MICROBIAL CLASSIFICATION

Other Publications of the
Society for General Microbiology

THE JOURNAL OF GENERAL MICROBIOLOGY
(*Cambridge University Press*)

MICROBIAL REACTION TO ENVIRONMENT
ELEVENTH SYMPOSIUM OF THE SOCIETY
(*Cambridge University Press*)

MICROBIAL GENETICS
TENTH SYMPOSIUM OF THE SOCIETY
(*Cambridge University Press*)

VIRUS GROWTH AND VARIATION
NINTH SYMPOSIUM OF THE SOCIETY
(*Cambridge University Press*)

THE STRATEGY OF CHEMOTHERAPY
EIGHTH SYMPOSIUM OF THE SOCIETY
(*Cambridge University Press*)

MICROBIAL ECOLOGY
EVENTH SYMPOSIUM OF THE SOCIETY
(*Cambridge University Press*)

BACTERIAL ANATOMY
SIXTH SYMPOSIUM OF THE SOCIETY
(*Cambridge University Press*)

MECHANISMS OF MICROBIAL PATHOGENICITY
FIFTH SYMPOSIUM OF THE SOCIETY
(*Cambridge University Press*)

AUTOTROPHIC MICRO-ORGANISMS
FOURTH SYMPOSIUM OF THE SOCIETY
(*Cambridge University Press*)

ADAPTATION IN MICRO-ORGANISMS
THIRD SYMPOSIUM OF THE SOCIETY
(*Cambridge University Press*)

THE NATURE OF VIRUS MULTIPLICATION
SECOND SYMPOSIUM OF THE SOCIETY
(*Cambridge University Press*)

THE NATURE OF THE BACTERIAL SURFACE
FIRST SYMPOSIUM OF THE SOCIETY
(*Blackwell's Scientific Publications Limited*)

MICROBIAL CLASSIFICATION

TWELFTH SYMPOSIUM OF THE
SOCIETY FOR GENERAL MICROBIOLOGY
HELD AT THE
ROYAL INSTITUTION, LONDON
APRIL 1962

CAMBRIDGE
Published for the Society for General Microbiology
AT THE UNIVERSITY PRESS
1962

PUBLISHED BY
THE SYNDICS OF THE CAMBRIDGE UNIVERSITY PRESS

Bentley House, 200 Euston Road, London, N.W.1
American Branch: 32 East 57th Street, New York, 22, N.Y.
West African Office: P.O. Box 33, Ibadan, Nigeria

©

THE SOCIETY FOR GENERAL MICROBIOLOGY
1962

Printed in Great Britain at the University Press, Cambridge
(Brooke Crutchley, University Printer)

CONTRIBUTORS

AINSWORTH, G. C., Commonwealth Mycological Institute, Kew, Surrey.

BISSET, K. A., Department of Bacteriology, The Medical School, University of Birmingham.

CAIN, A. J., Department of Zoology and Comparative Anatomy, University Museum, Oxford.

CORLISS, J. O., Department of Zoology, University of Illinois, Urbana, Illinois, U.S.A.

COWAN, S. T., National Collection of Type Cultures, Central Public Health Laboratory, Colindale, London, N.W. 9.

CUMMINS, C. S., Department of Bacteriology, London Hospital Medical College, London, E. 1.

DE LEY, J., Laboratorium voor Microbiologie, Faculteit der Weten-schappen, Ruksuniversiteit, Ghent, Belgium.

GILARDI, E., Istituto di Microbiologia, University of Milan, Italy.

HESLOP-HARRISON, J., Department of Botany, University of Birmingham.

HILL, L. R., Istituto di Microbiologia, University of Milan, Italy.

KREGER-VAN RIJ, NELLY J. W., Centraalbureau voor Schimmel-cultures, Julianalaan 67a, Delft, Netherlands.

LUND, J. W. G., Freshwater Biological Association, The Ferry House, Far Sawrey, Ambleside, Westmorland.

MURRAY, R. G. E., Department of Bacteriology and Immunology, University of Western Ontario, London, Ontario, Canada.

OAKLEY, C. L., Department of Bacteriology, University of Leeds.

PIRIE, N. W., Department of Biochemistry, Rothamsted Experimental Station, Harpenden, Herts.

ROPER, J. A., Department of Genetics, University of Sheffield.

ROSS, R., Department of Botany, British Museum (Natural History), Cromwell Road, London, S.W. 7.

SILVESTRI, L., Istituto di Microbiologia, University of Milan, Italy.

SMITH, G., Department of Biochemistry, London School of Hygiene and Tropical Medicine, Keppel Street, London, W.C. 1.

CONTRIBUTORS

SNEATH, P. H. A., National Institute for Medical Research, The Ridgeway, Mill Hill, London, N.W. 7.

STEEL, K. J., National Collection of Type Cultures, Central Public Health Laboratory, Colindale, London, N.W. 9.

TURRI, M., Istituto di Microbiologia, University of Milan, Italy.

WILDY, P., Institute of Virology, University of Glasgow.

CONTENTS

CONTENTS

EDITORS' PREFACE

That taxonomy is a fundamental branch of microbiology has always been recognized by the Society for General Microbiology. In September 1954 'The principles of microbial classification' was the subject of a one-day Discussion Meeting at Reading;* recently a Microbial Systematics Group has been established within the Society for the increasing number of members interested in taxonomy; here microbial classification is again reviewed.

Microbiology is not the sole preserve of bacteriologists, and while bacteria occupy a central position in this Symposium an effort has been made to consider the taxonomy of all the major groups of micro-organisms against a background sketched in by a zoologist and a botanist experienced in the taxonomy of larger organisms.

Each contribution is self-contained, but all are interrelated. Some, such as those on protozoa and algae, comprehensively survey the taxonomic treatments of single groups, some contrast different approaches to the taxonomy of one group, while others discuss the application to different groups of one taxonomic approach. This volume therefore reflects facts and uncertainties of present-day microbial classification, both theoretical and practical.

Help and advice from contributors and from other members of the Society in the preparation of the three Appendices is gratefully acknowledged.

G. C. AINSWORTH
P. H. A. SNEATH

Commonwealth Mycological Institute, Kew
and The National Institute for Medical Research, Mill Hill

* For a report see *J. gen. Microbiol.* **12**, 314–86, 1955.

THE EVOLUTION OF TAXONOMIC PRINCIPLES

A. J. CAIN

Department of Zoology, University Museum, Oxford

The purpose of studying the history of a scientific subject is to cast light on its present state. It is only too easy in any period to hold beliefs which are unformulated because unquestioned, and which are an actual hindrance to a more complete view of the subject. Perhaps there is no part of biology in which this is more true than it is in taxonomy, which for so long has progressed by a combination of tradition and rule of thumb.

Taxonomy is the science of classification (or, more broadly, arrangement) as applied to living things. Almost every advance in biology has had its effect on classification—nearly everyone has views on how things should be classified, and what are 'really' related and what only superficially similar, in biology as in every other science. Moreover, some sort of arrangement is inescapable for organizing our facts about the bewildering diversity of living things; and a nomenclature is equally essential as a quick and accurate method of reference and communication.

It is unnecessary for our purposes here to go back beyond Linnaeus, who is not only the accepted starting-point for nomenclature, but perhaps the most typical member of that school of taxonomy which began with Aristotle and his contemporaries and whose theories still influence taxonomy today. Yet very much of the so-called Linnean system of taxonomy as used today would be strange to Linnaeus, and most of what has been inherited from him is of rather doubtful value.

Linnaeus's principles of taxonomy can be summarized as follows (for a more detailed discussion see Cain (1958) and references therein).

(i) There are distinct *kinds* of living things without intermediates, each with its own peculiar characters or combination of characters. Each is separately created (or, as Linnaeus came to think later, evolved by hybridization from a limited number of originally created forms), breeds true, seldom, or only locally, hybridizes with others in the wild, and has a distinct role to play in the Economy of Nature. These are the *species*.

(ii) The species are constituents of higher groups which are themselves distinct and separate, each with its peculiarities, and these again are members of yet higher groups, and so on up to the group of all living things.

(iii) The best method of arranging living things is to find out what they

M S XII

'really are', what is their *essential nature*, and to *divide* all living things according to the modifications of this essential nature. Each division can itself be subdivided according to modifications of its essential characteristics, and so on down to the least divisions, the *species infimae* in the terminology of Aristotelian logic, which are Linnaeus's taxonomic species.

(iv) The most important characters for doing this are therefore the most essential ones, those that have the greatest influence in making the organism what it is, those in short that have the greatest *physiological importance*.

(v) The arrangement that most successfully carries out these principles is the most *natural* (because it expresses the *natures* of the things arranged). An arrangement that does not express the natures is an artificial one, which may be very useful for some special purpose. It may, for example, group things so that they can be readily identified, associating them in groups definable by some obvious but often trivial character which springs to the eye but does not indicate the 'true nature'.

Linnaeus's nomenclature accords closely with his theory and practice. Since, according to him, the species are the ultimate taxonomic units, then each should be given a distinct name. But, in practice, it was often difficult to name plants down to the species; and the higher groups of plants were not in his time generally agreed on, since most text-books used frankly artificial systems of arrangement, sometimes based on the leaf, sometimes on the corolla, sometimes on other parts of the plant, or on vague groupings intended to be natural. The genus, therefore, had for him an immense practical importance. All systematists, he thought, should know their genera by heart (he believed this to be perfectly possible) and then they would know at once with which kind of thing they were dealing. Consequently, he named genera for the easiest possible reference and the greatest memorability by giving each a single word which is a proper name. The species he named by a *differentia*, to follow the generic name; but his *differentiae* were often in effect lines of keys defining each species within the genus by stating some of their peculiar characters or character-combinations. As this meant that they could be up to twelve words long, and moreover, as they were liable to alteration if a new species was discovered, he produced also a single word, the *trivial epithet*, for each species, which he regarded as a mere catchword—in fact he never even bothered to give rules for its formation. It is this trivial name which has survived as the name distinguishing each species within a genus, since the *differentia* has become a line in what is explicitly a key, and has become a diagnosis in any more extended treatment of the group.

Linnaeus's principles of classification are based on the theory of Logical Division worked out by Aristotle, which held the field until the beginning of this century (later in some quarters) as the only good way of arranging anything. It was a most praiseworthy attempt to classify things by what they 'really are', and to avoid being misled by mere superficial resemblance. It failed because it was essentially deductive but was applied indiscriminately to situations where only inductive treatment was possible and never provided adequate criteria for deciding the meaning of the phrase 'what things really are'. A more detailed treatment of it is given by Cain (1958).

Logical Division can best be exemplified in such a subject as geometry. We can define exactly what we mean by a term such as circle or plane triangle. Then its definition states its *essence*—what it must be to be a circle, or triangle, at all. Any other attributes which a particular circle may have (e.g. its size, or the colour of the pencil used to draw it) are, in the technical sense, *accidental*. They can vary, without in the least causing it to be less or more a circle. But the number of sides of a plane triangle cannot vary, by definition. Furthermore, everything that follows rigidly from the essence or definition is a *property* of the circle or triangle, or other figure, always and necessarily possessed by every figure with that particular essence—for example the sum of the internal angles of any plane triangle must be 180°. Such constant characters would be of the utmost value in identifying the essential nature of a given entity, supposing that this were not already known. And since there are many sorts of triangle, we can divide the genus triangle into species by considering what is the essence of plane triangularity, and in what ways that essence can be expressed. If plane triangles are defined as plane figures bounded by three straight lines, then the logical choice for dividing them up into groups would be the proportions of these lines—and the usual division is into equilateral, isosceles and scalene. This is an excellent example of Logical Division; the essence of the kind (*genus*) of thing under consideration is first determined, and then the different forms (*species*) in which it can manifest itself are so determined that (*a*) they are mutually exclusive, with no overlapping classes, and (*b*) taken together they exhaust the genus, so that no species has been omitted. This sort of division was considered as excellent by Aristotle. We can easily see from it why he put immense emphasis on determining the essences of things, dividing up according to these essences, and disregarding mere accidental characters.

But suppose we try to apply this sort of procedure to living things. We can define an animal, but only descriptively. We do *not* know its essence; we cannot decide what are properties and what only accidentals. Certainly those characters that vary greatly within a group (from individual to individual within a species, or from genus to genus within a family, for example) must be accidental in that group. We might well think, by analogy with Logical Division, that those characters which are constant in a group, as far as our experience goes, are all properties. But this cannot be demonstrated; some, perhaps many, may be only accidentals that happen not to vary within our limited experience. Until Australia was discovered, it was possible to believe that whiteness is an essential character of swans (and therefore if a bird were not white, it could not possibly be a swan), but the discovery of black swans revealed colour as an accidental in this case.

Nevertheless, there has always been a considerable practical value in working out what characters are constant in a group, in order to define it. A horse is first shown to each of us in infancy by someone pointing to an example and pronouncing the name 'horse'. But the next one pointed out may be a different colour, or size, or with a longer tail... and so on. What is it that defines a given animal as a horse and not a cow? All the characters just mentioned vary greatly. The horsiness of a horse does not reside in the beast's colour, but in a multitude of anatomical and other characters found in combination in all horses. Such constant characters could be considered as properties, and a collection of them could be regarded as a definition of the essence, comparable with the definition of plane triangles, so that even in biology, the revered procedures of deductive thought could be approached. But in fact, such definitions are not of essences and allow of very little safe logical deduction. They are summaries of observations, useful for the definition of groups, but not the analysis of kinds, essentially inductive, and liable to upset by further discovery. They are invaluable for defining terms by means of which we can make sure that we are talking about the same sort of animal as someone else; and they are very useful summaries, making our classifications as concise as possible, and so the more easily scanned and (if necessary) memorized. Consequently, they have remained in use; but, unfortunately, they carried for centuries a prestige which was not theirs. The man who really knew what his subjects were and could reason about them deductively was obviously far better informed and more competent than he who could only group together those of his subjects that seem alike on mere observation without reasoning, an activity stigmatized by A. P. De Candolle as 'blind groping' (Cain, 1959a). Anyone, therefore, who could claim that he had definite principles on which animals or plants *must* be distributed into groups must be a better taxonomist than a mere grouper.

But, in fact, this blind groping was the only scientifically honest procedure. The logician Joseph (1916) has put it very clearly in relation to organic beings. 'If species were fixed: if there were in each a certain nucleus of characters, that must belong to the members of any species either not at all or all in all: if it were only upon condition of exhibiting at least such a specific nucleus of characters that the functions of life could go on in the individual at all; then this nucleus would form the essence of the kind. But such is not the case.... There may be deviation from the type, to a greater or lesser degree, in endless directions; and we cannot fix by any hard-and-fast rule the amount of deviation consistent with being of the species, nor can we enumerate all the points, of function or structure, that in reality enter into the determination of a thing's kind. Hence for definition, such as we have it in geometry, we must substitute classification; and for the demonstration of properties, the discovery of laws'—i.e. the inductive determination of regularities from actual observation of as many instances as possible

In the period from Linnaeus to Darwin, many workers had tried to find the 'natural classification', that which was based on the true natures of animals and plants (Cain, 1959 *a*, *b*). Almost always they had tried to do so on fixed *a priori* principles, in imitation of the deductive sciences, but often these would separate things which were so clearly related in every way that it was obvious that they must be kept together. A famous early example was the division of plants into woody and non-woody, on Aristotelian principles, which associated leguminous trees, for example, not with leguminous herbs, but with all other trees,—a ridiculous grouping, and recognized as such even before the time of Linnaeus. Merely as a result of taxonomic practice, it was becoming more and more evident that one could not lay down fixed principles on which to work, because they produced absurd results in some group or other; or some character of no importance according to the principles adopted was found to be of the greatest importance in defining a particular group—and therefore must really be important after all, which meant that the principles must be wrong.

The reason why it took so long to unmask the inadequacy of *a priori* division in biology is rather remarkable. Taxonomists were arguing in a circle without knowing it, and using one half of the circle as a separate argument from the other, which confirmed and strengthened it, thus increasing their confidence in their results. Two quite distinct and equally important taxonomic activities, at least as far as bi-sexually reproducing forms are concerned (which were the only forms considered until very recently), are the sorting of animals into different species, and the grouping of these species into higher and higher groups. The first involves such questions as 'Does this specimen belong only to a seasonal form, or a geographical race of an already known species; or is it a somewhat abnormal individual of one, or have I discovered a new species altogether?'—that is, a separate entity, genetically distinct from all others, and with its own mode of life. It leads to the distinguishing of the different *units* of animal life, so to speak. Its questions, as far as living things are concerned, can usually be settled by breeding experiments of a certain sort. The second activity involves such questions as 'Is the cheetah sufficiently different from the other great cats to require a group by itself, equal in rank to that containing all the others?' or 'Are the whales fishes or mammals?' or 'What animals should be put as the closest relatives of the common fox?' Such questions can never be settled decisively by experiment. They involve the weighing up of a large number of characters in all the forms considered, and some sort of overall comparison of similarities and differences against arbitrary standards. Such grouping is very readily done in an imprecise fashion by the human mind—anyone can 'see at a glance' that stoats and weasels and martens are far more like one another than like foxes and wolves. Such natural groupings—not according to natures in the Aristotelian sense, but according to mere 'blind groping'—have always been recognized. They are the real basis of early classification, and in fact, without them, classification could not even start. How was it that Cuvier, for example, could state what are the important characters of animals, and then proceed to distribute animals according to them on *a priori* principles? He could only do so because a natural group of animals (in contrast to plants) had *already* been recognized; after its recognition, the characters common to all animals could be sorted out from those possessed by only a few (which might then be used to define a natural subgroup of animals, or might be found to crop out sporadically in various natural subgroups, and have no diagnostic value). But if these characters had already been singled out as important on a natural grouping, there was no point in proclaiming that they must be important on principle, since the 'principle' was no more, very often, than a restatement of the fact that they were already found to be important. Nevertheless, many taxonomists including Cuvier (Cain, 1959*a*) *deduced* the physiological importance of various characters, and then claimed that as they could observe these characters to be very constant through large groups, they had confirmed their reasoning by observation. The question never asked was: 'How did we get our generally accepted groups of animals in the first place?', and the answer, which would not have been admitted because of deductive reasoning's high prestige, was 'By what you have called blind groping'.

Darwin and a few others were fully aware of the uselessness of the *a priori* principles that had been used. In the *Origin of Species* Darwin wrote, 'We must not, therefore, in classifying, trust to resemblances in parts of the organization, however important they may be for the welfare of the being in relation to the outside world [since this would group, for example, whales with fishes, or mice with shrews]. Perhaps from this cause it has partly arisen that almost all naturalists lay the greatest stress on resemblances in organs of high vital or physiological importance. No doubt this view of the classificatory importance of organs which are important [physiologically] is generally, but by no means always, true. But the importance for classification, I believe depends on their greater constancy throughout large groups of species; and their constancy depends on such organs having generally been subjected to less change in the adaptation of the species to their conditions of life...no one will say that rudimentary or atrophied organs are of high physiological or vital importance; yet undoubtedly, organs in this condition are often of high value in classification...'. In this he was perfectly right. At long last, deduction in imitation of the mathematical sciences was recognized as inapplicable in taxonomy, and pure observation of what characters were common within natural groups could be taken as the basic procedure for the second taxonomic activity. A. P. de Candolle had gone half-way to recognizing this fact (Cain, 1959 *a*).

But Darwin himself had theoretical principles which could be applied to taxonomy, and he proceeded to apply them. There was an unsolved problem in taxonomy, which on the theory of evolution was immediately explicable. Rudimentary organs had always been a puzzle. Aristotle himself could do no better than suppose that although Nature could produce animals of the same general plan but modified to lead different lives, she could not modify such a plan in any really essential features; and therefore rudiments of such features must always exist in the most modified forms 'for a token' of what the plan was in its unmodified state. In later times, a very similar interpretation was used. The rudiments served to show the main idea which the Creator had used in designing the modified forms. In tracing out these ideas, one was following the plan of creation. And many moralists pointed out how marvellous in ingenuity the Creator had been, to produce such infinitely diverse variations of a few themes and build up from them the complete Economy of Nature. This was a sublime interpretation. It graced with the beauty of holiness the study of natural history. But it was a subject for contemplation only, and gave no practical help to Science. Why should the Creator leave these tokens and rudiments? Moreover, if it was true that every sort of living thing was created perfect for its own role in the Economy of Nature, how was it that one did not find the same sort of animal performing the same service everywhere on the globe where that service could be performed? Why was it, for instance, that the place of the little auk as a small marine diving fish-eating bird was taken in the South Atlantic by a quite unrelated bird, the diving petrel, or that the large grazing mammals in Africa were antelopes but in Australia—in almost identical country—were large kangaroos?

The answer was obvious on the theory of evolution. The local stocks had been modified in each great region to occupy the available niches, and often they still bore the traces of their ancestral conditions. The reason why a natural group of vertebrates, or molluscs, or insects, could be recognized was simply that each did consist of variations on a single theme, but the theme was set by the ancestral form from which all the variations had been evolved by adaptation to different modes of life; the rudiments were there not as a token of the limited powers of Nature, nor of some mystical theme in the plan of Creation, but simply as relicts of a more ancestral condition. Community of descent, as Darwin said, was the bond between the members of a natural group.

This interpretation of the classification of living things into a hierarchy of groups was so convincing and so convenient that it was accepted unreflectingly by all the people who accepted evolution. At long last, the difficulty over rudimentary organs was disposed of; and taxonomists could go on exactly as before, merely interpreting their natural groups as groups which had a common ancestor. They had been tracing the course of evolution without knowing it, and needed only to acknowledge the fact.

But one may well wonder whether this simple equation of the classification with an evolutionary tree is not too simple. Many of the groups recognized in Darwin's day were badly known, and divided up on some principle or other rather than into natural subgroups. A complete overhaul was necessary before the equation was made. There was, moreover, one difficulty far more serious than this. Darwin had admitted, in his examples of the little auk and the diving petrel, the whale and true fish, the mouse and the shrew, that convergence could occur, by adaptation to the same, or a very similar mode of life. He never discussed convergence with any thoroughness and no example of it appears in the (hypothetical) ancestral tree he drew to illustrate his views on descent and classification. He appears to have assumed that convergence could never go so far as to produce virtually identical forms from different stocks. Now it may well be true that conditions over the face of the earth vary so much from place to place and from time to time that the chances of two very different stocks being continuously modified in the right directions for so long that they become virtually identical, are exceedingly small. But suppose that the stocks are already closely related and very similar: they might very well come to occupy the same mode of life (in different regions) by quite a small modification of each. And suppose further what is far more likely to be true than not, that we have no good fossil record of the group, how should we know that the very close resemblance between the end-products is only in part due to a common proximal ancestor, the remainder being convergent? But a classification which is professedly based on the course of evolution must always distinguish convergence from ancestral resemblance.

This difficulty has never been satisfactorily cleared up (Cain, 1959 *a*, *b*). For large parts of the animal and plant kingdoms, our best mode of classification is still by 'blind groping', by putting together those things that resemble each other most, all their characters being taken into consideration. In such groups we may *believe* that most are truly phyletic groups as well, each stemming from a common ancestor, but we have no way of checking how far this is true, and generalizations about the course of evolution which are based on them are insecure. For other groups, however, the fossil record is good enough to allow us to see a great part, if not all, of the course of evolution in them, and they afford our only firm basis for its study.

By equating taxonomic with ancestral relationship, Darwin, like Cuvier, adopted two criteria of the importance of characters. On the one hand, he said that those characters common to large groups (i.e. *natural* groups, although he did not say so explicitly) are more important than those common to groups containing little diversity. This is always right if only natural groups are to be made. But he also said (*a*) that those least likely to have been modified in relation to particular modes of life will be more important in showing ancestral affinity, and (*b*) that they can be recognized because they will be the most nearly constant ones within a natural group. But this assumes that natural groups are always phyletic or, in other terms, that convergence is never so great as to obscure or outweigh ancestral resemblance even in poorly known groups. He did not commit the earlier error of arguing in a circle. His principles of evolutionary importance were not derived from a pre-existing taxonomy, but from the results of artificial selection and from the study of heredity, variation and ecology. This is a point worth emphasizing. In many elementary text-books of biology, classification is treated as one of the lines of evidence for evolution. Darwin did not treat it thus; he discussed it quite late in the '*Origin*' as consonant with the theory of evolution, and explicable as a consequence of it. He never regarded it as primary evidence for evolution, and his caution was certainly justified. He only made a too simple equation between the accepted groups of his time and evolutionary groups. As a result of this revolution in the interpretation of classification, the good effects of abandoning deductive procedures were lost sight of as soon as they became visible. Everyone began to produce 'evolutionary' classifications of even the worst-known groups, never realizing that in many cases they might be foisting on to a very useful natural classification an interpretation almost as unjustified as the earlier *a priori* ones, except where the fossil record was really adequate.

A century ago, therefore, the old methods of classifying by logical division combined with a particular physiological theory were being abandoned, and evolutionary surmises (some good, some bad, many of untestable value) had taken their place. As yet, the actual units of classification, the species were in practice very much as in Linnaeus's day. But this state of affairs did not last, and it was removed by the accumulation of more taxonomic information. The present view of species has been reviewed elsewhere (Cain, 1954*b*) and need only be summarized here.

(i) Only for bi-sexually reproducing forms is there a distinct criterion for what must be included in any one species. Those forms that inter-breed freely (or are potentially capable of doing so, in the case of geographically separate populations) belong to the same species.

(ii) But species change in the course of evolution, and the breaking-up of a single continuous phyletic line must be arbitrary.

(iii) Bi-sexually reproducing species, clearly distinct from all others at any given locality, may vary geographically to such an extent that a number of descriptions is required to characterize populations in different areas—the species is no longer necessarily monotypic (Mayr, 1942).

(iv) Asexually reproducing forms can be broken up into 'species' only by some standard of overall difference, and in fact are only called species because often they must be fitted into genera alongside sexually reproducing forms, and because thereby they get the benefit of names agreed internationally and protected from homonymy and unwanted synonymy. However, it is certainly true that the species in bisexually reproducing forms is still the evolutionary unit, genetically separate from all other forms, and each evolutionary in its own way (Simpson, 1951). And this view of the species is of immense value in the taxonomy of very many groups of living things.

But very little indeed is left of the genus as Linnaeus conceived it (Cain, 1956). Instead of being as unitary as the species, and as important a taxonomic entity, it is now merely a collection of species which resemble each other closely. There is no reason at all to think of genera (as Linnaeus did) as necessarily distinct from one another; we may perfectly well have species that fall between two genera and could equally well be put into either. A genus need not even be definable— every character or character-combination confined to it may be lost or modified in one or other species that nevertheless, on their overall characters, are perfectly good members of it (Cain, 1954a). It has no greater importance than the family, order, class or any other group, yet the binominal nomenclature is so firmly embedded in the literature that we still have to put every species into a genus before we can give it a valid name (Cain, 1959c). In short, what we mainly inherit from Linnaeus are his excellent rules of homonymy and synonymy (the latter greatly modified), the taxonomic hierarchy of species, genus, order and class, now greatly expanded and interpreted on the basis of evolutionary theory, and a system of binominal nomenclature that corresponds, in part, to wholly discarded concepts.

It is time for taxonomists to recognize clearly what they are doing, and to face up to their own practice, disregarding irrelevant theory. In this, microbiologists have certain great advantages. First, they cannot take in at a glance immense numbers of characters, as can macrobiologists looking at their specimens. In consequence, microbiologists must make clear just what characters they are considering to a far greater extent than do macrobiologists. This should do away with a great deal of cryptotaxonomy (Cain, 1959c). Secondly, there is no fossil record, and no likelihood of one, and there should in consequence be very little interference in classification by theories of what must, or must not, be primitive characters or primitive micro-organisms. The technique of phylogenetic weighting is a very difficult one (Cain & Harrison, 1960) as has been proved only too often in the larger organisms; its prestige has been so great that many groups of large organisms with no good fossil record have been arranged on various pretended phylogenetic bases, with consequent instability of their classification. This should be far less likely to happen with micro-organisms. Lastly, in many micro-organisms, the species is not a valid concept. The practical unit is the strain, and this can be frankly recognized; all groups above it have exactly the same basis, namely that their constituents resemble each other on their overall characters to a given degree.

An arrangement on overall resemblance, devoid of any heterogeneity of units and of any irrelevant theoretical considerations, is probably the most useful one possible. It stores the greatest amount of information in its descriptions of the different groups formed, and it should have the greatest predictive value—when a new form is found that on its known features belongs to a particular group, its unknown features are most likely to be those given in the description of this group.

Moreover, if a numerical technique for expressing overall affinity can be found, then the values produced will serve to emphasize the artificiality of classifying into distinct groups when any degree of affinity may be found to occur. Here is one place where evolutionary theory is highly relevant to taxonomy; what we are to arrange is a scatter of forms taken more or less at random out of an evolutionary dendrite, not a set of clearly distinct entities groupable into a hierarchy of equally distinct groups.

The recognition that this sort of arrangement is the best is due to Adanson; but the prestige—to speak plainly, the snob-value—of the deductive method was great enough to ensure that his ideas were rejected for centuries (Cain, 1959a) and at present the snob-value of phylogenetic weighting may well hinder their application to groups in which no such weighting is possible. Only recently have analyses of the ideas involved in such arrangements been attempted (Cain & Harrison, 1958). Several procedures for making them as objective as possible have now been published (e.g. Michener & Sokal, 1957; Sneath, 1957a, b). There is no reason why microbial classification should not become the most firmly based of all biological classifications.

REFERENCES

CAIN, A. J. (1954a). Subdivisions of the genus *Ptilinopus* (Aves, Columbae). *Bull. Brit. Mus.* (*Nat. Hist.*), *Zoology*, **2**, 267.

CAIN, A. J. (1954b). *Animal Species and their Evolution.* London: Hutchinson.

CAIN, A. J. (1956). The genus in evolutionary taxonomy. *Syst. Zool.* **5**, 97.

CAIN, A. J. (1958). Logic and memory in Linnaeus's system of taxonomy. *Proc. Linn. Soc. Lond.* **169**, 144.

CAIN, A. J. (1959a). Deductive and inductive methods in post-Linnaean taxonomy. *Proc. Linn. Soc. Lond.* **170**, 185.

CAIN, A. J. (1959b). The post-Linnaean development of taxonomy. *Proc. Linn. Soc. Lond.* **170**, 234.

CAIN, A. J. (1959c). Taxonomic concepts. *Ibis*, **101**, 302.

CAIN, A. J. (1959d). Function and taxonomic importance. In A. J. Cain (ed.), *Systematics Association publication*, no. 3. London: Systematics Association.

CAIN, A. J. & HARRISON, G. A. (1958). An analysis of the taxonomist's judgement of affinity. *Proc. zool. Soc. Lond.* **131**, 85.

CAIN, A. J. & HARRISON, G. A. (1960). Phylogenetic weighting. *Proc. zool. Soc. Lond.* **135**, 1.

JOSEPH, H. W. B. (1916). *An Introduction to Logic.* Oxford.

MAYR, E. (1942). *Systematics and the Origin of Species.* New York.

MICHENER, C. D. & SOKAL, R. R. (1957). A quantitative approach to a problem in classification. *Evolution*, **11**, 130.

SIMPSON, G. G. (1951). The species concept. *Evolution*, **5**, 285.

SNEATH, P. H. A. (1957*a*). Some thoughts on bacterial classification. *J. gen. Microbiol.* **17**, 184.

SNEATH, P. H. A. (1957*b*). The application of computers to taxonomy. *J. gen. Microbiol.* **17**, 201.

PURPOSES AND PROCEDURES IN THE TAXONOMIC TREATMENT OF HIGHER ORGANISMS

J. HESLOP-HARRISON

University of Birmingham

INTRODUCTION: THE FUNCTIONS OF CLASSIFICATION

There can be few biologists who would not accept as one of the primary functions of biological systematics the production of a general classification of living things possessing at once the greatest possible content of information and the maximum convenience in use. Whatever other function may be attributed to taxonomy—such, for example, as investigating phylogeny—this one, the creation of a data storage and retrieval agency, is surely the inescapable one. Taxonomists can aim overtly at producing it and seek the most efficient means wherever they are to hand, or they can accept different aims and suppose that, *pari passu*, a classification still of utilitarian value will emerge; the more sanguine will hope that whatever the aim, the same classification will be thrashed out in the end. What sometimes goes unacknowledged is that the general purpose classification is not necessarily the most efficient for all purposes, and that it is not always desirable or indeed feasible to modify it to meet specialized demands.

During the last half-century there has been some divergence between zoological and botanical attitudes in this matter, exemplified by the utilization of the category system of orthodox taxonomy. While zoologists in general have been satisfied to accept the category system of Linnaeus without serious attempts at replacement or supplementation, botanists have repeatedly found it desirable to introduce secondary, special-purpose categories to accommodate variational units detected by other than morphological criteria. That there should be this difference is attributable both to dissimilarities in the material and to different preoccupations of workers in the two kingdoms. Systematists of the higher animal groups—who, on the whole, have set the zoological pace —have found that the comparative uniformity of breeding system permits a much wider extension of the 'biological' species concept (Mayr, 1942; Cain, 1954) so that a straight equating of the taxonomic species with this particular kind of evolutionary unit has seemed desirable. It is possible also that their modest satisfaction with the orthodox system may be attributable in part to the later, and as yet incomplete, development of cytotaxonomic studies in most vertebrate groups, which has permitted a whole dimension of variation to go almost undetected (Hamerton, 1958). The diversity of breeding system in higher plants, the static existence of plants with its consequences in conspicuous local ecological differentiation, the early popularity of botanical cytotaxonomy, and the wider application of breeding methods in plant taxonomic research have all combined to reveal, for botanists, inadequacies in the Linnean system as a means of expressing genetical and evolutionary relationships, and have led to the classification systems of so-called experimental taxonomy (Heslop-Harrison, 1960).

On the whole, the botanical experience is probably more relevant to microbial systematics than the zoological, if for no other reason than the greater community in the ways in which variation is generated in the microbial groups and higher plants. But it is not at all clear just what lessons are to be learned from this experience, for certainly it has not produced model solutions for all situations, providing at once a workable taxonomic system and a means of expressing evolutionary and genetical relationships. Thus forty years of experimental taxonomy have supplied no new recipe for handling the nomenclatural problems of agamic complexes, which, with a few notable exceptions, continue to be treated by monographers as they would have been two centuries ago. In a valuable recent survey of the impact of experimental upon orthodox taxonomy in flowering plants, Valentine & Löve (1958) have, however, suggested an eclectic approach to problems of this kind which has much to recommend it; and I shall expound similar views in what follows.

SPECIES: THE UNITS OF CLASSIFICATION

Currently, the International Codes of Nomenclature require all organisms to be referred to species for the purposes of naming, so that working systematists in all groups, if they wish their efforts to have legal sanction, have the unavoidable task of determining what variational units amongst all those they encounter can be fitted with least violence into this category. This pragmatic view of the function of the species category in the taxonomic hierarchy is forced upon one by the nomenclatural requirement, for the extension to all groups ensures that the word 'species' itself cannot be cornered for exclusive application to any *one* kind of variational unit.

By far the most widespread usage has undoubtedly been to accommodate assemblages of individuals placed together because of their general morphological similarity and dissimilarity from others. The great majority of the described and named species of plants and animals were based upon considerations of this kind in the first instance, and any current taxonomic journal will provide testimony that morphological distinction is still the commonest basis for species description in all groups.

In its most unsophisticated guise, the morphological criterion of species encourages a typological approach which attaches importance to meticulous description of individuals and leads to the cancerous proliferation of new binomials as finer and finer differentiae are encountered. In a more developed form, the morphological species conception takes cognizance of variation and the facts of distribution, and encourages the collation and description of populations rather than individuals. One of the wisest surveys of the application of this *morphological-geographical* principle in plant taxonomy is that of du Rietz (1930) who gives as a general definition of the species: '...the smallest natural populations permanently separated from each other by a distinct discontinuity in the series of biotypes...'.

The success of the morphological-geographical method in so many instances indicates with little room for doubt that the variational units it reveals have a degree of cohesion in nature, and it has long been accepted that in sexual groups this unity arises from the fact that the local population forms a breeding group. The elaboration of this idea to provide a theoretical basis for the so-called *biological species*, a group of panmictic populations set apart from other such groups by some form of reproductive isolation, has been a feature of the development of systematic theory in the last 30 years, fertilized to some extent (although, according to Mayr (1955), probably less than is commonly supposed) by the simultaneous growth of population genetics.

As Mayr (1955, 1957) has pointed out, the idea of the biological species subsumes two concepts of rather different kinds. On the one hand there is that derived from the criterion of reproductive isolation, observable when different species co-exist in the same locality, and on the other there is that of collectivity, inherent in such phrases as 'species are groups of actually or potentially interbreeding populations'. Although dispute is always possible as a consequence of the duality of the biological species concept, it is in fact a meaning of this kind that most commonly adheres to the word species in general biological use, even when the context of application is undefined. To some, especially those deeply conditioned by experience of dioecious groups, the only respectable species are of this nature.

It would be inappropriate here to detail all the strengths and weaknesses of the biological species concept among higher organisms, but two points do merit further attention, both concerned with reproductive isolation. The subtle arguments of Mayr and others place weight upon reproductive isolation in *one area at one time* as an immediate test of species distinction, but do not suppose that species limits can be determined positively by experimental tests for sterility or fertility where the status of groups of allopatric, i.e. geographically vicarious, populations is what is in question. However, there is no shortage of biologists who have no inhibitions about supposing that the sterility-fertility criterion can be developed into a direct and positive test of species rank. For Clausen, Keck & Hiesey (1939), for example, only those '...internal barriers that are of a genetic-physiologic nature' can be accepted as species-separating, while for van Steenis (1957) an experimental test of 'inmiscibility' is suitable for defining species limits irrespective of the behaviour of the populations in nature—provided, oddly enough, that the intersterility is not due to polyploidy or chromosome-structural change. The barriers which act to preserve reproductive isolation in nature are often of considerable subtlety, and I have emphasized elsewhere (Heslop-Harrison, 1955) the inadvisability of supposing that experimental tests of the capacity for gene exchange could ever provide an unequivocal means of establishing the limits of biological species among higher plants.

The second matter is the degree to which the biological species concept can in fact affect taxonomic practice in outbreeding groups. We have seen that the 'good' species of classical taxonomy have indeed the properties of the biological species, and that these good species have been based upon morphological-geographical considerations; from this it could be argued that, once sterility-fertility tests are put aside as not being especially relevant, the biological species concept merely provides a theoretical endorsement for the best type of existing practice. While this is true in some respects, the implications of the concept stretch further. For example, it demands 'population-thinking' in all outbreeding sexual groups, and so implies an out-and-out condemnation of all 'splitting' types of species-making which cut across breeding units. Furthermore, it provides the very strongest incentive for the refinement of distributional studies on a comparative basis, since it indicates that evidence concerning the distribution of populations, whether they are disjunct, continuous or overlapping, will almost inevitably be needed when decisions about status are involved.

Against these positive contributions to the rationalization of taxonomic procedure must be set some instances where the biological species concept provides little or no guidance for practical taxonomy, or where what it enjoins is not practicable in detail. Two contrasting situations, known both amongst animals and plants but probably more common in the latter, illustrate these limitations. The first is where remote populations are morphologically distinct and not connected by intermediates, although experiments may reveal the existence of complete interfertility. Here the decision on taxonomic rank can depend only upon comparative morphology, for whatever degree of interfertility may exist, the populations are already biological species in the sense that they are independent evolutionary lineages. The second is the case of sibling species, where reproductive isolation has developed without morphological divergence. Here 'non-experimental' taxonomy has no option but to treat the pair as one species until differentiae are available; although, as Nannfeldt (1938) has urged, there is good reason to make the split whenever consistent discriminating features are available, however minor they may be. We will allude to this issue also in discussing taxonomic criteria.

In sexual groups, one is perhaps justified in concluding that the species problem, if not solved, is now at least resolved. However, the practical and theoretical touchstones which can bring salvation in outbreeding groups lose much of their magic as soon as we attempt to apply them in groups where habitual inbreeding or apomixis is the rule. Indeed, the biological species concept is entirely inapplicable where sexuality, or the consequences of sexuality, are eliminated. From this we can conclude that in the context of agamic groups the word species must necessarily connote something different. The taxonomic problem arising from reproductive aberrations is acute in many plant genera, and knowledge of the cause of the anomalous variation patterns in these genera has contributed little to its solution. The brute fact is that where apomixis is prevalent or inbreeding is persistent a galaxy of minor variants is likely to be generated—e.g. clones, or homozygous pure lines, each more or less distinct from others genetically and showing low internal variability. What should be done about classification in these groups has puzzled generations of systematists; but the puzzle has been made worse by inattention to the question of why classification is needed at all.

If the answer to this question is simply that it is intrinsically a good thing that man should somewhere and in some form possess a detailed map of the variation, then the classificatory unit is inevitably the clone or homozygous biotype, and if we care to make this the unit to bear the binomial, it necessarily becomes the 'species' in the terms of the nomenclatural codes. We cannot then resent the nomenclatural morass which will be the consequence wherever the group is of any appreciable size; the product is the outcome of the principle with which we begin, and the principle is not invalidated merely because its operation embarrasses us. What is apparent is that the memorative value of the system of binomial nomenclature has been impaired—to put it mildly—in such an application, and this being so, its retention needs justification. The main argument *for* retention is that for the few who aim to attain familiarity with the detailed variation of the group, it still provides a more readily recalled means of identification than would a neutral system, say of numbers. To others the variational unit covered by the binomial in these circumstances appears so vastly different from that in sexual groups that to refer to it in the same kind of way seems improper.

Since there will always be comparatively few uses of a classification of an agamic complex in which *all* differential characteristics need to be taken into account, it is likely that there will always be a need for a less ambitious treatment than that which seeks to find a place for each distinguishable lineage. This will normally be one which makes use of discontinuities in the variational range at a higher level than the clone or pure line, or, where such discontinuities do not exist, takes cognizance of any variational foci there may be and carves taxa around them, establishing arbitrary boundaries if necessary. The product of this treatment is the collective or aggregate species.

Although commonly adopted in respectable floras, the aggregate species is sometimes criticized as perpetuating taxonomic imprecision. In fact, it only does so when it masquerades as something else: as a biological species comparable with those of a sexual group, or as an 'ultimate' subdivision—clone or pure line; and there are appropriate addenda to the binomial to ensure that this does not occur. No criticism can be entertained of aggregate species on the grounds that they are not 'proper' species; they are no more improper than any other sort, but merely based upon different criteria; and, as with other sorts, there are purposes for which they are useful, and purposes for which they are not.

The taxonomic challenge of agamic complexes would be severe enough if each possessed a variational pattern which, if sometimes intimidatingly complex, was at least static. Most also possess the disconcerting habit of generating new variation, and from time to time expunging or recombining the old. I have put forward the view elsewhere that the successful agamic complexes in higher plants are all of this nature (Heslop-Harrison, 1959), and have drawn the comparison with microorganisms capable of propagating indefinitely by sporulation but holding in reserve the capacity for sexual reproduction against the day when gene recombination is once more advantageous. The same biological end is served whether the agamic nebula is continuously reinforced from a basal assemblage of persistently sexual forms, or by the sporadic occurrence of sexual events in lineages which are otherwise free from recombination. It is obvious that in such groups no taxonomic system based upon the naming and classification of individual genotypes can hope to have permanence. Is this an argument against attempting to create one? Perhaps it is; but once more an analysis of motives gives some guidance. I cannot, for example, really think of a reason for keeping up to date with *Hieracium* section *Euhieracium* other than man's insatiable appetite for knowledge for its own sake about the organisms that inhabit this globe with him; but I can think of one for struggling along with *Poa*, where the apomicts may at least have some economic significance (Clausen, 1954).

THE CLASSIFICATORY PROCESS

'Artificial' and 'natural' classification

Given that it is species in one of the senses discussed above that are to be classified, the question remains how the classes of the system of higher rank than species are to be formed. With units presenting so many criteria of potential value as discriminants as species of higher organisms, there are obviously a great many ways in which groupings could be made, and—at least from the viewpoint of general taxonomic theory—none is necessarily more correct than the others if the goal is simply to produce *a* classification. It is usual, however, to distinguish between *artificial* and *natural* methods of classifying, and the implications of this distinction need examination.

The description *artificial* is applicable to any classification of organisms based upon resort to one or a few criteria as discriminants which happen to provide a ready means of subdivision. As Gilmour (1941, 1951) has stressed, such classifications are marked not only by the small number of criteria upon which they are based, but upon the small number of purposes they serve. This is not to say that the purposes are necessarily unimportant. Although a *key* is rather an analytical tool than a classification, it is constructed in the manner of an artificial classification, and none can deny the usefulness of keys for finding the name of an organism, the means by which its whole literature may be unlocked.

The adjective *natural* is notoriously imprecise, and applied to classifications it has hitherto conveyed at least three different ideas. The earliest is that of pre-evolutionary taxonomists like Linnaeus himself, for whom, as Cain (1958) has shown, a natural classification of organisms was intended to be founded on their real natures or essences in an Aristotelean sense (see p. 3).

A natural classification in the general theory of taxonomy is something quite different; it is one based upon overall resemblance or, in the jargon, the maximum correlation of attributes. Natural classification in this sense may appear at first sight to be different merely in degree and not in kind from artificial classification, the one being based upon few, and the other upon many properties of the organisms concerned. However, if I may paraphrase Orwell, it is not quite that all classifications are artificial but some are more artificial than others. At least in the taxonomy of living things there can be a further subtle difference in the basis of 'artificial' and 'natural' class formation.

Where the criteria are few, classes at every level in a hierarchy can readily be arranged so as to be defined uniquely by the possession, or lack of possession, of single attributes. In assembling such a system, the units, each characterized by a unique combination of the chosen attributes, would be placed together in progressively more inclusive classes by the selection seriatim of progressively more generalized properties. Each class at every level would accordingly be uniquely definable by the attributes shared in common by its component elements, and no individual would be tolerated in any class which did not conform to *all* the diagnostics of the class. This is an essential property of all logically constructed artificial classifications; but it is evident that natural classifications of organisms are *not* all like this.

A natural assemblage of organisms need not owe its unity to the possession by all members of one or a few characteristics in common, but to the fact that any pair share more characteristics in common than would any member with one of another such assemblage. To many biologists this situation is so familiar that they do not even recognize that it exists; and the principle is singularly rarely referred to in taxonomic texts, even when it is applied in practice. Taxonomic theorists have, however, commented upon it from time to time, including Bather (1927), who quotes Vicq-d'Azyr as stating the position with some clarity so early as 1786.

It is natural classes of this kind which systematists tend to form when they group according to overall likeness, whether this is done intuitively, or by following some method like the Adansonian one discussed below. It is usually said that classifications using classes of this kind are useful for more purposes, or permit the greatest number of inductive generalizations (Gilmour, 1941), but it is important to note just in what way this is true. By its very nature a natural classification cannot be expected to provide the sanction for predicating unique properties of all members of any class, for if this were so the classes could be defined by these properties, and the classification would to this extent be artificial. What can be said is that for any member correctly referred to a class in the classification there will be a large number of statements which will probably be true of it, and more probably true of it than if it were a member of any other class of equivalent rank.

'Phylogenetic classification'

The distinction between natural and artificial classification in the above sense is subtle enough to confuse, but the confusion has been worsened in post-Darwinian days by the confounding of the attempt to classify organisms (a legitimate activity) with the attempt to discover and express their phylogeny (another legitimate, but different, activity). Where the distinction has not been made, natural classification is equated directly with so-called phylogenetic classification (Sprague, 1941). This identification is unfortunate, for although a natural classification may be interpretable in terms of phylogeny, it cannot ever represent or express phylogeny. This has been accepted by the most avowed phylogeneticists (e.g. Simpson, 1945, 1959—see also Lawrence, 1951) and it is surprising that the point has not been more widely taken—indeed it can only be supposed that this is because it has not been generally understood.

It is historically demonstrable that good 'natural' classifications of parts of the living kingdoms were made before there could have been any intrusion of evolutionary ideas; so it is at once evident that a phylogenetic hypothesis is not a necessary tool for the formation of natural groupings. Nevertheless, phylogenetic speculation may affect the weighing up of criteria in the formation of groupings in the taxonomy of higher organisms; so it may be said that evolutionary ideas have come to affect taxonomic practice. But what is important is that the grouping is still carried on by comparison and contrast, and practically never with prior knowledge of phylogeny. Because of this, taxa can never be certified as monophyletic, since convergence is always a possibility, and one not totally excluded by any evidence whatever *except* knowledge of phylogeny.

It is quite true, of course, that the greater the number of independent characteristics shared in common by the members of a natural group of organisms the more probable it is that they belong to a single lineage and are thus monophyletic; but convergence to the extent of a polyphyletic origin of a single biological species is not unknown—as, for example, with polytopic allopolyploidy, where hybrids between the same two biological species assume fertility by chromosome doubling in different localities, and become, independently, the progenitors of what is effectively the same new species. The argument that a test of a true evolutionary group is that when a new criterion is applied, all its members measure up to it (Sprague, 1941) has little relevance. Such an observation simply increases the probability that the group is monophyletic, again without giving certainty; and the next new criterion could still reveal diversity.

It is hardly necessary here to dispose again of the view that the taxonomic hierarchy itself has some evolutionary significance, for few nowadays would be so ingenuous as to suppose that the categories can in some way be equated directly and neatly with the successive orders of branching of a phylogenetic tree. But even when this rather obvious pitfall has been avoided, there is still the chronic confusion which can arise through the confounding of the systematic chart and the genealogical tree. The presentations of Bessey (1915) and Hutchinson (1926, 1934) of the angiosperms permit just this error, although Hutchinson has himself warned against the confusion his diagrams invite. Lessons on how phylogenetic representations can be assembled have been given by Lam (1936), by Rodriguez (1950, 1956) for Bessey's and Hutchinson's systems, and by Sporne (1956, 1959). The symbolism suggested by these authors barely merits the description 'classification' at all except in a highly specialized sense, although all the schemes necessarily use the nomenclature of the natural groups of traditional taxonomy from whose properties they have been deduced.

CLASSIFICATORY CRITERIA

Sources

The criteria of Linnean-style taxonomy are derived principally from the comparative study of phenotypes. Some characteristics of phenotypes are readily observed; others are beyond unaided perception, and may be studied only with devices extending the human senses; and yet others are not expressed at all—or not expressed at the same time—unless conditions are provided which elicit them. But whatever the means of investigating phenotypes, the consequence for taxonomic purposes is simply to enlarge the body of 'characters' available. The value of criteria for classification is in no way related to the difficulty with which

they are observed, and it is not accordingly to be supposed that the
diagnostic value of, say, the disposition of the cellulose microfibrils of
the wall of a leaf hair cell is necessarily any greater than the shape of the
hair itself, notwithstanding the factor of forty thousand that separates
the costs of the instruments required to observe the two properties. It
would seem unnecessary to make this point, were it not that the recent
history of both plant and animal systematics has been punctuated by
hails of welcome for new kinds of criteria—almost invariably supposed
by their initiators or more vocal supporters to provide the corrective for
the 'fictions, errors and half-truths' of taxonomy.

The most obvious developments in the study of phenotypes in the
post-Linnean period have been in the field of micromorphology associated with the improvement and wider use of the microscope and its
various forms, and of preparatory techniques. The karyotype represents
a late step in the hunt for micromorphological criteria, although perhaps
not the ultimate, with the current rapid development of ultra-structure
research. Used as a classificatory tool, the karyotype can be divested of
all genetical significance and be drawn upon simply as a source of
morphological discriminants. The other and more important use of
cytological data as a basis for genetical deduction is discussed below.

The investigation of phenotypes in search of chemical differentiae,
long practised in the study of micro-organisms, has been gaining ground
for some time as a taxonomic procedure with higher plants and animals.
This extension of micromorphological study to the molecular level has
led to the revelation of important evidence concerning the taxonomic
distribution of molecules of known chemical structure and, through
chromatographic and immunological methods, also of chemically unknown but highly characteristic macromolecules. Bate-Smith (1958)
has pointed out that it is metabolically inert molecules of classes which
permit considerable structural diversity which are likely to prove of use
in supplying taxonomic discriminants. His own studies on plant
phenolics using chromatographic methods illustrate the kind of taxonomic data forthcoming from comparative investigations of relatively
simple molecules. Especially among the flowering plants secondary
products seem frequently to provide useful criteria (Hegnauer, 1956),
but the value of knowledge of the chemistry of metabolically important
compounds—wall materials, pigments and reserve products—has long
been appreciated in the taxonomy of other plant groups, more especially
algae and fungi.

The potentiality of immunological methods as a source of classificatory criteria is especially noteworthy. In so far as the proteins bear the

imprint of the genotype—if not directly, probably at no more than one step removed—they can form reliable and positive indicators of similarity and difference. In a paper reporting the first application of some modern immunological methods to flowering plant taxonomy, Gell, Hawkes & Wright (1960) suggest that serological characterization of the proteins from appropriate organs and tissues may help to elucidate genetic relations from the widest to the most minute.

Experimental culture is required to disclose some properties of the genotype of taxonomic significance, notably for exploration of phenotypic plasticity and the elucidation of life cycles. It needs no emphasis that it is part of the task of the systematist to ensure that his species descriptions truly embrace all aspects of infra-specific variability, taking into account not only the stage of the life cycle and genetically determined polymorphisms (especially those concerned with the breeding system), but also non-heritable variation arising from the impact of the environment. One of the major contributions of experimental taxonomic study of higher plants has been the elucidation of patterns of infra-specific variability involving both genetical and non-genetical components, since the capacity for direct plastic adaptation proves as much a property of the species as any other attribute. Phenotypic plasticity is less significant with higher animals as a consequence of their more efficient developmental regulation and freedom from the limitations of a sessile life. By the same token, it is frequently of *greater* significance with micro-organisms, where but a narrow range of potentialities may be expressed in any one environment. A testimony to this is the fact that transplant and varied-environment techniques (altogether insignificant in higher animal taxonomy) are still novelties used but occasionally by flowering-plant systematists, whilst their counterparts have long formed part of the every-day armoury of the microbial systematist.

Cytogenetical data

As classificatory adjuncts, the value of the chromosomes depends, as with other morphological attributes, upon the number of differentiae they have to offer and their stability. There is, however, another property that may reside in cytological data, namely that they may provide evidence for predicting breeding behaviour which may influence taxonomic decisions at and around the level of species. The existence of gross differences in chromosome number or structure between forms can form a reasonable basis for supposing that they would probably be at least partly intersterile, and so biospecifically distinct. Observations of this kind can thus replace experimental tests of interfertility with a reasonably high degree of certainty, and may therefore be acceptable as evidence of a peculiarly apposite kind when decisions about the taxonomic ranking of populations are involved. Löve (1951), for example, has developed an argument which almost amounts to suggesting that 'intraspecific' polyploidy should not be allowed to exist as a matter of taxonomic principle. Some animal cytologists have taken a less firm view (e.g. Hamerton, 1958), considering chromosome number alone as an inadequate basis for attempts to subdivide morphologically homogeneous population systems, and recently Löve has recognized the special taxonomic problem of cytologically distinct forms which show little or no morphological divergence (Valentine & Löve, 1958). The crucial issue is certainly the matter of morphological distinction. Where polyploids are in fact infallibly distinguishable by morphological features, it is reasonable to rank them as different species (Nannfeldt, 1938), although this is yet another situation where many purposes will be served well enough by the adoption of an aggregate binomial for the complex. Where consistent morphological discriminants are not available, the justification for awarding separate binomials to cytotypes is slight indeed. Nevertheless, it can be argued that the existence of different chromosome races should always act as a stimulus for further taxonomic study, and for this reason an addendum to the binomial of the aggregate species indicating that it is cytologically heterogeneous could be of value.

Very much the same considerations affect the taxonomic significance of experimental tests of interfertility. It has been noted that the biological species of Mayr and others is not definable simply by experimental tests of interfertility and the capacity for gene exchange; such tests merely expose intrinsic physiological barriers and cannot detect ethological and other barriers which may be of as much or greater importance in the wild. Obviously, however, when experiment does reveal the presence of a consistent sterility barrier between sexually breeding populations, they are biospecifically distinct, and the fact cannot be ignored when decisions about taxonomic rank are being made.

There is the further possibility that crossability tests might provide the evidence of relationship in the shaping of generic limits. Certainly the ability to produce an F_1 hybrid must itself indicate a degree of genetical compatibility; but genetical compatibility is, regrettably, not necessarily correlated with other attributes which might be regarded as taxonomically significant at a generic level, such as degree of morphological or genetical difference, or indeed the ages of lineages as independent evolutionary entities. A knowledge of crossability relationships is naturally of great significance in micro-evolutionary studies and in plant and animal breeding, but any classification based exclusively upon a sterility-fertility criterion is necessarily artificial.

Weighting

In the process of grouping which is the necessary first step in classification a decision has to be made as to how the available data shall be used. There are two possibilities: to give equal value to all observations, or to weight them differentially according to some agreed body of principles. It may be noted immediately that the severest discrimination that can be made between a pair of characters is to ignore one altogether, and since not all the facts about his organisms can ever be known to a systematist, he is already dealing with a weighted spectrum. But it may be supposed that the knowledge available will usually form a random sample of the whole universe of facts, and accordingly that it would be improbable that any other such sample would deviate radically. The sample can thus be treated as the whole, and the problem to weight or not to weight remains the same.

There are two bases on which weighting may be justified: (1) because there are *a priori* reasons why one character should be given greater prominence than another, and (2) because there are indications inherent in the available data that a classification of greater stability and possibly utility will arise by the promotion of some and the subordination of other characteristics. Weighting *a priori* may depend upon the application of principles determining what is and what is not essential in an Aristotelean sense, or upon some form of phylogenetical reasoning.

Cain (1959) has provided an admirable survey of the history of the *a priori* approach in taxonomy in the pre-evolutionary period. He has shown that most of the *a priori* reasoning of the early nineteenth century was superfluous, since the taxonomic results could have been reached in any event by grouping according to similarity, without weighting. Indeed the taxonomic principles of Lamarck, Cuvier and De Candolle were in large degree *a posteriori*, being based upon knowledge of groups already brought together by just this method (see p. 6).

In large measure this is also true of the principles of so-called phylogenetic taxonomy in the post-Darwinian period. The intention ostensibly motivating phylogenetic weighting as a taxonomic procedure seems straightforward enough. Essentially it arises from the belief that certain attributes of contemporary organisms give better indications than others of mutual relationships in an evolutionary sense, so that if the aim is to produce mono- or oligophyletic groupings, these characteristics should be given primary consideration and others played down or ignored. It is important to note the distinction between this activity and attempts to incorporate phylogenetic ideas in the *arrangement* of groupings resulting from classification according to maximum likeness. Bessey's 'Phylogenetic taxonomy of the flowering plants' (1915) is, for example, mostly a case of the second, not the first activity. In essence it is an arrangement of orders based upon twenty-eight dicta setting forth statements of opinion about the evolution of the group, including some twenty assertions of what is 'advanced' and what 'primitive'. We have already noted the confusion that can result from ingenuous attempts to interpret systems of arrangement like that of Bessey as phylogenetic trees.

Before any case for phylogenetic weighting in classification can be taken seriously, it must clearly be established how phylogenetically significant characteristics can be detected anyway. Cain (1959), in a penetrating analysis of these problems, suggests that the only incontestable evidence is that of an adequate fossil record, although a knowledge of the functional significance of certain characteristics may occasionally give reason to suspect evolutionary convergence. The reasonableness of accepting palaeontological evidence where such is available as providing an indication of what is and what is not phylogenetically significant seems unchallengeable; but the extent to which this can influence neontological classification is more debatable than at first sight may appear. Certainly there are many cases where 'improvement' in classification may be said to have resulted from an analysis of fossil evidence. Thus Florin's fine fossil researches have led to the resolution of many morphological puzzles in the gymnosperms, and have provided the justification for revisions like the removal of the Taxaceae from the Coniferales and the creation of an independent order, Taxales. On the other hand, attempts to argue from inadequate or under-analysed fossil material can merely lead to an amplification of dispute. It is salutary to read the conclusion of a distinguished pteridologist, after deploring the current confusion in the classification of vascular cryptogams, that '...this is chiefly due to the fact that the classification of the Pteridophyta is based upon fossil plants rather than living ones' (Pichi-Sermolli, 1959). The implication of this observation is simply that if a stable and agreed classification is what is desired it would be better to give up any pretence at 'phylogenetic classification' in this group and aim at a natural classification based upon maximum likeness amongst living forms.

In the total absence of relevant fossil evidence, there seems no means at all of introducing phylogenetic weighting into classification which does not involve an assertion of opinion, and the activity then becomes suspiciously like the *a priori* weighting of pre-evolutionists. The theory of evolution, after all, did not bring omniscience to taxonomists, but only a new way of looking at organic variation; and it is fruitful to consider just in what ways the mere possession of an evolutionary hypothesis *can* alter one's approach to the act of classification. Paradoxically enough, the answer is only by impelling one to adopt a less natural and more artificial basis for the delineation of groups; for the act of weighting itself involves a deliberate rejection as irrelevant of some of the knowledge available about the organisms under treatment, and so a narrowing of the range of criteria taken into consideration. Cain (1959) suggests that without fossil evidence the only characters which may validly be rejected in this manner are those known at the present day to be specializations for a highly specific mode of life, since such characters may well be attained polyphyletically under natural selection. Almost any other form of phylogenetic weighting he considers must be based upon hypotheses which on the whole are more likely to be wrong than right.

Nevertheless, it is widely supposed that taxonomists do always weight their data according to the evolutionary hypothesis they happen to hold for the groups they are treating (Whitehouse, 1954). If this were true, one might wonder how any stability in classification has been attained at all; but fortunately for biology it is largely a delusion. What weighting they do introduce is generally based upon a partly intuitive assessment of the patterns of correlation amongst the characters of the organisms before them. This assessment, together with a knowledge of practice in neighbouring groups, leads to the recognition of the characteristics which show the highest correlation *inter se* and can therefore sustain the greatest weight in framing higher categories. Phylogenetic speculation (along the lines that the high correlation of the characters indicates that they are 'primitive' or 'conservative') may or may not be grafted on afterwards.

It is instructive to consider in what ways a taxon based upon maximum likeness might be other than monophyletic (I have argued elsewhere (Heslop-Harrison, 1959) that the only useful sense of the word 'monophyletic' in relation to a taxonomic group is to imply that all its members have descended from a single ancestral population which would, if it existed today, be placed in the same group). Obviously this could only result from evolutionary convergence—when two or more originally diverse lineages have accumulated so many characters in common that they are more like each other today than like any others in existence. Adherence to a phylogenetic principle in classification would demand that if the evolutionary history were known, say from a fossil record, they should be separated and combined with other groups with which they share fewer common characters.

What if there were no fossil record? It is difficult to see in this case how the convergence can be detected for certain, although suspicion might arise whenever it is apparent that the unity of a group depends upon the possession of common characteristics adapted for a specialized form of life. It is considerations of this kind which demand that the Tasmanian wolf which resembles in so many respects the canine wolf should not be classified with it, and suggest that families like the Nymphaeaceae, the members of which share in common the habit of the water-lily and the structural adaptations this involves but precious little else, are ripe for subdivision.

The example of the Nymphaeaceae, however, illustrates that the gravest violation of phylogenetic principles is likely to arise not simply when adaptive characters are permitted to intrude into classification, but when they are allowed to dominate. Here not only phylogenetic principles are violated but also principles of natural classification, in that the groupings are based upon the common possession of a few major features and not upon reference to all those available. To correct the situation in many such cases what is necessary is not an exercise in phylogenetic speculation, but merely a translation of the basis of classification by taking more characteristics into consideration.

The key phrase is, of course, reference to all those characters available. In some groups, and more especially micro-organisms, the range of characters available is so small as almost to guarantee that classifications will be at once artificial and non-phylogenetic. The Fungi Imperfecti represents, *par excellence*, such an assemblage. Form genera are based upon similarities of growth and means of conidial dispersal which are necessarily strongly adaptive; they can thus barely avoid being poly-phyletic. But, once more, it is not a phylogenetic hypothesis that would be most effective in producing assemblage with a greater chance of being monophyletic, but simply the availability of a few more differential characteristics on which to found a natural classification.

I have referred above to a form of weighting of taxonomic charac-teristics often passing for phylogenetic weighting, which in fact is a by-product of grouping-by-likeness not dependent at all upon an evolutionary hypothesis. This is the special significance which comes to be attached to characters and constellations of characters found through a wide range of organisms in a fairly invariant form without at the same time being distributed universally in the group under treatment. In any system of classification these characteristics would tend to be emphasized in the definition of major groups; their elevation to greater significance is a product of hierarchical classification in general. With a background knowledge of what has already been accomplished in related groups, a taxonomist approaching an unfamiliar assemblage will necessarily refer to these elevated characteristics first. He will thus 'weight' them in the sense that he will permit them to give him his primary orientation and even to supply the basis of his first subdivisions. Now what is significant about this is that the procedure is logically based upon the facts ascertainable from existing organisms; the explanation of the constancy of the key characters is, of course, likely to be that they are phylogenetically ancient, but it is not knowledge of this fact or indeed any form of *a priori* evolutionary judgment at all which gave them their significance in the first instance, but merely their taxonomic usefulness in the context of the group under treatment. One may of course wish to *call* this activity phylogenetic weighting; but to do so does not make for clear thinking about the nature of taxonomic procedure.

The alternative to character weighting in the construction of taxonomic groups is to proceed by awarding equal value to all of the available characters. The first proponent of natural classification of this kind was Adanson (1763). Adanson's 'universal method' was essentially to create a succession of single-criterion classifications, and to determine which organisms came together in the greatest number; these were then placed together in a final classification as showing the greatest natural affinity. The criticisms of Adanson's universal method by his immediate successors appear in retrospect a little odd; they were that he succeeded in doing what he set out to do, namely to eliminate weighting as a taxonomic procedure. A criticism of greater substance is that the method demands an iterative treatment which can be far from economical in labour. This objection is less significant than formerly, since the actual operations of comparison can be mechanized and so rendered painless. Models for the application of Adansonian methods are available in the work of Michener & Sokal (1957) and Sneath (1957 *a, b*) for insect and bacterial groups, while Cain & Harrison (1958) have shown how closely allied is the procedure of a competent taxonomist in judging affinity by intuitive means.

The converse problem to that of grouping is that of discrimination, encountered in its most severe form in species or population complexes where intergrading variation tends to obscure what differences are present. Evidently the most useful procedure in attempting to separate and define taxa in such critical complexes will be one which takes into consideration the maximum number of characters, but which attaches significance to them according to their individual efficiency in providing the required discrimination. This approach, long adopted in anthropology, is finding a wider place in other fields of taxonomy. Anderson's 'hybrid index' (1936), much used in the analysis of interspecific hybridization in plants, is a form of discriminant function in which the character weighting is based upon subjective assessment. Fisher (1936) has supplied the full procedure for deriving the most efficient function for the discrimination of two groups using several metrical characters, and a model of its application to a small flowering plant complex is given by Whitehead (1954).

SPECIAL PURPOSE CLASSIFICATION

Whatever may be its demerits in detail and whatever objections may be launched against it on theoretical grounds, it is inconceivable that the taxonomic system in current use should be displaced in the foreseeable future as the main reference framework for the higher groups; after two centuries of use the Linnean method is ingrained so deeply in biology that abandonment now would scarcely be possible, and, in any event, a better general purpose-system has yet to be suggested. Nevertheless, there are many purposes for which classification of the traditional general-purpose form is likely to be found inadequate, not because of any inherent fault, but simply as an inevitable consequence of its being general. These are purposes for which, for one reason or another, a special criterion or small group of criteria has particular significance, so that a classification which does not place all the emphasis in the correct quarter is inappropriate. Such situations demand artificial classifications.

The obvious examples are those where the purpose immediately defines the criterion. The utilitarian classifications of materia medica, of economic botany—even of the fat stock market—are all of this nature: none has any particular need to use the framework of general taxonomy, except occasionally for the purpose of extracting a name for a label. All ecological classifications share a similar character, being based upon criteria such as feeding behaviour, habit, life form and the like which may or may not have a correlation with taxonomic position in the general system.

Biologists who acknowledge this occasionally have difficulty in accepting that also to be counted amongst artificial classifications are all those based exclusively on cytological or immunological data, or upon tests of interfertility, graft compatibility and the like. Yet it is obviously so, since only if the particular favoured characteristic should happen also to be that showing the highest average level of correlation with all other attributes would the classification accord with a natural one. The efflorescence of genetical and cytological research in the last half century has shown how unsafe this latter assumption can be, especially with plants; the groupings suggested by cytological and genetical criteria are by no means always congruent with those of a general classification based upon maximum correlation of attributes. It is this fact that has led to the proposal by experimental taxonomists of various special-purpose category systems.

Special-purpose categories

It should be evident, of course, that the category systems that have been a by-product of experimental taxonomy do not replace those of orthodox taxonomy but supplement them in those groups where experimental data have accumulated sufficiently to warrant a special treatment, and where, above all, a need has arisen. I have given elsewhere an introductory survey of the better known proposals (Heslop-Harrison, 1960). Forty years have elapsed since the first, that of Turesson (1922), was published—the familiary hierarchy, ecotype, ecospecies, coenospecies; a system which bore within itself evidence of its incomplete severance from orthodox taxonomy. The latest has been the deme system, which Gilmour and I developed in 1954 on the basis of a suggestion originally made by Gilmour & Gregor (1939). This we conceived as a special-purpose category system divorced totally from orthodox taxonomy, not necessarily hierarchical in structure, and of infinite flexibility.

The essence of the deme system is the construction of a series of category-terms by the addition of one or more virtually self-explanatory prefixes to the neutral suffix '-deme'. The suffix itself, always to be used in the terminology with a prefix, denotes any group of individuals of a specified taxon. The prefixes establish on what grounds they are individuals considered together; they thus carry information concerning the kind of *criterion* applied in forming the grouping, unlike any categories of nomenclatural taxonomy. There is a tendency among some biologists to employ the suffix alone, and to use the term *deme* in the sense of *topodeme* or *gamodeme* (see below): it is scarcely necessary to point out that this makes nonsense of the whole intention of the system. In the original exposition of the system, examples were given of its application to a particular, limited field, namely to the units of variation which are significant in the processes of micro-evolution in higher plants. Thus the term *topodeme* signifies a deme occurring in a specified geographical area; *gamodeme*, a deme composed of individuals which are so situated spatially and temporally that, within the limits of the breeding system, all can interbreed; *autodeme*, a deme composed of predominantly autogamous individuals; *agamodeme*, a deme composed of predominantly apomictic individuals, and so on. The categories are in no sense mutually exclusive, since the same population may be referable to several different categories according to which of its properties is taken into account, and the categories may be coincident or overlapping. In all derivatives concerned with dissimilarity, it is intended that 'difference' shall connote whatever the investigator cares to make it, which will naturally depend upon his technique and intention. The object of this stipulation is, of course, to focus attention upon the technique used in any study rather than upon the descriptive terminology itself.

The deme categories are not intended to form the basis of any formal nomenclatural system, but it is obvious that reference names or code numbers could be adopted wherever the need arises. Commonly these would be descriptive, or, in derivatives associated with locality or habitat, carry a geographical reference. A neutral system might be desirable in some cases, as, for example, in referring to infra-specific *serodemes*.

Whether or not the deme system will prove to have a function in analysing and referring to biological variation remains to be discovered, but it is difficult to see how any rational category system for special-purpose classifications can be devised which does not adopt something of the philosophy underlying it. The principal attributes of such a system are largely determined by the nature of artificial as opposed to natural classification. There are as many artificial classifications as there are criteria on which they can be based, so that the category system must make provision for indicating the kind of criterion in use in order that the particular classification can be identified. It follows also that it is imperative that nothing should preclude the inclusion of an individual in more than one category, since the groupings formed will necessarily differ according to the criterion applied. This in turn implies that no nomenclatural system comparable with that of orthodox taxonomy can be devised, but only reference nicknames linked inseparably to the category terms, themselves serving to identify the artificial classification in use. And, finally, only by the overt recognition that 'difference' is always a relative term to be established by context does it seem possible to avoid disputes about category definitions. The validity of an artificial classification is determined solely by its internal consistency, so that the purpose in view can always be allowed to govern the levels of difference to be adopted in establishing the subdivisions.

REFERENCES

ADANSON, M. (1763). *Familles des plantes*, 1. Paris: Vincent.

ANDERSON, E. (1936). Hybridisation in American Tradescantia. *Ann. Mo. bot. Gard.* 23, 511.

BATHER, F. A. (1927). Biological classification: past and future. *Quart. J. geol. Soc. Lond.* 83, lxii.

BATE-SMITH, E. C. (1958). Plant phenolics as taxonomic guides. *Proc. Linn. Soc. Lond.* 169, 198.

BESSEY, C. E. (1915). The phylogenetic taxonomy of flowering plants. *Ann. Mo. bot. Gard.* 2, 109.

CAIN, A. J. (1954). *Animal Species and their Evolution*. London: Hutchinson.

CAIN, A. J. (1958). Logic and memory in Linnaeus's system of taxonomy. *Proc. Linn. Soc. Lond.* 169, 144.

CAIN, A. J. (1959). Deductive and inductive methods in post-Linnean taxonomy. *Proc. Linn. Soc. Lond.* 170, 185.

CAIN, A. J. & HARRISON, H. G. (1958). An analysis of the taxonomist's judgment of affinity. *Proc. zool. Soc. Lond.* 131, 85.

CLAUSEN, J. (1954). Partial apomixis as an equilibrium system in evolution. *Caryologia* (vol. suppl. 1954), p. 469.

CLAUSEN, J., KECK, D. D. & HIESEY, W. M. (1939). The concept of the species based on experiment. *Amer. J. Bot.* 26, 103.

DU RIETZ, G. E. (1930). The fundamental units of biological taxonomy. *Svensk bot. Tidskr.* 24, 333.

FISHER, R. A. (1936). The use of multiple measurements in taxonomic problems. *Ann. Eugen.* 7, 87.

GELL, P. G. H., HAWKES, J. G. & WRIGHT, S. T. C. (1960). The application of immunological methods to the taxonomy of species within the genus *Solanum*. *Proc. roy. Soc.* B, 151, 364.

GILMOUR, J. S. L. (1941). Taxonomy and philosophy. In *The New Systematics*, p. 461. Oxford: Clarendon Press.

GILMOUR, J. S. L. (1951). The development of taxonomy since 1851. *Advanc. Sci., Lond.* 8, 70.

GILMOUR, J. S. L. & GREGOR, J. W. (1939). Demes: a suggested new terminology. *Nature, Lond.* 144, 333.

GILMOUR, J. S. L. & HESLOP-HARRISON, J. (1954). The deme terminology and the units of microevolutionary change. *Genetica*, 17, 147.

HAMERTON, J. L. (1958). Problems in mammalian cytotaxonomy. *Proc. Linn. Soc. Lond.* 169, 112.

HEGNAUER, F. (1956). Chemotaxonomic survey of the Leguminosae. *Pharmazie*, 11, 638.

HESLOP-HARRISON, J. (1955). The conflict of categories. In *Species Studies in the British Flora*, p. 161. Arbroath: Buncle.

HESLOP-HARRISON, J. (1958). The unisexual flower—a reply to criticism. *Phytomorphology*, 8, 177.

HESLOP-HARRISON, J. (1959). Apomixis, environment and adaptation. *Biosystematics Symposium, 9th Int. Bot. Congr., Montreal.* In *Advances in Botany.* Toronto: University of Toronto Press.

HESLOP-HARRISON, J. (1960). *New Concepts in Flowering-Plant Taxonomy.* London: Heinemann.

HUTCHINSON, J. (1926, 1934). *The Families of Flowering Plants.* I. *Dicotyledons;* II. *Monocotyledons.* London: Macmillan.

LAM, H. J. (1936). Phylogenetic symbols, past and present. *Acta Biotheoretica,* **2,** 153.

LAWRENCE, G. H. M. (1951). *Taxonomy of Vascular Plants.* New York: Macmillan.

LÖVE, A. (1951). Taxonomic evaluation of polyploids. *Caryologia,* **3,** 263.

MAYR, E. (1942). *Systematics and the Origin of Species.* New York: Columbia University Press.

MAYR, E. (1955). The species as a systematic and as a biological problem. *Biological Systematics,* p. 2. Cornvallis.

MAYR, E. (1957). Species concepts and definitions. In *The Species Problem,* p. 1. Washington, D.C.: Amer. Ass. Adv. Sci.

MICHENER, C. D. & SOKAL, R. P. (1957). A quantitative approach to a problem in classification. *Evolution,* **11,** 130.

NANNFELDT, J. A. (1938). *Poa maroccana* Nannf. sp.n. and *P. rivulorum* Maire & Trabut, two more tetraploids of sect. *Ochlopoa* A. & Gr. and some additional notes on *Ochlopoa. Svensk bot. Tidskr.* **32,** 295.

PICHI-SERMOLLI, R. E. G. (1959). Pteridophyta. In *Vistas in Botany,* **1,** 421. London: Pergamon.

RODRIGUEZ, R. L. (1950). A graphical representation of Bessey's taxonomic system. *Madroño,* **10,** 214.

RODRIGUEZ, R. L. (1956). A graphical representation of Hutchinson's taxonomic system. *Rev. Trop. Bot.* **4,** 35.

SIMPSON, G. G. (1945). The principles of classification and a classification of mammals. *Bull. Amer. Mus. Nat. Hist.* **85,** 1.

SIMPSON, G. G. (1959). Anatomy and morphology: classification and evolutions: 1859 and 1959. *Proc. Amer. phil. Soc.* **103,** 286.

SNEATH, P. H. A. (1957*a*). Some thoughts on bacterial classification. *J. gen. Microbiol.* **17,** 184.

SNEATH, P. H. A. (1957*b*). The application of computers to taxonomy. *J. gen. Microbiol.* **17,** 201.

SPORNE, K. (1956). The phylogenetic classification of the angiosperms. *Biol. Rev.* **31,** 1.

SPORNE, K. (1959). On the phylogenetic classification of plants. *Amer. J. Bot.* **46,** 385.

SPRAGUE, T. A. (1941). Taxonomic botany with special reference to the angiosperms. In *The New Systematics,* p. 435. Oxford: Clarendon Press.

TURESSON, G. (1922). The genotypical response of plant species to habitat. *Hereditas,* **3,** 211.

VALENTINE, D. & LÖVE, A. (1958). Taxonomy and biosystematic categories. *Brittonia, N.Y.* **10,** 153.

VAN STEENIS, C. G. G. J. (1957). Specific and infra-specific delimitation. *Flora Malesiana,* Ser. 1, **5,** pp. clxvii–ccxxxiv.

WHITEHEAD, F. H. (1954). An example of taxonomic discrimination by biometric methods. *New Phytol.* **53,** 496.

WHITEHOUSE, H. K. L. (1954). Review. *J. Ecol.* **42,** 563.

TAXONOMIC PROCEDURES IN CLASSIFICATION OF PROTOZOA

JOHN O. CORLISS

Department of Zoology, University of Illinois, Urbana, Illinois, U.S.A. *

Historically the science of systematics† has been considered divisible into three phases which are chronologically more or less independent: *alpha* taxonomy, the first or earliest stage, essentially limited to production of conventional descriptions of species and groups of species; *beta* taxonomy, the synthetic phase, concerned with proposals and treatment of schemes of natural classification embracing all levels in the taxonomic hierarchy; and finally the *gamma* stage, presumably the ultimate goal of all taxonomy, devoted principally to problems of evolutionary relationships at intraspecific, populational levels. In general the protozoologist is still in the dark ages of stage one, although for practical reasons, if no other, he must attempt a bit of *beta* taxonomy concomitantly. However, among students of animal groups, at least, he is far from being lonely in this respect: only certain vertebrate systematists and a scattering of investigators among the invertebrate specialists can profitably apply full time and talent to carrying on with the 'new systematics': 'detecting evolution at work' (Huxley, 1940).

DIVERSITY OF THE PROTOZOA

The tremendous diversity in the protozoan way of life and the taxonomic problems thus posed are not, I believe, generally appreciated by non-protozoological biologists. A few facts and figures will illustrate my point.

Consider the protozoan range in size. Omitting the amoeboid plasmodia of mycetozoa (which may measure more than a metre, over 10^6 μ, in a given direction), sizes vary from 1 to 4 μ for some small flagellates and sporozoa to 3000–5000 μ for large ciliates and rhizopod amoebae, to 70,000 μ for one stage in the life cycle of certain cnidosporidians, and even to 150,000 μ (15 cm.) for some fossil foraminiferidans! Volume-wise the size difference is even more striking: it has been calculated (Jahn & Jahn, 1949) that a cnidosporidian of the kind mentioned above

---

* I use the terms 'systematics' and 'taxonomy' indiscriminately throughout the present paper, following Mayr, Linsley & Usinger (1953), and others; but I am aware of distinctions recognized by such leaders as Simpson (1961).

† Address (1961–62): Department of Zoology, University of Exeter.

has a volume some 2×10^{12} times that of a leishmanian flagellate, whereas the size range among *all* vertebrates (by weight) is—by contrast —only about 10^9.

The cyto-architecture of the protozoa is also remarkable: whether they are considered to be unicellular or not (Baker, 1948; Corliss, 1957*a*; Dobell, 1911; Gregg, 1959; Hyman, 1959; Tartar, 1961), these micro-organisms have certainly demonstrated an amazing diversity in protoplasmic organization at what one may term the subcellular or organellar level. Features of this morphological differentiation of prime importance in systematics will be treated presently.

Physiologically, even if one considers nutritional habits alone, the range from autotrophy to complex heterotrophy, with exhibition of various kinds of phagotrophy and osmotrophy, nearly matches the extremes known for all organisms, plant, animal, and microbial. Exposure of many of the biochemical and physiological peculiarities— some surprisingly un-peculiar and metazoan-like on close inspection (Hutner, 1961)—of the protozoan way of life may be conveniently found in a recent series of volumes devoted expressly and exclusively to such an absorbing task: see Lwoff (1951), Hutner & Lwoff (1955), Hutner (1962).

The cosmopolitan nature of many protozoan species, both free-living and symbiotic, freshwater and pelagic, is taxonomically and evolutionarily discouraging to such biologists as vertebrate systematists and phylogenists who are accustomed to using factors of geographical distribution in their reconstructions. A myriad of problems remains to be solved with regard to ecological diversities of the protozoa (Kitching, 1957).

Finally, the possibility that thousands of present-day protozoan species are virtually unchanged descendants from perhaps a Cambrian or even pre-Cambrian ancestry rightly dismays the student of evolution and natural selection.

From a zoological, particularly vertebrate, point of view the outlook for achieving a comparably reasonable 'natural' scheme of classification for the protozoa is, in the final analysis, gloomy if not altogether hopeless (Corliss, 1960*a*). From the standpoint of a microbiologist, however, the protozoologist should be grateful for the relatively large favours granted him by his organisms. Indeed, their very heterogeneity, referred to so discouragingly in the preceding paragraphs, allows him to group and tangibly classify his wee animalcules with a practical facility which is surely the envy of his taxonomic colleagues in the fields of bacteriology, mycology, and virology. (Incidentally, I must say that it is a pleasant surprise for a protozoologist to be included in a symposium on micro-biology: so often he is just left forlornly dangling *between* the great field of bacteriology, on the one hand, and that of zoology proper, on the other.)

In the remainder of the present paper I wish to list and offer brief critical discussion of categories of characteristics, morphological and non-morphological, used or potentially useful in classifying protozoa; to consider general problems in the taxonomy of groups at different levels in the overall hierarchical system, illustrating such problems with selected examples; and, finally, to touch on nomenclatural aspects of systematics which have seemed to trouble so many protozoologists.

BASES FOR CLASSIFICATION OF PROTOZOA

Comparative morphology has always provided—and for some time will surely continue to do so—the principal source of data utilizable in recognition of relationships at all levels in the taxonomic hierarchy of protozoan forms. Of course this is generally true for all of the 'higher' plants and animals as well. It may be instructive to review here, briefly, the major categories of *anatomical* features of systematic value in study of protozoa; physiological, ecological, genetic, and other *non-morpho-logical* characteristics will be considered subsequently.

Morphological characteristics

(1) *Non-living products of the organism.* A sizeable percentage of the entire phylum Protozoa is treated taxonomically on the basis of the tests, shells, loricae, thecal plates, cyst or spore membranes, or internal skeletons which are remarkably assembled from external sources, precisely secreted by the organism itself, or ingeniously produced by a combination of the two methods. Major examples include the foramini-feridans, radiolaridans, and testaceous rhizopods among the so-called Sarcodina; the dinoflagellates, silicoflagellates, and coccolithophorids among the Mastigophora; the pelagic tintinnids among the Ciliophora; certain gregarines and coccidians among the Sporozoa *sensu stricto*; and large groups within the Cnidosporidia. What fossil records we have for the protozoa come principally from representatives of these groups. Precedence for use of 'hard parts' in comparative systematic study has, of course, been established long ago as indispensable in taxonomic investigation of much metazoan material.

(2) *Organelles of locomotion.* Pseudopodia, flagella, cilia—or their absence—have long served as 'key' characters in differentiating various

major protozoan taxa one from the other. As is well known, the conventional division of the phylum into four principal classes or subphyla is based on the predominant presence of one of these types of locomotor organelles or the complete absence of any of them. As pellicular structures and as organelles sometimes involved in feeding operations, they will be considered taxonomically valuable again in following paragraphs.

(3) *Body size and shape.* These are features often of dubious significance, although sometimes legitimately reliable at a given lower taxonomic level and of very general application in separation of certain major groups: for example, most gregarines are relatively large sporozoa while most haemosporidians are small; and most heterotrich ciliates are very conspicuous in their size while hymenostomes are often small and inconspicuous. Within some taxa of symbiotic or parasitic forms biometrical analyses of body sizes have provided very useful data.

(4) *Organelles of attachment to substrata.* Stalks, peduncles, thigmotactic ciliature, cemented-down loricae, filaments, suckers, hooks, and spines have been developed and elaborated by hundreds of protozoan species and have proven useful to their owners in maintenance of the body in a given ecological niche, either in fresh- or salt-water environments (on living or non-living substrata) or in digestive or coelomic cavities or tissue-cells of endoparasitized host organisms. In a very general way such adornments are of systematic value at the higher taxonomic levels; at the lowest levels they may be of considerable value, particularly when used in combination with other characters.

(5) *Colonial organization.* Scattered throughout most major groups of the protozoa are species whose normal form, at least in a predominant stage of the life cycle, is a *group* one; that is, the colonial organization has been adopted by these species. If the term 'colony' is defined rather loosely it may be considered to include not only the well known spheroid, discoid and arboroid types of association but also the more or less fortuitous kinds of aggregations of individuals into temporary chains, nets or gelatinous masses of irregular conformation. Specific usage of these characteristics in protozoan taxonomy, however, is rather limited, although genera such as *Volvox*, *Carchesium* and *Epistylis* are readily recognizable even to the non-protozoologist because of them.

(6) *Pellicular or 'superficial' differentiation.* Some phytoflagellates have distinctly sculptured periplasts or thecae, and cnidosporidian spores may be similarly decorated with ridges and other markings. The heavy pellicle of ophryoscolecid ciliates may be drawn out posteriorly into spines. External organelles of attachment in various groups have

already been mentioned: and numbers and arrangements of flagella also would come under this heading. But I have particularly in mind here the simple and compound ciliature of members of the subphylum Ciliophora: the structural diversity and patterns of topographical distribution of these organelles have long played important roles in schemes of classification for the ciliated protozoa, at all levels. Legitimately useful though such diagnostic characteristics are, however, it is being realized today (Corliss, 1961) that the superficial or external features of ciliation may sometimes exaggerate differences among the higher taxonomic groups: the value of the more conservative *infraciliature* is treated in the following paragraph.

(7) *Subpellicular bodies and fibrillar systems.* Basal 'granules', kinetodesmal fibrils, ciliary rootlets, and myoneme systems have been revealed in ciliates, many flagellates, and some other protozoa, most precisely by recent electron microscopical investigations (see the comprehensive review by Grimstone, 1961). Such structures lie within or just underneath the so-called pellicle and, with the exception of some myoneme systems, are associated directly with ciliary or flagellar organelles of locomotion or feeding. The basal bodies or kinetosomes, plus their related fibrils or kinetodesmata, comprise the 'infraciliature' of ciliates, a system of such universality and stability, and therefore reliability, that it has become exceedingly valuable in comparative taxonomic studies at all levels within the Ciliophora (Corliss, 1956*a*, 1961). Convenient methods (e.g. silver impregnation) for revealing its presence by conventional microscopical study have assured wide employment of this fundamental feature in modern revisions of ciliate taxa.

(8) *Feeding organelles.* Presence or absence of a cytostome or an oral apparatus and possession of structures (such as pseudopodia, ciliary organelles, tentacles) often of direct aid in phagotrophy are features of some, although rather general, value at the highest taxonomic levels. Morphology of the involved organelles, especially those used jointly in feeding and locomotion, is of obvious comparative value, as has been pointed out in a preceding paragraph. At ordinal levels and below, the 'mouth parts' of ciliates, particularly their infraciliary anatomy, are, for example, of considerable systematic significance. Recognition of possible homologies is essential in comparative taxonomic studies of such organelles (Corliss, 1959).

(9) *Internal differentiation and cytoplasmic inclusions.* Of limited taxonomic usage, in general, is the occurrence of organelles such as mitochondria, Golgi apparatus, contractile and other vacuoles, and crystalline inclusions of various sorts. Presence or absence of chroma-

tophores (chloroplasts, plastids) furnishes the basis for a major dichotomy among the flagellated protozoa, but the existence of apochlorotic strains and species (laboratory-induced or naturally occurring) reveals the taxonomic folly of applying the distinction, as Calkins (1933) did, too rigidly. Pigmentation and food reserves will be mentioned below, under non-morphological characteristics. Distribution of trichocysts throughout the phylum represents a matter of cytological interest but it affords no real basis for much taxonomic separation. Of striking importance, however, are the elements of the 'mastigont system'. Features of this essentially internally developed system are to the comparative taxonomy of zooflagellates what the ciliary organelles (and their infraciliature) are to the systematics and postulated evolutionary relationships of the ciliated protozoa (for the flagellate structures and their value see Kirby (1944, 1950) and papers cited therein). These 'flagellar units' comprise the flagella proper and such associated organelles as blepharoplasts (basal bodies) or blepharoplast-complexes, axostyles, parabasal bodies (recently revealed as Golgi material by electron microscopy), and, scattered throughout various taxa, the costa, cresta, pelta, aciculum, and un-named minor fibrils. When a single nucleus is intimately associated with such organelles, the entire set—which may be duplicated many times over in a single flagellate's body—is known as a karyomastigont; when the nuclei are spatially dissociated, akaryomastigonts are recognized.

(10) *Nuclear characteristics.* Nuclear monomorphism sets all other protozoa apart from the Ciliophora. At lower taxonomic levels size, shape, and internal composition of nuclei are more important in some groups than in others: indispensable, for instance, in differentiating various genera and species of symbiotic amoebae (e.g. see Hoare, 1959 b), but generally of no consistent value in separating groups of ciliates at suprageneric grades (Corliss, 1959, 1961). Chromosome studies are of as great potential value in taxonomic considerations of protozoa as of any group of organisms, but technical difficulties have, to date, prevented much advance in this area of protozoan cytogenetics. Even sorting out the differences between true chromosomes and chromosome-aggregates (Devidé & Geitler, 1947) plagues the ciliate cytologist; and in some of the otherwise most ideal species the number of chromosomes is rather high or variable (e.g. note Dippell (1954) on *Paramecium aurelia*, in which five races within a single variety were shown to have a range in diploid chromosome number from 66 to 102!). Investigators using *Tetrahymena pyriformis* are fortunate in these respects: the diploid number is only ten and all chromosomes are easily

detectable (Ray, 1956); on the other hand, the number in the neighbouring species *T. rostrata* is estimated to be several times that number (Corliss, 1956*b*).

Further improvements can and will be made, of course, in utilization of any and all of the 'morphological' approaches to recognition and taxonomic differentiation of protozoan groups considered in the preceding pages. Among these are more precise cytological techniques (e.g. witness the tremendous amount of significant data being made available today through electron microscopy); more elegant methods of collecting comparative data, and increased application of improved statistical methods of analysis to the information so obtained; wider recognition of differences between homologous and analogous structures and organelles; increased awareness of the intimate relationship of physiological and ecological factors to morphological differentiation; more widespread realization of the necessity of studying the organism throughout its entire life cycle, so that such important features as polymorphism will not be overlooked.

Non-morphological characteristics

I have noted our overwhelming dependence in protozoology on morphology as a source of taxonomic criteria in treating all levels comprising classificational schemes. Yet many features of a non-morphological nature are in use already, and it is not over-optimism on my part to predict increased utilization of such factors as our knowledge continues to grow and to become more refined. Major categories which provide such characters may be considered briefly.

(1) *Ecological considerations of free-living forms.* This is a neglected area of potentially richly rewarding protozoological research yet precise studies of outstanding, broadly applicable value can nearly be counted 'on the fingers of one thumb' (to borrow a well-known literary phrase). In spite of the seemingly ubiquitous nature of so many species, careful investigation of ecological niches and of factors limiting the occupancy of given habitats has in the past revealed information of use in taxonomy and could do so in the future on a much wider scale. In a general way 'ecology' has, of course, long been useful in separation of marine from freshwater forms, polysaprobic from oligosaprobic, microphagous from macrophagous, anaerobic from aerobic, sedentary from mobile, etc. Kitching (1957) has offered the most recent review of the status of ecology with reference to free-living protozoa; an example of an investigation published since then which is of potential significance

taxonomically is the accurate, detailed study by Heal (1961) on testaceous amoebae found in fens and bogs in northern England.

(2) '*Host-parasite*' *relationships of symbiotic forms.* In some instances here perhaps too much taxonomic weight has been given to such factors as 'host-specificity', although it is most encouraging to note such statements as the one made in the novel parasitological treatise recently produced by Noble & Noble (1961, p. 637): 'No longer does the parasitologist assume that a parasite in a new host is a new species.' At the lower levels, however, many important observations on the ecology of protozoan parasites have had a direct bearing of great value on the classificational systems of the micro-organisms implicated. The reader is referred to general text-books of parasitology and protozoology, which abound with excellent examples of application of host-symbiont factors to protozoan taxonomy. In going a step further—attempting to relate groups of free-living forms to those comprised of commensals or parasites—one must keep clearly in mind the many morphological and physiological changes which may have been undergone in adaptation to life on or within a host organism.

(3) *General physiological characteristics.* These include reaction to various stimuli, types of locomotion, modes of nutrition, specific patterns of behaviour (seldom studied rigorously), etc. Such features are often employed in taxonomic diagnoses, generally in combination with anatomical ones; but, so far, their independent use in systematics is only significant in scattered cases. One may note, in passing, the alleged potential value of pseudopodial behaviour in classification of rhizopod amoebae, as recently stressed by Bovee (Bovee, 1954; Bovee & Jahn, 1960); and among the ciliates even the direction of spiralling when swimming has been put forward as a factor of taxonomic significance (Bullington, 1939).

(4) *Biochemical and serological characteristics.* A vast amount of work is being done today on protozoan metabolism; yet the resulting data have not, in large measure, been directly applicable to taxonomic problems. Part of the difficulty lies in the variableness of the information obtained in study of forms known for certain to be closely related on morphological and other grounds. Furthermore, biochemical likenesses may appear between forms from widely separated taxa. Measure of affinity by means of antigenic similarities is more promising. Such serological methods have already been used to advantage at strain and species levels, in works on both free-living forms (e.g. species of *Paramecium*) and, especially, parasitic species (e.g. haemoflagellates and various sporozoa).

(5) *Pigments, coloration in general, characteristic food reserves.* Although general body coloration is a feature of restricted taxonomic usage in protozoology, the kinds of pigments present in the chromatophores of phytoflagellates are of definite systematic value at suprafamilial levels. In fact, kinship of these forms with a number of algal groups has long been recognized through comparative study of their photosynthetic systems (a recent treatment of such phylogenetic considerations is that by Dougherty & Allen, 1960). Food reserves are also considered of taxonomic significance among groups of phytoflagellates, but less often among other kinds of protozoa; for example leucosin is a carbohydrate reserve uniquely characteristic of the order Chrysomonadida.

(6) *Morphogenetic and ontogenetic features: attention to full life cycles.* Here the characteristics actually studied are principally morphological in nature; it is the emphasis which is different. I maintain that the study of ontogeny in protozoa can be taxonomically as fruitful—and advisable —as it is for metazoa or metaphyta. We need to know more about the habits of larval forms and whether or not we are missing the occurrence of polymorphism among so many incompletely studied life histories of both free-living and symbiotic protozoa. Surely profitable would be thorough investigation of the patterns of the complex morphogenetic movements which may be involved in such phenomena as binary or multiple fission, stomatogenesis, en- and ex-cystation, regeneration—in fact, in processes of de- and re-differentiation in general at the protozoan level. I have discussed some employment of such approaches in ciliate classification elsewhere (Corliss, 1956a, 1961).

(7) *Genetic factors.* The systematic value of genetics needs neither defence nor explanation. To date, however, the protozoa have not been very co-operative in this respect, greatly limiting recruitment of geneticists into the area. In what little *gamma* taxonomy has been possible with protozoan material, genetic factors have been fully exploited (e.g. see the comprehensive, authoritative review by Sonneborn, 1957). The elusiveness of sex in so many protozoan groups remains a stumbling block in refined taxonomic-genetic approaches to their classification at specific and subspecific levels. I might say, in passing, that I associate myself with the optimistic school of thought which believes that all protozoa have (and we just have not caught them at it yet or have not been able to recognize the form of its existence) or have had sexuality *of some sort*: this view is diametrically opposed to that which upholds the 'primitive sexlessness' of certain protozoa.

(8) *Phylogenetic considerations.* The difficulties encountered in

carrying out proper phylogenetic or evolutionary studies of most protozoan groups, as I have discussed in some detail elsewhere (Corliss, 1960a, 1962), are nearly insurmountable. Yet, obviously, results must be obtained before they can be applied to systematic problems! So much speculation is involved that there is great danger of unwittingly finding oneself in the realm of protozoan mythology rather than reality. Promulgation of phylogenetic hypotheses, however, need not 'degenerate into a kind of scholarly indoor past-time', as one experimental biologist recently expressed it. Lack of a usable fossil record for most protozoan groups is the major handicap in postulating directly supportable ideas of ancestral relationships; one is obliged to assume that certain extant forms represent groups little changed over great periods of time. Factors of polyphyly, convergence, and parallel evolution must be taken into account, particularly when treating groups whose members have adopted a symbiotic mode of life; and even under the best of circumstances we can never do more than suggestively conclude that the characteristics we have chosen to study comparatively *may* be valid indicators of community of descent.

A phylogenetic tree, perhaps more properly a 'dendrogram', which attempts to illustrate possible interrelationships among the major taxa comprising the protozoan subphylum Ciliophora is offered in Fig. 1. In recent years there has been a flurry of publication of new 'trees', especially of the algal-flagellate protistan groups, of interest to protozoologists (see Corliss, 1960a; Dougherty & Allen, 1960; and references therein). I believe it is worth while having a definite 'frame of reference' even if it is of a transitory nature, such as this obviously highly oversimplified ciliate tree—if for no other reason than to offer something concrete to attack in the future when we are armed with new data and fresh ideas.

PROTOZOAN TAXONOMY AT THE HIGHER LEVELS

There has recently been a revival of disagreement concerning the most 'natural' division of the 'phylum' (or kingdom of several phyla?) Protozoa at the highest levels (e.g. see discussion in Corliss, 1960a). This may be considered a healthy sign of progress! The Honigberg Committee (a ten-man 'Committee on Taxonomy' of the international Society of Protozoologists) debated a number of the problems involved before meetings of the Society held in Oklahoma in 1960 and Prague in 1961. Such activity is most commendable. Revisions of conventional schemes of classification are bound to result. Changes are going to stem from new interpretations of older data, stimulating syntheses of current

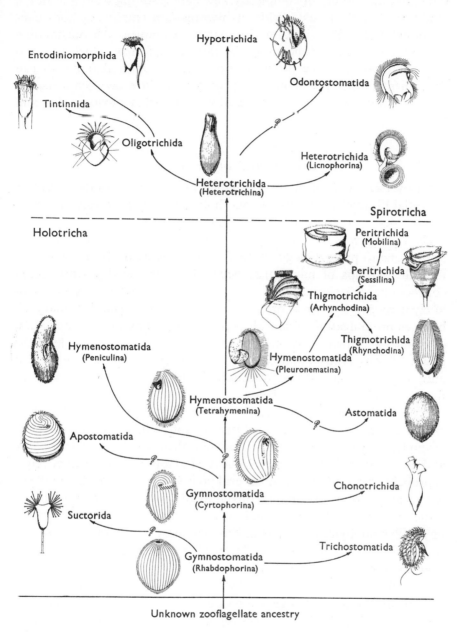

Fig. 1.

A genealogical tree of the ciliated protozoa which attempts to show postulated
evolutionary lines at ordinal level (after Corliss, 1960*a*).

data, and availability of completely new data resulting from additional studies in 'new' or 'old' fields of investigation employing both conventional and freshly discovered research techniques. An outstanding very recent example, concerning the ultimate effect of which it is too early to predict, is the proposal advanced by Jahn that an alleged fundamental difference in mode of protoplasmic flow between members of two major groups of the 'Sarcodina' is of great phylogenetic, and hence classificational, significance (Jahn, Bovee & Small, 1960).

General areas of controversy

Controversial areas of discussion which may involve points of real or potential disagreement (always, one hopes, eventually resolvable) may be considered briefly under five headings.

(1) *The break with tradition.* This perennial problem in taxonomy is not unique to protozoology; in fact, it is probably much more serious for other groups of micro-organisms where drastic departures from conventional vertebrate-styled schemes of classification may be absolutely necessary if any real progress is to be realized. The customary lag between promulgation of new ideas (not only in the field of systematics, of course) and their appearance in text-books is a good example of the power of conservatism and conventionalism and of the weight of past authority. Elements of the 'tradition' problem are evident in most of the other points considered below.

(2) *Practical convenience and stability* versus *extensive theoretical 'improvements'.* This serious problem cannot be lightly dismissed. For example, the suggestion that the 'phylum' Protozoa is more reasonably and more naturally represented by several taxonomically distinct phyla is probably a sound one, from several points of view. Copeland (1956), for instance, boldly distributes conventional 'protozoan' groups among some five phyla within his kingdom Protoctista: by name, the Phaeophyta, Pyrrhophyta, Protoplasta, Fungilli and Ciliophora. (The protozoologist *sensu stricto*, as opposed to the 'protistologist', will never have heard of any of these save the last.) One tends to shudder at this action principally, I believe, because of the impractical aspects of such disruption of taxa containing organisms discussed as a single assemblage of forms in teaching and in general research in the traditionally unitary field of 'protozoology'. Thus we tend to conclude, 'Such action may be sound, but it is premature'; or 'carrying on for a while longer with the standard "phylum Protozoa" is virtually demanded on the basis of practical necessity' (guilty party: Corliss, 1960*a*!).

There *is* a genuine need for stability in taxonomy, yet, paradoxically, the science must remain fluid and dynamic to properly serve its purposes. Most of us believe that the problem is to maintain a desirable degree of continuity while simultaneously incorporating revisions and improvements. But, one may muse, it might be better to sweep everything away and start afresh with a Dobellian spirit, as exemplified in that trenchant essay on the principles of protistology in which the subject is decisively introduced with the blunt statement (Dobell, 1911, p. 271): 'The present paper is largely analytic and destructive: but it is so of necessity, for it is useless to attempt to build upon a rotten foundation.'

(3) *Definition of the limits of a given taxonomic rank.* How encompassing should higher (or lower, for that matter) taxa be? Many protozoologists have been disturbed by the elevation of a number of groups which are conventionally considered to be families to the ordinal level in the first fascicule of the extensive treatises on the protozoa edited by Grassé (1952, 1953); for the most recent attack, see Hyman (1959). In the class 'Zooflagellata' alone some fourteen orders, representing a threefold increase over conventional classifications, are recognized; these contain only two families each, on the average. In certain cases, it is true, little-known or essentially monogeneric groups were thus given a status possibly not warranted by the facts available. There is the danger, too, that the overall system might become unbalanced if characteristics of minor value are used to separate major ranks. On the other hand, what is *the* criterion or what are the major criteria for recognizing separateness of groups of protozoan species at, for example, the ordinal level? What degree of morphological or physiological differentiation justifies establishment of separate orders or suborders, within any group of organisms, plant, animal, or microbial? One relies on the considered judgement of the so-called 'experts' (only expert, it sometimes seems, if their conclusions agree with one's own preconceived or tradition-bound notions?) who arrive at their decisions essentially by subjective approaches. It is difficult to be objective via subjectivity!

The familiar battle between the conservatively minded lumpers and the arch-splitters is waged just as fiercely among protozoan taxonomists as among systematists of any other group of organisms. I believe myself that there should be a high correlation of agreement between the scope, extent, or definition of an 'order' in each of the major subdivisions of the phylum; without such equivalence or parallelism—or an honest approach to it—some groups will, relatively speaking, always be mistreated. Yet achievement of such a goal is obviously difficult because of differences in the characteristics employed from group to group, in the philosophies of the specialists or experts involved, in the very nature of the protozoa concerned, and in the amount of information we have accumulated for each of the various groups.

(4) *The partially solved problem.* It is practically impossible to revise totally or even substantially improve all parts of a scheme of classification (at the higher levels) at one fell swoop. This causes difficulties, particularly, one may note sympathetically, for text-book writers. For example, Kirby (1947), fifteen years ago, erected a new zooflagellate order, the Trichomonadida, defining it so admirably that there seemed no question of its immediate wide acceptance and adoption. His taxonomic action, however, left in its wake the remnants of an ill-defined 'Polymastigida' —some eight families—which have been treated in quite different ways by authors of recent text-books or over-all protozoological treatises (e.g. contrast the results in Doflein & Reichenow, 1949–53; Grassé, 1952; Hall, 1953; Kudo, 1954; Levine, 1961; Mackinnon & Hawes, 1961; Manwell, 1961). It is to be hoped that very recent proposals by Honigberg (1962) will authoritatively clear up the problems of what to do with the families left more or less 'order-less' by Kirby's otherwise fully commendable major taxonomic decision. This situation occurs even more frequently at lower taxonomic levels.

(5) *The soundness of radical revisions.* Major changes are, rightly, viewed and reviewed with caution and suspicion, but, theoretically, not with too much biased prejudice! The bases for such taxonomic revisions must be sound and clearly presented; new approaches and new techniques are quite acceptable if their application on a broader scale produces generally consistent results, especially with regard to the neighbouring, unchanged taxa. One example at the ordinal level may suffice to illustrate the point.

The position of the curious chonotrichs among the major ciliate taxa has long vexed protozoan taxonomists. These stalked, sedentary organisms, ectocommensal on certain marine or freshwater crustaceans, manifest a vase-shaped body form in the mature stage of their life history which seems morphologically unique (see figure labelled 'Chonotrichida', Fig. 1, lower right). 'Peristomial' (actually vestibular) ciliature adorns the funnel-like anterior 'lips' of the sessile creature; reproduction is by budding. Following their discovery in the late nineteenth century, chonotrichs were generally classified as a special section of the peritrichs (themselves set widely apart from other ciliates), or occasionally of the heterotrichs. Relatively uncommon and thus not thoroughly studied, the organisms were considered by Poche (1913) to constitute an independent group at a high taxonomic level, being treated as equivalent to the holotrichs, spirotrichs, and peritrichs, as those groups were then recognized. This position was consolidated in the authoritative monograph by Kahl (1930–35), whose conclusion has been universally followed. But during the past decade, a series of studies, which concentrated on all stages in the chonotrich life history, employed such ideal techniques as silver impregnation, the Feulgen nuclear reaction, and electron microscopy, and recognized infraciliary homologies and the value of morphogenetic phenomena in comparative taxonomy, have combined to throw new light on the proper relationship between the seemingly enigmatic chonotrichs and other ciliates (see Corliss, 1956a, 1959; Fauré-Fremiet, 1950, 1953, 1957a, b; Fauré-Fremiet & Guilcher, 1947; Fauré-Fremiet, Rouiller & Gauchery, 1956; Guilcher, 1951; Tuffrau, 1953). Considered very closely related to certain cyrtophorine holotrich gymnostomes, in the works just listed, the Chonotrichida may now be classified as one of nine orders within the subclass Holotricha (see Fig. 1), a position well justified and likely to be accepted widely in due time, although it represents a radical revision in the taxonomic status of these protozoa.

Application of similar approaches to problems of other ciliate ordinal groups may turn out to be equally successful (see Corliss, 1961).

Trends in classificational revisions

Seventy-five years ago the classification of the phylum Protozoa had progressed to the state shown in Table 1, a tremendous advance over the first schemes published some 50–100 years earlier by such pioneers in the field as Müller (1786) and Ehrenberg (1838). Names and ranks of the taxa in the table are based on the work of that great 'architect of protozoology', O. Bütschli (1880–89), although the order of his classes is altered to match the arrangement used in Table 2.

In Table 2 may be seen a scheme of classification representing approximately the current or at least a well established, modern arrangement of the higher protozoan taxa. It is based primarily on the system published by Kudo (1954), which strongly resembles that of Doflein & Reichenow (1949–53); three order-level groups have been added (from Hall, 1953) and names of the two subphyla, 'Plasmodroma' and 'Ciliophora', have been omitted. The expansion since Bütschli's time is readily evident, and revised areas are universally agreed to represent substantial improvement over older schemes.

The tremendous growth of the phylum in number of species is truly phenomenal: even within the past thirty years over 500 species have

4-2

Table 1. *The suprafamilial scheme of classification of the phylum*
Protozoa according to Bütschli (1880–1889)

Class I. MASTIGOPHORA
    Order 1. Flagellata
        Suborder (1) Monadina
            (2) Euglenoidina
            (3) Heteromastigoda
            (4) Isomastigoda
    Order 2. Choanoflagellata
    Order 3. Dinoflagellata
            (1) Adinida
            (2) Dinifera
    Order 4. Cystoflagellata

Class II. SARKODINA
    Subclass 1. Rhizopoda
    Order 1. Rhizopoda
        Suborder (1) Amoebaea
            (2) Testacea
            (3) Perforata
    Subclass 2. Heliozoa
    [with several orders]
    Subclass 3. Radiolaria
    [with many orders, after Haeckel]

Class III. SPOROZOA
    Subclass 1. Gregarinida
        Order 1. Monocystidea
            2. Polycystidea
    Subclass 2. Myxosporidia
    Subclass 3. Sarcosporidia
    [appended: the Microsporidia]

Class IV. INFUSORIA
    Subclass 1. Ciliata
        Order 1. Gymnostomata
            2. Trichostomata
        Suborder (1) Aspirotricha
        [including the opalinids]
            (2) Spirotricha
        Section (i) Heterotricha
            (ii) Oligotricha
            (iii) Hypotricha
            (iv) Peritricha
    [appended: the Trichonymphidae]
    Subclass 2. Suctoria

been described as new annually (Corliss, 1960 a). Since Bütschli's time,
the number of higher categories of ciliates alone has increased from
eight (orders, suborders and 'sections') to twenty-six (orders and suborders) in the most recent classification; and the number of species,
from some 500 to an estimated 6000 (Corliss, 1961)! Thus classificational schemes for the protozoa must be changed, if only to accommodate properly the addition of so many new forms or groups of forms not
all of which can be expected to fit into anciently established taxa.

Hyman (1959), perhaps a little wishfully, has mentioned the present-
day 'stability' of the protozoan classificational scheme. Yet certain
(further) changes are bound to come; and although I shall not be
audacious enough to predict the situation *seventy-five* years hence, I
submit that even before the end of the present decade major revisions
or additions will be accepted or under favourable discussion in several
broad areas, with the result that the scheme of 1970 may resemble less
the current one (Table 2) than the latter does that of seventy-five years
ago (Table 1). Here are my rather conservative predictions:

(1) The 'Mastigophora' and 'Sarcodina' will be united under some
common subphylum-heading, in recognition of the fact that they are
probably more closely related than conventionally indicated. Certain
minor 'sarcodinid' groups may be eliminated entirely from consideration as protozoa.

Table 2. *A modern suprafamilial scheme of classification of the phylum Protozoa (principally after Kudo, 1954)*

Class I. MASTIGOPHORA
Subclass 1. Phytomastigina
  Order 1. Chrysomonadina
    2. Cryptomonadina
    3. Phytomonadina
    4. Euglenoidina
    5. Chloromonadina
    6. Dinoflagellata
Subclass 2. Zoomastigina
  Order 1. Rhizomastigina
    2. Protomonadina
    3. Trichomonadina
    4. Polymastigina
    5. Hypermastigina

Class II. SARCODINA
Subclass 1. Rhizopoda
  Order 1. Proteomyxa
    2. Mycetozoa
    3. Amoebina
    4. Testacea
    5. Foraminifera
Subclass 2. Actinopoda
  Order 1. Heliozoa
    2. Radiolaria

Class III. SPOROZOA
Subclass 1. Telosporidia
  Order 1. Gregarinida
    2. Coccidia
    3. Haemosporidia

Subclass 2. Cnidosporidia
  Order 1. Myxosporidia
    2. Microsporidia
    3. Actinomyxidia
    4. Helicosporidia
Subclass 3. Acnidosporidia
  Order 1. Haplosporidia
    2. Sarcosporidia

Class IV. CILIATA
Subclass 1. Protociliata
  [the opalinids]
Subclass 2. Euciliata
  Order 1. Holotricha
    Suborder (1) Astomata
      (2) Gymnostomata
      (3) Trichostomata
      (4) Hymenostomata
      (5) Thigmotricha
      (6) Apostomea
  Order 2. Spirotricha
    Suborder (1) Heterotricha
      (2) Oligotricha
      (3) Tintinnoinea
      (4) Entodiniomorpha
      (5) Ctenostomata
      (6) Hypotricha
  Order 3. Chonotricha
    4. Peritricha

Class V. SUCTORIA

(2) The current 'Sporozoa' will be split into two groups of equal status (probably considered subphyla), essentially a revival of proposals made over fifty years ago, with possibly complete rejection of certain minor groups now afforded refuge therein.

(3) The 'Protociliata' (the opalinids) will be removed from the subphylum Ciliophora, or at least reduced to the status of an appended, specialized group rather than maintained as a main-line, primitive ancestral group to the ciliates proper. In the most recent remarks on the subject, Wessenberg (1961), although disagreeing with Grassé (1952), the writer (Corliss, 1955), and others who support the flagellate affinities of these curious protozoa, concluded that the opalinids are not closely related to either ciliates *or* flagellates.

(4) The ciliate groups 'Suctoria', 'Chonotricha', and 'Peritricha' will be incorporated as ordinal taxa within the (subclass) Holotricha; and a major dichotomy of the Ciliophora, into holotrichs and spirotrichs, will be recognized (see Fig. 1).

(5) The number of orders and suborders will be increased in practically all groups to accommodate forms previously poorly known or in overdue recognition of the desirability of having more uniformity in the degree of separateness of co-ordinate taxa belonging to the several major subdivisions of the phylum. New names will need to be proposed, and there will be some general changing of names.

(6) Some reasonably mild system of uniform endings for the names of the higher taxonomic categories will be adopted, although not without encountering considerable resistance. (The problem of achieving uniformity of suffix for names at a given suprafamilial level, not under the jurisdiction of the *International Rules of Zoological Nomenclature*, is treated on pp. 61–2.)

Most aspects of the 'predictions' listed above have already been discussed to a certain extent in other publications (Corliss, 1960*a*, 1962) in which I have acknowledged their general origin in suggestions and viewpoints put forth by a number of modern protozoan taxonomists.

A new, summarizing attempt of my own, incorporating a number of the ideas just discussed, appears in the tentative scheme offered as Table 3 (p. 67) inserted, like this paragraph, in the proofs. In formulating such a skeletal classification (lack of space prevents inclusion of the 49 suborders which I recognize) I have been influenced most recently by discussions at the protozoological congress at Prague in August, 1961. But the table should not be construed to represent the unanimous or 'official' views of Dr Honigberg's Committee on Taxonomy (see p. 46) of which I am a member. Treatment of major differences between the arrangements seen in Tables 2 and 3 is not possible here; but comparative inspection of the two classifications may serve as a conveniently useful point of departure for subsequent debate and discussion.

PROTOZOAN TAXONOMY AT THE LOWER LEVELS

While there are only several score of suprafamilial taxa with which to contend, there are thousands of protozoan families, genera and species. Problems among the lower taxonomic groups are thus much more numerous, although of a kind similar to those already discussed in this paper and naturally less often of such broad importance.

Family-group problems

Having just completed a review of some 130 families assignable to the subphylum Ciliophora (Corliss, 1961), I am acutely aware of the shortcomings of many of the diagnoses available in the literature for these protozoa, and I doubt if the situation is much improved among the other major groups comprising the phylum. There seems to be a tremendous unevenness in defining the limits of a familial group. Many families contain but a single genus and species, and sometimes these appear very closely related to neighbouring monogeneric families. For example, the holotrich trichostome families Trichospiridae Kahl, 1926, and Spirozonidae Kahl, 1926, are separated primarily on the basis of the direction of winding of a band of somatic ciliature,* a difference conceivably attributable to a relatively simple genetic mutation. On the other hand, such families as the Buetschliidae Poche, 1913, Enchelyidae Ehrenberg, 1838, Frontoniidae Kahl, 1926, and Oxytrichidae Ehrenberg, 1838, are considered to contain from thirty to half a hundred generic groups (very large by protozoological standards), and some of these genera seem strikingly dissimilar to others in the same family. Yet the large family Folliculinidae Dons, 1914, contains thirty genera all very likely closely related. In the case of the Frontoniidae, I have suggested removal of about a dozen genera to three other families (one new and two resurrected) and reduction of the number of 'true' frontoniids to four or five (Corliss, 1961). But, paralleling the problem discussed for Kirby's order Trichomonadida (see p. 50), this action has only incompletely solved the problem, since some twenty genera are left dangling, familyless.

I have already mentioned (see p. 49) the unpopular treatment of a number of flagellate familial groups by Grassé (1952), viz. raising them to an ordinal status in recognition of the apparent extent of their differences. One of the most controversial areas today, at the family level, is to be found among the rhizopod amoebae. Some of the knotty problems involved—morphological, taxonomic and nomenclatural—are treated, or referred to, in the recent works of Bovee (1954), Deflandre (1959), Loeblich & Tappan (1961), Singh (1952) and Vickerman (1962); but an over-all definitive, synthetic review is yet to appear. The exemplary series of papers on zooflagellate families and genera published by the late Professor H. Kirby, between 1924 and 1952, did much to establish precise taxonomic standards for these important mastigophoran groups (see Kirby, 1950, and references cited therein).

---

* Incidentally, the significance of dextral versus sinistral winding of buccal membranelles, a characteristic conventionally employed to separate such groups as the peritrichs from all other ciliates, is greatly weakened by the realization that some species within a single ordinal taxon (the Hymenostomatida) show a counterclockwise turning of the membranelles, while others manifest a clockwise arrangement of these ciliary structures (Corliss, 1956a).

Problems at the generic level

Revisions of protozoan genera are badly needed, particularly of groups containing relatively undifferentiated species of small size or little studied by modern techniques. The persistently troublesome problem described briefly with regard to the ordinal level (see p. 49), concerning the boundaries consistently assignable to allegedly equivalent ranks throughout an extensive heterogeneous assemblage of micro-organisms, is just as significant here. Does the definition or diagnosis of the genus *Amoeba* (= *Chaos*, according to some workers; but see Kudo, 1959) embrace the same amount of diversity as that of *Euglena, Paramecium, Plasmodium, Tetrahymena* or *Trypanosoma*? Because of the wide differences in differential characteristics employed in recognizing species and species-groups within the generic taxa just listed, I despair that even statistical approaches to weighting of relevant characters can ever solve the matter satisfactorily. Interesting proposals are being made with respect to possible solution of the problem of generic boundaries for certain well known protozoan groups. The cases of two genera some of whose species are of outstanding medical and socio-economic importance to man may be briefly considered in illustration: the haemosporidian genus, or genus-complex, *Plasmodium* and the haemoflagellate genus *Trypanosoma*.

Based primarily on our newly acquired knowledge of patterns of exo-erythrocytic schizogony, it is now becoming evident that the old malarial genus *Plasmodium sensu lato* includes species which quite definitely are not congeneric. Saurian and avian malarial species are assignable to the genus *Haemamoeba*, reserving *Plasmodium* for most, but not all, of the mammalian parasites. The causative agent for malignant tertian malaria, '*P.' falciparum*, shows several striking differences in its physiological life cycle, its cytology, and its effect on the host: it has thus been allocated to the genus *Laverania* by some, notably British, workers. *Hepatocystis, Nycteria* and *Polychromophilus* have been proposed for certain erstwhile *Plasmodium* species from insectivorous bats and, in the case of *Hepatocystis*, also from African apes and several other mammalian hosts. The differences between these three last-mentioned genera and *Plasmodium sensu stricto* are considered so great (in life cycles, cytology, vectors, etc.) that they are even removed from the family Plasmodiidae to the Haemoproteidae, alongside the well established genera *Haemoproteus* and *Leucocytozoon*, whose species infect birds and reptiles. Professor P. C. C. Garnham, London School of Hygiene and Tropical Medicine, is the acknowledged authority on these particular taxonomic problems and the above discussion is based on work by Garnham (1951, 1953; Garnham *et al.* 1961), Bray (1957), and others cited in those publications.

General infrageneric groupings of species of *Trypanosoma*, the cause of sleeping sickness, have long been recognized on such bases as the vectors involved, position of parasite in the vector, kinds of hosts, and degrees of pathogenicity. Some such groupings have not agreed with those proposed by other workers and seldom, with any consistency, have the subdivisions been given legal taxonomic status. Dr C. A. Hoare, Wellcome Laboratories of Tropical Medicine, an authority on trypanosomes and trypanosomiases, is contemplating erection of some eight subgenera within the genus *Trypanosoma* as a means of formally separating what he considers to be natural groups of those species parasitizing mammalian hosts (personal communication from Dr Hoare). Much of the background work for these proposals has already been carried out in detail; for example, see his extended series of 'morphological and taxonomic studies on mammalian typanosomes', the most recently published of which is Hoare (1959*a*); also see Hoare (1957*a*). In passing, Hoare's (1957*b*, 1959*b*) excellent observations on the comparative systematics of genera and species among the sporozoan coccidians and the parasitic amoebae also might be appropriately mentioned here.

The 'species problem' in protozoology

I hope that no microbiologist will disagree with the sentiment expressed so aptly by the late Dr W. T. Calman: 'The most urgent task confronting the systematist...is not that of adding to the number of named species but that of revising and putting in order the species that are supposed to be already "known"' (Calman, 1949). Hyman (1959) complains of the 'disease of raising ranks'; a second malady, characteristic of *alpha* taxonomists in particular, is that of naming new species. Unfortunately there *are* hundreds of undescribed protozoan forms legitimately deserving of specific epithets: but unless it is unavoidable, let us leave them in their peaceful state of anonymity!

In addition to potentially new proper species, only in need of careful description, there are four other principal sources of 'new' species: (1) forms already described but rather poorly and perhaps long ago, thus conveniently re-named as new by subsequent workers; (2) forms already described—and adequately enough—but in publications overlooked because of their age or rarity; (3) forms which are merely unrecognized stages in the life cycle of a polymorphic species; (4) forms named as new which would be better considered merely as strains or subspecies of existing species. In all instances by study of the organism, conscientiousness in searching the literature, serious attempts to evaluate the significance of differences found, and firm resolution not to describe something as new purely for the sake of describing something as new will help greatly in keeping short the columns of 'new species' appearing annually in the *Zoological Record*.

The problems of boundaries of specific diagnoses for the vast majority of protozoan species are similar to those discussed for higher taxa. In general, common sense, reasonably objective subjectivity, and custom dictate the limits of a protozoan species. In the last analysis, we are at the mercy of the experts; or, to express it more graciously, we are dependent on the good judgement of the specialists.

The genetic approach, so ideal from a theoretical point of view, at least, is at present very restricted in application to the protozoa. Because of the rigid requirements for such a refined approach—diploidy, heterosexuality, laboratory culturability and manipulativeness of the organisms —it is unlikely to ever prove useful on a large scale in protozoan systematics. Some taxonomically valuable information, however, has already been obtained by the pioneering series of studies by Professor T. M. Sonneborn and associates (see Sonneborn, 1957). The 'biological', 'physiological', or 'genetic' species—conventionally referred to as varieties, now as *syngens* by Sonneborn—which comprise such a well known 'morphological' species as, for example, *Paramecium aurelia*, have not yet been split up into taxonomically independent species. Sonneborn's philosophy is that the term 'species' should be reserved for groups of organisms morphologically (generally) distinguishable, readily identifiable, one from the other; and the term syngen should be used for the 'evolutionary unit', members of which share a potentially common gene pool. Thus his syngen is the 'biological species' of the genetically oriented animal systematist. It is undeniable, as Sonneborn has emphasized, that the overwhelming majority of described animal species—not only the 'asexual species' of many protozoan groups—are of the 'morphological type'. The reader interested further in this 'species problem at the protozoan level' is referred to Sonneborn's review (Sonneborn, 1957). Some biologists (e.g. Hairston, 1958) have disagreed with Sonneborn concerning the advantages or disadvantages and the difficulties of designating and recognizing the sexual varieties of *Paramecium* species as truly separate species in their own right.

Consideration of infraspecific categories is beyond the scope of the present paper. In general, subspecies are seldom described among the protozoa: wisely, in my opinion, since our knowledge is so limited concerning factors which conventionally serve as bases for precise characterization of such units of *gamma* taxonomy. Incidentally, subfamilial and subgeneric taxa are also, on the whole, infrequently recognized by protozoologists. Phycologists, I believe, often describe 'varieties', and thus protozoan phytoflagellate species are sometimes so treated. But, from a zoological point of view, varieties have no legal nomenclatural status (Hemming, 1958). Strains and races are important, though unofficial, units of designation in certain cases of species widely employed in physiological and biochemical research (e.g. *Tetrahymena pyriformis*: see Corliss, 1954) or parasitological investigation (see examples in Hoare, 1943, 1952, 1955, 1957a; Manwell, 1957).

NOMENCLATURAL PROCEDURES IN PROTOZOOLOGY

The *International Rules of Zoological Nomenclature* (see Hemming, 1958; Keen & Muller, 1956; and Appendix I) allow little freedom of choice in the matter of naming animals and groups of animals at familial levels and below. The stabilizing effect this should have on the taxonomy of any group is welcome. At the higher levels 'no holds are barred'; but, in wrestling with the problems involved, ethical decency and a modicum of common sense should prevail.

At the risk of being branded a traitor to my profession, I must nevertheless make the observation that protozoologists, as a group, seem to me to be more often guilty of infringement of the *Rules* than certain other groups of biologists, e.g. vertebrate systematists (or is it just my ignorance of mistakes made by those working with organisms on the multicellular side of the animal kingdom?). But if my perfidy is justified, perhaps the explanation hinges on the fact that protozoologists are generally nearly a century behind in the field of taxonomy, through no fault of the investigators themselves working in the area but by the very nature of their organisms.

It is an interesting fact that very few names of protozoa appear in the *Official List of Generic Names in Zoology*, 1958, or in the *Official Index of Rejected and Invalid Generic Names in Zoology*, 1958. Type specimens are seldom available (fossil foraminiferidans are a notable exception), a condition incredible to most other zoological taxonomists when they first learn of this deficiency. Representation in culture collections, some international in coverage, is on the increase, but most protozoan species cannot yet be cultivated sufficiently conveniently to be so treated (see the recent list in Provasoli *et al.* (1958) of strains and species which are available).

Inexcusable nomenclatural shortcomings

Some shortcomings, real or apparent, are easier to overcome than others. Eight inexcusably careless faults all too common in the taxonomic protozoological literature are the following:

(1) Proposal of familial names not based on names from among those of the included genera; or forming them improperly from generic names.

(2) Total disregard for type genera and dates of their establishment when shifting genera from family to family or amalgamating several erstwhile separate familial groups.

(3) Citation of text-book writers or other such 'reviewers' as authors of taxonomic names included in their general works, rather than bothering to search through the original literature for the proper authorships and dates; and a general lack of attempt at accuracy in citation of names and dates.

(4) Inattention to priority with reference to synonyms if it conflicts with biased personal preference. (I have, myself, been guilty of favouring stability over priority in what I believe to be reasonable circumstances, but I confess to the 'crime' when doing it and include mention of the stricter alternative so that it is available to the purist, who may prefer it: see Corliss, 1961.)

(5) Failure to check sources such as Neave (1939–50) and Schulze *et al.* (1926–54) before proposing 'new' generic names. This is the most common origin of homonyms which are then a source of later taxonomic confusion. Among the names of some 840 recognized genera of ciliated protozoa I recently discovered nearly 100 homonymous names which had to be disposed of by one means or another (Corliss, 1960*b*). A less frequent source of trouble results from well meant replacement of a name which, however, was *not* truly a homonym and thus did not require replacement, or was indeed a homonym but had already been replaced by an earlier worker. Also junior homonyms for which junior synonyms are available need not be replaced by new names.

(6) Placement of a former generic name of a species in the position officially reserved for the subgeneric name (if one exists): this lamentable and most confusing practice is carried on wholesale in a number of major taxonomic works and textbooks in the field of protozoology. It is difficult to understand why such a flagrant disregard for the *International Rules* persists in this particular case: there are other ways of indicating former generic vehicles of a species than by usurping the place of the subgeneric name.

(7) Assignment of credit for the name of a suprafamilial taxon to the worker who most recently merely altered the spelling of its suffix; and proposal of new names for higher taxa for which perfectly good names are already in existence. Admittedly there are no official rules in the *Code* covering these matters, but I feel strongly that it is committing a deplorable injustice to the original 'name-maker' to change a terminal letter of the suffix, for example, and then blithely claim the name as one's own.

(8) Ignorance of or failure to survey properly the literature, be it limited or extensive, pertinent to any nomenclatural-taxonomic problem which is being treated. Such inconsideration unnecessarily multiplies the labours of a more conscientious subsequent reviewer.

The lack of names of protozoan genera in the *List* and *Index* is, as far as I can discover, simply a reflection of collective indolence on the part of all protozoologists, the writer included. Perhaps because most of us have not been trained in the allegedly rigorous vertebrate school of taxonomic practices, we are not sufficiently inclined or motivated to spend time in carrying out such an activity, worthwhile though it might prove to be.

The problem of type specimens

There are good excuses for the general lack of type specimens. The vast majority of protozoan species known to date have been described either totally from examination of fresh, living material (sometimes perhaps supplemented with temporarily stained preparations) or, less often, from study of so-called permanent preparations which may contain specimens retainable in a worthwhile, recognizable state for only a few years. Also it is important to recall that many characteristics employed in specific diagnoses of protozoa are never, or not always, preservable in a fixed condition on a slide (or in a vial): these may include body form, coloration, delicate processes of various sorts, modes of locomotion and feeding, and a host of other physiological, genetic, and behavioural traits. In comparative taxonomic work good drawings, supplemented with photomicrographs when possible (plus, of course, a thorough presentation in the text of the publication), are usually an adequate, perhaps superior, substitute for having a fixed preparation of the described organism itself. On the other hand, for groups of protozoa which technically can now be so handled, I am all in favour of depositing type specimens in an established central location. The usual advantages in later comparative work are obvious; and if such a regulation were made practically obligatory it might even act as a prophylactic to the disease of new-species-naming!

In addition to the forminiferidan students, it is only fair—and most encouraging—to note that there are other, if lonesomely scattered, examples of protozoologists who designate type specimens and make them generally available to authorized investigators. And it should be noted that Dr Jaroslav Weiser, of Prague, has been working tirelessly to arouse more international interest in this important matter.

The controversy over uniform endings

The nomenclatural problems stirred up by the controversy over whether or not to employ uniform endings for all taxa of the same rank may be mentioned briefly, from the point of view of their application to protozoan systematics. Above the level of family, the *International Rules* sensibly make no requirements regarding terminations of taxonomic names; in fact, the Copenhagen Decisions (Hemming, 1953) state that such a regulation would be 'inadvisable'. Personally I certainly agree that to attempt to force all zoological systematists to use identical suffixes for any given high-level taxonomic rank would be foolish: altogether too much upsetting would be caused, a general loss of some very important stability in our systems would be brought about, and endless wrangling over the most suitable terminations would result. Much has been published on this subject in the zoological literature of the past decade, but I have no intention of reviewing it all here.

Concerning the phylum Protozoa, however, I ally myself (Corliss, 1956a, 1957b, 1961) with the group of investigators who believe that a certain amount of uniformity in endings is a desirable goal. Jahn & Jahn (1949) and Hall (1953) have been leaders in this, with their adoption of the endings suggested earlier, for all animal groups, by Pearse (1936); actually Delage & Hérouard (1896) employed a very logical set of uniform endings for the protozoa in their oft-neglected treatise published more than half a century ago. I believe that it is reasonable and sensible to employ uniform suffixes for orders (-ida) and suborders (-ina) in particular, since these groups are the most numerous and the most important suprafamilial protozoan categories. I do think the terminations should be moderate; in this respect I cannot endorse the rather lengthy and unwieldy suffixes suggested and used by Levine (1959, 1961), in spite of their idealistic precision.

It is logical and convenient to be able to recognize the rank of a major taxon by its ending (e.g. note names in Fig. 1). A number of the names of higher protozoan groups were originally proposed with such endings; the alteration required in any case is not great: for example, Dinoflagellata needs to be transformed only into Dinoflagellida; Foraminifera into Foraminiferida; Gymnostomata, Gymnostomatida; Hypermastigina, Hypermastigida; Hypotricha, Hypotrichida; Suctoria, Suctorida; Heliozoa, Heliozoida; etc. The fear that the first user of the name with the uniform termination will thereafter be credited with authorship of that name should be completely allayed, as I see it. Since the stem of the name is the important thing, both historically and from the point of view of the student obliged to remember it, the use of uniform suffixes will work no hardship nor bring discredit to any early investigator: on the other hand, its advantages are obvious.

ACKNOWLEDGEMENTS

Support of Grant no. 10666 from the National Science Foundation, Washington, D.C., is gratefully acknowledged. Much of the present paper was prepared while the author was an Honorary Research Associate in the Department of Zoology, University College London, during the first year (1960–1961) of a two-year leave from the University of Illinois.

REFERENCES

BAKER, J. R. (1948). The status of the protozoa. *Nature, Lond.* **161**, 548–51, 587–9.

BOVEE, E. C. (1954). Morphological identification of free-living Amoebida. *Proc. Iowa Acad. Sci.* **60**, 599–615.

BOVEE, E. C. & JAHN, T. L. (1960). Locomotion and the classification of Amoebida and Testacida. (Abstr.) *J. Protozool.* **7** (Suppl.), 8.

BRAY, R. S. (1957). *Studies on the Exo-Erythrocytic Cycle in the Genus* Plasmodium. London School of Hygiene and Tropical Medicine Memoir No. 12. 192 pp. London: H. K. Lewis and Co.

BULLINGTON, W. E. (1939). A study of spiraling in the ciliate *Frontonia* with a review of the genus and a description of two new species. *Arch. Protistenk.* **92**, 10–66.

BÜTSCHLI, O. (1880–89). Sarkodina und Sporozoa...(Abt. I, 1880–82); Mastigophora (Abt. II, 1883–87); Infusoria und System der Radiolaria (Abt. III, 1887–89). In *Klassen und Ordnung des Thier-Reichs*, **1**, 1–2035. Edited by H. G. Bronn. Leipzig: C. F. Winter.

CALKINS, G. N. (1933). *The Biology of the Protozoa*, 2nd ed. 607 pp. Philadelphia: Lea and Febiger.

CALMAN, W. T. (1949). *The Classification of Animals. An Introduction to Zoological Taxonomy*, 54 pp. London: Methuen and Co.

COPELAND, H. F. (1956). *The Classification of Lower Organisms*, 302 pp. Palo Alto, California: Pacific Books.

CORLISS, J. O. (1954). The literature on *Tetrahymena*: its history, growth, and recent trends. *J. Protozool.* **1**, 156–69.

CORLISS, J. O. (1955). The opalinid infusorians: flagellates or ciliates? *J. Protozool.* **2**, 107–14.

CORLISS, J. O. (1956a). On the evolution and systematics of ciliated protozoa. *Syst. Zool.* **5**, 68–91, 121–40.

CORLISS, J. O. (1956b). Occurrence and study of autogamy in diverse strains of *Tetrahymena rostrata*. (Abstr.) *J. Protozool.* **3** (Suppl.), 3.

CORLISS, J. O. (1957a). Concerning the 'cellularity' or acellularity of the protozoa. *Science*, **125**, 988–9.

CORLISS, J. O. (1957b). Nomenclatural history of the higher taxa in the subphylum Ciliophora. *Arch. Protistenk.* **102**, 113–46.

CORLISS, J. O. (1959). An illustrated key to the higher groups of the ciliated protozoa, with definition of terms. *J. Protozool.* **6**, 265–81.

CORLISS, J. O. (1960a). Comments on the systematics and phylogeny of the protozoa. *Syst. Zool.* **8** (yr. 1959), 169–90.

CORLISS, J. O. (1960b). The problem of homonyms among generic names of ciliated protozoa, with proposal of several new names. *J. Protozool.* **7**, 269–78.

CORLISS, J. O. (1961). *The Ciliated Protozoa: Characterization, Classification and Guide to the Literature*, 310 pp. London and New York: Pergamon Press.

CORLISS, J. O. (1962). Application of phylogenetic considerations to protozoan systematics. *Proc. 1st int. Conf. Protozool., Prague, August* 1961 (in the Press).

DEFLANDRE, G. (1959). Rhizopoda and Actinopoda. In *Ward and Whipple's Fresh-Water Biology*, pp. 232–64, 2nd edition. Edited by W. T. Edmondson. New York: Wiley and Sons.

DELAGE, Y. & HÉROUARD, E. (1896). *La Cellule et les Protozoaires*. In *Traité de Zoologie Concrète*, 1, 1–584. Paris: Schleicher Frères.

DEVIDÉ, Z. & GEITLER, L. (1947). Die Chromosomen der Ciliaten. *Chromosoma*, 3, 110–36.

DIPPELL, R. V. (1954). A preliminary report on the chromosomal constitution of certain variety 4 races of *Paramecium aurelia*. *Proc. IX int. Congr. Genetics*, Bellagio, Italy, 1953. Published in *Caryologia*, 6 (Suppl.), 1109–11.

DOBELL, C. (1911). The principles of protistology. *Arch. Protistenk.* 23, 269–310.

DOFLEIN, F. & REICHENOW, E. (1949–53). *Lehrbuch der Protozoenkunde*... 6th Edition. 1214 pp. Jena: G. Fischer.

DOUGHERTY, E. C. & ALLEN, M. B. (1960). Is pigmentation a clue to protistan phylogeny? In *Comparative Biochemistry of Photoreactive Systems*, pp. 129–44. *Symp. Comp. Biol*. Vol. I, edited by M. B. Allen. New York: Academic Press.

EHRENBERG, C. G. (1838). *Die Infusionsthierchen als Vollkommene Organismen*, 612 pp. Leipzig.

FAURÉ-FREMIET, E. (1950). Morphologie comparée et systématique des ciliés. *Bull. Soc. zool. Fr.* 75, 109–22.

FAURÉ-FREMIET, E. (1953). Morphology of protozoa. *Ann. Rev. Microbiol.* 7, 1–18.

FAURÉ-FREMIET, E. (1957*a*). Le macronucleus hétéromere de quelques ciliés. *J. Protozool.* 4, 7–17.

FAURÉ-FREMIET, E. (1957*b*). *Trichopus lachmanni*, n.sp.; structure et morphogenèse. *J. Protozool.* 4, 145–50.

FAURÉ-FREMIET, E. & GUILCHER, Y. (1947). *Trochilioides filans*, n.sp., infusoire holotriche de la famille des Dysteriidae. *Bull. Soc. zool. Fr.* 72, 106–12.

FAURÉ-FREMIET, E., ROUILLER, C. & GAUCHERY, M. (1956). Structure et origine du péduncule chez *Chilodochona. J. Protozool.* 3, 188–93.

GARNHAM, P. C. C. (1951). Patterns of exoerythrocytic schizogony. *Brit. med. Bull.* 8, 10–15.

GARNHAM, P. C. C. (1953). Terminology of Haemosporidiidea. *Communications V Congr. int. Med. trop. Palud., Istanbul*, 2, 228–31.

GARNHAM, P. C. C., HEISH, R. B. & MINTER, D. M. (1961).The vector of *Hepatocystis*, (= *Plasmodium*) *kochi*; the successful conclusion of observations in many parts of tropical Africa. *Trans. roy. Soc. trop. Med. Hyg.* 55, 497–502.

GRASSÉ, P. P., Editor (1952). *Traité de Zoologie. Anatomie, Systématique, Biologie.* Vol. I, fasc. 1: *Phylogénie. Protozoaires: Généralités, Flagellés*. 1071 pp. Paris: Masson et Cie.

GRASSÉ, P. P., Editor (1953). *Traité de Zoologie. Anatomie, Systématique, Biologie.* Vol. I, fasc. 2. *Protozoaires: Rhizopodes, Actinopodes, Sporozoaires, Cnidosporidies*. 1160 pp. Paris: Masson et Cie.

GREGG, J. R. (1959). On deciding whether protistans are cells. *Phil. Sci.* 26, 338–46.

GRIMSTONE, A. V. (1961). Fine structure and morphogenesis in protozoa. *Biol. Rev.* 36, 97–150.

GUILCHER, Y. (1951). Contribution à l'étude des ciliés gemmipares, chonotriches et tentaculifères. *Ann. Sci. nat. Zool.* (sér. 11), 13, 33–132.

HAIRSTON, N. G. (1958). Observations on the ecology of *Paramecium*, with comments on the species problem. *Evolution*, 12, 440–50.

HALL, R. P. (1953). *Protozoology*, 682 pp. New York: Prentice Hall.

HEAL, O. W. (1961). The distribution of testate amoebae (Rhizopoda: Testacea) in some fens and bogs in northern England. *J. Linn. Soc. Zool.* **44**, 369–82.

HEMMING, F. (1953). *Copenhagen Decisions on Zoological Nomenclature*, 135 pp. London: International Trust for Zoological Nomenclature.

HEMMING, F. (1958). Official text of the 'Règles Internationales de la Nomenclature Zoologique' as it existed up to the opening of the Paris Congress in 1948. *Bull. zool. Nom.* **14**, i–xxviii.

HOARE, C. A. (1943). Biological races in parasitic protozoa. *Biol. Rev.* **18**, 137–44.

HOARE, C. A. (1952). The taxonomic status of biological races in parasitic protozoa. *Proc. Linn. Soc. Lond.* **163**, 44–7.

HOARE, C. A. (1955). Intraspecific biological groups in pathogenic protozoa. *Ref. Vet.* **12**, 258–63.

HOARE, C. A. (1957a). The classification of trypanosomes of veterinary and medical importance. *Vet. Revs. Annot.* **3**, 1–13.

HOARE, C. A. (1957b). Classification of Coccidia Eimeriidae in a 'periodic system' of homologous genera. *Rev. brasil. Malariol.* **8**, 197–202.

HOARE, C. A. (1959a). Morphological and taxonomic studies on mammalian trypanosomes. IX. Revision of *Trypanosoma dimorphon*. *Parasitology*, **49**, 210–31.

HOARE, C. A. (1959b). Amoebic infections in animals. *Vet. Revs. Annot.* **5**, 91–102.

HONIGBERG, B. M. (1962). A contribution to systematics of the non-pigmented flagellates. *Proc. 1st int. Conf. Protozool., Prague, August*, 1961 (in the Press).

HUTNER, S. H. (1961). The environment and growth: protozoan origins of metazoan responsitivities. *Symp. Soc. gen. Microbiol.* **11**, 1–18.

HUTNER, S. H., Editor (1962?). *Biochemistry and Physiology of Protozoa*. Vol. III. New York: Academic Press. (In preparation.)

HUTNER, S. H. & LWOFF, A., Editors. (1955). *Biochemistry and Physiology of Protozoa*. Vol. II, 388 pp. New York: Academic Press.

HUXLEY, J., Editor. (1940). *The New Systematics*, 583 pp. Oxford: Clarendon Press.

HYMAN, L. H. (1959). *The Invertebrates: Smaller Coelomate Groups*. Vol. V, 783 pp. New York: McGraw-Hill. [Phylum Protozoa, pp. 698–713, in Chap. 23: 'Retrospect'.]

JAHN, T. L., BOVEE, E. C. & SMALL, E. B. (1960). Mechanisms of movement: the basis for a new major dichotomy of the Sarcodina. (Abstr.) *J. Protozool.* **7** (Suppl.), 8.

JAHN, T. L. & JAHN, F. F. (1949). *How to know the Protozoa*, 234 pp. Dubuque, Iowa: Brown.

KAHL, A. (1930–35). Urtiere oder Protozoa. I: Wimpertiere oder Ciliata (Infusoria). Parts 18, 21, 25, 30, in *Die Tierwelt Deutschlands*, pp. 1–886. Edited by F. Dahl. Jena: G. Fischer.

KEEN, A. M. & MULLER, S. W. (1956). *Schenk and McMasters' Procedure in Taxonomy*, 3rd ed. 119 pp. Stanford, California: Stanford University Press.

KIRBY, H. (1944). Some observations on cytology and morphogenesis in flagellate protozoa. *J. Morph.* **75**, 361–421.

KIRBY, H. (1947). Flagellate and host relationships of trichomonad flagellates. *J. Parasitol.* **33**, 214–28.

KIRBY, H. (1950). Systematic differentiation and evolution of flagellates in termites. *Rev. Soc. Mex. Hist. Nat.* **10** (yr. 1949), 57–79.

KITCHING, J. A. (1957). Some factors in the life of free-living protozoa. In *Microbial Ecology. Symp. Soc. gen. Microbiol.* **7**, 259–86.

KUDO, R. R. (1954). *Protozoology*, 4th ed. 966 pp. Springfield, Illinois: Thomas.

KUDO, R. R. (1959). *Pelomyxa* and related organisms. *Ann. N.Y. Acad. Sci.* **78**, 474–86.

LEVINE, N. D. (1959). Uniform endings for the names of higher taxa. *Syst. Zool.* **7** (1958), 134–5.

LEVINE, N. D. (1961). *Protozoan Parasites of Domestic Animals and of Man*, 412 pp. Minneapolis: Burgess.

LOEBLICH, A. R., Jr. & TAPPAN, H. (1961). Suprageneric classification of the Rhizopodea. *J. Paleontol.* **35**, 245–330.

LWOFF, A., Editor. (1951). *Biochemistry and Physiology of Protozoa*, **1**, 434 pp. New York: Academic Press.

MACKINNON, D. L. & HAWES, R. S. J. (1961). *An Introduction to the Study of Protozoa*, 506 pp. Oxford: Clarendon Press.

MANWELL, R. D. (1957). Intraspecific variation in parasitic protozoa. *Syst. Zool.* **6**, 2–6.

MANWELL, R. D. (1961). *Introduction to Protozoology*, 642 pp. New York: St Martin's Press.

MAYR, E., LINSLEY, E. G. & USINGER, R. L. (1953). *Methods and Principles of Systematic Zoology*, 328 pp. New York: McGraw-Hill.

MÜLLER, O. F. (1786). *Animalcula Infusoria Fluviatilia et Marina*, 367 pp. Havniae et Lipsiae.

NEAVE, S. A. (1939–50). *Nomenclator Zoologicus*, **1–5**. 4113 pp. Zoological Society of London.

NOBLE, E. R. & NOBLE, G. A. (1961). *Parasitology, the Biology of Animal Parasites*, 767 pp. Philadelphia: Lea and Febiger.

PEARSE, A. S., Editor. (1936). *Zoological Names. A List of Phyla, Classes, and Orders*, 24 pp. Durham, North Carolina: Duke University Press.

POCHE, F. (1913). Das System der Protozoa. *Arch. Protistenk.* **30**, 125–321.

PROVASOLI, L., BALAMUTH, W., BECKER, E. R., CORLISS, J. O., HALL, R. P., HOLZ, G. G., Jr., LEVINE, N. D., MANWELL, R. D., NIGRELLI, R. F., STARR, R. C. & TRAGER, W. (1958). A catalogue of laboratory strains of free-living and parasitic protozoa (with sources from which they may be obtained and directions for their maintenance). *J. Protozool.* **5**, 1–38.

RAY, C., Jr. (1956). Meiosis and nuclear behavior in *Tetrahymena pyriformis*. *J. Protozool.* **3**, 88–96.

SCHULZE, F. E. *et al.* (1926–54). *Nomenclator Animalium Generum et Subgenerum*, Vols. I–V. 3716 pp. Berlin: Preuss. Akad. Wiss.

SIMPSON, G. G. (1961). *Principles of Animal Taxonomy*, 247 pp. New York: Columbia University Press.

SINGH, B. N. (1952). Nuclear division in nine species of small free-living amoebae and its bearing on the classification of the order Amoebida. *Phil. Trans.* B, **236**, 405–61.

SONNEBORN, T. M. (1957). Breeding systems, reproductive methods and species problems in protozoa. In *The Species Problem*, pp. 155–324. Edited by E. Mayr. Washington, D.C.: AAAS Publications.

TARTAR, V. (1961). *The Biology of* Stentor, 413 pp. New York and London: Pergamon Press.

TUFFRAU, M. (1953). Les processus cytologiques de la conjugaison chez *Spirochona gemmipara* Stein. *Bull. biol. Fr. Belg.* **87**, 314–22.

VICKERMAN, K. (1962). Patterns of cellular organisation in *limax* amoebae: an electron microscope study. *Exp. Cell Res.* (in the Press).

WESSENBERG, H. (1961). Studies on the life cycle and morphogenesis of *Opalina*. *Univ. Calif. Publ. Zool.* **61**, 315–69.

ADDENDUM

(For explanation see p. 54)

Table 3. *A tentative scheme of classification of the phylum Protozoa
(above the level of suborder)*

Subphylum I. MASTIGAMOEBAEA
Class I. FLAGELLATA

    Subclass 1. Phytomastigophora
      Order 1. Chrysomonadida
          2. Silicoflagellida
          3. Coccolithophorida
          4. Xanthomonadida
          5. Cryptomonadida
          6. Dinoflagellida
          7. Ebriida
          8. Phytomonadida
          9. Euglenida
        10. Chloromonadida

    Subclass 2. Zoomastigophora
      Order 1. Rhizomastigida
          2. Choanoflagellida
          3. Kinetoplastida
          4. Retortamonadida
          5. Diplomonadida
          6. Oxymonadida
          7. Trichomonadida
          8. Hypermastigida

Class II. PARAFLAGELLATA
    Order Opalinida

Class III. SARCODINA

    Subclass 1. Rhizopoda
      Superorder (1) Lobosida
      Order 1. Amoebida
          2. Arcellida
      Superorder (2) Filosida
      Order 1. Aconchulinida
          2. Gromiida
      Superorder (3) Mycetozoida
      Order 1. Acrasida
          2. Plasmodiophorida
          3. Eumycetozoida

    Subclass 2. Piroplasmata
    Order Piroplasmida

    Subclass 3. Reticulosa
    Order 1. Athalamida
         2. Monothalamida
         3. Foraminiferida
         4. Xenophyophorida
         5. Proteomyxida

    Subclass 4. Actinopoda
    Order 1. Heliozoida
         2. Acantharida
         3. Radiolarida

Subphylum II. SPOROZOA
Class I. TELOSPORIDIA

    Subclass 1. Gregarinomorpha
      Order 1. Archigregarinida
          2. Eugregarinida
          3. Neogregarinida

    Subclass 2. Coccidiomorpha
      Order 1. Protococcida
          2. Eucoccida
          3. Haemosporida

Class II. HAPLOSPORIDIA
    Order Haplosporida

Class III. SARCOSPORIDIA
    Order 1. Toxoplasmida
         2. Sarcosporida

Subphylum III. CNIDOSPORIDIA
    Order 1. Myxosporida
         2. Microsporida
         3. Actinomyxida
         4. Helicosporida

Subphylum IV. CILIOPHORA
    Class CILIATA

    Subclass 1. Holotricha
      Order 1. Gymnostomatida
          2. Trichostomatida
          3. Chonotrichida
          4. Suctorida
          5. Apostomatida
          6. Astomatida
          7. Hymenostomatida
          8. Thigmotrichida
          9. Peritrichida

    Subclass 2. Spirotricha
      Order 1. Heterotrichida
          2. Oligotrichida
          3. Tintinnida
          4. Entodiniomorphida
          5. Odontostomatida
          6. Hypotrichida

CLASSICAL AND MODERN CRITERIA USED IN ALGAL TAXONOMY WITH SPECIAL REFERENCE TO GENERA OF MICROBIAL SIZE

J. W. G. LUND

Freshwater Biological Association, Ambleside, England

INTRODUCTION

The classical morphological and anatomical criteria used to distinguish genera are still so important that they can form a basis for reviewing algal taxonomy at this level. Space precludes more than passing reference to species. Though the larger algae should not be included in a symposium on microbial classification, some reference will be made to them because, among algae, there are all gradations over a vast range of size. There are also all gradations between animals and plants, while some algae are difficult to distinguish from bacteria. The range of structure, physiology and biochemistry is so great that a heterogeneous taxonomy is not unexpected. The modern realization of the diversity of algae is seen in the frequent erection of each of the main groups of algae to the same rank (divisio or phylum) as the Flowering Plants (or of all the Higher Plants) on the grounds that these arose from the same stock as the Green Algae (Chlorophyta). The system followed here is that of Fott (1959a) which is similar to that of Fritsch (1935, 1945).

Considering characters one by one is unsatisfactory, for an attempt to produce a natural classification usually involves comparing several features. However, the alternative method of presentation, the consideration of each division separately, is less concise because the same or similar features appear repeatedly (Fritsch, 1935, p. 27). The main purpose is to provide information. Special emphasis is given here to small algae and those which have been used as experimental organisms by microbiologists.

Because of the diversity of the organisms called algae, and so of their taxonomic criteria, this short account is something of a catalogue. It is hoped that, with the help of the literature cited, it may help microbiologists who wish to find their way through the taxonomic jungle.

THE FLAGELLUM

The structure and the number, position and length of the flagella are often generic characters.

In Flagellates

In the Volvocales (Chlorophyta, Green Algae) their number may be the sole criterion for generic distinctions (Figs. 1–22). *Chlamydomonas* and *Carteria* have two and four, respectively, as have the colourless *Polytoma* and *Tetrablepharis* (by colourless is meant the absence of chromatophores or photosynthetic pigments). This seems a stable character. No viable quadriflagellate *Chlamydomonas* or biflagellate *Carteria* clones have been produced experimentally, despite the occasional appearance of such cells (Pascher, 1929 a). The motile zygotes of some biflagellate species retain temporarily the flagella of both gametes. *C. ovata* is the planozygote of *Chlamydomonas variabilis* (Behlau, 1939). *Chlorobrachis* may be the motile zygote of the colonial *Pyrobotrys* or a separate unicellular genus (Schulze, 1927; Strehlow, 1928–29; Behlau, 1935; Korshikov, 1938 a; Lee, 1951; Hansen & Gerloff, 1952; Silva & Papenfuss, 1953). A comparison of the chromosomes of such algae is difficult because they are so small. Most species of *Pyramimonas* (*Pyramidomonas*) have four flagella but *P. octociliata* Carter (1937) has eight. Its retention in the genus is justified by the occasional octociliate specimens in asexual populations of normally quadriciliate species (Geitler, 1925; Pascher, 1929 a; Conrad, 1939).

It seems then that the number of flagella in the Volvocales is a good specific character but, unless combined with other features, is doubtfully justified as a generic one. It is convenient for identification. There is bound to be prejudice in favour of its retention because *Chlamydomonas* alone has about 500 species. The structure of the flagella of most Green Algae is uniform and if two or more are present they are of equal length (for exceptions see Carter, 1937; Starr, 1955 a; Lewin, 1958; Butcher, 1959).

In the Chrysophyceae (Chrysophyta) the number of flagella is considered to be of great or little taxonomic importance according to their structure or the opinion of the authority concerned. Three arrangements exist (Figs. 58–64): (*a*) uniflagellate and pantonematic (Fig. 58); (*b*) biflagellate, with one flagellum pantonematic and usually much longer than the other acronematic one (heteromorphic, Fig. 59); (*c*) biflagellate with both flagella acronematic (homoeomorphic) and of equal (Fig. 61) or subequal (Fig. 62) length. In the second case the

pantonematic flagellum has a more undulatory motion than the acronematic one (heterodynamic, Fig. 60) and in the third case this may
(heterodynamic, Fig. 63) or may not (homodynamic, Figs. 61, 62) be so.
Only the 'double organism' *Didymochrysis* has two flagella of each kind
(Pascher, 1929 *a*). Organisms with two acronematic flagella often have
a third filiform appendage, the haptonema (Fig. 64) (Parke, Manton &
Clarke, 1955), which may be a valuable diagnostic feature.

There seems no doubt that the two sets, (*b*) and (*c*), of biflagellate
genera are quite separate (Parke, 1961). The old view that uniflagellate
and heteromorphic biflagellate genera belonged to different groups is no
longer tenable. This difference is even of doubtful value at the level of
species (Fott, 1959*b*; Lund, 1960; Parke, 1961). However, several
pairs of genera are so distinguished, for example *Chromulina* and
Ochromonas (Figs. 29, 30). In many species of the latter the short
flagellum is so minute that it is easily overlooked. In *Chromulina
psammobia* electron microscopy shows that there is a second short
flagellum within the cell (Fauré-Frémiet & Rouiller, 1957). It is unknown
if this is so in other species, but the difference between an internal
flagellum and an external functional one justifies the continued separation of the genera. Similarly, it seems that the minute structure found
near the pantonematic flagellum of *Mallomonas* is also the remnant of
a second acronematic one (Magne in Bourrelly, 1957). In the parallel
genus *Mallomonopsis* (Matvienko, 1941, 1954; *Ochromallomonas* Lund,
1942) this flagellum is so long (Figs. 48, 49) that their separation seems
justifiable.

The taxonomy of the loricate *Kephyrion* and its allies (Schmid, 1934;
Conrad, 1942; Fott, 1959*b*; Lund, 1960) is more difficult. Some
parallels between the uniflagellate and biflagellate genera are so striking
that one must suspect that, in the former, a minute second flagellum has
been overlooked. Fott (1959*b*) considers that it may be present or
absent, so that it is of no specific importance. The records of uni- or
biflagellate specimens in *Lepochromulina* (Scherffel, 1911; Geitler, 1948;
Fott, 1953; Petersen & Hansen, 1960) support this view.

The Chrysophyceae have been considered at length because, as will be
seen, the taxonomy of this group is undergoing great changes and
because of the importance of the flagella in the new system which is
arising. In the remaining groups the flagella either are of constant type
or arrangement (e.g. in the classes of the Phaeophyta) or are of little
value in separating genera. In the Xanthophyceae (Chrysophyta) the
number of motile genera is too small for useful consideration but the
same criteria probably apply as in the Chrysophyceae. In the Eugleno-

phyta (Figs. 65–70) the number of flagella is a generic character. Thus *Euglena* has one and *Eutreptia* two. As in *Mallomonas*, however, a rudiment of a second flagellum is present in *Euglena*. Colourless Euglenophyta show considerable variety in the number and length of the flagella present (cf. Fritsch, 1935, pp. 734 *et seq.*) often combined with other divergent characters. Pyrrophyta, Chloromonadophyceae and Cryptophyceae have uniform flagella. It is true that, in the last, *Monomastix* has only one flagellum but there are good grounds for considering it to be a uniflagellate Green Alga.

In non-motile forms

In the Chlorophyta the majority of the genera have biflagellate motile reproductive stages, though quadriflagellate ones are not uncommon. The multiflagellate genera belong to specialized groups (Oedogoniineae; Derbesiaceae). Variations in the number are rarely used as in *Characium* and *Pseudocharacium* Korshikov (1953) because other characters are available. In the Ulotrichineae this seems to be the only feature separating *Ulothrix* from *Chlorohormidium* Fott (*Hormidium* Kütz.).

In view of the two apparently fundamentally different biflagellate types in the Chrysophyceae they may be expected to become sound criteria for distinguishing orders and certainly of genera. The separation of orders on the presence of a single acronematic flagellum or of it and a pantonematic one (Bourrelly, 1957) seems unsound. Whether non-motile genera should continue to be separated by such differences in the flagella of their swarmers involves the questions already discussed (p. 69). The same problem arises in the Xanthophyceae where, at present, both uniflagellate and biflagellate (presumably heteromorphic) species may be found in one genus, e.g. *Pleurochloris*, *Heterogloea* (Pascher, 1937–39).

THE CELL WALL

Presence or absence

The terms walled or naked are commonly used but what is meant by them, and consequently their taxonomic value, is uncertain. Picken (1960) says: 'the point at which, by reason of stability and rigidity, the outer layers of a cell are recognized as a "wall" is an arbitrary one, and the distinction between "inert membranes" and the "physiological cell surface" ignores the fact that what ends as an inert membrane usually begins as a structure inseparable from the physiological surface'. This is a consideration of importance in the Chrysophyceae (see Lund, in the press) and allied groups, but phycologists often mean by a wall an outer membrane which is not involved directly in the cleavages of a cell undergoing reproduction.

In the Volvocales (Chlorophyta) the presence or absence of a wall is the sole generic difference between several pairs of genera (Figs. 1–17). The wall in such algae is usually visible but, in case of doubt, the essential difference between this and the 'membrane' around the protoplast is seen during division. The wall takes no part in this. When a wall is absent the whole cell divides longitudinally into two. Additional features are that when walled cells are placed in plasmolysing solutions the protoplast alone contracts and, in a naked cell, changes of shape are possible without any concomitant increase in size. The former is not trustworthy in species with very thin walls. The latter, as used at the generic level in the Chlorococcales (Starr, 1955a), is not wholly free from doubt. The elongate 'naked' zoospores may appear to be as 'walled' as those said to have a wall, in that they do not change in shape while swimming. When they settle down in preparation for a new non-motile phase of growth the naked zoospores round-off while the 'walled' zoospores do not. As zoospores do not divide this wall problem cannot be solved at present but the difference in behaviour supplies a useful taxonomic character. The wall of *Chlamydomonas* may be cellulosic (Lewin, Owen & Melnick, 1951) but that of *Platymonas* is not (Lewin, 1958), so that there may not be clear chemical differences between 'walls' and 'membranes'.

No walled Volvocales have been turned into naked ones, or vice versa, in the sense that self-perpetuating clones have been obtained. However, a common feature of cultures of *Chlamydomonas* and related organisms is the appearance of 'twinning' (Lewin, 1952). 'Twin' cells appear to have undergone longitudinal division like a *Dunaliella*, but there is no evidence concerning the presence or absence of a wall. Mutants with a substantial proportion of such mis-divisions show impaired growth. In genetical experiments twinning behaves as a single gene mutation (Lewin, 1952).

There is a number of loricate Volvocales (the Phacotaceae) in which nearly all the cell surface lies some distance within a firm outer membrane which is often encrusted with various compounds (Figs. 23–28). This is also called a capsule, theca or envelope. Insufficient is known about these algae to be sure how many have walls within this capsule which might well be the true wall. The cell division of some (e.g. *Phacotus lenticularis*; Conrad, 1931) suggests that there is such a wall so that it will differ from the naked loricate genera of other groups (e.g. Chrysophyceae, Euglenophyceae). On the other hand, the opposite may be the case in *Dysmorphococcus* (Bold & Starr, 1953), a genus in which the 'cell' usually lies close to the capsule. Here the position may be that a rough and coloured wall has been mistaken for an outer capsule. Even if the Phacotaceae is an artificial family the characters of the alleged capsule are such that several good genera and species can be distinguished.

It is not certain that any naked non-motile Chlorophyta exist. Apart from certain palmelloid genera, it is clear that the cells possess a wall. When an alga, such as *Chlamydomonas* on agar, becomes non-motile but continues to multiply to form a mucilaginous mass of cells it is said to be palmelloid. Many species exist for a considerable time in this state in nature, notably terrestrial forms. From such species there is a continuous series of algae leading to definitely non-motile forms in which zoospores or gametes are the only motile stages (Figs. 91–96; 102–104). Therefore there can be no satisfactory distinction between Volvocales and Chlorococcales while generic distinctions may be even more subjective than usual. In many genera which (though palmelloid) have clear-cut characteristics, any cell may become motile. In these it may be difficult to determine where the cell wall ends and the mucilaginous investment begins, if indeed there is any demarcation (cf. Picken, 1960). The common genera *Tetraspora*, *Gemellicystis* and *Paulschulzia* (Lund, 1956) are examples. The cells can lose their pseudocilia, replace them by flagella and swim away, though growth of the colony is by means of cell-division in the non-motile phase. A superficial appearance of longitudinal division of the whole cell, as in naked forms, is not borne out by careful examination. It seems, then, that these are walled cells and the present exclusion of generic distinctions on the basis of the presence or absence of a wall is justifiable.

In the Chrysophyceae and Xanthophyceae palmelloid algae commonly have naked cells. Nevertheless, the question as to what is a wall is very important because of the taxonomic emphasis laid on it. In these groups Picken's (1960) statement quoted earlier seems to apply only too well. Even in the flagellate forms this difficulty arises. Thus Lund (1942) describes two species of *Chromulina* in which reproduction takes place within a membrane which might well be called a wall. As there is no evidence that the motile cells divide, as they should if the name *Chromulina* is strictly applied, these algae perhaps represent separate genera. In the capsal organization (Pascher, 1925; Fott, 1959a) the cells are solitary or in mucilaginous colonies of the palmelloid type, while in the coccal group they have a firm wall. The cells of many capsal forms are undoubtedly naked, they exhibit changes in shape (metaboly) and show no sign of an external membrane which can be called a wall in that it does not divide with the rest of the cell. Yet careful examination of others leads to doubt. There appears to be a delicate membrane around the cells within which the division of the protoplast takes place, four daughter cells often arising as in the autosporic Chlorococcales. It seems impossible at present to answer the question 'When is a wall not a wall?' (Lund, in the press). The distinction of genera on such grounds is one of the causes of the unsatisfactory classification in this class. In the Xanthophyceae the same problem exists but the clearly walled or coccal genera are the more numerous.

The cells of the Euglenophyceae may have a very rigid external membrane (periplast), for example in *Phacus* and *Lepocinclis* or, as in some *Euglena* spp., one which is highly ornamented. The periplast is, however, an integral part of the protoplast since it divides with it and so the cell is naked. This is also true of the loricate *Trachelomonas*. Other naked though not necessarily metabolic flagellates are typical of the Cryptophyceae and Chloromonadinophyceae. In Phaeophyta there are no naked genera but the zoospores are always naked.

In the Dinophyta we return to terminological difficulties which are by-passed by avoiding the use of the word wall. The terms armoured or unarmoured are generally used according to whether the periplast is covered by plates or not (Figs. 81–90). Several generic distinctions are based on the shape, structure and arrangement of the plates. The word naked is also often avoided, which is just as well in a genus such as *Gymnodinium* (see Schiller, 1933, pp. 323–434) where plates may (e.g. *G. coronatum* Wolosz. = *Woloszynskia coronatum* (Wolosz.) Thompson, 1950) be quite easily seen or, apparently, be absent (cf. Kofoid & Swezy, 1921). Indeed, if the words naked or walled were used in the same sense as elsewhere a number of new and artificial groups would have to be erected. In some armoured genera the whole cell, including the plates, undergoes fission: e.g. *Ceratium* (Fott, 1959a, Fig. 215), *Gonyaulax*, and *Dinophysis*, and in others only the protoplast within. Though the latter situation holds for the vast majority of the species of *Peridinium*, the former is seen in a small minority (Lefèvre, 1932).

Structure of the wall and other outer membranes

In the Chlorococcales several genera are distinguished by the structure of the wall (Figs. 119–126). However in *Scenedesmus* a wide range of structure is used solely for distinguishing species (Figs. 105–116) but there is disagreement about the value of such characters (e.g. Smith,

1916; Chodat, 1926; Yaguzhinskii, 1936, 1937; Skuja, 1948; Dedusenko-Shchegoleva, 1949; Hortobágyi, 1959–60, 1960; Fott & Komárek, 1960).

Here there are three difficulties which are common to a variety of simple organisms and the cause of similar disagreements in other algal groups (e.g. Xanthophyceae, Cyanophyta). First, there is no sexual reproduction so that, as in many micro-organisms (e.g. Fungi Imperfecti) and even in, for example, the apomictic hawkweeds (*Hieracium*, see Clapham, Tutin & Warburg, 1961) differences arising by mutation are perpetuated. Secondly, there are so few visible structural differences for the taxonomist to use. Thirdly, the chromosomes are so minute that, as yet, they cannot be studied. The result is that any difference is utilized in order to assist identification. The prejudice of most present-day algal taxonomists is in favour of splitting genera or, at least, keeping pre-existing genera as small as possible. This is a useful practical outlook, but there is justification for the opposite view in relation to *Scenedesmus*, in which the wall ornamentation shows so much intergrading variation that it is difficult to see how the genus could be split.

In the desmids (Conjugatophyceae) several of the genera either come very close to or merge imperceptibly with one another (Figs. 157–164). Here, as in the Chlorococcales and Mischococcales (Figs. 117–149; 165–179), it is difficult to separate a discussion of the structure of the wall from one of cell shape (see p. 84). However, the arrangement of the spines in *Xanthidium* may be so simplified that some species come close to those of *Staurodesmus* (= *Arthrodesmus* p.p.). Distinction is largely a matter of convenience in relation to ecological and other studies, a situation which is obvious when considering species of desmids, notably the planktonic *Staurastrum* (Brook, 1959). It is probably true to say that the vast number of specific and infra-specific taxa in desmids is largely the result of the infinite variety in their shape and in the detailed ornamentation of the wall which fascinates the microscopist and tempts the taxonomist.

The last sentence probably could be applied to diatoms (Bacillariophyceae) too, where the structure of the silicified wall is one of the three main taxonomic characters. At the generic level the symmetry and structure of the wall are most important (Figs. 188–215). Investigations with the electron microscope (see pictures in Helmcke & Krieger, 1953–54) have not altered taxonomists' views on genera and seem unlikely at present to lead to much change in speciation (Hendey, 1959). Nevertheless, the separation of species is often based on fine structure. In discoid diatoms the disposition of the structural units may give patterns which can be used taxonomically (e.g. Figs. 188–193). The finer details, however, are either discerned with difficulty with the light microscope or only with the electron microscope, and then, '...Similar patterns of microstructure are to be found in species of diatoms belonging to widely differing taxonomic groups' (Hendey, 1959). This is why it seems unlikely that electron microscopy will lead to much change at the generic level either. On the other hand, the large number of electron micrographs published still only represents a fraction of the known species. In *Navicula* and *Nitzschia*, containing some 1000 and 700 species, respectively, two of the main specific characters are the arrangement and density of the fine lines or dots visible under a light microscope. The detailed differences revealed by the electron microscope may lead to changes here, including transfers to other genera (Hendey, 1959). For further consideration of structure reference may be made to the valuable review of Hendey (1959) and standard floras (e.g. Hustedt, 1930–59; Cleve-Euler, 1951–55). Siliceous coverings are also common in the Chrysophyceae, as well as calcareous ones (coccolithophorids), and are important even at the generic level.

Among flagellates, *Microglena* has lens-shaped granules of silica, *Synura* and *Mallomonas* overlapping scales which generally bear long bristles, and *Conradiella* annular plates (Figs. 47–50). In the last three the diversity of structure in the scales and spines is used for specific distinctions, but in the Coccolithineae also for distinguishing genera (Schiller, 1930; Deflandre, 1952; Deflandre & Fert, 1954; Halldal, 1955). This difference in outlook is based on the belief that the diversity of structure of the scales of *Mallomonas* and *Synura* is less striking than that of the coccoliths which, as will be seen, are also of importance in relation to the taxonomy of filamentous forms. Scales which are apparently neither calcified nor silicified supply specific characters in *Chrysochromulina* and its allies (Parke *et al.* 1955–59; Parke, Lund & Manton, in the press). These, too, are complex but can only be studied with an electron microscope. Some detail can be seen in the scales and spines of *Mallomonas* and *Synura* with a light microscope if the best lenses and procedures are used, but this is not always clearly indicated. Nevertheless, it is only with the electron microscope that their full structure is revealed or, in very small species, that any detail is visible (Manton, 1955; Harris & Bradley, 1957, 1958, 1960; Asmund, 1955, 1956, 1959; Fott, 1959*a*, fig. 27). This can also be true of Coccolithophorids (Hasle, 1960).

In the loricate Chrysophyceae (Figs. 32–35, 38–45) the common distinction between *Dinobryon* and *Hyalobryon* is based on the construction of this case which, in the latter genus, consists of a series of rings fitting into one another. However, *Dinobryon* is said to have a similar case though the margins of the rings are only visible after special treatment (cf. Fritsch, 1935, fig. 174). Skuja (1948, 1956) depicts species of *Dinobryon* with the *Hyalobryon* type of case. It may be that distinction here is a matter of convenience based on tradition (Mack, 1953). There are, however, species of *Dinobryon* (e.g. Sect. Epipyxis and Fig. 44) in which the envelope is built up of overlapping scales and it is still not certain that the common colonial, free-swimming species of *Dinobryon* have a ring structure (Petersen & Hansen, 1958).

Zygospores and resting spores with strongly ornamented walls are very common in Green Algae but are not used as generic features. They are very important for delimiting species in the Oedogoniales and Zygnematales (see Kolkwitz & Krieger, 1941–44; Gemeinhardt, 1939–40; Randhawa, 1959). The fact that the highly ornamented zygospores of desmids are not used taxonomically while those of the Zygnematales are, may be related to the diversity of shape and ornamentation of the vegetative cells in the former and its absence in the latter. A further difficulty is that zygospores are not common in the desmids, though this is also true of some Zygnematales (e.g. *Mougeotia* spp.). If, using culture techniques (Starr, 1955b, 1959), sexual reproduction could be induced more freely, then the taxonomy of genera such as *Staurastrum* and *Cosmarium* might be improved. The zygotes of *Chlamydomonas* and allied genera also have ornamented walls. Too few examples are known to enable them to be of much use, while experiments show that they may be prevented from producing their full ornamentation, without loss of viability, by conditions which could occur in nature (Lewin, 1957).

The asexual spores of Blue-Green algae may supply important specific characters (e.g. *Anabaena*, Fritsch, 1939b; Komárek in Komárek & Ettl, 1958) but here, too, they may be more variable than was believed (Demeter, 1956). In the Chrysophyceae the cysts are only used at the level of species, and then only in certain genera. Conrad's (1931) chromulinoid genera based on their ornamentation have not been upheld. Yet at the level of species the description of many Chromulinae in which cysts are unknown is regrettable because the characters used, such as shape, size and cell contents, can vary so greatly. The same is true of allied genera (concerning *Ochromonas* see Pringsheim, 1952, 1955) where, in the absence of cysts, clone cultures may be essential. However, it seems unlikely that cysts can be used very extensively, for those of many Chrysophyceae are so similar in size and shape, while micro-structure (of the types seen in the walls of diatoms and other Chrysophycean flagellates) is absent.

The fate of the wall during reproduction or growth may supply useful characteristics which are considered later (p. 89).

CONTRACTILE VACUOLES

These have recently been used in the Volvocales to re-classify *Chlamydomonas* and its allies (Figs. 1–12). All the *Chlamydomonas* species with more than two contractile vacuoles distributed irregularly throughout the cell have been transferred to *Chlorogonium* (Ettl in Komárek & Ettl, 1958; but see also footnotes by Fott, 1959a, pp. 235–36). This has resolved the difficulty of distinguishing the genera by shape. Moreover, the location of the contractile vacuoles is a stable character. Against the view that several species of *Chlorogonium*, including the type *C. euchlorum*, have a characteristic type of chromatophore (Fig. 13), can be set the fact that among the species placed in *Chlamydomonas* by all the authorities is found every type of chromatophore known in Green Algae. Nevertheless, the classical species of *Chlorogonium*, as well as more recent ones (e.g. *C. maximum*, Skuja, 1939, 1956), have a characteristic type of chromatophore and a more or less narrow protoplasmic strand which lies at some distance from the wall and joins the cell apex to that of the chromatophore. Skuja (1956) records only two anterior contractile vacuoles in young cells of *C. maximum* and in the adult ones of *C. perforatum*, though it is not clear that they are orientated as in *Chlamydomonas* sensu Ettl. A few species of *Chlamydomonas* have four apical contractile vacuoles. In *C. pulsatilla* their constant and characteristic position is similar to that of the bivacuolate species, so that Ettl (1959) does not transfer it to *Chlorogonium*.

The absence of any clear distinction between flagellate and coccoid Chlorophyta has been mentioned. One of the last features of the flagellate state to disappear or, if we follow Chadefaud's (1959) evolutionary sequence, to appear, is the contractile vacuole, as is well seen in the Chlorangiales of Ettl (Komárek & Ettl, 1958) and the Tetrasporineae (as demarcated by Fritsch, 1935). *Characiochloris* (see Komárek & Ettl, 1958) differs from *Characium* in their presence, though their number and distribution seems to differ from those in the zoospores of the latter. *Hypnomonas* Korshikov (1926) differs from *Chlorococcum* (as defined by Silva & Starr, 1953) in the presence of contractile vacuoles in the vegetative cells. Fritsch & John (1942) and Starr (1955a), however, have found them in species which would otherwise belong to

Chlorococcum. Further they may not be a constant feature during the life of a cell. It seems, then, that too much stress may be laid on this feature. Though contractile vacuoles may be useful at the generic level, their use for delimiting higher taxa such as the Vacuolatae of Korshikoff (1926, 1932, 1953) is unsound.

Contractile vacuoles are commonly present in non-motile Chryso-phyceae and Xanthophyceae and occasionally in diatoms. However, their number and position do not appear to supply useful characters. One difficulty is the suspicion that many records of monovacuolate species are erroneous. Their presence or absence is used by Pascher (1937–39) to separate *Pleurochloridella* from *Pleurochloris*, although, in some species of the latter, contractile vacuoles may be present in young vegetative cells. The position is the same as in *Hypnomonas*, to which Pascher refers, and *Chlorococcum*. Another similar pair are *Characidiop-sis* and *Characiopsis*. The former has species with a stigma.

A practical difficulty in using contractile vacuoles as diagnostic characters is their absence in marine species. Thus Butcher (1959) says that some of his non-vacuolate species of *Chlamydomonas* are very similar to vacuolate freshwater forms. This may be an insuperable difficulty but Ettl (1959) has shown that non-contractile vacuoles may be present after a freshwater species has been transferred to a medium containing 1% glucose or NaCl, and Guillard (1960) suppressed their formation by increasing the osmotic pressure of the culture medium. The latter also showed that a mutant without vacuoles could only live in special media of high osmotic value and could be crossed with the parent vacuolate strain. We now need to test marine species to see if contractile vacuoles can appear.

CHROMATOPHORES (INCLUDING CHLOROPLASTS). PYRENOIDS

Presence or absence

The presence or absence of chromatophores is commonly used as a single character for separating genera, for example *Chlamydomonas* and *Polytoma* (Chlorophyta); *Euglena* and *Astasia* (Euglenophyceae); *Ochromonas* and *Monas* (Chrysophyta); *Cryptomonas* and *Chilomonas* (Figs. 1, 7, 29, 36, 65, 69, 79, 80). Yet in the Dinophyta colourless and pigmented species (Figs. 81–87) are common in *Gymnodinium, Kato-dinium* (*Massartia*) and *Amphidinium* and are also known in *Peridinium* (cf. *Mallomonas*, Chrysophyta; Conrad, 1927). Among diatoms, the only authenticated colourless species is in the genus *Nitzschia* (Pringsheim,

1951 a). In the Euglenophyceae an ambivalent attitude prevails. Colourless Euglenae are commonly placed in *Astasia* but exceptions occur in those resembling *E. acus*. Pringsheim (1956) has reviewed the unresolved arguments concerning these algae, for some of which the genera *Khawkinea* and *Cyclidiopsis* have been erected on the grounds of differences in the occurrence of stigma, the shape of the paramylon grains and the location of the anterior canal. In *Phacus*, Pringsheim (1936) places an undoubtedly colourless species in *Hyalophacus* but Pochmann (1942) retains it in *Phacus*. In *Trachelomonas*, Pringsheim (1957) does not erect a new genus for the colourless species.

Observations on many species give the impression that, among such pairs of genera, the non-phagotrophic are more sharply distinct than the phagotrophic ones. There is no difficulty in distinguishing between *Chlamydomonas* and *Polytoma* or *Cryptomonas* and *Chilomonas*. In such genera, viable colourless mutants of the pigmented species are unknown and there is no record of a colourless species producing pigmented cells. Even in *Euglena* there is only one species (*E. gracilis*) in which colourless, viable mutants have been produced experimentally and even then this was only successful with some races (Pringsheim, 1956).

Distinguishing *Monas* from *Ochromonas* and the uniflagellate *Oikomonas* from *Chromulina* may be difficult. One has the impression that every gradation between the pigmented and colourless state exists. The more organisms an *Ochromonas* ingests, the paler and smaller the chromatophore is likely to become. The subjective impression, therefore is that if conditions continue to favour phagotrophy, particularly if the illumination is poor, the cells will become colourless. The same is true of organotrophy, which is also possible for these versatile organisms. However, this seems to be an erroneous view, for either cells without chromatophores are not produced or, if they are, they do not seem to be able to multiply for long enough to produce colourless populations of appreciable size. It is very difficult to determine by observation whether or not a chromatophore is present but occasional colourless specimens are recorded for *Poteriochromonas stipitata* (Scherffel, 1911; Pringsheim, 1959). In *Ochromonas* Pringsheim (1952) obtained several apparently colourless cells but, when isolated, these either produced pigmented populations or died.

Even in the Dinophyta, where no such generic separations are made, the only record of mixed pigmented and colourless populations seems to be that of Skuja (1939) for *Amphidinium luteum*, and this needs verification by isolation tests.

The resolution of these problems depends on morphological and physiological investigations. The present system is illogical but is unlikely to be changed as yet because it is hallowed by time. Moreover, prejudice against large genera is such that there will be resistance to the extension of the system in the Dinophyceae to the Chrysophyceae. The apparently clear-cut distinction in the non-phagotrophic pairs of genera may be a cause of satisfaction to the taxonomist but there is a hint of difficulty here too. In *Furcilla* and *Pseudofurcilla* (which Skuja (1956) equates with *Furcilla*), there appear to be both colourless and pigmented forms (Skuja, 1927; Pascher, 1927; Jane, 1944*b*), while Korshikov (1939) says the cells can be at first colourless and later pigmented as in *Phacotus pallidus* (Korshikov, 1938*b*). A similar situation may exist in *Polytomella* (Skuja, 1939), and Strehlow (1928–29) found that the zygotes of the colourless *Polytoma fusiforme* developed chlorophyll. Presumably such algae are never modifications of the same species.

Among coccoid algae, *Chlorella* has received much non-taxonomic attention and numerous colourless mutants have been produced. Therefore the separation of the parallel apoplastidic *Prototheca* must be reconsidered. A stumbling block here is the unsatisfactory state of the taxonomy of *Chlorella* (Pringsheim, 1959). Names such as *C. vulgaris* and *C. pyrenoidosa* are used with a freedom which almost amounts to levity. Pringsheim (1959) says that apochlorotic mutants of *Chlorella* are microscopically indistinguishable from *Prototheca*. However, they are said to be physiologically different (Ciferri, 1956; Ciferri, Montemartini & Ciferri, 1957). The statement that *P. zopfii* has chloroplast grana (Rabinowitch, 1956, p. 1725) needs confirmation. Other such pairs of coccoid Chlorophyta are *Ankistrodesmus* and *Hyaloraphidium* and the colourless species of *Characium* (Pascher, 1929*b*) which, logically, should be in a separate genus.

In other groups, colourless genera are rare or absent. It is unknown how far this is because of the difficulty of distinguishing such algae from other micro-organisms. For example, many colourless filamentous Cyanophyta (e.g. Oscillatoriaceae, see Skuja, 1956) and similar organisms (Pringsheim, 1949, 1951*b*) are known, while criteria for distinguishing colourless coccoid forms from some non-motile bacteria remain to be found. Colourless Xanthophyceae might also be difficult to recognize because the characteristic bipartite cysts are not common even in pigmented forms.

On the other hand, colourless coccoid Chrysophyceae and Dinophyceae should be detectable. In the latter division such organisms do exist as parasites (Schiller, 1933–37) and, at times, produce gymnodinioid swarmers. If there are others without swarmers their detection may soon prove possible because of the recent work on the nuclear structure of Dinophyceae (Skoczylas, 1958–59; Stosch, 1958–59; Dodge, 1960).

The type of chromatophore. Pyrenoids

Very varied taxonomic importance is given to the shape and structure of the chromatophores. For example, in the coccoid Green Algae studied by Starr (1955a), the shape and location of the chromatophore, and the presence or absence of a pyrenoid are primary generic characters (Figs. 127–137). In *Chlamydomonas* and its allies the variety of the chromatophores and the presence of many pyrenoids or none ensure that considerable caution is shown even for specific delimitation (Gerloff, 1940; Lund, 1947b; Ettl, 1959). Both approaches seem justifiable. In the first case striking differences occur without intergrading and these can be combined with other structural characteristics. In the second case intergrading forms can be found, even during the growth of one cell. Sometimes the emphasis laid on the chromatophores seems less satisfactory. *Eremosphaera* has only one other distinguishing feature, namely its large size. *Muriella* Boye Pet. em. Vischer (1936) differs from *Chlorella* in the presence of more than one chromatophore in the adult cells and the absence of a pyrenoid. Nevertheless, in such characterless algae, it is natural to seize on any available visible difference. *Mougeotiopsis* is also separated by the absence of a pyrenoid, but the large number of species of Zygnematales, all with a pyrenoid, makes it a striking exception.

In the Xanthophyceae and Chrysophyceae the chromatophores are usually parietal disks, plates or bands and the few genera with axile ones generally have other characteristics justifying their separation. In the Bacillariophyceae (diatoms) it may seem that the striking ornamentation of the frustules has led to the wall receiving too much importance relative to the chromatophores and pyrenoids. However, the less common types of chromatophore are found among a variety of genera which are clearly distinguished by the symmetry and shape of the cells. To some extent, too, elaboration of the chromatophore can be related to the size of the cells.

The chromatophores of most Phaeophyta are of the same type but may differ in the haploid and diploid phases; more diversity occurs in Rhodophyta. For a general review of these divisions see Fritsch (1942). Considerable differences may be seen in different parts of a plant or stages in the life history. Belcher (1960) found different chromatophores in stages of *Bangia atropurpurea* which were unlike morphologically but apparently had the same number of chromosomes. For the most part such algae have a multitude of other characters for generic delimitation.

Though all pyrenoids in Green Algae appear to be of similar constitution, a variety of such bodies is said to be present in other groups. If these are as different as suspected (Hollande, 1942) they deserve more attention from taxonomists.

SHAPE AND SYMMETRY OF CELLS

Shape and ornamentation are widely used as generic characters. Once again, whether justified or not, such separations are usually convenient.

In unicellular flagellates shape can only be used if it is not too variable. Therefore there is less emphasis on this in the Chrysophyceae, where most of the flagellates are naked and metabolic (i.e. show changes of shape), than in the Chlorophyceae where most are walled or, if naked, are less metabolic.

In the Volvocales examples of distinction by shape are illustrated in Figs. 14–22. As has been mentioned, too much emphasis was laid by some workers on shape in distinguishing between *Chlamydomonas* and *Chlorogonium*. Ettl, who has tried to find a better basis for their separation has, however, used shape to create new genera (Ettl, H. & Ettl, O., 1959). *Costatochloris* includes species previously placed in *Carteria* which have a longitudinally ridged wall and differ from *Diplostauron* in the number of flagella. *Pyramichlamys* includes *Carteria* species with an apical depression and, in some, the shape is similar to that of the naked *Pyramimonas*. *Chlamydonephris* and *Chlamydomonas* are a similar pair (Figs. 1, 14).

In the Chrysophyceae, *Monochrysis* (Skuja, 1948) basically is a bilaterally symmetrical *Chromulina* (cf. *Nephrochloris*; Pascher, 1937–39). There are many loricate genera in this division (Figs. 32–35, 38, 39, 43–45). There is a divergence of opinion on structural grounds as to the limits of most of these genera (Pascher, 1913; Conrad, 1942; Fott, 1959*b*; Lund, 1960; see also p. 70).

In the Cryptophyceae, the typical genera have a very similar basic shape, and those which have not are mainly of uncertain position or more correctly placed in the Chlorophyceae (e.g. *Monomastix, Heteromastix*). In the Euglenophyceae (Figs. 71–74), shape is important for both generic and specific separation. *Phacus* differs from *Euglena* in the rigid and generally leaf-like shape and *Lepocinclis* from both in being

6-2

neither flattened nor metabolic. This arrangement is generally satisfactory. Pringsheim (1956) has considered the species which form a bridge between *Euglena* and *Lepocinclis* in shape but says they come closer to the former genus. Some species of *Phacus* and *Euglena* could be placed in either genus. *P. tripteris* is placed in *Phacus* by Pochmann (1942) and in *Euglena* by Pringsheim (1956) who points to its close relationship with other species but adds: 'the decision is of course a matter of expediency'. Pochmann (1942) expresses similar views in relation to the species of *Phacus* grouped round *P. pyrum*, also called *E. pyrum* and *Lepocinclis pyrum*. He says: 'so gibt es Formen, die weit mehr an eine *Lepocinclis* erinnern als an einem *Phacus*...die aber aus formalen Gründen vorderhand bei *Phacus* verblieben müssen'. Similar problems exist in colourless Euglenineae.

In the Dinophyceae (Figs. 81–90), the shape and the structure of the external membrane, discussed earlier, are the main generic characters. Thus the unicellular dinoflagellates, which are unarmoured or lack the marked plating of *Peridinium* etc., include three similar genera, *Gymnodinium*, *Amphidinium* and *Katodinium*, differing in the relative sizes of the upper and lower halves of the cell. The two halves in *Gymnodinium* can be somewhat unequal so that separation depends on what the specialist considers is a great inequality. The same is true about the degree of spiralness in the course of the transverse groove which should justify generic separation.

Many genera of coccoid algae are based on cell shape and ornamentation, notably in the Chlorophyceae and Xanthophyceae. In the Chlorococcales Korshikov (1953) has laid the foundations of a better arrangement by his careful studies of development and reproduction (see p. 89). Examples of similar genera are illustrated in Figs. 119–126. In the Mischococcales Pascher (1937–39) separated many genera by shape. The cells of *Chloridella*, *Ellipsoidion* and *Monallanthus* are globose, oval-ellipsoid and shortly cylindrical, respectively. *Monodus* has species which are so fusiform that they grade into *Chlorocloster* (Figs. 165–178). Among genera of more striking shape, those Bourrelly (1951) has united in *Pseudostaurastrum* should be kept distinct if *Chloridella*, *Ellipsoidion*, etc. are to be separated.

A case might be made for uniting such desmid genera as *Staurastrum*, *Cosmarium* and *Xanthidium* as well as their recent offshoots *Staurodesmus* and *Actinotaenium*. Their separation is largely for convenience. However, the genera *Staurodesmus* and *Actinotaenium* (Teiling, 1948, 1954) do resolve some of the ambiguities surrounding *Cosmarium* and *Penium* on the one hand and *Arthrodesmus* and *Staurastrum* on the other. In the latter pair, the distinction was one of radiation, *Arthrodesmus* being biradiate and *Staurastrum* tri- to multiradiate (Figs. 162–164). The same problem arises between the generally biradiate *Cosmarium* and triradiate *Staurastrum* (Fritsch, 1953) so that some species may be assigned to either genus. Studies by Kallio (1951, 1953), Waris (1950) and Starr (1958) suggest that triradiate cells of normally biradiate species are diploid. With further experimental and cytological work it may be possible to reduce the emphasis placed on symmetry so that a species, though plastic in this respect, may still be placed in its correct genus (cf. Teiling, 1950).

Emphasis is laid on shape (Figs. 216–228) in the Cyanophyta (Chroococcales) in such pairs of genera as *Gloeocapsa* and *Gloeothece*, and *Aphanothece* and *Aphanocapsa*. On the other hand, such differences are permitted within *Microcystis* (*Diplocystis* Trevis.). Drouet & Daily (1956) and Komárek (Komárek & Ettl, 1958) have stressed the importance of the plane in which cell division takes place. The former pair of authors have radically revised the whole order, but most phycologists keep to the classical system (Geitler, 1930–32, 1960; Elenkin, Gollerbakh, Polyanskiĭ & Kosinskaya, 1936–49; Komárek & Ettl, 1958; Desikachary, 1959).

COLONIES

The ways in which cells are united together and their arrangement relative to one another and the plant as a whole are important characters for separating colonial algae. These combined with other features make most generic distinctions quite clear in the motile Chlorophyceae and Chrysophyceae. At the level of species delimitation is sometimes more difficult (e.g. *Dinobryon*).

Among the coccoid Chlorophyceae the arrangement of the cells is very widely used (cf. Korshikov, 1953). The greatest confusion is among those palmelloid genera where there is little distinction between a heap of cells resulting from multiplication in one place and an organized colony. Even palmelloid stages of *Chlamydomonas* may show a certain amount of organization (e.g. Skuja, 1956, Taf. xvii and xviii). Genera such as *Palmella*, *Gloeocystis* and *Asterococcus* (Figs. 92–94) are all ill-defined and the absence of a dividing line between such motile and non-motile algae has been mentioned. An example is *Gloeococcus* Braun (1851; Iyengar, 1954; Lund, 1957) a name often erroneously applied to *Sphaerocystis*), which can be considered as a motile *Chlamydomonas* surrounded by mucilage or a simple palmelloid colony in which the cells are slightly motile (Fig. 92).

It is equally impossible to restrict the word colonial to algae with a definite arrangement of a limited number of cells. The palmelloid Green Alga *Tetraspora* has a virtually limitless number of cells arranged more or less clearly in fours and comes very close to *Paulschulzia* (Lund, 1956) in which, so far as is known, the colony never has more than 256 cells and usually less than 64. In the latter genus the arrangement of the cells in the colony reflects the enclosure of three generations in a common membrane derived from the grandparental cell. Nevertheless, their separation and that of *Apiocystis* seem justified by the absence of intergrades (Figs. 101–104).

Less satisfactory generic separations are found in some of the clearly coccoid forms such as Korshikov's (1953) *Coenococcus*, *Coenocystis* and *Coenochloris*, and *Sphaerocystis* Chod. as delimited by modern taxonomists. Similar criteria are applied to genera of other groups, for example, in the Cyanophyta (Figs. 218–228). *Coelosphaerium* differs from *Microcystis* in the restriction of the cells to the outer layers of the mucilaginous colony. The laminar colonies of *Merismopedia* differ from those of *Eucapsis* in consisting of one layer of cells and from those of *Holopedium* in the quadrate groups of cells. Drouet & Daily (1956) do not accept these generic limits.

As a general rule, if cells of the same shape and structure live alone they belong to one genus but, if they are enclosed in mucilage or otherwise grouped together, they belong to another. A well known exception is *Ankistrodesmus* (Figs. 140, 142, 145). Since there appear to be all gradations between colonial and non-colonial species this may seem reasonable. Nevertheless, it is probable that, in some species, other characters of taxonomic importance are ignored and that the taxonomy of this and related genera (see Korshikov, 1953) should be revised.

FILAMENTS

A filament consists of cells joined together to form a thread whose method of construction varies from group to group but not usually from genus to genus.

The presence or absence of branching may characterize families or higher groupings. *Ulothrix* and *Uronema* are unbranched and usually placed in a different order or suborder from the branched *Stigeoclonium* (Figs. 249, 250, 262). Similar systems have been erected for Chrysophyceae and Xanthophyceae (Fritsch, 1935; Pascher, 1937–39; Bourelly, 1957; Fott, 1959a). In the diatoms (and desmids) the terms filamentous and colonial can be applied equally to the linear series of cells, and there is good reason to suspect this is so in nearly all Chrysophyta (Lund, in the press; Parke, 1961). In diatoms the arrangement of the cells in the colony may be the only character separating genera, for example *Fragilaria* and *Synedra* which, in turn, scarcely differ in structure from *Asterionella* and *Thalassiothrix*. The first three genera can produce similar bands when grown on agar. However, on transference to liquid, the cells return to the system seen under natural conditions. It may seem surprising that the old distinction between the solitary *Eunotia* and the filamentous *Himantidium* has been given up. Such arrangements are often compounds of convenience and conviction. It is convenient to separate the large and rather characterless genera *Fragilaria* and *Synedra*. The curious raphe and the shape of *Eunotia* lead to the conviction that the arrangement of the cells is a minor matter. Similar viewpoints apply to the wide separation of *Ulothrix* from *Stigeoclonium* and the mere generic separation of *Oedogonium* from *Oedocladium*.

In the Rhodophyta it is the aggregation and diversification of filaments which underlie the diversity of external form. This is so in some Phaeophyta and Chlorophyta (Siphonales), but in others the structure is parenchymatous. The taxonomy of such large or relatively large plants is not considered here.

Simple aggregations of filaments supply generic characters in the Cyanophyta, where what appear to be trivial differences are often utilized. *Phormidium* differs from *Lyngbya* in the union of threads by mucilage into papery or gelatinous strata (Figs. 235–237). Single threads of the former may predominate in nature so that they can be mistaken for species of the latter. This is particularly so in soil (Lund, 1947 *a*). *Microcoleus* and *Hydrocoleus*, and *Schizothrix* and *Porphyrosiphon* are other closely allied pairs of genera.

Just as complex systems of branching are used for delimiting the genera of many large algae, so are simpler ones for smaller genera. *Draparnaldia* differs from *Stigeoclonium* (Figs. 262–264) in the clear distinction between broad main branches of unlimited growth and narrow short bushy ones; in culture this feature disappears. Several species of *Stigeoclonium* are heterotrichous (Fritsch, 1939 *a*, 1942, 1949), that is, they have a basal, horizontally spreading system of branches and an upright one. The relative predominance of one or other branching system is one of the distinctions between some Green Algae belonging to Chaetophorales of Fritsch (1935) and also among many Phaeophyta (Fritsch, 1943).

In the Cyanophyta two main types of branching are possible. Either the so-called true-branching, which is similar to that of the algae just mentioned, or false-branching. In the latter, the trichome, the part of the filament within the sheath, is interrupted in some way and the two halves so formed are able to grow out through the sheath (cf. Fritsch, 1945, pp. 842 *et seq*.). The way in which these false branches arise and their position in relation to the enigmatic cells called heterocysts (Fritsch, 1951) are much used as generic characters. In some genera the latter character does not afford a clear-cut distinction so that there are disagreements about generic and specific limits. This is notably so in *Tolypothrix* and *Scytonema* (cf. Bhâradwâja, 1933, 1934), while *Plecto-nema* only differs from these genera in the absence of heterocysts (Figs. 238–241).

In unbranched filaments with simple methods of reproduction, features used for distinguishing non-filamentous algae become valuable. *Stichococcus* differs from *Chlorohormidium* (= *Hormidium*), in the absence of a pyrenoid and the common fragmentation into single cells so that it can be mistaken for a coccoid alga (Figs. 251, 252, 258, 261). In *Raphidonema* filaments are so rarely developed, and then so feebly, that it is only by careful observation of cell division that it can be distinguished from the coccoid *Ankistrodesmus* under whose name many of the records must lie (Figs. 140, 141). *Microspora* is characterized both by the chromatophore and the method of forming new cells. The latter feature, repeated in the Xanthophycean genus *Tribonema*, may be difficult to see in small species. In *Tribonema* this wall structure must be seen in order to separate it from *Bumilleria* and *Heterothrix*.

Among Cyanophyta, *Oscillatoria* differs from *Spirulina* in not having spirally wound filaments. A few species have somewhat undulate filaments and those of *Spirulina* (incl. *Arthrospira*) may have very lax spirals so that the difference is one of degree (Figs. 229–231). On the other hand, straight and spirally wound species are both placed in *Anabaena* (Figs. 242, 246).

REPRODUCTION AND LIFE HISTORIES

Methods of reproduction are universally held to be of great importance in taxonomy and classification, particularly above the rank of genus.

The taxonomic value of the structure of zoospores has already been considered (pp. 69–71) and non-motile genera may be delimited by their presence or absence. Early workers placed an azoosporic coccoid Green Algae such as *Chlorella* in a different suborder from the otherwise similar zoosporic *Chlorococcum*. Such a division of the Chlorococcales (Brunnthaler, 1915) has been given up because it undoubtedly obscures affinities. It is a convenient difference for separating genera. The system used in the Green Algae is also applied in the Xanthophyceae and Chrysophyceae.

The methods by which zoospores are developed and their fate are of taxonomic importance, as is well seen in the modern re-organization of the Chlorococcales, begun by Korshikov (1953) and Fott (1957, 1958, 1959 a), and sure to be carried further. Geitler (1924) suggested that the method of cleavage of the protoplasm in the formation of zoospores and non-motile analogues, variously called autospores, aplanospores, etc., was significant. It can be successive (*sukzedane*), in that nuclear and cytoplasmic division go hand in hand, or simultaneous (*progressive*) in that the cells are multinucleate before a general more or less synchronous cleavage of the cytoplasm takes place. Both types of cleavage may be found in algae which in other respects cannot be separated generically (e.g. *Chlorococcum*; Starr, 1955 a; Arce & Bold, 1958).

The method by which the spores are liberated is a useful character. In Chlorococcales, for example, the wall may deliquesce, enlarge or break up in a characteristic manner. The spores may escape by diverse methods, such as through a pore or after an apical lid opens. In *Hydrianum* (Korshikov, 1953) and *Chlororhabdion* Jane (1944 a) one of the spores develops within the old sporangium wall. These methods, so important taxonomically in the aquatic phycomycetes (Sparrow, 1960), are likely to become much more generally used for coccoid algae.

Too much emphasis may be placed on the fate of the wall. In *Dictyosphaerium* the autospores remain attached to the tips of the four lobes into which the cell splits but there are some species (e.g. *D. simplex*, *D. minutum*; Lund, 1947 a) which come very close to *Chlorella* in the looseness of the attachment of the cells and the absence of the rolling up of the old segments of the wall (Figs. 150–153). Such minute algae, particularly terrestrial ones, have to be investigated in culture and here the likelihood that they will remain so attached is increased by their remaining in one position for long periods.

The modern extensive use of unialgal cultures may lead to the union of species and genera by supplying unequivocal proof that they are phases in the life history of one organism. Thus three little known Chlorococcales have recently been found to be stages of the common and supposedly well known *Schizochlamys delicatula* (Thompson, 1956). It is again among the Chrysophyceae that some of the greatest changes are foreshadowed by work which is still in an early stage. Details may be found in Parke (1961). Coccolithophorineae have long been known from the sea and because of their remarkable exoskeleton (see p. 76) have often been examined. Some of these are the motile stage or swarmers of known or unrecognized coccoid forms, and have a haptonema in addition to the two isomorphic flagella. Others are similarly related to species of filamentous genera; or flagellate, coccoid and filamentous plants may all be stages of one species which is found under two or three generic names. This is another example of the uncertain generic limits in this class.

The life history and methods of development of sexual or asexual phases may be characteristic of genera or larger groups. Papenfuss (1960) has emphasized the importance of the way in which the sporeling develops in *Ulva* and allied genera. Other examples are the stages of *Spongomorpha*, *Urospora* and *Cladophora* which were previously referable to the genera *Codiolum* and *Chlorochytrium* (Archer & Burrows, 1960), and the absence of inversion in the coenobial development of *Astrophomene* and its presence in *Volvulina* (Pocock, 1953; Stein, 1958). Life history and development are vital taxonomic features in many Rhodophyta and Phaeophyta, though often at suprageneric levels.

Oogamy is rarely considered to justify generic separation. This is because it is often only present in a small minority of the species in a genus (e.g. *Chlamydomonas*, *Carteria* and *Chlorogonium*). Researches into the reproduction of diatoms have shown that oogamy occurs in several centric and one pennate diatom (Stosch, 1955, 1956, 1958), but the species concerned are retained in the same genera as before on the morphological grounds discussed earlier. On the other hand, Geitler (1957) has shown that variations in the type of sexual reproduction occur in some species of pennate diatoms and has erected some new infra-specific taxa.

DISCUSSION

It has been necessary to pay most attention to single characters though generic distinctions are ideally based on a combination of features. Table 1 will, to some extent, rectify this narrow viewpoint since it shows the main features used for the delimitation of the genera of smaller algae. The diagrammatic Figs. 1–265 portray examples.

At the level of the genus or species algae are grouped largely on the basis of convenience. Therefore the different systems depend on different authorities' ideas of what is convenient and will continue to do so until there is a good understanding of what controls the observed differences. Improvements both in convenience and in taxonomy may be expected from various procedures.

Type material, if it exists, should be carefully examined (see Drouet & Daily, 1956; Papenfuss, 1960). It is often lacking or is in such a condition that it cannot be studied properly. It would be helpful to try and devise methods appropriate for the preservation of even such delicate *to delimit the genera of the smaller algae*

Rhodophyta, Phaeophyta, Charophyceae and Bryopsidales (Siphonales) are excluded. Nomenclature of Fott (1959a). Chrysophyta: B, Bacillariophyceae (diatoms); Chr, Chrysophyceae; X, Xanthophyceae. Chlorophyta, Co; Cyanophyta, Cy; Chloromonadophyceae, Cm.; Cryptophyceae, Cr; Dinophyta, D; Euglenophyta, E; Chr (si), Silicoflagellineae.)

1. Flagellate algae

(a) Unicellular

Character	
Flagella, number, location, relative length, structure	Chr, X, Co, E, Cr
Wall, presence or absence, structure	Co
External siliceous, calcareous or organic bodies	Chr
Internal siliceous skeleton	Chr (Si)
External organic plating (armour)	D
Lorica, shape and structure	Chr, Co, E
Cell, shape and symmetry	Chr, X, Co, Cr, Cm, D, E
Contractile vacuoles, number and location	Co
Chromatophore, presence or absence	Chr, Co, Cr, Cm, E
Chromatophore, shape	Chr, Co
Pigments	Cr

(b) Colonial

Character	
Flagella (see 1(a))	Chr, Co
Shape of colony and arrangement of cells	Chr, Co, B, X, Cy
External siliceous bodies	Chr
Development	Co

2. Filamentous algae

(a) Branched or unbranched

Character	
Branches, presence or absence	Chr, X, Co, Cy
Zoospores, presence or absence, flagella (see 1(a))	Chr, Co
Sporangia, type and position	Co
Akinetes, presence or absence, position and structure	Co, Cy
Heterocysts, presence or absence	Cy
Filaments solitary or in groups, arrangement in such groups	Cy
Type of sexual reproduction	Co
Life history	Co, Chr

(b) Unbranched.

Character	
Cell structure, especially at base or apex	Co, Cy
External sheath or mucilage, presence or absence, structure	Co, Cy
Chromatophores, structure	Co
Pyrenoid, presence or absence	Co

(c) Branched

Character	
Heterotrichy, degree and kind, presence or absence	Chr, Co, Cy
Branches and main axes, type and relationship to one another	Co, Cy
Method of initiation of branches	Cy
Hairs, presence or absence, structure	Co
Asexual reproductive body, type	Cy
Sexual reproduction, type	Co

3. Coccoid, palmelloid, rhizopodial or other non-filamentous or non-flagellate algae

(a) Unicellular.

Character	
Rhizopodial or amoeboid	Chr, X, E, D
Zoospores, presence or absence structure (see 1(a))	Chr, X, Co, D
Gametes, presence or absence, structure	Co
Other reproductive bodies (auto-spores, akinetes, etc.), presence or absence, structure	Chr, X, Co, Cy
Method of release of spores, fate of sporangium wall	Co
Contractile vacuoles, presence or absence, location	X, Co
Mucilage, presence or absence, structure	Co, Cy
Chromatophores, presence or absence	Co
Chromatophores, structure	Chr, X, Co
Pyrenoids, presence or absence	Co
Cell shape and symmetry	B, Chr, X, Co, Cy, D
'Wall', presence or absence	Chr, X
'Wall', structure and ornamentation	B, X, Co
Development, especially in relation to reproduction	Co

(b) Colonial

Character	
Plasmodial organization	Chr, X
Arrangement of cells in colony	B, Chr, X, Co, Cy
Shape and symmetry of cells	B, Chr, X, Co, Cy
Structure of cell walls	B, Co

objects as many flagellates. It would also help if nomenclaturists would be prepared to accept special criteria for the typification of 'difficult' algae. The question as to whether cultures can be accepted is under discussion.

Descriptions of algae should ideally be based on material from nature as well as enrichment and clone cultures. Cultures are often essential. Many soil and aerial algae may be unidentifiable in nature (Starr, 1955; Arce & Bold, 1958; Vischer, 1936, 1937, 1945, 1953, 1960). Essential characters may only be detectable if very large populations are grown or special media used. Examples are pigment analysis in *Botryococcus* and *Vaucheria* (Belcher & Fogg, 1955; Rieth & Sagromsky, 1959) and the presence or absence of starch in azoosporic coccoid Chlorophyta and Xanthophyceae (Vischer, 1936).

Electron microscopy has already had a considerable influence on taxonomy, as has been seen in the sections devoted to flagellates, and there can be no doubt that it would help elsewhere. Here, too, clonal cultures ensure ample material and that the organism so examined is also that seen under the light microscope.

The chromosome numbers of a moderate number of algae are known, and where the chromosomes are large they may supply valuable taxonomic characters as has been strikingly shown by Godward (1950, 1953, 1954, 1956). Now that so many algae can be cultivated and methods for cytological investigation are in general use, genetical experiments should be more common. It may be said that they are, but very few are concerned with taxonomy. Pascher's (1916) classical work on *Chlamydomonas* and the investigations of Starr (1958, 1959), Transeau (1951) and Turner (1922) show how this may help at the specific level. Few attempts have been made to cross species of allegedly different genera. Strehlow (1928–29) tried to cross *Chlamydomonas* and *Chlorogonium*. It is among such genera that useful work could be done since, as has been seen, many of them form pairs differing in a single character, often its presence or absence. Bliding (1936) says that in the taxonomically difficult genera *Cladophora* and *Enteromorpha* (Bliding, 1938–39, 1944) speciation based on external morphological characters alone is unsatisfactory and that knowledge is needed of developmental stages (cf. Papenfuss, 1960, for *Ulva* and allied genera), and of chromosome numbers together with breeding experiments. The first two desiderata have been widely achieved in Rhodophyta and Phaeophyta.

ACKNOWLEDGEMENTS

The author's thanks are due to Dr J. H. Belcher and Miss E. Swale for reading and discussing the manuscript, and to Mr E. Marshall for checking the references.

Figs. 1–28

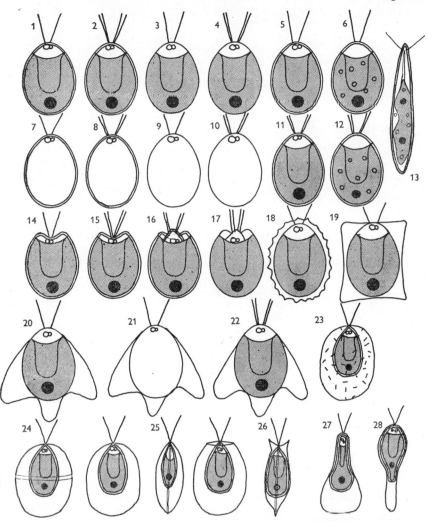

In these and succeeding figures features distinguishing genera are illustrated diagrammatically. No diagram is meant to represent a given species. In this first series unicellular Volvocales (Chlorophyta) are represented. Figs. 1–12, genera differing in the number of flagella, presence or absence of a wall or of a chromatophore, or the number and distribution of the contractile vacuoles; Fig. 13, the 'classical' conception of *Chlorogonium* to which Ettl (Komárek & Ettl, 1958) joins multivacuolate species of *Chlamydomonas* (see p. 78). Figs. 14–22, genera differing in cell shape, number of flagella, presence or absence of chromatophores or of a wall. Figs. 23–28, loricate genera; 25, 26 showing front and side views. In Figs. 1–17 cells with a double line round them are walled. Circles, white inside, contractile vacuoles; all black, pyrenoids. Figs. 1, 5, *Chlamydomonas*; 2, 11, *Carteria*; 3, *Dunaliella*; 4, *Quadrichloris*; 6, 13, *Chlorogonium*; 7, *Polytoma*; 8, *Tetrablepharis*; 9, *Hyaliella*; 10, *Polytomella*; 12, *Pseudocarteria*; 14, *Chlamydonephris*; 15, 16, *Pyramichlamys*; 17, *Pyramimonas*; 18, *Lobomonas*; 19, *Diplostauron*; 20, *Brachiomonas*; 21, *Hyalobrachion*; 22, *Chlorobrachis*; 23, *Coccomonas*; 24, *Hemitoma*; 25, *Phacotus*; 26, *Pteromonas*; 27, *Tingitanella*; 28, *Cephalomonas*.

Figs. 29–64

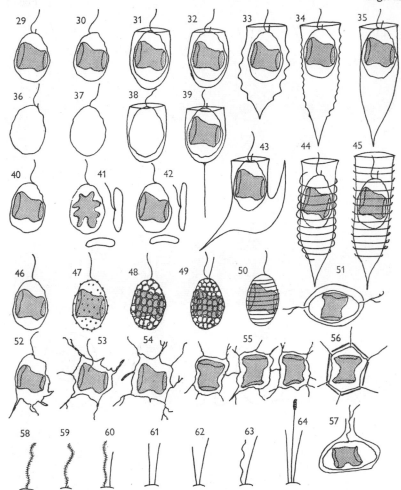

Figs. 29–50, flagellate and rhizopodial genera of the Chrysophyceae (Chrysophyta) differing in number and length of flagella; presence or absence of chromatophores; shape of the cell; absence or presence of loricae or a siliceous exoskeleton and their shape or structure. Figs. 51–7, rhizopodial genera differing in the presence or absence of a flagellum, colonial habit, or absence or presence of a lorica and its shape. Figs. 58–63, the types of flagella in Chrysophycean flagellates and the haptonema. Xanthophyceae are mainly classified on the same principles.

Fig. 29, *Ochromonas*; 30, 40, 46, *Chromulina*; 31, *Kephyrion*; 32, *Pseudokephyrion* or *Kephyriopsis*; 33, *Pseudokephyrion* or *Kephyriopsis* or *Dinobryon*; 34, 35, 44, *Dinobryon*; 36, *Oikomonas*; 37, *Monas*; 38, *Calycomonas*; 39, *Poteriochromonas*; 41, *Phaeaster*; 42, *Monochrysis*; 43, *Chrysolykos*; 45, *Hyalobryon*; 47, *Microglena*; 48, *Mallomonas*; 49, *Mallomonopsis*; 50, *Conradiella*; 51, *Chrysoamphitrema*; 52, rhizopodial stage of a *Chromulina*; 53, *Chrysamoeba*; 54, *Rhizochrysis*; 55, *Chrysidiastrum*; 56, *Heliochrysis*; 57, *Lagynion*.

Flagella: Fig. 58, one, pantonematic; 59, two, heteromorphic, the long one pantonematic and the very short one acronematic; 60 as 59 but with longer acronematic flagellum; 61, two acronematic, of equal length, 62 as 61 but of unequal length; 63, two acronematic but heterodynamic; 64 as 61 but with a haptonema between the flagella. Nomenclature after Bourrelly (1957).

Figs. 65–90

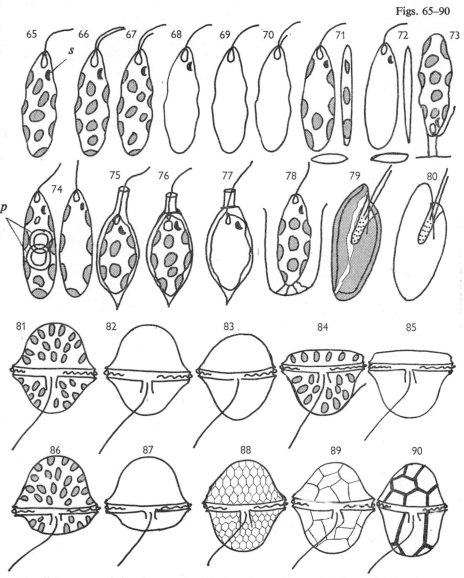

Flagellate genera belonging to the Euglenophyta, Cryptophyceae and Dinophyceae (Pyrrophyta). Figs. 65–78, Euglenophyta differing in number and length of flagella, absence or presence of a chromatophore or of a stigma, cell shape, absence or presence of a lorica and its structure, or attachment to the substratum. Figs. 79 and 80, Cryptophyceae with and without chromatophores. Figs. 81–90, Dinophyceae differing in the shape of the cell, or the absence or presence of superficial plating (armour) and its type. Figs. 71, 72, cells seen from the three sides and 74 from two sides. *s*, stigma; *p*, paramylon.

Fig. 65, *Euglena*; 66, *Eutreptia*; 67, *Eutreptiella*; 68, *Khawkinea*; 69, *Astasia*; 70, *Distigma*; 71, *Phacus*; 72, *Hyalophacus*; 73, *Colacium*; 74, *Lepocinclis*; 75, *Strombomonas*; 76, 77, *Trachelomonas*; 78, *Klebsiella*; 79, *Cryptomonas*; 80, *Chilomonas*; 81–83, *Gymnodinium*; 84, 85, *Amphidinium*; 86, 87, *Katodinium*; 88, *Woloszynskia* or *Gymnodinium*; 89, *Glenodinium*; 90, *Peridinium*.

Figs. 91–116

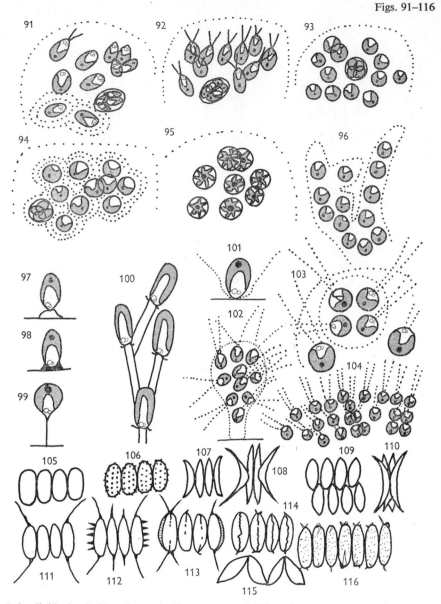

Palmelloid, dendroid and pseudociliate genera of Chlorophyceae, and *Scenedesmus* spp. Diagrams of parts of colonies in Figs. 91–96 and 103 and 104, edge of mucilage dotted. In Figs. 101–104 pseudocilia also dotted.

Fig. 91, *Chlamydomonas*, palmella stage; 92, *Gloeococcus*; 93, *Palmella*; 94, *Gloeocystis*; 95, *Asterococcus*; 96, *Palmodictyon*; 97, *Chlamydomonas* attached to substratum by its flagella; 98, *Chlorophysema*; 99, *Stylosphaeridium*; 100, *Chlorangium*; 101, *Chaetochloris*, a Chlamydomonas type of cell with the flagella replaced by pseudocilia; 102, *Apiocystis*; 103, *Paulschulzia*; 104, *Tetraspora*; 105–116, species of *Scenedesmus* differing in the shape and arrangement of cells and the ornamentation of the wall; 110 also called *Tetradesmus*.

Figs. 117–149

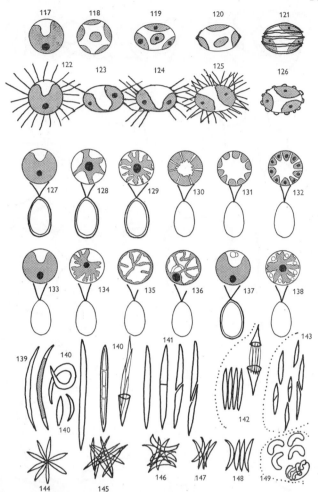

Generic delimitation in Chlorococcales (Chlorophyta). Figs. 117–126, azoosporic genera differing in shape, number of chromatophores, presence or absence of pyrenoids and the ornamentation of the wall. Figs. 127–138, zoosporic genera, all of similar shape but differing in the number and type of the chromatophores, absence, presence and number of pyrenoids (black circles) or contractile vacuoles (white circles), or in the type of zoospore. Zoospores walled or naked, with flagella of equal or unequal length. Figs. 139–149, azoosporic solitary or colonial genera mainly of very uncertain delimitation, except 141 which is filamentous.

Fig. 117, *Chlorella*; 118, *Muriella*; 119, 120, *Oocystis*; 121, *Scotiella*; 122, *Golenkinia*; 123, 124, *Chodatella*; 125, *Franceia*; 126, *Siderocelis*; 127, *Chlorococcum*; 128, *Nautococcus*; 129, *Macrochloris* (*Radiosphaera*); 130, *Dictyococcus*; 131, *Bracteococcus*; 132, *Planktosphaeria*; 133, *Neochloris*; 134, *Trebouxia* (*Cystococcus*); 135, *Dictyochloris*; 136, *Spongiochloris*; 137, *Hypnomonas* (*Chlorococcum*); 138, *Actinochloris*; 139, *Hyaloraphidium*; 140, *Ankistrodesmus* (this and succeeding forms have a chromatophore though its type is not of diagnostic importance and is not indicated in the diagrams); 141, *Raphidonema*; 142, *Quadrigula* (or *Ankistrodesmus*); 143, *Elakatothrix*; 144, *Actinastrum*; 145, *Ankistrodesmus*; 146, *Selenastrum* (or *Ankistrodesmus*); 147, *Scenedesmus* (or *Selenastrum* or *Ankistrodesmus*); 148, *Scenedesmus*; 149, *Kirchneriella*. Nomenclature of Starr (1955a) and Korshikov (1953).

Figs. 150–164

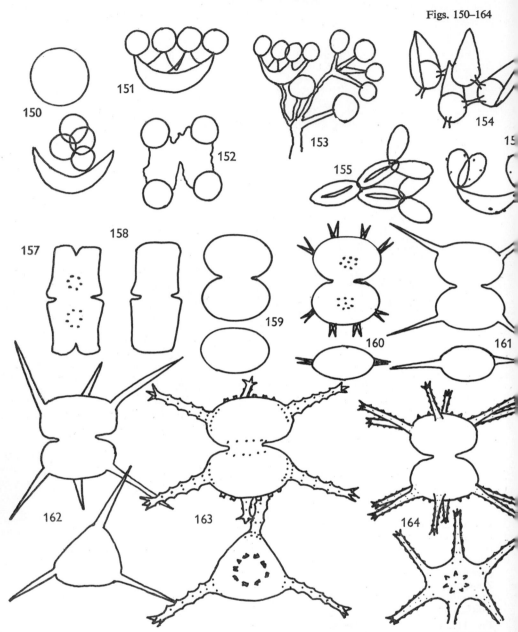

Figs. 150–156, azoosporic Chlorococcales whose cells are united into colonies by the remains of the parental walls. Fig. 157–164. Conjugatophyceae, desmids (Chlorophyta), genera distinguished by the shape and symmetry of the cells. Chromatophores not indicated because they are not generically important.

Fig. 150, *Chlorella* (unicellular genus); 151, 152, *Chlorella* or *Dictyosphaerium*; 153, *Dictyosphaerium*; 154, *Coronastrum*; 155, *Dichotomococcus*; 156, *Quadricoccus*; 157, *Euastrum*; 158, 159, *Cosmarium*; 160, *Xanthidium*; 161, 162, *Staurodesmus*; 163, 164, *Staurastrum*.

Figs. 165–187

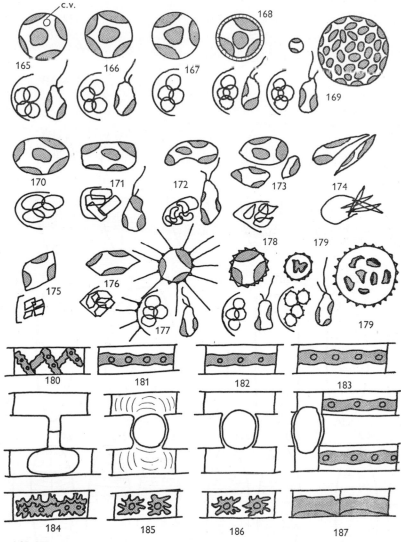

Figs. 165–179, genera of coccoid Xanthophyceae (Chrysophyta) separated largely by the shape of the cell, a classification representing the views of Pascher (1937–39). Figs. 179–187, Conjugatophyceae (Chlorophyta), unbranched, filamentous genera distinguished by the type of chromatophore and method of conjugation.

Fig. 165, *Pleurochloridella* (has contractile vacuole, *c.v.*); 166, *Pleurochloris* (lacks contractile vacuole); 167, *Chloridella* (no zoospores); 168, *Sklerochlamys* (porose wall); 169, *Botrydiopsis* (adult cells, relatively, very large); 170, *Ellipsoidion*; 171 *Monallanthus*; 172, *Nephrodiella*; 173, *Monodus*; 174, *Chlorocloster*; 175, *Rhomboidiella*; 176, *Prismatella*; 177, *Akanthochloris*; 178, *Trachycystis* (parietal chromatophores); 179, *Endochloridion* (chromatophores not parietal); 180, *Spirogyra*; 181, *Debarya* (gametangial cells filled with pectic material); 182, *Mougeotia*; 183, *Temnogametum* (small gametangial cells); 184, *Sirocladium* (also has special method of conjugation); 185, *Zygnemopsis* (conjugation as *Debarya*); 186, *Zygnema* (conjugation as *Mougeotia*); 187, *Mougeotiopsis* (no pyrenoids)

Figs. 188–215

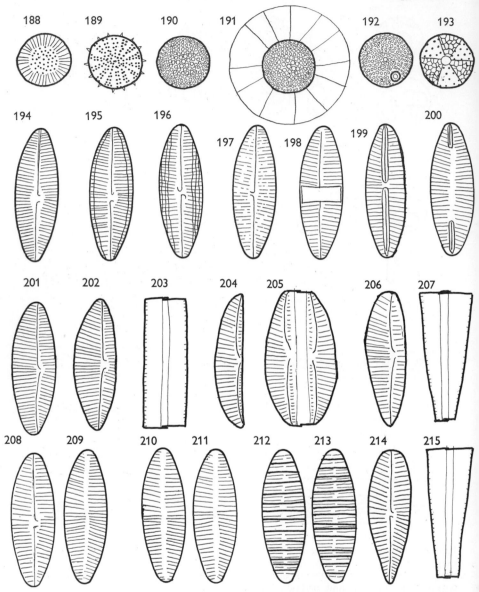

Genera of centric (Figs. 188–193) and pennate (Figs. 194–200) diatoms (Chrysophyta) differing in the structure of the wall, and also (Figs. 201–215) in the symmetry of the cell.

Fig. 188, *Cyclotella*; 189, *Stephanodiscus*; 190, *Coscinodiscus*; 191, *Planktoniella*; 192, *Actinocyclus*; 193, *Actinoptychus*; 194, *Navicula*; 195, *Caloneis*; 196, *Neidium*; 197, *Anomoeoneis*; 198, *Stauroneis*; 199, *Frustulia*; 200, *Amphipleura*; 201, 202, 203 (girdle view), *Cymbella*; 204, 205 (ventral girdle view), *Amphora*; 206, 207 (girdle view), *Gomphocymbella*; 208, 209, upper and lower valves of *Achnanthes*; 210, 211 of *Synedra* or *Fragilaria* and 212, 213 of *Diatoma*; 214, 215 (girdle view), *Gomphonema*.

Figs. 216–248

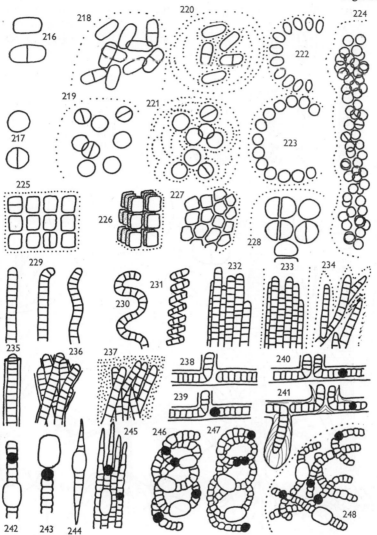

Genera of Cyanophyta distinguished by the shape and aggregation of the cells (Figs. 216–228) and filaments (Figs. 229–248). Filamentous genera also differing in absence or presence and position of heterocysts (black circles), spores (large oval-oblong cells), absence or presence and then development of a sheath, degree of twist and branching. Mucilage sheaths dotted. Nomenclature after Geitler (1930–32).

Fig. 216, *Synechococcus*; 217, *Synechocystis*; 218, *Aphanothece*; 219, *Aphanocapsa*; 220, *Gloeothece*; 221, *Gloeocapsa*; 222, 223, *Coelosphaerium*; 224, *Microcystis*; 225, *Merismopedia*; 226, *Eucapsis*; 227, *Holopedium*; 228, *Chroococcus*; 229, threads of *Oscillatoria* showing transitions to 230; 230, 231, *Spirulina* (*Arthrospira*); 232, *Oscillatoria* or *Trichodesmium*; 233, *Microcoleus* or *Hydrocoleus*; 234, *Schizothrix*; 235, *Lyngbya*; 236, *Symploca*; 237, *Phormidium*; 238, *Plectonema*; 239; *Tolypothrix*; 240, *Scytonema*; 241, *Petalonema* (*Scytonema*) (position of lower branch of no taxonomic significance); 242, 246, *Anabaena*; 243, *Cylindrospermum*; 244, *Raphidiopsis*; 245, *Aphanizomenon*; 247, *Anabaenopsis*; 248, *Nostoc*.

Figs. 249–265

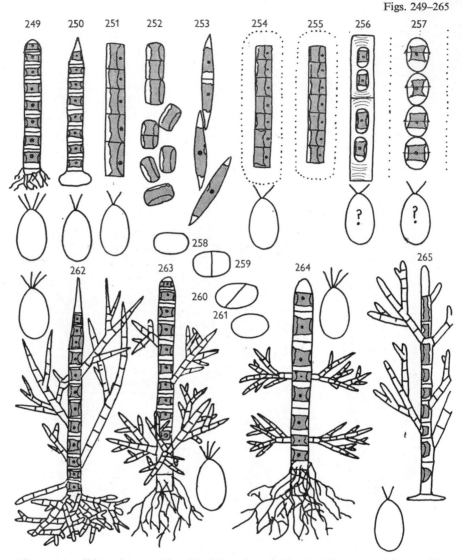

Filamentous Chlorophyceae. Figs. 249–261, unbranched genera distinguished by structure or shape of the cells, especially at the apex and base, presence or absence of zoospores (? = existence uncertain) and the number of their flagella, development of mucilage (dotted outline), presence or absence of pyrenoids and dissociation of the threads. The last feature leading to unicellular genera of uncertain position and delimitation (Figs. 258–262). Figs. 262–265, branched genera differing in degree of development of basal system (262 is heterotrichous, 263, 264 only have attaching rhizoids), and of lateral axes, the number of flagella in the zoospores and the presence or absence of pyrenoids (black circles).

Fig. 249, *Ulothrix*; 250, *Uronema*; 251, *Chlorohormidium* (*Hormidium*); 252, *Stichococcus*; 253, *Raphidonema*; 254, *Gloeotila*; 255, *Geminella*; 256, *Binuclearia*; 257, *Radiofilum*; 258, 259, *Stichococcus* or *Nannochloris*; 260, 261, *Coccomyxa*; 262, *Stigeoclonium*; 263, *Draparnaldia*; 264, *Draparnaldiospis*; 265, *Microthamnion*.

REFERENCES

Russian and Ukrainian titles are transliterated according to the system proposed by the Royal Society.

ARCE, G. & BOLD, H. C. (1958). Some Chlorophyceae from Cuban Soils. *Amer. J. Bot.* **45**, 492–503.

ARCHER, A. & BURROWS, E. M. (1960). Heteromorphic life-history as a family criterion in the Cladophorales. *Brit. phycol. Bull.* **2**, 31–3.

ASMUND, B. (1955). Electron microscope observations on *Mallomonas caudata* and some remarks on its occurrence in four Danish ponds. *Bot. Tidsskr.* **52**, 163–8.

ASMUND, B. (1956). Electron microscope observations on *Mallomonas* species and remarks on their occurrence in some Danish ponds. II. *Bot. Tidsskr.* **53**, 75–85.

ASMUND, B. (1959). Electron microscope observations on *Mallomonas* species and remarks on their occurrence in some Danish ponds and lakes. III. *Dansk bot. Ark.* **18**, 7–50.

BEHLAU, J. (1935). Die Spondylomoraceen-Gattung *Chlamydobotrys. Beitr. Biol. Pfl.* **23**, 125–64.

BEHLAU, J. (1939). Der Generationswechsel zwischen *Chlamydomonas variabilis* Dangeard und *Carteria ovata* Jacobsen. *Beitr. Biol. Pfl.* **26**, 221–49.

BELCHER, J. H. (1960). Culture studies of *Bangia atropurpurea* (Roth) Ag. *New Phytol.* **59**, 367–73.

BELCHER, J. H. & FOGG, G. E. (1955). Biochemical evidence of the affinities of *Botryococcus. New Phytol.* **54**, 81–3.

BHÂRADWÂJA, Y. (1933). False branching and sheath-structure in the Myxophyceae, with special reference to the Scytonemataceae. *Arch. Protistenk.* **81**, 243–83.

BHÂRADWÂJA, Y. (1934). The taxonomy of *Scytonema* and *Tolypothrix*, including some new records and new species from India and Ceylon. *Rev. algol.* **7**, 149–78.

BLIDING, C. (1936). Über die Fortpflanzungskörper einiger Marinen *Cladophora*-Arten. *Svensk bot. Tidskr.* **30**, 529–36.

BLIDING, C. (1938–39). Studien über der Entwicklung und Systematik in *Enteromorpha*. I–II. *Bot. Notiser* (1938), pp. 83–90; (1939), pp. 134–44.

BLIDING C. (1944). Zur Systematik der Schwedischer Enteromorphen. *Bot. Notiser* (1944), pp. 831–56.

BOLD, H. C. & STARR, R. C. (1953). A new member of the Phacotaceae. *Bull. Torrey bot. Cl.* **80**, 178–86.

BOURRELLY, P. (1951). Xanthophycées rares ou nouvelles. *Bull. Mus. Hist. nat. Paris*, 2 ser. **23**, 666–72.

BOURRELLY, P. (1957). Recherches sur les Chrysophycées: Morphologie, phylogénie systématique. *Rev. algol.*, Mem. Hors. Ser. no. 1, 412 pp.

BRAUN, A. (1851). *Betrachtungen über die Erscheinung der Verjungung in der Natur.* Leipzig.

BROOK, A. J. (1959). *Staurastrum paradoxum* Meyen and *S. gracile* Ralfs in the British freshwater plankton, and a revision of the *S. anatinum* group of radiate desmids. *Trans. roy. Soc. Edinb.* **63**, 589–628.

BRUNNTHALER, J. (1915). Protococcales. *Süsswass.-Fl. Dtschl. Öst. Schweiz*, **5**, 52–205.

BUTCHER, R. W. (1959). An introductory account of the smaller algae of British coastal waters. Pt. 1. Introduction and Chlorophyceae. *Fish. Invest., Lond.* Ser. IV, 1–74.

CARTER, N. (1937). New or interesting algae from the brackish water. *Arch. Protistenk.* **90**, 1–68.

CHADEFAUD, M. (1959). Les Végétaux non Vasculaires (Cryptogamie): Chadefaud, M. & Emberger, L. *Traité de Botanique*, 1. Paris: Masson.

CHODAT, R. (1926). *Scenedesmus*. Étude de génetique, de systématique experimentale et d'hydrobiologie. *Z. Hydrol.* 3, 3–4, 71–258.

CIFERRI, O. (1956). Thiamin-deficiency of *Prototheca*, a yeast-like achloric alga. *Nature, Lond.* 178, 1475–76.

CIFERRI, R., MONTEMARTINI, A. & CIFERRI, O. (1957). Caratteristiche morphologiche e assimilative e speciologia delle Protothecae. *Nuovi Ann. Igiene Microbiol.* 8, 554–63.

CLAPHAM, A. R., TUTIN, T. G. & WARBURG, E. F. (1961). *Flora of the British Isles*, 2nd edition. Cambridge University Press.

CLEVE-EULER, A. (1951–55). Die Diatomeen von Schweden und Finnland. *K. Svensk. VetenskAkad. Handl.* Ser. 4, 2 (1); 3 (3); 4 (1); 4 (5); 5 (4).

CONRAD, W. (1927). Essai d'une Monographie des genres *Mallomonas* Perty and *Pseudomallomonas* Chod. *Arch. Protistenk.* 59, 423–505.

CONRAD, W. (1931). Recherches sur les Flagellates de Belgique. 1. Flagellates des étangs des 'eaux douces' a Vieux-Héverlé-lez-Louvain. *Mém. Mus. Hist. nat. Belg.* no. 47, 65 pp.

CONRAD, W. (1939). Notes protistologiques. XI. Sur *Pyramidomonas amylifera*. n.sp. *Bull. Mus. Hist. nat. Belg.* 15, no. 42, 10 pp.

CONRAD, W. (1942). Notes protistologiques. XXV. A propos des genres *Kephyrion* Pascher 1913 et *Pseudokephyrion* Pascher 1913. *Bull. Mus. Hist. nat. Belg.* 18, 1–6.

DEDUSENKO-SHCHEGOLEVA, N. T. (1949). Species atque varietates novae generis *Scenedesmus* Meyen. *Notul. syst. Sect. Cryptog. Inst. bot. Nom. Komarov. Acad. Sci. URSS.* 6, 27–33.

DEFLANDRE, G. (1952). Classe des Ebriédiens; des Silicoflagellidés; des Coccolithophoridae. In Grassé, P–P, *Traité de Zoologie* 1, 1, 407–70. Paris: Masson.

DEFLANDRE, G. & FERT, C. (1954). Observations sur les Coccolithophoridés actuels et fossiles en microscopie ordinaire et électronique. *Ann. Paléont.* 40, 117–76.

DEMETER, O. (1956). Über Modifikationen bei Cyanophyceen. *Arch. Mikrobiol.* 24, 105–33.

DESIKACHARY, T. V. (1959). *Cyanophyta*, 686 pp. New Delhi: Indian Council for Agricultural Research.

DODGE, J. D. (1960). Nuclei, nuclear division and taxonomy in the Dinophyceae. *Brit. phycol. Bull.* 2, 14–15.

DROUET, F. & DAILY, W. A. (1956). Revision of the coccoid Myxophyceae. *Butler Univ. bot. Stud.* 12, 1–218.

ELENKIN, A. A., GOLLERBAKH, M. M., POLYANSKIǏ, V. I. & KOSINSKAYA, E. E. (1936–49). *Monographia algarum cyanophycearum aquidulcium et terrestrium in finibus URSS inventarum.* Inst. Bot. Acad. Sci. URSS.

ETTL, H. (1959). Bemerkungen zur Artabgrenzung einiger Chlamydomonaden (Zur Kenntnis der Klasse Volvophyceae V). *Nova Hedwigia*, 1, 167–93.

ETTL, H. & ETTL, O. (1959). Zur Kenntnis der Klasse Volvophyceae. II. (Neue oder wenig bekannte Chlamydomonadalen.) *Arch. Protistenk.* 104, 51–112.

FAURÉ-FRÉMIET, E. & ROUILLER, C. (1957). Le flagelle interne d'une Chrysomonadale, *Chromulina psammobia*. *C.R. Acad. Sci., Paris*, 244, 2655–7.

FOTT, B. (1953). Nové řasy a bičíkovci. *Preslia*, 25, 143–56.

FOTT, B. (1957). Taxonomie der mikroskopischen Flora einheimischer Gewässer. *Preslia*, 29, 278–319.

FOTT, B. (1958). Zur Kenntnis der Gattung *Rhopalosolen* (Chlorococcales). *Ann. Inst. biol. Tihany*, 25, 343–51.

FOTT, B. (1959a). *Algenkunde*. Jena: G. Fischer.

FOTT, B. (1959b). Zur Frage der Sexualität bei den Chrysomonaden. *Nova Hedwigia*, **1**, 115–27.

FOTT, B. (1960). Taxonomische Übertragungen und Namensänderungen unter den Algen. *Preslia*, **32**, 142–54.

FOTT, B. & KOMÁREK, J. (1960). Das Phytoplankton der Teiche im Teschner Schlesien. *Preslia*, **32**, 113–41.

FRITSCH, F. E. (1935). *The Structure and Reproduction of the Algae*, **1**. Cambridge University Press.

FRITSCH, F. E. (1939a). The heterotrichous habit. *Bot. Notiser* (1939), pp. 125–33.

FRITSCH, F. E. (1939b). The genus *Anabaena*, with special reference to the species recorded from India and from the adjacent Asiatic mainland. *J. Indian bot. Soc.* **28**, 135–16.

FRITSCH, F. E. (1942). Studies in the comparative morphology of the algae. 1. Heterotrichy and juvenile stages. *Ann. Bot., Lond.*, N.S. **6**, 397–412.

FRITSCH, F. E. (1943). Studies in the comparative morphology of the algae. III. Evolutionary tendencies and affinities among Phaeophyceae. *Ann. Bot., Lond.*, N.S. **7**, 63–87.

FRITSCH, F. E. (1945). *The Structure and Reproduction of the Algae*, **2**. Cambridge University Press.

FRITSCH, F. E. (1949). The lines of algal advance. *Biol. Rev.* **24**, 94–124.

FRITSCH, F. E. (1951). The heterocyst: a botanical enigma. *Proc. Linn. Soc. Lond.* **162**, 194–211.

FRITSCH, F. E. (1953). Comparative studies in a polyphyletic group, the Desmidiaceae. *Proc. Linn. Soc. Lond.* **164**, 258–80.

FRITSCH, F. E. & JOHN, R. P. (1942). An ecological and taxonomic study of the algae of British Soils. II. Consideration of the species observed. *Ann. Bot., Lond.*, N.S. **6**, 371–95.

GEITLER, L. (1924). Die Entwicklungsgeschichte von *Sorastrum spinulosum* und die Phylogenie der Protococcales. *Arch. Protistenk.* **47**, 440–7.

GEITLER, L. (1925). Zur Kenntnis der Gattung *Pyramidomonas*. *Arch. Protistenk.* **52**, 356–70.

GEITLER, L. (1930–32). Cyanophyceae. *Rabenhorst's Kryptogamenflora*, **14**.

GEITLER, L. (1948). Symbiosen zwischen Chrysomonaden und Knospenden bakterienartigen Organismen, sowie Beobachtungen über Organisationseigentümlichkeiten der Chrysomonaden. *Öst. bot. Z.* **95**, 300–24.

GEITLER, L. (1957). Die sexuelle Fortpflanzung der pennaten Diatomeen. *Biol. Rev.* **32**, 261–95.

GEITLER, L. (1960). *Schizophyceen*. Berlin: Nikolassee.

GEMEINHARDT, K. (1939–40). Oedogoniales. *Rabenhorst's Kryptogamenflora*, **12** (4). Leipzig.

GERLOFF, J. (1940). Beiträge zur Kenntnis der Variabilität und Systematik der Gattung *Chlamydomonas*. *Arch. Protistenk.* **94**, 311–502.

GODWARD, M. B. E. (1950). On the nucleolus and nucleolar-organizing chromosomes of *Spirogyra*. *Ann. Bot., Lond.*, N.S. **14**, 39–53.

GODWARD, M. B. E. (1953). Geitler's nucleolar substance in *Spirogyra*. *Ann. Bot., Lond.*, N.S. **17**, 403–16.

GODWARD, M. B. E. (1954). The 'diffuse' centromere or polycentric chromosomes in *Spirogyra*. *Ann. Bot., Lond.*, N.S. **18**, 143–56.

GODWARD, M. B. E. (1956). Cytotaxonomy of *Spirogyra*. I, *S. submargaritata*, *S. subechinata* and *S. britannica*. *J. Linn. Soc. (Bot.)*, **55**, 532–46.

GUILLARD, R. R. L. (1960). A mutant of *Chlamydomonas moewusii* lacking contractile vacuoles. *J. Protozool.* **7**, 262–8.

HALLDAL, P. (1955). Comparative observations on Coccoliphorids in light and electron microscopes and their taxonomical significance. *Rapp. Comm. 8me Congr. int. Bot. Paris, 1954*, 122–23.

HANSEN, I. & GERLOFF, J. (1952). Beitrag zur Kenntnis einiger Volvocales. *Ber. dtsch. bot. Ges.* **65**, 87–93.

HARRIS, K. & BRADLEY, D. E. (1957). An examination of the scales and bristles of *Mallomonas* in the electron microscope using carbon replicas. *J. R. micr. Soc.* **76**, 37–46.

HARRIS, K. & BRADLEY D. E. (1958). Some unusual Chrysophyceae studied in the electron microscope. *J. gen. Microbiol.* **18**, 71–83.

HARRIS, K. & BRADLEY, D. E. (1960). A taxonomic study of *Mallomonas*. *J. gen. Microbiol.* **22**, 750–77.

HASLE, G. R. (1960). Plankton Coccolithophorids from the subantarctic and equatorial pacific. *Nytt. Mag. Bot.* **8**, 77–88.

HELMCKE, J. G. & KRIEGER, W. (1953–54). *Diatomeenschalen im elektronenmikroskopischen Bild.* **1** (1953), **2** (1954), Berlin: Wilmersdorf. [A new and enlarged edition is in the press as a supplement to *Nova Hedwigia*.]

HENDEY, N. I. (1959). The structure of the diatom cell wall as revealed by the electron microscope. *J. Quekett micr. Cl.*, Ser. 4, **5**, 147–75.

HOLLANDE, A. (1942). Étude cytologique et biologique de quelques flagellés libres. *Arch. Zool. Exp.* **83**, 1–268.

HORTOBÁGYI (1959–60). Algen aus den Fischteichen von Buzsák. 1–3, *Scenedesmus*-Arten. *Nova Hedwigia*, **1**, 41–64; 345–81; **2**, 173–90.

HORTOBÁGYI, T. (1960). Das mehrmonatige Leben von Algen eines austrockenden Teichbettes unter erschwerten Bedingungen (im Laboratorium). *Acta Biol. Acad. Sci. Hungar.* **10**, 299–330.

HUSTEDT, F. (1930–59). Die Kieselalgen. *Rabenhorst's Kryptogamenflora*, **7**. Jena.

IYENGAR, M. O. P. (1954). A note on *Gloeococcus* A. Braun. *Rapp. Comm. Sect.* 17 *8me Congr. int. Bot. Paris, 1954*, 98–99.

JANE, F. W. (1944*a*). *Chlororhabdion*, a new genus of the Xanthophyceae. *J. R. micr. Soc.* **64**, 16–25.

JANE, F. W. (1944*b*). Studies on the British Volvocales. *New Phytol.* **43**, 36–48.

KALLIO, P. (1951). The significance of nuclear quantity of the genus *Micrasterias*. *Ann. (bot.-zool.) Soc. zool.-bot. fenn. Vanamo (bot.)*, **24**, no. 2, 1–212.

KALLIO, P. (1953). The effect of continued illumination on the desmids. *Arch. Soc. zool.-bot. fenn. Vanamo*, **8**, 58–74.

KOFOID, C. A. & SWEZY, O. (1921). The free-living unarmoured *Dinoflagellata*. *Mem. Univ. Calif.* no. 5, 1–562.

KOLKWITZ, R. & KRIEGER, H. (1941–44). Zygnemales. *Rabenhorsts' Kryptogamenflora*, **13** (Abt. 2). Leipzig.

KOMÁREK, J. & ETTL, H. (1958). *Algologische Studien*. Prague: Ceskoslovenska Akad. ved. Praha.

KORSHIKOV, A. A. (1926). On some new organisms from the groups Volvocales and Protococcales, and on the genetic relations of these groups. *Arch. Protistenk.* **55**, 439–503.

KORSHIKOV, A. A. (1932). Studies in the Vacuolatae. 1. *Arch. Protistenk.* **78**, 559–612.

KORSHIKOV, A. A. (1938*a*). Volvocineae. *Viznachnik prisnovodnikh Vodorostei Ukr. RSR. IV.* Kiev: Akad. Nauk Ukr. RSR.

KORSHIKOV, A. A. (1938*b*). O nekotorykh novykh vidakh semeistva Phacotaceae. *J. Inst. bot. Acad. Sci. Ukr. 1938*, 137–49.

KORSHIKOV, A. A. (1939). K morfologii i sistematike roda *Furcilla* Stokes. *Bot. Zh. S.S.S.R.* **21**, 397–407.

KORSHIKOV, O. A. (1953). *Viznachnik prisnovodnisc vodorostei Ukrains'koi RSR.* v Pidklas Protokovi (Protococineae). Kiev: Ukr. Akad. Nauk.

LEE, K. T. (1951). Notes on some Volvocales from Shanghai, I–II. *Sinensia*, **2**, 25–36.

LEFÈVRE, M. (1932). Monographie des espèces d'eau douce du genre *Peridinium* Ehrb. *Arch. Bot. Mém., Caen*, **2** (1928), no. 5, 210 pp.

LEWIN, R. A. (1952). Ultraviolet induced mutations of *Chlamydomonas moewusii* Gerloff. *J. gen. Microbiol.* **6**, 233–48.

LEWIN, R. A. (1957). The zygote of *Chlamydomonas moewusii*. *Canad. J. Bot.* **35**, 795–804.

LEWIN, R. A. (1958). The cell walls of *Platymonas. J. gen. Microbiol.* **19**, 87–90.

LEWIN, R. A., OWEN, M. J. & MELNICK, J. L. (1951). Cell-wall structure in *Chlamydomonas. Exp. Cell Res.* **2**, 708–9.

LUND, J. W. G. (1942). Contributions to our knowledge of British Chrysophyceae. *New Phytol.* **41**, 274–92.

LUND, J. W. G. (1947*a*). Observations on soil algae. II. Notes on groups other than diatoms. *New Phytol.* **46**, 35–60.

LUND, J. W. G. (1947*b*). Observations on soil algae. III. Species of *Chlamydomonas* Ehr. in relation to variability within the genus. *New Phytol.* **46**, 185–94.

LUND, J. W. G. (1956). On certain planktonic palmelloid green algae. *J. Linn. Soc. (Bot.)*, **55**, 593–613.

LUND, J. W. G. (1957). Four new green algae. *Rev. algol.*, N.S. **3**, 26–44.

LUND, J. W. G. (1960). New or rare Chrysophyceae. 3. New records and observations on sexuality and classification. *New Phytol.* **59**, 349–60.

LUND, J. W. G. (in the Press). Unsolved problems in the classification of the non-motile Chrysophyceae with references to those in parallel groups. *Preslia.*

MACK, B. (1953). Untersuchungen an Chrysophyceen I–III. *Öst. bot. Z.* **100**, 147–52.

MANTON, I. (1955). Observations with the electron microscope on *Synura caroliniana* Whitford. *Proc. Leeds phil. lit. Soc. (Sci. Sect.)*, **6**, 306–16.

MATVIENKO, A. M. (1941). Do sistematiki rodu *Mallomonas. Trud. nauk.-dosl. Inst. Bot. Kiïv.* **4**, 41–7.

MATVIENKO, A. M. (1954). Zolotisty Vodorosli. *Opredel. presnovod. Vodorosl. SSSR.* **3**. Moscow.

PAPENFUSS, G. F. (1960). On the genera of the Ulvales and the status of the order. *J. Linn. Soc. (Bot.)*, **56**, 303–18.

PARKE, M. (1961). Some remarks concerning the class Chrysophyceac. *Brit. Phycol. Bull.* **2**, 47–55.

PARKE, M., LUND, J. W. G. & MANTON, I. (in the Press). Observations on the biology and fine structure of the type species of *Chrysochromulina, C. parva* Lackey, in the English Lake District.

PARKE, M., MANTON, I. & CLARKE, B. (1955–59). Studies on marine flagellates. II (1955): Three new species of *Chrysochromulina*; III (1956): Three further species of *Chrysochromulina*; IV (1958): Morphology and microanatomy of a new species of *Chrysochromulina*. V (1959): Morphology and microanatomy of *Chrysochromulina strobilus* sp.nov. *J. mar. biol. Ass. U.K.* **34**, 579–609; **35**, 387–414; **37**, 209–28; **38**, 169–88.

PASCHER, A. (1913). Chrysomonadineae. *Süsswass.-Fl. Dtschl. Öst. Schweiz*, **2**, 7–95.

PASCHER, A. (1916). Über die Kreuzung einzelliger, haploider Organismen: *Chlamydomonas. Ber. dtsch. bot. Ges.* **34**, 228–42.

PASCHER, A. (1925). Die braune Algenriche der Chrysophyceen. *Arch. Protistenk.* **52**, 489–564.

PASCHER, A. (1927). Volvocales = Phytomonadineae. Flagellatae IV = Chlorophyceae I. *Süsswass.-Fl. dtschl. Öst. Schweiz.*

PASCHER, A. (1929a). Beiträge zur allgemeinen Zellehre. I. Doppelzellige Flagellaten und Parallelentwicklungen zwischen Flagellaten und Algenschwärmern. *Arch. Protistenk.* **68**, 261–304.

PASCHER, A. (1929b). Eine neue farblose Chlorophyceae. *Beih. bot. Zbl.*, Abt. I, **45**, 390–400.

PASCHER, A. (1937–39). Heterokonten. *Rabenhorst's Kryptogamenflora*, **11**. Leipzig.

PETERSON, J. B. & HANSEN, J. B. (1958). On some neuston organisms. I. *Bot. Tidsskr.* **54**, 93–110.

PETERSON, J. B. & HANSEN, J. B. (1960). On some neuston organisms. II. *Bot. Tidsskr.* **56**, 197–234.

PICKEN, L. E. R. (1960). *The Organization of Cells and other Organisms.* Oxford University Press.

POCHMANN, A. (1942). Synopsis der Gattung *Phacus. Arch. Protistenk.* **95**, 81–252.

POCOCK, M. A. (1953). Two motile multicellular green algae, *Volvulina* Playfair and *Astrophomene*, a new genus. *Trans. roy. Soc. S. Afr.* **34**, 103–27.

PRINGSHEIM, E. G. (1936). Zur Kenntnis saprotropher Algen und Flagellaten. 1 Mitteilung: Über anhäufungskulturen polysaprober Flagellaten. *Arch. Protistenk.* **87**, 43–96.

PRINGSHEIM, E. G. (1949). The relationship between Bacteria and Myxophyceae. *Bact. Rev.* **13**, 51–98.

PRINGSHEIM, E. G. (1951a). Über farblose Diatomeen. *Arch. Mikrobiol.* **16**, 18–27.

PRINGSHEIM, E. G. (1951b). The Vitreosillaceae: a family of colourless, gliding, filamentous organisms. *J. gen. Microbiol.* **5**, 124–49.

PRINGSHEIM, E. G. (1952). On the nutrition of *Ochromonas. Quart. J. micr. Sci.*, Ser. 3, **93**, 71–96.

PRINGSHEIM, E. G. (1955). Kleine Mitteilungen über Flagellaten und Algen. Über *Ochromonas danica* n.sp. und andere Arten der Gattung. *Arch. Mikrobiol.* **23**, 181–92.

PRINGSHEIM, E. G. (1956). Contributions towards a monograph of the genus *Euglena. Nova Acta Leop. Carol.*, N.F., No. 125, 168 pp. Leipzig.

PRINGSHEIM, E. G. (1957). Two species of *Trachelomonas* (Euglenineae) without chlorophyll. *Nature, Lond.* **180**, 1296–97.

PRINGSHEIM, E. G. (1959). Heterotrophie bei Algen und Flagellatem. In *Handbuch der Pflanzenphysiologie*, **11**, 303–26. Berlin: Springer.

RABINOWITCH, E. I. (1956). *Photosynthesis and Related Processes*, **2**, Pt. 2. New York: Interscience. 2 vols.

RANDHAWA, M. S. (1959). *Zygnemaceae.* 478 pp. New Delhi: Indian Council of Agricultural Research.

RIETH, A. & SAGROMSKY, H. (1959). Untersuchungen an *Vaucheria* halophiler Standorte des Neapeler Gebeites. *Pubbl. Staz. zool. Napoli*, **31**, 90–7.

SCHERFFEL, A. (1911). Beitrag zur Kenntnis der Chrysomonadineen. *Arch. Protistenk.* **22**, 299–344.

SCHILLER, J. (1930). Coccolithineae. *Rabenhorst's Kryptogamenflora*, **10**, 2. Leipzig.

SCHILLER, J. (1933–37). Dinoflagellatae (Peridineae). *Rabenhorst's Kryptogamenflora*, **10**, 1, 2. Leipzig.

SCHMID, G. (1934). Die Chrysomonadengattungen *Kephyrion, Pseudokephyrion* und *Stenocalyx* in Gewässern bei Wien. *Öst. bot. Z.* **83**, 162–72.

SCHULZE, B. (1927). Zur Kenntnis einiger Volvocales (*Chlorogonium, Haematococcus, Stephanosphaera, Spondylomorum, Chlorobrachis*). *Arch. Protistenk.* **58**, 508–76.

SILVA, P. C. & PAPENFUSS, G. F. (1953). A systematic study of the algae of sewage oxidation ponds. *Publ. St. Water Pollut. Control Bd. Sacramento*, 7.

SILVA, P. C. & STARR, R. C. (1953). Difficulties in applying the International Code of Botanical Nomenclature to certain unicellular algae, with special reference to *Chlorococcum*. *Svensk. bot. Tidskr.* 47, 235–47.

SKOCZYLAS, O. (1958–59). Über die Mitose von *Ceratium cornutum* und einige anderen Peridinein. *Arch. Protistenk.* 103, 193–228.

SKUJA, H. (1927). Über die Gattung *Furcilla* Stokes und ihre Systematische Stellung. *Acta Hort. bot. Univ. latv.* 2, 117–24.

SKUJA, H. (1939). Beitrag zur Algenflora Lettlands. II. *Acta Hort. bot. Univ. latv.* 11–12, 40–169.

SKUJA, H. (1948). Taxonomie des Phytoplanktons einiger Seen in Uppland, Schweden. *Symb. bot. upsaliens.* 9, (3), 399 pp.

SKUJA, H. (1956). Taxonomische und biologische Studien über das Phytoplankton Schwedischer Binnengewässer. *Nova Acta Soc. sci. upsal.*, Ser. IV, 16 (3), 404 pp.

SMITH, G. M. (1916). A monograph of the algal genus *Scenedesmus*, based upon pure culture studies. *Trans. Wis. Acad. Sci. Arts Lett.* 18, 422–530.

SPARROW, F. K. (1960). *Aquatic Phycomycetes*, 2nd edition. Ann Arbor, Mich.: Univ. Michigan Press.

STARR, R. C. (1955a). A comparative study of *Chlorococcum meneghinie* and other spherical, zoospore-producing genera of the Chlorococcales. *Ind. Univ. Publ.* 20, pp. 111.

STARR, R. C. (1955b). Isolation of sexual strains of placoderm desmids. *Bull. Torrey bot. Cl.* 82, 261–5.

STARR, R. C. (1958). The production and inheritance of the triradiate form in *Cosmarium turpinii*. *Amer. J. Bot.* 45, 243–8.

STARR, R. C. (1959). Sexual reproduction in certain species of *Cosmarium*. *Arch. Protistenk.* 104, 155–64.

STEIN, J. R. (1958). A morphological study of *Astrophomene gubernaculifera* and *Volvulina Steinii*. *Amer. J. Bot.* 45, 388–97.

STOSCH, H. A. VON (1955). Die Oogamie von *Biddulphia mobiliensis* und die bisher bekannten Auxosporenbildungen bei den Centrales. *Rapp. Comm. 8me Congr. int. Bot.* 1954, Sect. 17, 58–68.

STOSCH, H. A. VON (1956). Entwicklungsgeschichtliche Untersuchungen an zentrischen Diatomeen. II. Geschlechtszellenreifung, Befruchtung und Auxosporenbildung einiger, grundbewohnender Biddulphiaceen der Nordsee. *Arch. Mikrobiol.* 23, 327–55.

STOSCH, H. A. VON (1958). Kann die oogame *Rhabdonema adriaticum* als Bindglied zwischen den beiden grossen Diatomeengruppen angeschen werden? *Ber. dtsch. bot. Ges.* 71, 241–49.

STOSCH, H. A. VON (1958–59). Zum Chromosomenformwechsel der Dinophyten Sowie zur Mechanik und Terminologie von Schrauben. *Arch. Protistenk.* 103, 229–40.

STREHLOW, K. (1928–29). Über die Sexualität einiger Volvocales. *Z. Bot.* 21, 625–92.

TEILING, E. (1948). *Staurodesmus*, genus novum. *Bot. Notiser* (1948), 49–83.

TEILING, E. (1950). Radiation of desmids, its origin and its consequences as regards taxonomy and nomenclature. *Bot. Notiser* (1950), 299–327.

TEILING, E. (1954). *Actinotaenium*, genus desmidiacearum resuscitatum. *Bot. Notiser* (1954), 376–426.

THOMPSON, R. H. (1950). A new genus and new records of fresh-water Pyrrophyta in the Desmokontae and Dinophyceae. *Lloydia*, 13, 277–99.

THOMPSON, R. H. (1956). *Schizochlamys gelatinosa* and *Placosphaera opaca*. *Amer. J. Bot.* **43**, 665–72.

TRANSEAU, E. N. (1951). *The Zygnemataccae*. 327 pp. Columbus, Ohio: Ohio State University.

TURNER, C. (1922). The life history of *Staurastrum Dickiei* var. *parallelum* (Nordst.). *Proc. Linn. Soc. Lond.* **134**, 59–63.

VISCHER, W. (1936). Über Heterokonten und Heterokonten-ähnliche Grünalgen. *Ber. schweiz. bot. Ges.* **45**, 372–410.

VISCHER, W. (1937). Über einige Heterokonten (*Heterococcus, Chlorellidium*) und ihren Polymorphismus. *Ber. schweiz. bot. Ges.* **47**, 225–50.

VISCHER, W. (1945). Heterokonten aus alpinen Böden, speziell dem Schweizerischen Nationalpark. *Ergebn. wiss. Unters. schweiz. NatParks.* **1**, N.F., 481–512.

VISCHER, W. (1953). Über primitivste Landpflanzen. *Ber. schweiz. bot. Ges.* **63**, 169–93.

VISCHER, W. (1960). Reproduktion und Systematischer Stellung einiger Rinden- und Bodenalgen. *Schweiz. Z. Hydrol.* **22**, 330–49.

WARIS, H. (1950). Cytophysiological studies on *Micrasterias*. II. The cytoplasmic framework and its mutation. *Physiol. Plant.* **3**, 236–46.

YAGUZHINSKII, S. N. (1936). Nablyudeniya nad izmenchivost'yu ostistykh vidov roda *Scenedesmus* Meyen. *Bull. Sta. biol. Bolchevo*, **9**, 67–95.

YAGUZHINSKII, S. N. (1937). Nablyudeniya nad izmenchivost'yu v klonakh bezo- stitnykh vidov roda *Scenedesmus* Meyen. *Bull. Sta. biol. Bolchevo*, **10**, 125–48.

THE MORPHOLOGICAL APPROACH TO THE TAXONOMY OF MICROFUNGI

GEORGE SMITH

London School of Hygiene and Tropical Medicine

In the early days of descriptive mycology—the days of Persoon, Link, Ehrenberg, Nees von Esenbeck, Fries and Corda—the morphological approach to classification was predominant. The main trouble in evaluating the findings of these pioneers is that their descriptions of fungi were, by modern standards, very imperfect, partly because of the indifferent optical equipment available at the time, and partly because the describers had no idea of the extent of the Fungus Kingdom, and found that brief diagnoses were sufficient to separate the few forms they knew. In connexion with the accuracy of descriptions it is interesting to note that in Corda's *Icones* (1837–54), the standard of the illustrations improves markedly after the first volume, and the illustrations in Corda's *Pracht-Flora* (1839) are beautiful. It is probably significant that in the early 1830's important improvements were made, particularly by Lister in England, in the quality of microscope objectives, and that such lenses gradually became known all over Europe.

With the realization that fungi are the cause, and not the result, of plant diseases, the idea gradually gained ground that every plant has its own distinct fungus flora, and, as a corollary, that fungi belonging to the same genus, but found to parasitize different plants, are, of necessity, different species. The result has been that many genera have been cluttered up with specific epithets derived from the names of the host plants. For example, in Saccardo's *Sylloge* (Saccardo, 1882–1931), there are brief descriptions of some 270 so-called species of *Cladosporium*, very many of the specific epithets being based on the names of the hosts, although these are very rarely truly parasitic, but, in most cases, are the common *C. herbarum* growing on the honey-dew secreted by aphides. The situation regarding the stem and leaf parasites, *Phoma* and *Phyllosticta*, is even worse, with well over 3000 names, and with no essential morphological difference between the two genera (cf. p. 252).

SACCARDO'S SPORE GROUPS

However, although the *Sylloge* includes thousands of names based entirely on host relationships, Saccardo was really the first to use morphology of the microfungi to develop a more or less workable scheme of classification. For the primary subdivision of the fungi he used types of sporing structures, such as sporangia, perithecia, asci, apothecia, basidia, pycnidia, acervuli, coremia, or simple loose webs of hyphae. Below this level the chief basis of classification was the characteristics of the spores, such as colour, shape and septation, the different classes of which were divided into two series according as to whether they were hyaline or dark, given group names (see Table 1), and used as a grid by which many species could be conveniently, if at times most unnaturally, catalogued. Saccardo had no real appreciation of differences in the methods of spore production (one of the most important criteria today), although the mode of occurrence of the spores, whether singly, in chains, or in balls, was taken into account. In spite of its limitations, Saccardo's spore-system of classification has proved very useful for the classification and identification of ascomy-

Table 1. *Saccardo's spore groups.*

Spores			Colour of spores and/or mycelium	
			Hyaline or pale	Dark
1-celled		Amerosporae	Hyalosporae	Phaeosporae
2-celled		Didymosporae	Hyalodidymae	Phaeodidymae
2 or more cross septa		Phragmosporae	Hyalophragmiae	Phaeophragmiae
Muriform (i.e. having both cross and longitudinal septa)		Dictyosporae	Hyalodictyae	Phaeodictyae
Thread-like		Scolicosporae	——	——
Spirally coiled		Helicosporae	——	——
Star-shaped		Staurosporae	——	——

cetes, but, although in general use, it has not proved satisfactory for classifying hyphomycetes.

If we consider in turn the various classes of fungi, we find that the degree to which morphology has contributed to classification depends, in general, on the number of morphological criteria which are available for classificatory purposes. Thus yeasts are virtually impossible to classify on purely morphological considerations, so that all who have studied these important organisms have been driven to use biochemical characters. Phycomycetes are more complex, and show a fair number of morphological characters by which they may be classified, such as sporangia, asexual spores, oogonia and oospores in the Oomycetidae, and sporangia and spores, chlamydospores, gemmae, columellae, zygospores and modes of conjugation in the Zygomycetidae. In any case the number of phycomycetes is small compared with the numbers of ascomycetes and fungi imperfecti.

In the Ascomycetes the number of criteria is large, including colour, shape and mode of occurrence of the perithecia or apothecia, shape and size of asci and number of spores therein, characteristics of ascospores, and also types of accessory spore forms. This class does, however, raise other problems of classification. In particular I consider it important that some attempt be made to standardize, as far as possible, taxonomic criteria. At present, differences which, in one order, are used to separate genera and even families, are, in another order, not of sufficient importance to define species. In the Fungi Imperfecti the number of criteria useful for classification is limited, and it is not surprising that a great deal of effort has gone in attempts to provide a satisfactory scheme of classification for this important group of fungi.

VUILLEMIN'S SPORE GROUPS

Whilst Saccardo was completing his first eight volumes of the *Sylloge*, covering all the classes of fungi, Costantin (1888) had an inkling of what have since proved to be more valid characteristics to use for classification of the enormous assembly of fungi included in the Hyphomycetes. In some respects he foreshadowed Vuillemin (1910a, b, 1911, 1912). The work of the latter is of particular importance, since, for the first time, a bold attempt was made to classify hyphomycetes on the basis of methods of spore production, and not mainly on the characteristics of the spores themselves, as in Saccardo's system. Unfortunately Vuillemin never applied his system to the classification of all the known genera, so that it cannot be used as a basis for identifications. The main points of his system are the recognition of the following types (see Table 2):

Table 2. *Vuillemin's spore groups.*

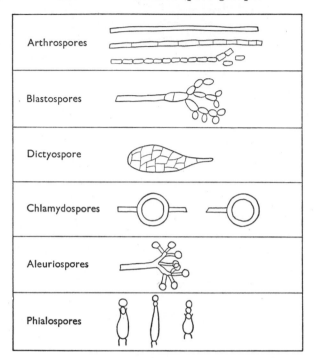

Arthrospores	
Blastospores	
Dictyospore	
Chlamydospores	
Aleuriospores	
Phialospores	

1. THALLOSPORES

Spores which are not distinct, *ab initio*, from the mycelium which bears them. This main type is further subdivided into:

(*a*) *Arthrospores*, formed by fragmentation of the mycelium, as in *Geotrichum*.

(*b*) *Blastospores*. These arise as buds from pre-existing cells. They may form chains by further budding, the chains being frequently branched, due to the formation of more than one bud from a single cell. Examples are *Pullularia* (*Aureobasidium*) and *Cladosporium*.

(*c*) *Dictyospores*. Many-celled spores with both cross and longitudinal septa. Examples are *Alternaria* and *Stemphylium*.

(*d*) *Chlamydospores*. Thick-walled spores, terminal or intercalary, found in all groups of fungi, and functioning as resting cells.

(*e*) *Aleuriospores*. Small terminal chlamydospores, resembling conidia, attached by the whole width of the parent hypha, and liberated by the decay of the latter. Examples are *Trichothecium*, *Sepedonium* and *Aleurisma* (*sensu* Vuillemin).

2. CONIDIOSPORES

Spores which arise on the thallus as newly and distinctly formed elements. They are separated from the thallus by the action of the fungus itself, and not merely by decay of the parent hyphae, as in the previous subgroup.

(a) *No definite conidiophores.* Conidia borne on small projections or denticles at any points along the hyphae. Typified by *Sporothrix* (= *Sporotrichum* as understood by medical mycologists).

(b) *Conidiophores definite, but the spores not produced on phialides.* A typical example is *Botrytis*, in which the spores are produced on tiny pegs covering the surface of the swollen ends of the stiff, much-branched conidiophore.

(c) *Spores produced from phialides.* These are what Vuillemin called *conidia vera.* In true phialides the spores are formed endogenously, the cell contents being extruded more or less continuously, and being cut off at intervals by cross-walls to form the spores. The latter are always thin-walled, and form unbranched chains. Phialospores are produced in *Aspergillus, Penicillium, Verticillium,* and many other genera. Also it has been shown by a number of subsequent workers that more or less inconspicuous phialospores are produced in many other genera which are classified on the basis of other spore forms, e.g. *Sepedonium, Botrytis* and *Trichothecium.*

Mason (1933, 1937, 1941), in a study largely devoted to the conidial states of ascomycetes, discussed Vuillemin's scheme of classification, and clarified a number of the latter's conceptions. For the type of spores produced singly on tiny pegs he proposed the term 'radula spore', from the similarity of the spore-bearing surface to a nutmeg grater.

HUGHES'S SPORE GROUPS

The next serious advance in the study of the Hyphomycetes was by Hughes (1953). The genera discussed are divided into eight main groups, based entirely on methods of spore production. Some of the criteria used in the classification are far from easy to understand, and the examples chosen to illustrate the various types are taken mostly from fungi which are specialized saprophytes on decaying parts of plants, and many genera of common moulds are not mentioned at all. The labour of classifying all the known genera of hyphomycetes in such a scheme would be considerable, but, until this is done, the curators of some of our most important herbaria can hardly be blamed for classifying their collections according to Saccardo's system, out-of-date though it is.

Hughes first separates the various types into two main divisions. The first, which includes seven of the eight sections, comprises all species in which any extension of the conidiophore is confined to the apical region. The remaining section VIII includes species in which the growth of the conidiophore is always basal. Section I*a* corresponds roughly to Vuillemin's 'blastospores', the conidia developing in acropetal succession on conidiophores which, when once formed, do not increase in length. Section I*b* includes fungi with comparatively wide mycelium, not only the species with spore production similar to that in section I*a*, but also species forming what Mason termed 'radula spores'.

In section II the conidiophore produces a terminal spore, and then extends by a new growing point to one side of the conidium and produces a second spore, this process being repeated to give, usually, an 'ear' of spores.

Section III is perhaps the most interesting of all the sections from the point of view of its effect on classification. The first spores are formed as terminal aleuriospores (*sensu* Vuillemin), but, instead of only one spore being produced, the conidiophore or sporiferous cell elongates through the scar left by abscission of the first spore, to produce a second spore, and so on, an unbranched chain of conidia being eventually formed. The spore-producing cell gradually elongates, and the scars left by separation of successive spores are visible as faint rings on the terminal portion of the cell. Hence, Hughes has termed such spore-producing cells 'annellophores'. In some genera the annellophores have previously been regarded as phialides, but the two types of cell are quite distinct, phialides producing a succession of spores without any increase in length, annellophores gradually lengthening with each conidium produced. A typical example of this section is *Scopulariopsis*, in the past regarded as distinct from, but closely related to, *Penicillium*. However, it is significant that all taxonomists who have studied species of *Scopulariopsis* have remarked on the very variable length of the 'phialides', and on their being almost cylindrical rather than typically bottle-shaped as the name implies. Annellophores are not easy to detect, so it will be some time before all the cases of this method of spore formation are brought to light, but, in my experience, annellophore production is fairly common among hyphomycetes, quite a number of so-called phialides having proved to be annellate when critically examined.

Hughes's section IV includes all the fungi which form their conidia from phialides. In section V the conidial chains merge imperceptibly into the supporting conidiophore, and the conidia mature very slowly, so that a single chain may have one-celled spores at the lower end, phragmospores in the middle, and large dictyospores at the upper end. This type is found chiefly amongst the coelomycetes, that is fungi which produce their conidia in pycnidia or acervuli. Section VI covers a somewhat miscellaneous variety of methods of spore production. The spores are thick-walled, solitary or in whorls, or in acropetal chains, and the conidiophores may proliferate through the terminal pore or may, as in section II, continue growth from just below the previously formed conidium. Section VII accommodates fungi which form what Vuillemin termed 'arthrospores', the conidiophore gradually breaking up into spores from the tip backwards, *Geotrichum* and *Oidiodendron* being typical examples.

A number of other workers in various parts of the world are interested in a general classification of the hyphomycetes. Tubaki (1958), in particular, has somewhat amplified Hughes's scheme. Hughes's section III (annellosporae) is divided into three subsections: A, producing typical annellophores; B, producing solitary aleuriospores, hence no annellophores, e.g. *Trichocladium*; C, forming separating cells between conidiophore and spore, these breaking down to liberate the conidia, e.g. *Tetrachaetum* and *Keratinomyces* (but not *Beltrania*, in which the separating cells do not break down). Section IV (phialosporae) is divided into two subsections: A, the *Penicillium* type, in which spore production is apparently exogenous; B, spores produced endogenously as in *Thielaviopsis*. Tubaki states that Hughes's section VIII is more complex than the original description would indicate, but he does not attempt to sort it out. Finally Tubaki makes a new section IX, to include a number of genera which Hughes does not discuss, *Trichothecium*, *Monosporium* and *Cylindrophora*.

CONCLUSIONS

The problem of a satisfactory classification of the hyphomycetes has been considered in some detail because this group is, with the possible exception of the coelomycetes (also Fungi Imperfecti) in most urgent need of a comprehensive scheme to cover all known genera. To attain a satisfactory classification of the fungi imperfecti two lines of attack are necessary. On the one hand, in spite of a very welcome revival of interest in taxonomy during the last two decades, we need many more monographic treatments of individual genera, which will emphasize real relationships and ignore the spurious similarities which have, in the past, brought together in one genus a miscellaneous assortment of species. The other requirement is, as stated above, for an extension of some scheme, such as that of Hughes, to include all the known genera, or at least all the genera for which types are available. It is unfortunate that many genera have been founded on specimens or cultures which have not been preserved. In some such cases the descriptions and figures are adequate for recognition, but many diagnoses, mostly but by no means exclusively in the older literature, are hopelessly inadequate, and the names virtually meaningless. Nevertheless, there are sufficient 'good species' to provide plenty of problems for taxonomists for some time to come.

REFERENCES

CORDA, A. C. J. (1837–54). *Icones fungorum hucusque cognitorum*, 6 vols. Prague.

CORDA, A. C. J. (1839). *Pracht-Flora europaeischen Schimmelbildungen*. Leipzig and Dresden.

COSTANTIN, J. (1888). *Les Mucedinées simples*. Paris: Klingsieck.

HUGHES, S. J. (1953). Conidia, conidiophores and classification. *Canad. J. Bot.* **31**, 577–659.

MASON, E. W. (1933). Annotated account of fungi received at the Imperial Mycological Institute. List II, Fasc. 2. *Mycol. Pap.* no. 3.

MASON, E. W. (1937). Annotated account of fungi received at the Imperial Mycological Institute. List II, Fasc. 3 (general part). *Mycol. Pap.* no. 4.

MASON, E. W. (1941). Annotated account of fungi received at the Imperial Mycological Institute. List II, Fasc. 3 (special part). *Mycol. Pap.* no. 5.

SACCARDO, P. A. (1882–1931). *Sylloge fungorum omnium hucusque cognitorum*, 25 vols. Pavia.

TUBAKI, K. (1958). Studies on the Japanese Hyphomycetes. V. Leaf and stem group, with a discussion of the classification of Hyphomycetes and their perfect stages. *J. Hattori bot. Lab.*, no. 20, 142–244.

VUILLEMIN, P. (1910*a*). Matériaux pour une classification rationelle des Fungi Imperfecti. *C.R. Acad. Sci., Paris*, **150**, 882–4.

VUILLEMIN, P. (1910*b*). Les Conidiosporés. *Bull. Soc. Sci. Nancy*, Sér. 3, **11**, 129–72.

VUILLEMIN, P. (1911). Les Aleuriosporés. *Bull. Soc. Sci. Nancy*, Sér. 3, **12**, 151–75.

VUILLEMIN, P. (1912). *Les Champignons. Essai de classification*. Paris: O. Doin et Fils.

FINE STRUCTURE AND TAXONOMY
OF BACTERIA

R. G. E. MURRAY

*Department of Bacteriology and Immunology, University of
Western Ontario, London, Canada*

Bacterial morphology has acquired new dimensions in the past twenty
years. This is due in large part to the high resolution and analytical
possibilities provided by the present-day microscopical and biochemical
studies of cell structure. The developments have been reflected in the
First and the Sixth Symposia sponsored by this Society, and in one or
more chapters in most of the others; in a growing series of books and
compendia; and, not the least important, in changes in the introductory
chapters of text-books for elementary students. The result is a number
of detailed and profusely illustrated views of the present state of knowledge, and this is amplified with every issue of the specialist journals.
The present contribution emphasizes some consequences of current
work on thoughts about bacterial taxonomy and descriptions of
bacteria.

It must be clear that very little of the current work on shape and form
and fine structure is directed towards the needs of taxonomy. There are
the detailed studies of individual strains of *Escherichia coli*, *Bacillus
megaterium* and a rather short list of other bacteria that serve as the
test-objects for new methods of divining structure and function. This
provides the morphologist with the information he must have about the
biochemistry and the physical state of cell components, just as the
reverse flow provides the biochemist with the information he needs on
structure. The taxonomist needs—but does not yet have—wide-ranging,
detailed observations of organisms in culture and in natural habitats.
This detail must be reduced to bare essentials, for the taxonomist must,
of necessity, take a more general view-point. But there are remarkably
few *comparative* studies. The result is that the application of the newer
adjuncts of morphology for taxonomic purposes entails generalization
from limited cases. A further consequence is that the data can first be
applied only in the broadest and most inclusive sense (e.g. at the present
rank of Class) or in the narrowest sense (e.g. species or, perhaps, genera).
That which is in between remains untouched.

Taxonomy has always relied heavily upon morphological criteria or characters to define groups at all levels. Among plants and animals this has obvious advantage where a scattering of fossil specimens has allowed development of a natural order based on morphological sequences. The bacteria have not only failed to leave us a fossil record useful in this regard but their morphology (the classical criteria concerning size, shape, growth habit, motility, capsulation, sporulation and staining reactions) is limited, in contrast to the range of capability in terms of habitats, interactions in specialized environments, and metabolic potential. Furthermore, the morphological characters concern the structure and attributes of a *cell* of small dimensions—a problem admittedly shared, but less acute, with the other divisions of microbiology.

Our forebears soon found that you could classify bacteria in a number of ways and 'form genera' became intermixed with 'physiological genera', 'pigment genera', 'disease genera' and so forth. The morphological groups, repeating (or retaining) the permutations and combinations of a relatively small selection of characters, return several times in different physiological disguises. It is unfortunate, as van Niel (1946) pointed out, that it was not recognized how these various and somewhat arbitrary choices of classifying characters could form a *number* of overlapping keys for the identification of organisms according to the circumstances of the isolation. Few, if any, of the arrangements give much semblance of a 'natural order'; they are much too practical. This is at last recognized by a key, devised by Skerman (1949, 1957, 1959), pretending to be nothing but practical and utilizing all sorts of characters chosen for apparent reliability in the separation of already-described genera. From here the specialized generic keys of compilations such as *Bergey's Manual* (Breed, Murray & Smith, 1957) can take over the task of identification.

The fact that such an arbitrary key is needed draws attention to the continuing inadequacy of descriptions, and any improvement will require concerted effort of re-description using the very best available techniques (Skerman, 1949, 1959). Furthermore, it will have to be the people who isolate and identify bacteria who must do this and not merely the experimentalist who must work with a more limited range of 'type' cultures. Skerman's (1949) prescriptions for reform should be read again.

The 'form genus' of the bacteriologist is not quite the same as the 'form genus' of the mycologist and zoologist (van Niel, 1955). The form in the bacteria is that of a single cell or the relations of a small, relatively undifferentiated consortium rather than the development and fruition of a multicellular animal or plant. Growth habit and patterns of division may be available to us but not complex differentiation and recapitulated phylogeny. So, what we must do is describe our charges *as cells* and compare them with other kinds of cells. Although the present-day 'morphologist' produces a considerable variety of artifacts for us to sort out, the resulting pictures have relevance because they describe the cell as a whole. We have now, developing, a new comparative anatomy at the cellular level that is particularly advantageous to the bacteriologist because he can contribute on equal terms with the rest of biology (although facing slightly unequal difficulties).

This new anatomy of bacteria was the special concern of the Sixth Symposium at which Bradfield (1956) drew attention to the new differences in structure evident in comparing bacterial cells to the rest. There has been since then only a very superficial sampling of bacteria, but there is enough information to add considerably to our knowledge of the uniqueness (Stanier, 1954) of bacteria. Furthermore, we can clear up the impasse (and the consequent discouragement) noted, so short a time ago, by van Niel (1955), when it was still not possible to make a clear distinction between plant, blue-green algal and bacterial cells.

FEATURES OF BACTERIAL STRUCTURE

It has always been difficult to be precise about the characters that differentiate bacteria as a taxon. The difficulty and the need for new characters can best be illustrated by consulting the description of the Class Schizomycetes prepared by the late Professor R. S. Breed for the 7th edition of *Bergey's Manual* (Breed *et al.* 1957, p. 33); certainly he wrote from experience and with the greatest possible precision. We may now be able to select some structural characters of the bacteria and see what newer information can add to the description.

The fact is that the many variable properties of size, shape, photosynthesis and so forth give no definitive properties to the class; they can only apply clearly to individual taxa of lower order. The operative definition is that they are 'typically unicellular plants' and, unless the cells are recognizable in terms of the structure of an idealized plant cell (Whaley, Mollenhauer & Leech, 1960; Porter & Machado, 1960; Hodge, McLean & Mercer, 1955), this is of little help. The other differentiating characters are descriptive of taxa differentiated within the class, yet the characters are also unique.

Recent cytological techniques, including the morphological and chemical study of cell fractions and sections, have allowed something much more definitive (Robinow, 1961) than the 'small size and glassy cytoplasm' of former days. We can refer to the specialized structure of cytoplasm (Murray, 1960), nucleoplasm (Kellenberger, 1960) and the contribution of the cytoplasmic membrane to their structure (Giesbrecht, 1960; Fitz-James, 1961); to the cell-walls and their chemical composition (Salton, 1961); to gliding and flagellar motility (Weibull, 1960), and even to the sort of mechanisms of genetic segregation that are not found in bacteria (Hayes, 1960). It is becoming evident that many of these involve characters distinctive enough to be used to define a taxonomic group that includes the bacteria.

Cytoplasm and the cytoplasmic membrane

The bacteria do indeed have a peculiar cytoplasm: it is packed with dense ribosomal particles (this is especially true in the active growth phase) and it is relatively free of membranous structures by comparison with the cells of plants and animals (Pls. 1–4).

The cytoplasm is bounded by a plasma or cytoplasmic membrane (Kellenberger & Ryter, 1958) shown to be separate from the enveloping cell-wall (Robinow & Murray, 1953; and Pl. 4, fig. 3), and it is the effective permeability barrier of the cell. Undoubtedly many functions must be crammed into its 60–100 Å. thickness. For a while it was thought that the plasma membrane was not only hard to demonstrate but stayed at the cytoplasmic surface; this appeared to be an overwhelming characteristic of bacterial cytoplasm (Bradfield, 1956; Murray, 1957). But vastly improved techniques of fixation and embedding (Maaløe & Birch-Andersen, 1956; Ryter & Kellenberger, 1958a, b; Kellenberger, Ryter & Séchaud, 1958; Glauert & Glauert, 1958) make it certain that many types of bacteria (so far all aerobes, or facultative aerobes grown aerobically) have intrusions of the plasma membrane into the cytoplasm. The most extreme of these (Pl. 1, fig. 3; Pl. 2, fig. 2) show various sorts of rolling up of the membrane into structures giving whorl-like profiles and tubules (Shinohara, Fukushi, Suzuki & Sato, 1958; Glauert & Hopwood, 1959; Giesbrecht, 1960; Glauert, Brieger & Allen, 1961; Van Iterson, 1961), which may be called chondrioids (Ryter & Kellenberger, 1958a) or mesosomes (Fitz-James, 1961) to choose the most neutral terms. They seem to remain attached to the superficial plasma membrane and in this regard they may be looked upon as the simplest form of membrane system in cytoplasm, in contrast to the elaborate membranous organelles of animal and plant cells. They may not be constant or consistent in bacteria; but they appear to be unique. Their function remains uncertain and, even if they are proved to contain cytochrome oxidase and to have a mitochondrion-like function, there is no reason to equate them to the distinct morphological elements of higher cells, the mitochondria, as Giesbrecht (1960) has done. They seem to be identical with the 'peripheral bodies' of Chapman & Hillier (1953) and are related in space (if not function) to the formation of septa, dividing chromatic bodies (Van Iterson, 1961) and the forespore (Fitz-James, 1961).

The ribosomes (Pls. 2, 3), or ribonucleic acid-protein (RNP) particles, are very similar in form and physical behaviour (Huxley & Zubay, 1960) to those of higher cells. Whether or not the synthesis of these RNP associations takes place at the plasma membrane—for certainly membrane fractions (Spiegelman, 1958) and chromatin (Ezekiel, 1961) both show high activity—ribosome-studded membranes are *not* the prominent feature in the bacteria that they are in so many other cells.

Specialized vesicles and membranes of a different sort appear in the cytoplasm of photosynthetic bacteria (Vatter & Wolfe, 1958). These are not grouped in the organellar fashion of plant chloroplasts with grana and stroma enclosed by a membrane (Hodge *et al.* 1955). They appear to contain all the photosynthetic pigments (Schachman *et al.* 1952) and hence deserve the name of chromatophores. Although new arrangements may be found (see Drews, 1960; Vatter, Douglas & Wolfe, 1959) the fact is that, when they occur, the chromatophores differ from plant plastids by not being enclosed in a membrane. They are formed only in cells grown in light, and there is still much doubt about their origin (Hickman & Frenkel, 1960).

In suitable environments bacteria will store energy as phosphorus or lipid compounds, polymetaphosphate (volutin) and poly-β-hydroxybutyrate. These are easily recognizable morphological entities (Pl. 2) and are of considerable functional interest (Doudoroff & Stanier, 1959; Wilkinson & Duguid, 1960). Polymetaphosphate is not confined to bacteria. It is rather common in all the protists including fungi, algae and protozoa. β-Hydroxybutyrate, on the other hand, which certainly is widely distributed in bacteria, may be less common in other organisms. However, detailed discussion of these and other inclusions (e.g. sulphur) belongs more properly to comparative biochemistry, although the kind, appearance and assortment of inclusions may have diagnostic value (e.g. *Beggiatoa*).

Chromatin bodies and nucleoplasms

The nuclear material of bacteria is peculiar and is endowed with distinct properties.

(1) The cytoplasm is extremely basophilic in active growth (due to ribosomes in large part), and consequently the classical character of chromatin—ready and marked stainability with basic dyes—is rather overshadowed by the neighbouring cytoplasm. Even so the majority of chromatin bodies do *not* stain readily with basic dyes (Robinow, 1956*b*), even with the Romanowsky methylene blue-eosin series which were developed to overcome a similar reluctance on the part of the nuclei of malaria parasites. The chromatin is easily stained following suitable pretreatment—e.g. with HCl as for a Feulgen reaction—and most conclusions on its disposition in bacteria is based on such preparations. The cells are peculiarly reluctant to reveal details of internal structure in life except by phase-contrast microscopy (Mason & Powelson, 1956).

(2) The chromatin bodies are not obviously chromosomal at any time in their growth cycle. Indeed they seem to ramify in the central portion of the cytoplasm. The precise arrangement is determined to some extent by the physiological state of that particular cell and the environment (Whitfield & Murray, 1956) but it can also be a genetic character (Lieb, Weigle & Kellenberger, 1955). Each one then behaves as a unit and it is this unit which divides, *directly*, and without spindle formation, more or less in phase with cell division (Robinow, 1956*a*, *b*). A slight asynchrony of these divisions commonly leads to cells with two or four or more chromatin bodies during phases of active growth. But normally when growth ceases there is left a 'resting cell' having a single unit of chromatin. Each of the units in the multinucleate filaments seems to be totipotential and complete (Witkin, 1951; Munson & McLean, 1961). The genetical evidence (see Hayes, 1960) is that these bodies contain the genetical information in a single linkage group, as if the chromatin body were effectively a single chromosome. The vegetative cell is haploid and only transiently diploid during recombination; a contrast to the normal diploid state of cells of most higher organisms, which are characteristically only transiently haploid in the gametes. However, it is hard to know what genetic generalizations can be made from a very small sampling of bacterial species.

(3) In most kinds of living things the deoxyribonucleic acid (DNA) is associated with basic proteins. The consistent experience in bacteria, however, is that the appropriate histochemical tests give no result for the latter. This, together with the other peculiar staining properties,

may indicate that the 'nucleoprotein' is of unusual composition (Robinow, 1956b). Furthermore, because polyamines have been found associated with phage DNA (Ames, Dunin & Rosenthal, 1958), and phages could be said, perhaps, to be intimate genetic parasites of bacteria, a rather similar peculiarity might be expected in the nucleus parasitized. The chemical evidence is still inconclusive as to whether or not there are histones in bacteria (Belozersky, 1947; Chargaff & Saidel, 1949; Palmade, Chevallier, Knoblauch & Vendrely, 1958; Zubay & Watson, 1959); the results seem to depend on the technique.

(4) The electron microscope shows a finely stranded nucleoplasm (Kellenberger et al. 1958; Kellenberger, 1960; van Iterson & Robinow, 1961). It matters little that the interpretation of fine structure is still open to debate (Murray, 1960), but it is important that the nucleoplasm is not bounded from the cytoplasm by a nuclear membrane (Pl. 1, fig. 2; Pls. 2, 3, 4). The primitive forms of membrane structures in the cytoplasm of many bacteria do not extend to surround the nuclear area, although they may penetrate to it (Pl. 2) and be contiguous (Giesbrecht, 1960; Van Iterson, 1961). These observations and the special case of *Thiovulum majus* (Fauré-Fremiet & Rouiller, 1957), which has a more elaborate membrane system without nuclear membrane, lend some support to the concept that the nuclear membrane may be the innermost elaboration of the endoplasmic reticulum rather than a special system of its own giving rise to the reticulum (Porter & Machado, 1960). In fact, the latter authors suggest that the reticulum system might be looked upon as 'an instrument of differentiation' rather than a thing to be differentiated.

Cell-wall and other surface structures

The bacterial protoplast is corseted in an unique and fascinating cell-wall that confers strength, form and rigidity on to cell. These cell-walls are extraordinary for the chemical diversity of their structure and the uniqueness of a few of their components (see Salton, 1960, 1961). Proteins, lipids and carbohydrates are all represented. The cellulose of the equally distinct plant cell-wall and the chitin of the fungal cell-wall are not present, although two organisms, the well known *Acetobacter xylinum* and now *Sarcina ventriculi* (Canale-Parola, Borasky & Wolfe, 1961), seem to secrete cellulose into their environment.

There is a mucopeptide complex found in all bacteria so far studied, which seems to confer strength and form to the walls, and acts as if it were a tough fabric in the midst of complex layers (Work, 1957). The peptide part seems to consist of a small number of amino acids: alanine and glutamic acid, either lysine or diaminopimelic acid (occasionally both), and a small number of the amino acids glycine, aspartic acid, serine and threonine. These are attached to a carbohydrate moiety of an *N*-acetyl-hexosamine and of muramic acid (3-*O*-carboxyethyl-D-glucosamine), which probably form the backbone of the structure and have been found in all bacterial walls studied. It is this kind of muco-peptide that is characteristic of bacteria and it is peculiar in the high proportion of D-amino acids. The unique amino sugar component muramic acid, and glucosamine form the basis of mucopolysaccharides, the other part of the mucocomplex. Here indeed resides the substrate of lysozyme and the sensitivity of bacteria to penicillin, and in many Gram-positive organisms the mucocomplex (both mucopeptide and muco-polysaccharide) may constitute almost the entire wall. There is a steadily growing list of peculiarities of bacterial cell-walls of lower taxa, but the broad taxonomic import does not yet seem so clear as in the case of the mucopeptide and mucopolysaccharide components (Cum-mins & Harris, 1956; Salton, 1961).

The cell-wall is a structural unit that undoubtedly contributes to the ruggedness and the survival, as well as the shape, of bacteria but it is not essential to the continuity of cellular function. Provided the environ-ment is suitably adjusted in osmotic pressure, in the presence of penicillin the cell-wall of *Escherichia coli* can be made to lose its strength and rigidity and then revert to the original form on removal of the penicillin (Lederberg, 1956; Lederberg & St Clair, 1958). This does not involve total loss of wall components. However, some cultures will form stable (i.e. non-reverting) L-forms (see Klieneberger-Nobel, 1960), and these seem to have lost most if not all cell-wall components to judge from biochemical and morphological criteria (Sharp, Hijmans & Dienes, 1957; Liebermeister, 1960; Kandler & Kandler, 1960). This problem is still shrouded in mysteries since the true protoplasts and the sphero-plasts (i.e. those retaining some wall structure) formed by lysozyme action seem incapable of reversion to normal form and the true proto-plasts seem to be incapable of multiplication (Salton, 1960; McQuillen, 1960). Stability is not immediately established; it requires some generations and must involve more than a single loss. The stable L-form, which is known to be derived from bacteria, and the pleuropneumonia-like organism (PPLO) of less certain origin seem to be at least morpho-logically equivalent, and the multiplication process is of the same kind (Liebermeister, 1960). There is every reason to retain the PPLOs among the bacteria until we know more of their nature.

Motility

The motility of those bacteria that swim is effected by flagella that are not equivalent to the flagella and cilia of certain plant and animal cells (see Weibull, 1960). These are truly unique structures of great thinness (100–200 Å.) and a variety of arrangements. They consist of a single protein that has been studied in some detail, and seems to belong to the keratin-myosin group. They originate from the cell, since protoplasts retain flagella, but there is still no real evidence on the sites of synthesis or origin and no understanding of their energy mechanism.

Gliding motility, although a character of Beggiatoales and Myxobacterales, is more characteristically a property of the blue-green algae. The mechanism is unknown. In general, gliding bacteria do not form sheaths.

Endospores

These specialized structures (see Robinow, 1961) develop within the cytoplasm of *Bacillus* and *Clostridium* species, and more scattered representatives of other bacterial genera: e.g. *Sarcina, Spirillum, Oscillospira* and *Metabacterium*. Since spores seem to have survival value (resistance to heat, desiccation and radiation), they have often been looked upon as a mechanism for averting disaster. However, sporulation is a complicated business requiring suitable cellular preparation (Murrell, 1961) and must be presumed to involve a complex genetic mechanism to order such an array of structure (Jacob, Schaeffer & Wollman, 1960). There is no suspicion (except in the case of *Metabacterium*) that spores represent a growth mechanism, since the ratio of spores to vegetative cells is rarely greater than 1:1. If the position of *Oscillospira* is unequivocally bacterial, then there is not much doubt that endospores are peculiar to bacteria.

The morphological interest is made the greater by the curious means of loculation of the forespore by a septum formed by the cytoplasmic membrane and mesosomes (Pl. 3, fig. 1). This divided portion of the protoplasm then sinks into the remainder and matures into a spore (Young & Fitz-James, 1959 a; Fitz-James, 1961); the remainder decays. Furthermore, some insect-pathogenic varieties of *Bacillus cereus* (and some of unknown pathogenicity) form parasporal bodies when they sporulate (Hannay, 1956), which consist mostly of a specific, toxic protein.

THE COMPARATIVE ANATOMY OF BACTERIA
AND BLUE-GREEN ALGAE

It is well known that the morphological groups of blue-green algae (Schizophyceae) have their counterpart among bacteria. Some of these bacteria are distinguished by flagellar motility (e.g. *Caryophanon*) rather than the gliding motility characteristic of blue-green algae (e.g. *Oscillatoria*); the distinction is even less clear with the gliding forms *Beggiatoa* and *Thiothrix* (Pringsheim, 1949); and resemblance is carried further by the sharing of gliding motility and somewhat specialized colonial habits (e.g. by the bacterium *Leucothrix* and the algae Rivulariaceae), so that the particular sort of photosynthesis remains the only distinction. The list can be multiplied many times over and includes coccal and helical forms.

The Schizophyceae seem to be no more closely related to other algae and higher plants than are the Schizomycetes. The distinction of chromatoplasm and centroplasm (Ris & Singh, 1961) seems to be a matter of the peripheral distribution of lamelliform chromatophores, which are penetrated by cytoplasmic elements, and in a few bacteria (e.g. *Rhodomicrobium vannielii*) the situation is very similar (Vatter *et al.* 1959; Costerton, 1960). The centroplasm contains all the elements of bacterial protoplasm including ribosomes and a nucleoplasm that is not partitioned off by nuclear membrane (Bradfield, 1956; Hopwood & Glauert, 1960; Costerton, 1960; Ris & Singh, 1961). The red algae are ruled out of consideration by the demonstration (Brody & Vatter, 1959) that they possess nuclear membranes and well developed cytoplasmic organelles, as have all the other algae.

The centroplasm in blue-green algae contains chromatin bodies that are morphologically equivalent to those of bacteria (Cassell & Hutchinson, 1954) and react similarly to stains. They appear to divide directly and to be without visible chromosomes. The nucleoplasms in electron micrographs of sections have all the same appearances as those of bacteria (Ris & Singh, 1961) and react similarly to the composition of the fixative (Drews & Niklowitz, 1956; Fuhs, 1958; Hopwood & Glauert, 1960), although in one case (*Anabaena cylindrica*) there was an unusually enhanced electron opacity (Hopwood & Glauert, 1960). One peculiarity may have significance: the presence of finely structured granules, as much as 0.25–0.5 μ diam., seemingly associated with the chromatin. Perhaps they are 'protein bodies' (Costerton, 1960) because they stain with mercuric-bromphenol blue of Mazia, Brewer & Alfert (1953); however, they do not respond to the alkaline fast green technique of Alfert & Geschwind (1953) and (as in bacteria) nor does the adjacent chromatin. The many 'granules', 'bodies' and 'vacuoles' in both centroplasm and chromatoplasm noted in practically all recent studies of sections need systematic and critical study.

The cytoplasm, i.e. the portion of the centroplasm that is not chromatin, contains none of the membranous structures (mesosomes) that similar sections of bacteria have shown. This must be interpreted cautiously since the origins of the lamellar chromatophores is not known and could involve the plasma membrane (Costerton, 1960), although there seems to be no connexion (Hagedorn, 1960).

The cell walls are complex in section and not unlike those of many bacteria. Of the various layers the inner table takes part in septum formation and seems to represent the structural part of the cell-wall. The superficial resemblance has chemical support because diaminopimelic acid has been detected (Work & Dewey, 1953), and it is said that the bacterial type of wall mucopeptide is also present (Salton, 1960; H. H. Martin, personal communication). The walls of some species, *Oscillatoria princeps* (Ris & Singh, 1961) and *O. formosa* (Costerton, 1960), have the peculiarity of pores that may contain protrusions from the cytoplasm; but the fine structure of the wall has received even less study than in the bacteria. As in the latter, there may be a variety of structures if one looks for it.

So the basis of the objections expressed by Fritsch (1945) and Pringsheim (1949) to the alliance of the bacteria and blue-green algae has been partly removed. The two classes cannot be equated entirely: the Schizophyceae are entirely photosynthetic. But could non-photosynthetic variants be distinguished from bacteria (e.g. *Vitreoscilla* Pringsheim, 1951; see Costerton, Murray & Robinow, 1961)? Bacterial photosynthesis, although undoubtedly basically similar (Stanier, 1961), still does not evolve oxygen, and the associated pigments of the two classes differ. The Schizophyceae are only motile on surfaces by that curious and inexplicable gliding motility whereas bacteria have other means of motion as well as the gliding exhibited by the Beggiatoales and Myxobacterales.

A SUMMARY DEFINITION OF THE CLASS SCHIZOMYCETES
VON NAEGELI 1857

We may now summarize the elements of structure characteristic of bacteria. The outline for this description has purposely retained and extended the elements of the current description in *Bergey's Manual*

(Breed *et al.* 1957, p. 33). The description attempts a synthesis of the nature of bacterial cells without considering them as plants, as demonstrated by their cytological properties.

Bacteria are: ubiquitous small cells, 10–0·1 μ diam., without obvious internal differentiation in life. They are frequently motile: either swimming *by means of flagella* of bacterial type or gliding on surfaces.

Cell multiplication is by fission, usually binary but occasionally unequal and even by budding. Cells may remain attached after division, thus causing special or random arrangements of the cells. Some show a *true branching*, mycelial habit with filamentous cells of bacterial dimensions (*ca.* 1 μ). There may be differentiation of cells in groups or trichomes to form holdfast cells, and motile or non-motile disseminative cells. *Endospores* are formed by some species and sporocysts by others. *Heterocysts* (see p. 88) are not formed.

They are not eunucleate; they possess one or more chromatin bodies (nucleoids) per cell, showing stages of direct division in a growing cell. There is no spindle apparatus. The nucleoplasm does not show cyclical changes in texture or show chromosome formation; it is not separated from the cytoplasm by a membrane, and includes no obvious nucleolus or *protein bodies*. They are usually haploid.

The cytoplasm is bounded by a plasma membrane. *In some species this forms intrusive tubules or lamellae or more complex structures* (mesosomes). Endoplasmic reticulum is not formed. The membrane takes part in cell division by septum formation or constriction.

A complex cell-wall encloses the protoplast. Among the constituents is a mucopeptide, containing muramic acid, glucosamine and, sometimes, diaminopimelic acid. Some bacteria-like organisms (Mycoplasmatales) may have bacterial features but lack part or all of the cell wall mucocomplex.

Various inclusions may be present, including polymetaphosphate, polyhydroxybutyrate, granulose, sulphur and other materials both organic and inorganic. Some species are pigmented.

Photosynthetic species have either *bacterio-chlorophyll* with *aliphatic carotenoids* or one of two *chlorobium chlorophylls* with *monocyclic carotenoids*, associated in simple cytoplasmic chromatophores (see Stanier's survey of photosynthesis patterns (1961) for greater detail). *Phycocyanin is not present.*

The bacteria are saprobic free-living or parasitic cells; they may be pathogenic in plants or animals.

The italicized portions of the description are to indicate some characters that may distinguish the blue-green algae from the bacteria.

They are indeed so closely related that one has the impression of as great differences *within* the Schizomycetes as between them and the Schizophyceae. However, they can be maintained as separate taxa of equal rank as long as a limbo between the two is recognized (see Pringsheim, 1949; Stanier, 1954; *Bergey's Manual*, 1957, p. 854). The position of all members of this anomalous group without photosynthetic apparatus cannot yet be decided on morphological grounds (see Costerton *et al.* 1961) because we do not know what characters to look for other than gliding and photosyntheisis.

SOME REMARKS ON BROAD CLASSIFICATION

There thus seems to be support for the long contended theory that bacteria are closely related to the blue-green algae (Cohn, 1875), a theory which seems to be tacitly accepted in many modern classifications; there is a surprisingly quiet acceptance of the possibility that three or more kingdoms are needed to describe the nature and the relations of living things (see Whittaker, 1959; Copeland, 1938; Stanier & van Niel, 1941; Breed *et al.* 1957).

Two kingdoms have seemed to be a stable part of biology for a long time, and there is strength in this sort of simplicity as long as it expresses the conclusions drawn from observation. But there have been a number of alternative proposals and all stem from the many observations of organisms, mostly of minute size, that lack the distinctive and largely morphological characteristics of undoubted plants and animals.

Whittaker (1959) points out, in a most interesting review, that the alternatives have the useful function of forcing clarification of the concepts of broad relations in the living world, and this is valuable even if they remain as minority view-points. They have been the concern of microbiologists for the most part, since the major discontinuity is afforded by what we may call the protists, after Haeckel.

Of most immediate importance to us in a complex history is that many authors have proposed that the bacteria and the blue-green algae should be included in a new kingdom and separated from the 'higher' forms (Copeland, 1938, 1956; Stanier & van Niel, 1941). This amounts to distinguishing two levels of organization—cells with and without nuclear membranes (Whittaker, 1959). To my mind this distinction is amply justified.

If we accept the premises: (1) that morphological characters have a primary import in taxonomy (see p. 135; and van Niel, 1955) and that this includes cellular structure, in particular; and (2) that there is a consistent and fundamental difference in the organization of the cells of Schizomycetes and Schizophyceae compared to those of plants and animals; then, a separation of high rank is justified. Stanier & van Niel (1941) adopted Copeland's kingdom Monera (Copeland, 1938), 'Organisms without nuclei, the cells solitary or physiologically independent', to include the bacteria and blue-green algae. They added two more negative characters: absence of plastids and absence of sexual reproduction. In the following fifteen years chromatin bodies were accepted as nuclear equivalents; photosynthetic bacteria were found to have chromatophores, and genetic recombination was discovered. van Niel (1955) felt that these developments threatened 'the very basis of the characterization of the kingdom' and that new and adequate criteria were required. New criteria are available, as we have outlined, to distinguish chromatin bodies from true nuclei and chromatophores from plastids. Absence of sexual reproduction does not yet constitute a valid character, and is not really needed. We can accept a new kingdom of bacteria and blue-green algae but it may have to be called Mychota (Enderlein, 1925) rather than Monera as Copeland (1947, 1956) has pointed out.

To my mind the subdivision of a new kingdom Protista into subkingdoms Monera and Eunucleata (as proposed by Whittaker, 1959, for a four-kingdom system) is attractive but still has the disadvantage of putting together fundamentally dissimilar organisms and thus blurring their distinctions. I am more sympathetic to a six-kingdom system such as that suggested by Jahn & Jahn (1949)—Archetista (or viruses), Mychota (monera), Protista (to include protozoa and nucleate algae), fungi, metaphyta and metazoa. At least this recognized what we recognize ourselves as specialist microbiologists and in our divisions of biological science. However, experience tells us that such sweeping changes are unlikely to be accomplished in a hurry. I am quite willing to accept a kingdom Mychota (or whatever proves to be nomenclaturally acceptable) so that we may recognize the bacteria and blue-green algae for what they are. One can but echo Prévot (1940): 'Pourquoi ne pas avoir le courage de dire: le Règne bactérien?'

PERSPECTIVES FOR LOWER TAXONS

General morphology is the main basis for separation of orders and, to a variable extent, families and lower taxa, in present-day classifications of the bacteria. The vicissitudes of the application of the classical criteria of size, form and arrangement have been chronicled in detail in various compendia (e.g. Breed, Murray & Hitchens, 1948) and there are many criticisms of the ways in which these and physiological characters have been used (van Niel, 1946; Winogradsky, 1952; Skerman, 1949). But the fact is that the sorts of morphological *characters* being used today are not very different from those of sixty years ago as a reading of, for instance, A. Fischer's book on bacterial structure (Fischer, 1900) will show. One cannot expect to be able to ring many new changes under the circumstances.

Skerman (1949) has pointed out that the descriptions available to the taxonomist (and also the diagnostician) are woefully inadequate and it is hard to see how they could be modified. One can only agree. Perhaps a programme of re-description of at least type species might be attempted by some organized effort and using some agreed approaches.

There is little doubt that the kind of general cytological characters already discussed can be applied to broad taxonomic purposes. As these characters are defined more exactly new types of difference must appear. The way in which this type of approach will apply to lower taxa is not certain. There are many problems, not the least being: (1) the accumulation of enough special information, i.e. the encouragement of adequately detailed and reliable description; (2) the relative weight (or reliability) of characters.

Applications of microscopy to description

Much more could be expected if the methods and principles, hard won by the cytologists, could be carried over into the more practical everyday affairs of determinative bacteriology. Skerman (1959) has made an important innovation by including a clear statement of methods that work as far as characters for his key are concerned. Some stimulating but not restrictive approach to morphological descriptions is needed.

The classical dried film, heated, stained and observed in oil is not suitable to making decisions about cell structure (Robinow, 1945; Bisset, 1950; Robinow & Murray, 1953; Robinow, 1956a) any more than is an ordinary 'hanging-drop' for phase microscopy of the living cell (Mason & Powelson, 1956). Methods that take full advantage of the resolution and other possibilities of the light microscope are *not* more difficult to perform. And some classical methods now almost forgotten should be revived, such as the nigrosin film technique for quick decisions about form and arrangement, or even looking at cell fractions. Such simple applications would surely soon show returns in descriptions, modifications of old descriptions, and important new possibilities. For example, the rediscovery of parasporal bodies (Hannay,

1956) and subsequent extensive investigations (Young & Fitz-James, 1959 a, b; Hannay, 1961) stemmed from such morphological observations. It is clear that there will be some wasted effort; but one cannot measure the stimulating return from, for instance, Pijper's contentions on flagella (Pijper, 1946) in the now considerable information on flagella (Stocker, 1956; Weibull, 1960).

The establishment and consolidation of sound morphological criteria, obtained with the electron microscope, as a basis for classification cannot be considered to be more than started. Although the *general* character of bacterial cytoplasm is quite distinct from that of other living things, as we have already seen, the degree of difference in specific instances is much less easy to establish. For instance some organisms frequently show complex cytoplasmic intrusions or mesosomes, others do not seem to show them. *Escherichia coli* has been among the latter and many of us believed that this organism did not have them at all; yet, I have twice seen micrographs in the past year (E. Vanderwinkle and A. Glauert, personal communications) that show an undoubted mesosome; so they exist, but rarely, in the species. This is the sort of information that will be slow to accumulate, even for type species. At any rate, a start has been made and electron microscopes (and the suitable skills for biological studies) are becoming so widely available that a considerable addition to our descriptions must be expected.

In the studies of some specific groups there will be a considerable delay in the production of taxonomically useful results. An outstanding current example is that of the stable L-forms and the PPLOs. Their nature has not been fully revealed by the most devoted and painstaking morphological approaches (see Kleineberger-Nobel, 1960) and many mysteries remain. The physical state and behaviour of the reproductive units are still not understood (Liebermeister, 1960). It was to be hoped that electron micrographs of sections would provide us with much needed information. But the delicate forms of the reproductive elements have proved hard to capture and even the development of new fixatives has been required (Hofschneider, 1960). The studies of Van Iterson & Ruys (1960) further revealed an extremely small organism (0.3–$0.4\,\mu$ diam.) that has the structural components of a bacterial cell (Van Iterson & Robinow, 1961), is capable of independent growth and was associated with several PPLO cultures that they worked with (Pl. 3, fig. 2). Undoubtedly, we will have to wait longer for usable taxonomic data on this group than in the case of many of the Eubacteriales.

The weight of characters

The primacy of morphological criteria has been accepted almost as a tenet of taxonomic faith. It has been a valuable principle in the establishment of phylogenetic arrangements in plants and animals. In the bacteria it has been more difficult to justify without question although many authors have concluded that 'morphology remains the first and most reliable guide' (Kluyver & van Niel, 1936) despite all temptations offered by physiological criteria. The fact is that any major morphological character must be considered as being of extreme complexity, involving many processes or interacting systems. Provided this structure is basically stable (a prime argument for comparative cytology) this character should be recognizable even if there are superficial variations.

It is absurd to consider that all characters have equal importance in making taxonomic distinctions, yet this seems to be a very general attitude that has led us into troubles enough. The non-selectivity (or even lack of criticism) may originate with a paucity of characters to begin with, but is still not excusable.

An outstanding general example of weighting may be provided by the Rickettsiales, long separated from the bacteria because they are small and obligate intracellular parasites. It becomes more probable that the rickettsia will turn out to be very specialized bacteria, to judge from the morphological and structural characters found by Schaechter *et al.* (1957), whereas the viruses proper have less clear affinities. So the alliance between the rickettsia and viruses may resemble the ancient one of whales and fishes. There is no doubt that size alone is deceiving and the requirements leading to obligate cellular parasitism are likely to vary considerably. Such organisms, of bacterial appearance, are rather widely distributed and often only poorly studied; difficulties of cultivation place the burden of identification on morphology (e.g. the symbiotic bacteria in cockroach oocytes studied by Bush & Chapman, 1961). It looks as if their taxonomy will rest on morphological characters of the sorts we have discussed.

Cell-walls illustrate the full range of structural taxonomic problems and have the most detail for study. As has already been stated, the walls provide an outstanding characteristic of a taxon of high rank. Further biochemical dissection of their complexity (Salton, 1952, 1961) showed that the Gram reaction was actually a neat way of separating bacteria into two fundamental groups: Gram-positive cells having walls of limited amino acid content, no aromatic or S-containing amino acids, low lipid content, and consisting in large part of the complex of mucopeptides and mucopolysaccharides; and Gram-negative cells containing a wide range of amino acids (including aromatic and S-containing ones), relatively large amounts of lipid and relatively low quantities of the mucocomplex (10–20% of the weight of the wall). So that this old, morphologically derived character of the Gram reaction has substantial expression in the complexity of wall. In fact, it is probable that the reason for the Gram 'reaction' lies in the permeability of the wall for the extraction of the iodine-crystal violet complex (Salton, 1960), since damage to the integrity of the wall by lysozyme converts Gram-positive cells to Gram-negative ones. At any rate, the Gram reaction provides a character of considerable weight. The structure of the walls in section is generally quite distinct (Pls. 1–4): Gram-positive organisms have a thick homogeneous layer close to the plasma membrane, whereas Gram-negative organisms have a thin dense-light-dense complex in that position; what lies outside this is quite variable in both cases.

Still finer dissection (Cummins & Harris, 1956; Salton, 1961; Baddiley et al. 1956) showed that each genus tends to have a characteristic pattern of cell-wall components, whether one measures amino acids, monosaccharide constituents, or the techoic acids (poly-glycerol and ribitol phosphates). Some are genus specific patterns, others are more general, and some provide separations between species. It seems premature to do more than refer to this as an approach of promise for taxonomy, e.g. in *Staphylococcus* (*Micrococcus*) (Salton & Pavlik, 1960), *Lactobacillus* (Ikawa & Snell, 1960) and *Corynebacterium* (Cummins & Harris, 1956).

How this is reflected in cell-wall fine structure is not certain. A macromolecular monolayer has been found by Houwink (1953) in shadowed preparations of isolated walls of *Spirillum*, forming a hexagonal pattern of globules 120–140 Å. diam. This sort of thing may not be uncommon, for a similar structure has been found in *Spirillum serpens*, *Rhodospirillum rubrum* (Salton & Williams, 1954) and *Halobacterium halobium* (Houwink, 1956), but an unidentified Gram-positive bacterium showed a rectangular array of similar particles (Labaw & Mosley, 1954). Perhaps these macromolecules resemble the protein-mucopeptide R-layer of the wall of *Escherichia coli* (Weidel, Frank & Martin, 1960). Certainly, cataloguing and identifying these parts of walls will not be a simple matter. In view of the seeming homogeneity of the walls of many Gram-positive bacteria it seems possible that the structures seen may be protein macromolecules overlaid on the structural layers containing mucopeptide, as seems to be the case in the study on *E. coli* quoted above.

We have found a much more complex pattern in a tetrad-forming coccus using the phosphotungstate 'negative stain' technique (Brenner & Horne, 1959) on isolated cell-wall fragments. There is a double layer of hexagonally arrayed 'pegs' on a membrane with a spacing of about 150 Å. (Pl. 4, fig. 2). There has not been enough of a morphological survey to show the distribution of such structures in the several genera showing tetrad-formation. Our experience is that this structure is rare among cocci and is only shared (R. W. Horne & M. Thornley, private communication) with a seemingly identical organism discovered by Anderson *et al.* (1956) that has been called *Micrococcus radiodurans*. This sort of approach may prove to have value in generic definition and be sufficiently simple in application.

The last and finest order of structure will be measured by, for example, the order of amino acids in the peptide and the order of the component amino sugars and linkages in the 'backbone' structure of the mucopeptide. This is now getting down to almost the same order of fineness as the immunological analyses (Westphal, 1959) and probably will be open to the same sort of taxonomic traps.

These criteria, whether based on physical or chemical methods of divination, can be expressed in two ways. The morphological way would concern the overall construction of the wall (in this instance with information in both section and plan, in addition to the 'cytochemical' data e.g. Gram reaction). This cruder expression (not cluttered, perhaps, with too much detail) could be supplemented by the chemical data on materials, their proportions and the presence or absence of some selected components. It is probable that, in the end, the biochemistry will provide structural information in the form of general mechanisms of synthesis such as those now being worked out (Strominger & Threnn, 1959). This type of approach may avoid the confusion likely when the presence or absence of individual components is given too much significance; more often than not, the reason for their success in taxonomy is that they are part of a complex, stable component. The 'either-or' situations (such as the presence of ribitol or glycerophosphate polymers and of diaminopimelic acid or lysine) cannot be given so much significance.

What we must guard against is the ready acceptance of mutable and unstable characters for taxonomic separations at the lower levels. It would be better to multiply the number of groups so that differences become as evident as similarities, and so stimulate the critical evaluation that is so badly needed.

There are, in this set of examples provided by cell-walls, a series of levels of significance for taxonomic purposes. These are, in descending order: (1) a 'basal' structure of bacterial cell-walls, applicable to the highest ranks, Kingdom and Class; (2) the three major structural groups (Order or higher) expressed almost exactly by the presence of rigid cell-walls and the Gram reaction; (3) finer groupings according to components and linkages that are not yet fully correlated (possibly Order down to Species). It would seem to me that there is a sound basis for dividing the Schizomycetes into: (1) those with cell-walls of Gram-positive type; (2) those with cell-walls of Gram-negative type; (3) those 'wall-less' organisms presently considered with Mycoplasmatales.

The time will come, and examples both helpful and cautionary can be given, when there is sufficiently organized morphological and morphological-chemical information to be of real help in the classification of lower taxa. The possibilities unveiled in the past few years give promise of this. The main thing is to assess the new features found for their stability as taxonomic characters and assign them some weight or value in the taxa they define. What we lack the most are characters and adequate descriptions.

ACKNOWLEDGEMENTS

The author is indebted to the Royal Society of Canada and the National Research Council of Canada for their support of the research of his laboratory; to Professor E. Kellenberger and the Laboratoire de Biophysique, Université de Genève, for help and hospitality during the writing of this paper, and to Dr E. Vanderwinkel, Dr Antoinette Ryter and Dr Woutera van Iterson for illustrative material.

REFERENCES

ALFERT, M. & GESCHWIND, I. I. (1953). A selective staining method for the basic proteins of cell nuclei. *Proc. nat. Acad. Sci., Wash.* **39**, 991.

AMES, B. N., DUNIN, D. T. & ROSENTHAL, S. M. (1958). Presence of polyamines in certain bacterial viruses. *Science,* **127**, 814.

ANDERSON, A. W., NORDAN, H. C., CAIN, R. F., PARRISH, G. & DUGGAN, D. (1956). Studies on a radio-resistant *Micrococcus*. I. Isolation, morphology, cultural characteristics, and resistance to gamma radiation. *Food Tech., Champaign,* **10**, 575.

BADDILEY, J., BUCHANAN, J. G., CARSS, B., MATHIAS, A. P. & SANDERSON, A. R. (1956). The isolation of cytidine diphosphate glycerol, cytidine diphosphate ribitol and mannitol-1-phosphate from *Lactobacillus arabinosus*. *Biochem. J.* **64**, 599.

BELOZERSKY, A. N. (1947). On the nucleoproteins and polynucleotides of certain bacteria. *Cold Spr. Harb. Symp. quant. Biol.* **12**, 1.

BISSET, K. A. (1950). *The Cytology and Life-History of Bacteria*. Edinburgh: E. and S. Livingstone.

BRADFIELD, J. R. G. (1956). Organization of bacterial cytoplasm. *Symp. Soc. gen. Microbiol.* **6**, 296.

BREED, R. S., MURRAY, E. G. D. & HITCHENS, A. P. (1948). *Bergey's Manual of Determinative Bacteriology*, 6th edition. Baltimore: Williams and Wilkins.

BREED, R. S., MURRAY, E. G. D. & SMITH, N. R. (1957). *Bergey's Manual of Determinative Bacteriology*, 7th edition. London: Baillière, Tindall and Cox.

BRENNER, S. & HORNE, R. W. (1959). A negative staining method for high resolution electron microscopy of viruses. *Biochim. biophys Acta*, **34**, 103.

BRODY, M. & VATTER, A. E. (1959). Observations on cellular structures of *Porphyridium cruentum*. *J. biophys. biochem. Cytol.* **5**, 289.

BUSH, G. L. & CHAPMAN, G. B. (1961). Electron microscopy of symbiotic bacteria in developing oocytes of the American cockroach, *Periplaneta americana*. *J. Bact.* **81**, 267.

CANALE-PAROLA, E., BORASKY, R. & WOLFE, R. S. (1961). Studies on *Sarcina ventriculi*. III. Localization of cellulose. *J. Bact.* **81**, 311.

CASSELL, W. A. & HUTCHINSON, W. G. (1954). Nuclear studies on the smaller Myxophyceae. *Exp. Cell Res.* **6**, 134.

CHAPMAN, G. B. & HILLIER, J. (1953). Electron microscopy of ultra-thin sections of bacteria. I. Cellular division in *Bacillus cereus*. *J. Bact.* **66**, 362.

CHARGAFF, E. & SAIDEL, H. F. (1949). On the nucleoproteins of avian tubercle bacilli. *J. biol. Chem.* **177**, 417.

COHN, F. (1875). Untersuchungen über Bacterien. II. *Beitr. Biol. Pfl.* **1**, Heft 3, 141.

COPELAND, H. F. (1938). The kingdoms of organisms. *Quart. Rev. Biol.* **13**, 383.

COPELAND, H. F. (1947). Progress report on basic classification. *Amer. Nat.* **81**, 340.

COPELAND, H. F. (1956). *The Classification of Lower Organisms*. Palo Alto, California: Pacific Books.

COSTERTON, J. W. F. (1960). Cytological studies of the Schizophyceae and related organisms. *Thesis, University of Western Ontario, London, Canada*.

COSTERTON, J. W. F., MURRAY, R. G. E. & ROBINOW, C. F. (1961). Observations on the motility and the structure of *Vitreoscilla*. *Canad. J. Microbiol.* **7**, 329.

CUMMINS, C. S. & HARRIS, H. (1956). The chemical composition of the cell wall in some Gram-positive bacteria and its possible value as a taxonomic character. *J. gen. Microbiol.* **14**, 583.

DOUDOROFF, M. & STANIER, R. Y. (1959). Role of poly-β-hydroxybutyric acid in the assimilation of organic carbon by bacteria. *Nature, Lond.* **183**, 1440.

DREWS, G. (1960). Untersuchungen zur Substruktur der 'Chromatophoren' von *Rhodospirillum rubrum* und *Rhodospirillum molischianum*. *Arch. Mikrobiol.* **36**, 99.

DREWS, G. & NIKLOWITZ, W. (1956). Beiträge zur Cytologie der Blaualgen. II. Zentroplasma und Granuläre Einschlüsse von *Phormidium uncinatum*. *Arch. Mikrobiol.* **24**, 147.

ENDERLEIN, G. (1925). *Bakterien-Cyclogenie*. Berlin and Leipzig: De Gruyter.

EZEKIEL, D. H. (1961). Increase in ribonucleic acid in the bacterial chromatin body during chloramphenicol treatment. *J. Bact.* **81**, 319.

FAURÉ-FREMIET, E. & ROUILLER, C. (1958). Étude au microscope électronique d'une bactérie sulfureuse, *Thiovulum majus* Hinze. *Exp. Cell Res.* **14**, 29.

FISCHER, A. (1900). *The Structure and Function of Bacteria*. Oxford: Clarendon Press.

FITZ-JAMES, P. C. (1961). Participation of the cytoplasmic membrane in the growth and spore formation of bacilli. *J. biophys. biochem. Cytol.* **8**, 507.

FITZ-JAMES, P. C. & YOUNG, I. E. (1959). Comparison of species and varieties of the genus *Bacillus*. Structure and nucleic acid content of spores. *J. Bact.* **78**, 743.

FRITSCH, F. E. (1945). *The Structure and Reproduction of the Algae*, **2**. Cambridge University Press.

Fuhs, G. W. (1958). Untersuchungen an Ultradünnschnitten von *Oscillatoria amoena* (Kütz) Gomont. *Protoplasma*, **49**, 523.

Giesbrecht, P. (1960). Über 'Organisierte' Mitochondrien und andere Feinstrukturen von Bacillus megaterium. *Zbl. Bakt.* 1 *Abt. Orig.* **179**, 538.

Glauert, A. M., Brieger, E. M. & Allen, J. M. (1961). The fine structure of vegetative cells of *Bacillus subtilis. Exp. Cell Res.* **22**, 73.

Glauert, A. M. & Glauert, R. H. (1958). Araldite as an embedding medium for electron microscopy. *J. biophys. biochem. Cytol.* **4**, 191.

Glauert, A. M. & Hopwood, D. A. (1959). A membranous component of the cytoplasm in *Streptomyces coelicolor. J. biophys. biochem. Cytol.* **6**, 515.

Hagedorn, H. (1960). Elektronenmikroskopische Untersuchungen an Blaualgen. *Naturwissenschaften*, **47**, 430.

Hannay, C. L. (1956). Inclusions in bacteria. *Symp. Soc. gen. Microbiol.* **6**, 318.

Hannay, C. L. (1961). Fowler's bacillus and its parasporal body. *J. biophys. biochem. Cytol.* **9**, 285.

Hayes, W. (1960). The bacterial chromosome. *Symp. Soc. gen. Microbiol.* **10**, 12.

Hickman, D. D. & Frenkel, A. W. (1960). The structure of *Rhodospirillum rubrum. J. biophys. biochem. Cytol.* **6**, 277.

Hodge, A. J., McLean, J. D. & Mercer, F. V. (1955). Ultrastructure of the lamellae and grana in the chloroplasts of *Zea mays. J. biophys. biochem. Cytol.* **1**, 605.

Hofschneider, P. H. (1960). Zur Wandstruktur von *E. coli* B Sphaeroplasten. *Proc. Reg. Conf. Electron Microscopy*, Delft.

Hopwood, D. A. & Glauert, A. M. (1960). The fine structure of the nuclear material of a blue-green alga, *Anabaena cylindrica* Lemm. *J. biophys. biochem. Cytol.* **8**, 813.

Houwink, A. L. (1953). A macromolecular monolayer in the cell wall of *Spirillum* spec. *Biochim. biophys. Acta*, **10**, 360.

Houwink, A. L. (1956). Flagella, gas vacuoles and cell wall structure in *Halobacterium halobium*; an electron microscope study. *J. gen. Microbiol.* **15**, 146.

Huxley, H. E. & Zubay, G. (1960). Electron microscope observations on the structure of microsomal particles from *Escherichia coli. J. molec. Biol.* **2**, 10.

Ikawa, M. & Snell, E. E. (1960). Cell-wall composition of lactic acid bacteria. *J. biol. Chem.* **235**, 1376.

Jacob, F., Schaeffer, P. & Wollman, E. L. (1960). Episomic elements in bacteria. *Symp. Soc. gen. Microbiol.* **10**, 67.

Jahn, T. L. & Jahn, F. F. (1949). *How to know the Protozoa*. Dubuque, Iowa: W. C. Brown.

Kandler, O. & Kandler, G. (1960). Die L-phase der Bakterien. *Ergebn. Mikrobiol. (Ergebn. Hyg. Bakt.)* **33**, 97.

Kellenberger, E. (1960). The physical state of the bacterial nucleus. *Symp. Soc. gen. Microbiol.* **10**, 39.

Kellenberger, E. & Ryter, A. (1958). Cell wall and cytoplasmic membrane of *Escherichia coli. J. biophys. biochem. Cytol.* **4**, 323.

Kellenberger, E., Ryter, A. & Séchaud, J. (1958). Electron microscope study of DNA-containing plasms. II. Vegetative and mature phage DNA as compared with normal bacterial nucleoids in different physiological states. *J. biophys. biochem. Cytol.* **4**, 671.

Klieneberger-Nobel, E. (1960). L-Form of bacteria. In *The Bacteria*, **1**, 361. New York: Academic Press.

Kluyver, A. J. & van Niel, C. B. (1936). Prospects for a natural system of classification of bacteria. *Zbl. Bakt.* (2 *Abt.*), **94**, 369.

LABAW, W. & MOSLEY, V. M. (1954). Periodic structure in the flagella and cell walls of a bacterium. *Biochim. biophys. Acta,* **15,** 325.

LEDERBERG, J. (1956). Bacterial protoplasts induced by penicillin. *Proc. nat. Acad. Sci., Wash.* **42,** 574.

LEDERBERG, J. & ST CLAIR, J. (1958). Protoplasts and L-type growth of *Escherichia coli. J. Bact.* **75,** 143.

LIEB, M., WEIGLE, J. J. & KELLENBERGER, E. (1955). A study of hybrids between two strains of *Escherichia coli. J. Bact.* **69,** 468.

LIEBERMEISTER, K. (1960). Morphology of the PPLO and L-forms of *Proteus. Ann. N.Y. Acad. Sci.* **79,** 326.

MAALØE, O. & BIRCH-ANDERSON, A. (1956). On the organization of the 'nuclear material' in *Salmonella typhimurium. Symp. Soc. gen. Microbiol.* **6,** 261.

MASON, D. J. & POWELSON, D. M. (1956). Nuclear division as observed in live bacteria by a new technique. *J. Bact.* **71,** 474.

MAZIA, D., BREWER, P. A. & ALFERT, M. (1953). The cytochemical staining and measurement of protein with mercuric bromphenol blue. *Biol. Bull., Woods Hole,* **104,** 57.

McQUILLEN, K. (1960). Bacterial protoplasts. In *The Bacteria,* 1, 249. New York: Academic Press.

MUNSON, R. J. & MacLEAN, F. I. (1961). The nature of radiation sensitivity of the long forms of *Escherichia coli. J. gen. Microbiol.* **25,** 29.

MURRAY, R. G. E. (1957). On the fine structure of microbes. *Canad. J. Biochem. Physiol.* **35,** 565.

MURRAY, R. G. E. (1960). Internal structure of bacteria. In *The Bacteria,* 1. New York: Academic Press.

MURRELL, W. G. (1961). Spore formation and germination as a microbial reaction to environment. *Symp. Soc. gen. Microbiol.* **11,** 100.

NIEL, C. B. VAN (1946). The classification and natural relationships of bacteria. *Cold Spr. Harb. Symp. quant. Biol.* **11,** 285.

NIEL, C. B. VAN (1955). Classification and taxonomy of the bacteria and bluegreen algae. In *A Century of Progress in the Natural Sciences* 1853–1953, p. 89. San Francisco: California Academy of Sciences.

PALMADE, C., CHEVALLIER, M. R., KNOBLAUCH, A. & VENDRELY, R. (1958). Isolement d'une desoxyribonucleohistone à partir d'*Escherichia coli. C.R. Acad. Sci., Paris,* **246,** 2534.

PIJPER, A. (1946). Shape and motility of bacteria. *J. Path. Bact.* **58,** 325.

PORTER, K. R. & MACHADO, R. D. (1960). Studies on the endoplasmic reticulum IV. Its form and distribution during mitosis in cells of onion root tip. *J. biophys. biochem. Cytol.* **7,** 167.

PRÉVOT, A. R. (1940). *Manuel de classification et de détermination des bactéries anaérobies.* Paris: Masson.

PRINGSHEIM, E. G. (1949). The relationship between bacteria and Myxophyceae. *Bact. Rev.* **13,** 47.

PRINGSHEIM, E. G. (1951). The Vitreoscillaceae: a family of colourless, gliding, filamentous organisms. *J. gen. Microbiol.* **5,** 124.

RIS, H. & SINGH, R. N. (1961). Electron microscope studies on blue-green algae. *J. biophys. biochem. Cytol.* **9,** 63.

ROBINOW, C. F. (1945). Addendum to *The Bacterial Cell.* R. J. Dubos. Cambridge, Mass: Harvard University Press.

ROBINOW, C. F. (1956a). The chromatin bodies of bacteria. *Symp. Soc. gen. Microbiol.* **6,** 181.

ROBINOW, C. F. (1956b). The chromatin bodies of bacteria. *Bact. Rev.* **20,** 207.

ROBINOW, C. F. (1961). Outline of the visible organization of bacteria. In *The Cell*, 4, 45. New York: Academic Press.

ROBINOW, C. F. & MURRAY, R. G. E. (1953). The differentiation of cell wall, cytoplasmic membrane and cytoplasm of Gram-positive bacteria by selective staining. *Exp. Cell Res.* 4, 390.

RYTER, A. & KELLENBERGER, E. (1958*a*). Etude au microscope électronique de plasmas contenant de l'acide désoxyribonucléique. I. Les nucléoïdes des bactéries en croissance active. *Z. Naturf.* 13*b*, 597.

RYTER, A. & KELLENBERGER, E. (1958*b*). L'inclusion au polyester pour l'ultramicrotomie. *J. Ultrastructure Research*, 2, 200.

SALTON, M. R. J. (1952). The nature of the cell walls of some Gram-positive and Gram-negative bacteria. *Biochim. biophys. Acta*, 9, 334.

SALTON, M. R. J. (1960). Surface layers of the bacterial cell. In *The Bacteria*, 1, 97. New York: Academic Press.

SALTON, M. R. J. (1961). *Microbial Cell Walls*. New York: John Wiley and Sons.

SALTON, M. R. J. & PAVLIK, J. G. (1960). Studies of the bacterial cell wall. VI. Wall composition and sensitivity to lysozyme. *Biochim. biophys. Acta*, 39, 398.

SALTON, M. J. R. & WILLIAMS, R. C. (1954). Electron microscopy of the cell walls of *Bacillus megaterium* and *Rhodospirillum rubrum*. *Biochim. biophys. Acta*, 14, 455.

SCHACHMAN, H. K., PARDEE, A. B. & STANIER, R. Y. (1952). Studies on the macromolecular organization of microbial cells. *Arch. Biochem.* 38, 245.

SCHAECHTER, M., TONSIMIS, A. J., COHN, Z. A., ROSEN, H., CAMPBELL, J. & HAHN, F. E. (1957). Morphological, chemical and serological studies of the cell walls of *Rickettsia mooseri*. *J. Bact.* 74, 822.

SHARP, J. T., HIJMANS, W. & DIENES, L. (1957). Examination of the L-forms of group A streptococci for the group specific polysaccharide and M protein. *J. exp. Med.* 105, 153.

SHINOHARA, C., FUKUSHI, K., SUZUKI, J. & SATO, K. (1958). Mitochondrial structure of *Mycobacterium tuberculosis* relating to its function. *J. electron Micr.* 6, 47.

SKERMAN V. B. D. (1949). A mechanical key for the generic identification of bacteria. *Bact. Rev.* 13, 175.

SKERMAN, V. B. D. (1957). In Breed, Murray & Smith (1957), p. 987.

SKERMAN, V. B. D. (1959). *A Guide to the Identification of the Genera of Bacteria*. Baltimore, Md.: Williams and Wilkins.

SPIEGELMAN, S. (1958). Protein and nucleic acid synthesis in subcellular fractions of bacterial cells. In *Recent Progress in Microbiology*, p. 81. Stockholm: Almquist and Wiksell.

STANIER, R. Y. (1954). Singular features of bacteria as dynamic systems. In *Cellular Metabolism and Infections*, p. 3. New York: Academic Press.

STANIER, R. Y. (1961). Photosynthetic mechanisms in bacteria and plants: development of a unitary concept. *Bact. Rev.* 25, 1.

STANIER, R. Y. & VAN NIEL, C. B. (1941). The main outlines of bacterial classification. *J. Bact.* 42, 437.

STOCKER, B. A. D. (1956). Bacterial flagella: morphology, constitution and inheritance. *Symp. Soc. gen. Microbiol.* 6, 19.

STROMINGER, J. L. & THRENN, R. H. (1959). The optical configuration of alanine residues in a uridine nucleotide in the cell wall of *Staphylococcus aureus*. *Biochem. biophys. Acta*, 33, 280.

VAN ITERSON, W. (1961). Some features of a remarkable organelle in *Bacillus subtilis*. *J. biophys. biochem. Cytol.* 9, 183.

VAN ITERSON, W. & ROBINOW, C. F. (1961). Observations with the electron microscope on the fine structure of the nuclei of two spherical bacteria. *J. biophys. biochem. Cytol.* 9, 171.

VAN ITERSON, W. & RUYS, A. C. (1960). The fine structure of the Mycoplasmataceae. I. *Mycoplasma hominis*, *M. fermentans* and *M. salivarium*. *J. Ultrastructure Res.* **3**, 282.

VATTER, A. E., DOUGLAS, H. C. & WOLFE, R. S. (1959). Structure of *Rhodomicrobium vannielii*. *J. Bact.* **77**, 812.

VATTER, A. E. & WOLFE, R. S. (1958). The structure of photosynthetic bacteria. *J. Bact.* **75**, 480.

WEIBULL, C. (1960). Movement. In *The Bacteria*, **1**, 153. New York: Academic Press.

WEIDEL, W., FRANK, H. & MARTIN, H. H. (1960). The rigid layer of the cell wall of *Escherichia coli* strain B. *J. gen. Microbiol.* **22**, 158.

WESTPHAL, O. (1959). Die Struktur der Antigene und der Wesen der immunologischen Spezifität. *Naturwiss.* **46**, 50.

WHALEY, W. G., MOLLENHAUER, H. H. & LEECH, J. H. (1960). The ultrastructure of the meristematic cell. *Amer. J. Bot.* **47**, 401.

WHITFIELD, J. F. & MURRAY, R. G. E. (1956). The effects of the ionic environment on the chromatin structures of bacteria. *Canad. J. Microbiol.* **2**, 245.

WHITTAKER, R. H. (1959). On the broad classification of organisms. *Quart. Rev. Biol.* **34**, 210.

WILKINSON, J. F. & DUGUID, J. P. (1960). The influence of cultural conditions on bacterial cytology. *Int. Rev. Cytol.* **9**, 1.

WINOGRADSKY, S. (1952). Sur la classification des bactéries. *Ann. Inst. Pasteur*, **82**, 125.

WITKIN, E. M. (1951). Nuclear segregation and the delayed appearance of induced mutants in *Escherichia coli*. *Cold Spr. Harb. Symp. quant. Biol.* **16**, 357.

WORK, E. (1957). Biochemistry of the bacterial cell wall. *Nature, Lond.* **179**, 841.

WORK, E. & DEWEY, D. L. (1953). The distribution of diaminopimelic acid among various micro-organisms. *J. gen. Microbiol.* **9**, 394.

YOUNG, I. E. & FITZ-JAMES, P. C. (1959a). Chemical and morphological studies of bacterial spore formation. I. The formation of spores in *Bacillus cereus*. *J. biophys. biochem. Cytol.* **6**, 467.

YOUNG, I. E. & FITZ-JAMES, P. C. (1959b). Chemical and morphological studies of bacterial spore formation II. Spore and parasporal protein formation in *Bacillus cereus* var. *alesti*. *J. biophys. biochem. Cytol.* **6**, 483.

ZUBAY, G. & WATSON, M. R. (1959). The absence of histone in the bacterium *Escherichia coli*. I. Preparation and analysis of nucleo-protein extract. *J. biophys. biochem. Cytol.* **5**, 51.

EXPLANATION OF PLATES

PLATE 1

Micrographs to show aspects of cell structure of *Spirillum serpens*, fixed after the fashion of Kellenberger and embedded in Vestopal.

Fig. 1. A general view of cytoplasmic architecture showing the ribosomal packing of cytoplasm, profiles of tubular intrusions, a metachromatic granule (*MG*, damaged by electron beam), and profiles of tubular intrusions of plasma membrane (arrows). The lack of ready distinction of chromatin areas should be noted. × 36,000. (Micrograph by Dr E. Vanderwinkel.)

Fig. 2. Section at region of cell division showing two mesosomes (*M*), the fine strands of the nucleoplasm (*n*) between ribosome packed areas, and the disposition of cell-wall over a delicate plasma membrane (right-hand border). The cell-wall is fairly typical of Gram-negative organisms, although the more usual form is shown in Pl. 4, fig. 3. × 48,000.

Fig. 3. The origin of intrusions at the plasma membrane.

PLATE 2

Fig. 1. The general construction of *Bacillus megaterium*. Dense cytoplasm containing nucleoplasms (*n*), a large mesosome in the centre adjoining a nucleoplasm and lipid droplets (low density areas). The cell-wall shows the dense homogeneous layer common to most Gram-positive organisms, and there is a septum in formation. The plasma membrane shows as a delicate double track, intimately applied to the cytoplasmic surface. × 50,000.

Fig. 2. A section of *Bacillus subtilis* containing a large and complex mesosome that seems to be within the nucleoplasm. The origin from the plasma membrane is seen at the right. × 48,000. (Micrographs by Dr E. Vanderwinkel.)

PLATE 3

Fig. 1. A section of sporulating *Bacillus subtilis* to show the separation of the forespore by a plasma membrane septum with mesosome. × 80,000. (Micrograph by Dr A. Ryter.)

Fig. 2. A micrograph of a very small coccus associated with cultures of *Mycoplasma*. It shows a cell-wall, possibly a plasma membrane, and a nucleoplasm in a dense cytoplasm. × 200,000. (Micrograph by Dr W. Van Iterson.)

PLATE 4

Fig. 1. A tetrad-forming coccus (similar to *Micrococcus radiodurans* Anderson) to show general features and cell-wall of Gram-positive type. No mesosomes have been found in this organism. Some structure is seen in the inner wall (arrow). × 30,000.

Fig. 2. Isolated inner cell wall of Fig. 1 prepared by phosphotungtie acid 'negative staining' technique. × 72,000.

Fig. 3. Portion of *Escherichia coli* a few minutes after T5 phage infection, showing an outer paired cell-wall and inner plasma membrane of strikingly similar profile. × 78,000.

PLATE 1

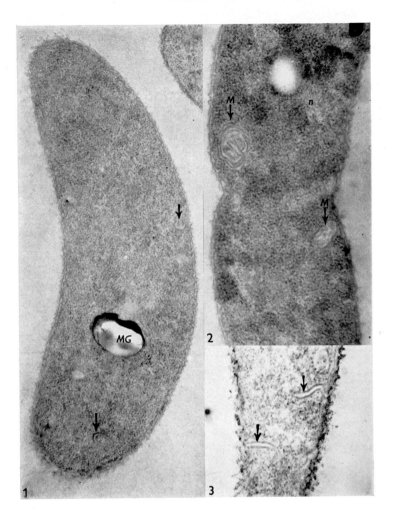

PLATE 2

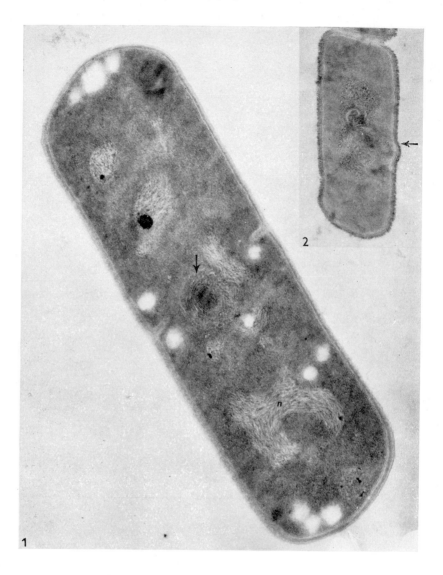

PLATE 3

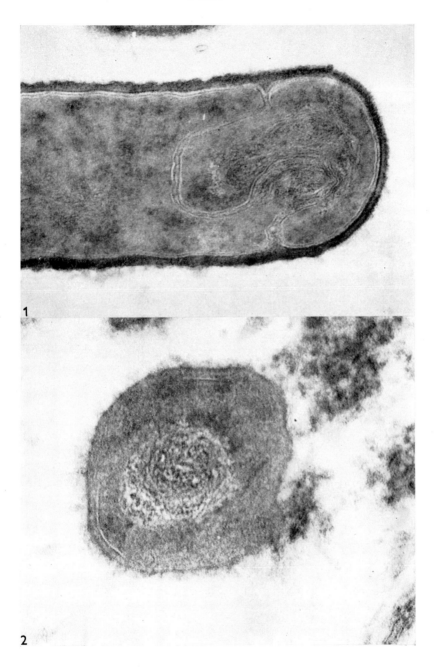

PLATE 4

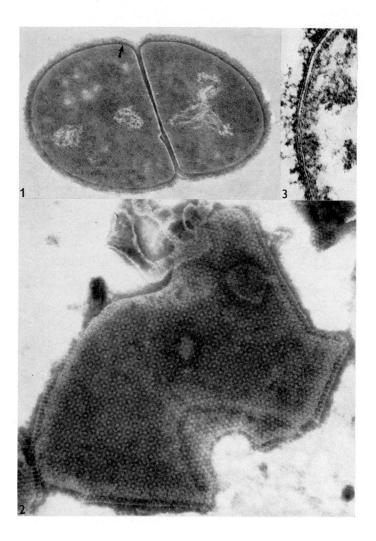

CLASSIFYING VIRUSES AT HIGHER LEVELS: SYMMETRY AND STRUCTURE OF VIRUS PARTICLES AS CRITERIA

P. WILDY

Medical Research Council Experimental Virus Research Unit, Institute of Virology, University of Glasgow

In this article I shall consider the possibility of classifying viruses at higher levels. Surveying viruses as a whole, certain similarities of pattern stand out and, whilst there is wide variation, there exist a number of groups of like strains which seem to be closely related. The relationships between the strains of a group have in several instances been well defined. What is more difficult, and this is what concerns us here, is to determine if and how these groups are related.

There is no need to dwell upon the purposes of classification (see Cowan, 1955; Bawden, 1955; Sneath, 1957*a*). Since, however, we are dealing with possible relationships between groups, we are not concerned with utilitarian classifications. What does interest us is the degree of similarity and dissimilarity between virus strains. If this can be estimated for enough strains, we may begin classifying, though the resulting classification is unlikely to be phylogenetically valid in its entirety.

Many of the difficulties encountered with microbial taxonomy apply also to viruses. There is no fossil or embryological evidence; viruses multiply and mutate (and hence may evolve) very rapidly by the human time scale (cf. Cowan, 1955; Andrewes & Sneath, 1958). Besides this, virology has grown from four more or less separate disciplines concerning plant viruses, vertebrate viruses, insect viruses and bacteriophages. Each has developed its own methods of study and the emphasis of each has been conditioned partly by the interests of the workers in each field and partly by the amenability of the different host materials to different techniques. Thus, strict comparisons of only a few features are yet possible. In fact, our ignorance is so great that we are not yet in a position to begin serious comparisons and no attempt at arrangement will be undertaken here. But however classification is eventually attempted, it is first necessary to collect suitable data. Much of this discussion will therefore concern the suitability and practicability of a number of criteria.

NATURE OF VIRUSES

In the third Marjory Stephenson Memorial Lecture, Lwoff (1957) concluded that viruses are viruses, thus freeing us from the need to think of them in particular as degenerate microbes, aberrant pieces of host cell material or macromolecules. In this contribution we shall consider only entities believed to fulfil the following generalizations:

(1) Viruses multiply only in living cells, giving rise usually to like progeny, but like other living organisms they are subject to genetic variation.

(2) They possess two well marked phases, extracellular and intracellular.

(3) Extracellular virus occurs in the form of particles, any one of which is potentially able to infect a susceptible cell. They have the following properties:

(*a*) The complete infective particle consists of one or other kind of nucleic acid wrapped in a protein coat, the *capsid* (see Lwoff, Anderson & Jacob, 1959), which is composed of serologically specific protein. (These are minimal requirements: some viruses have additional structures.)

(*b*) The particle has no energy-producing mechanisms.

(*c*) Unlike bacteria, rickettsiae and the psittacosis group of organisms, virus particles probably contain no muramic acid (Allison & Perkins, 1960).

(*d*) Though formal proof is lacking, the nucleic acid, whether deoxyribonucleic acid (DNA) or ribonucleic acid (RNA), probably fulfils the role of genetic material, since particles deficient in nucleic acid are non-infective (Markham & Smith, 1949) and under appropriate conditions extracted nucleic acid is able to infect a cell giving rise to new virus particles (Gierer & Schramm, 1956; Colter, Bird & Brown, 1957).

(*e*) When a particle infects a cell, the genetic material passes into the cell and the virus particle ceases to exist.

(*f*) Finally, all evidence suggests that far from being randomly associated the nucleic acid and protein capsid are highly integrated so that the particle is found to have well defined symmetry (see discussions by Crick & Watson, 1956, 1957; Klug & Caspar, 1961; Horne & Wildy, 1961).

(4) Two intracellular phases are recognized:

(*a*) All viruses by definition exhibit a vegetative phase in which new viral components are synthesized and assembled to form new particles. The precise mechanisms of this process may differ amongst different viruses.

(*b*) Some viruses (temperate bacteriophages) have another intracellular phase in which prophage (presumed to be phage nucleic acid) becomes attached to host chromosomes and multiplies with them. After a number of generations the prophage may pass once again into the vegetative phase. So far there is no unequivocal evidence that such a phase exists for animal or plant viruses.

The constant feature of all phases of a virus is the genetic pattern and probably also the actual material in which it is carried. There is little need to emphasize that in classifying viruses we are in reality comparing their genetic patterns.

Heterogeneity, origin and evolution

It is important to recognize that the above similarities do not imply that all viruses are phylogenetically related. All we have done is to group together a number of entities possessing several arbitrary features in common. In fact, viruses are plainly heterogeneous. They have entirely different host ranges, their particles extend over the range 20–300 mμ and have several shapes and degrees of complexity. They even contain different sorts of nucleic acid. There is a danger, however, that the differences between some animal and some plant viruses are over-emphasized through lack of strict comparisons between various strains.

The main question is whether all viruses have a common ancestry and have evolved divergently leading to a wide spectrum of entities, or whether they have arisen from separate stems and evolved convergently so that common features have been imposed by their habit. It is conceivable, for example, that their size alone may be responsible for many common properties (cf. Crick & Watson, 1957). Notice that it is of secondary importance whether viruses originated from free living organisms (Green, 1935; Laidlaw, 1938) or from cell constituents (Lwoff, 1957). All that can be stated is that the heterogeneity is so great that any common ancestry must be extremely remote, and for practical purposes it is prudent to assume that it does not exist.

There is, however, good reason to suppose that once a virus has become recognizable as such it may evolve by mutation and selection. There is abundant evidence for mutation amongst bacterial, plant and animal viruses. In fact, not only does the mechanism exist, but it has been seen at work in nature; the behaviour of influenza viruses provide excellent examples (Francis, 1959). The existence of groups of similar viruses suggests that these have common ancestry, and Burnet (1955) has postulated parallel evolution of virus and host (e.g. herpes virus and B virus in man and monkey). Such considerations strongly suggest that some groups of viruses may have common origins. Of particular interest are the speculations of Andrewes (1957), which not only reveal the futility of classifying certain groups of arthropod-transmitted viruses as vertebrate viruses or plant viruses, but suggest that they indeed may have originated in arthropods. Andrewes further pointed out that other groups of viruses, no longer transmitted by arthropods, might also have had similar origins.

Very little can be concluded about the origins of viruses. It seems probable that they are not all phylogenetically related though the strains of some groups evidently are. Further, there may be intergroup relationships and it is not unreasonable to suppose that some of these may cut across the conventional divisions of virology. It is part of our eventual task to decide which these are and for this reason it is both justifiable and necessary to examine viruses as a whole.

GROUPING VIRUSES AT LOWER LEVELS—TESTS FOR RELATEDNESS

We have already referred to a number of groups of viruses whose members show certain common properties. Some of these groups probably consist of phylogenetically related members, others are doubtfully related. To form these groups logically would require comparisons of large numbers of strains using many criteria and the use of a technique such as has been developed by Sneath (1957 *a*, *b*). Andrewes & Sneath (1958) have indeed made such a comparison on 25 strains of vertebrate viruses using 49 characteristics (see p. 319) but this was frustrated largely by lack of information. For this reason the groups we recognize have been formed largely on a common-sense basis and the relatedness of strains within the groups has been tested usually by serological methods. Various writers have suggested that the results of mixed infections might be used to show relatedness and the applicability of these also requires consideration.

Serological characteristics

That the sharing of antigenic determinants between organisms may have phylogenetic significance has been known since the pioneer studies of Landsteiner (1945). The general applicability of the method is well known in other disciplines, and serology forms the most powerful and delicate tool available for grouping viruses. Not only may the sharing of antigenic determinants between strains be demonstrated quantitatively, but in some instances, notably with more complex virus particles, the antigens may be situated in different sites. Thus with the influenza viruses the V antigen (detectable by haemagglutination inhibition, virus neutralization and, with appropriate sera, by complement fixation) shows high strain specificity, whereas the specificity of the internal component usually detected by complement fixation has wider specificity

amongst groups of strain. Though serological methods have their draw-
backs, for example, the conversion of D to C antigen in poliovirus
(Le Bouvier, Schwerdt & Schaffer, 1957), they have been generally and
successfully applied in one form or another amongst the plant, vertebrate and bacterial viruses and have formed the main criterion for
determining relatedness between strains.

Results of mixed infection

Mixed infections of cells have been studied at various levels with a
number of virus-host systems, and to some extent the results seem to
indicate degrees of relatedness. It is important to distinguish two sorts
of observations on mixed infection; (a) where two viruses are applied to
a cell or cells in such a way as to achieve more or less simultaneous
infection, and (b) when cells (or host tissues) already infected with one
virus are challenged with a second. The first kind of observation may be
interpreted at the cellular level, the second usually may not.

(a) *Simultaneous infection.* When simultaneous infection is studied at
the cellular level one of five phenomena may be observed. The first
involves genetic interaction between the viruses, giving rise to genetically
stable progeny with mixed characters of the two parent strains. This has
been reported amongst a number of bacteriophages and animal viruses
(see Hirst, 1959; Burnet, 1959). Genetic interaction may also be
demonstrated by applying two genetically damaged viruses to a cell,
giving rise to stable progeny (multiplicity reactivation, Luria, 1947).
Such genetic interaction obviously implies close relationships between
strains and suggests that they belong to the same species in the commonly
accepted sense (cf. Andrewes & Sneath, 1958).

A second result that may be detected is the formation of mixed particles which do not breed true but give rise to progeny like the original
virus strains. With phenotypic mixing the particles may have the host
range or serological characters of both parents but only give rise to
progeny of one parental type (Streisinger, 1956; Fraser, 1953). This is
presumably because the mixed particles have the nucleic acid of one
parent (determining the type of progeny) but capsids with properties of
the other parent, or both (determining host range and serology). In
some instances so-called 'heterozygotes' are formed, where one particle
appears to possess two genomes. The progeny of such particles are
found to consist of both parental types (Gottlieb & Hirst, 1954). Mixed
particles have been reported with a number of related viruses, and it is
reasonable to suppose that this may occur only when the components

of the parent strains are sufficiently alike to give a good fit. Taken at their face value, the results suggest that mixing requires a lesser degree of relatedness. For example, while genetic interaction has been reported between influenza A virus strains (Burnet & Lind, 1951) and between influenza B virus strains (Perry & Burnet, 1953) it has not been found between influenza A and B strains or between influenza A and NDV, whereas mixed particles have (Gottlieb & Hirst, 1954; Granoff & Hirst, 1954). Similarly, no genetic interaction has been demonstrated amongst the enteroviruses, but phenotypic mixing has been found between poliovirus strains (Sprunt, Mountain, Redman & Alexander, 1955) and between ECHO 7 and Coxsackie A9 virus strains (Itoh & Melnick, 1959).

A third phenomenon which Fenner & Woodroofe (1960) have suggested may be of taxonomic use is the reactivation found between members of the pox group.

Finally, the remaining possibilities are mutual exclusion at the cellular level and independent multiplication of both strains. These probably do not constitute reliable criteria for classification, for although mutual exclusion occurs between some unrelated strains of bacteriophage and not between related strains, this is not invariable (Adams, 1959). Furthermore, the occurrence of two sorts of inclusion body in cells infected with widely different animal viruses (Anderson, 1942; Syverton & Berry, 1947; Reissig, 1959) at least indicate simultaneous activity of two viruses in a cell though they do not necessarily imply that both are growing nor that the cells were necessarily infected simultaneously.

(b) *Challenge by a second virus.* If an infected host is challenged with another virus strain, the second strain may or may not become established and produce specific symptoms. This forms the basis for the cross-protection test (see Bennett, 1953). When a plant or tissue is infected with one strain of virus it usually becomes partially or wholly immune to challenge by related strains, though not by unrelated strains. There are, however, exceptions to this rule. Though the rationale is not understood, it is evident that for maximum protective effect sufficient time must elapse before challenge, possibly relating to the spread of the first virus through the host.

Turning to a different situation, the immunity of a lysogenic bacteria to superinfection by closely related strains but its ready acceptance of other temperate phages (see Adams, 1959) at once suggests a means of determining relationships between temperate phages. The existence, however, of mutants which can overcome the immunity means that it is not a reliable index of relatedness.

Instances of type-specific interference are known amongst the animal viruses (Henle & Rosenberg, 1949), and it has been shown that a virus may superinfect cells previously infected with an unrelated virus (Reissig, 1959). But it is unlikely that the cross-protection test could successfully be applied, because of non-specific interference due to interferon (Isaacs & Lindemann, 1957).

Summarizing, virus groups should be discernible provided sufficient characters are compared using a method such as that of Sneath (1957a, b). In fact, they have been constructed from strains with similar characteristics, special emphasis being paid to serological data. The relatedness of strains within groups may be tested serologically, and by the behaviour of mixed infections. Of these, only the cross-protection test has proved generally useful. When two strains are found to recombine genetically or to form mixed particles, it seems on general grounds that they must be related. However, it would be extremely unwise to interpret negative results as indicating non-relatedness.

CHOICE OF CRITERIA FOR DISTINGUISHING GROUPS OF VIRUSES

Whatever criteria are used, there is general agreement that they should concern as many attributes of viruses as possible. The eight criteria suggested at Rio de Janeiro ten years ago (Andrewes, 1951) in fact attempt just this. It is interesting that these criteria were applicable not only to vertebrate viruses but were also largely applicable to insect viruses (Bergold, 1953), with slight alteration to plant viruses (Knight, 1959) and partially at least to bacteriophage (Adams, 1959). However, in the past decade attention has been focused more and more on the fundamental properties of viruses. It is amongst these fundamental properties that we must look if we are to discover degrees of similarity between groups of viruses. For example, as Cooper (1961) has noted, host range is a useful criterion for classification at lower levels (i.e. the arrangement of strains in groups) but is of little value at the higher levels. Again, 'pathology' and 'symptomatology' may be useful in distinguishing constituent strains of the tobacco mosaic virus (TMV) group, or myxovirus group, but are plainly impossible to apply in comparing the two groups owing to inherent differences in the host cells. Another reason for confining ourselves to fundamental criteria is to avoid redundancy; as Sneath (1957a) has pointed out, if features A and B are used for comparison and feature B is a necessary consequence of A, it becomes redundant. For this reason we should look for characteristics which are as basic as possible and remember that as knowledge advanced, the characteristics used as criteria will change.

The nature of virus at once suggests that we should use two groups of criteria (*a*) features of extracellular virus—i.e. the virus particle, and (*b*) features of the intracellular phases. Unfortunately we are unable to make comparisons of the intracellular phase, partly because our knowledge is in any case very scrappy, and partly for technical reasons. Though admittedly the comparisons will be incomplete, they may be made on the properties of virus particles. This is roughly equivalent to classifying multicellular organisms solely on the properties of their gametes; the result may be distorted. In the next section we shall discuss a number of basic characteristics which are at present of varying practicability.

PROPERTIES SUITABLE AS CRITERIA FOR CLASSIFICATION

We have in the past been accustomed to using various features of the intact infective virus particle for classification. It is still desirable to do so at lower levels, but it is evident that if the component parts of the particle are sufficiently characterized, the properties of the intact particle become redundant and may even be misleading. This may be illustrated by two examples. First, if a particle contains lipid as an integral part of its surface, it is likely to be sensitive to ether and other lipid solvents. Secondly, the shape and size of a virus particle is dependent upon the size, shape and symmetry of its capsid, and the presence or absence of accessory structures. Thus, it seems more logical to score the myxovirus particle as comprising a helical capsid encased in an envelope which contains lipid than to score it as a pleomorphic spherical (sometimes filamentous) ether-sensitive particle.

Accordingly we shall consider the properties of the capsid, the properties of the nucleic acid, and the properties of various accessory components.

(1) *The capsid*

The capsid is composed of a number of symmetrically arranged protein molecules (see Lwoff *et al.* 1959; Crick & Watson, 1956, 1957) which are frequently arranged as symmetrical morphological subunits, the *capsomeres* (Lwoff *et al.* 1959). We thus find a series of potentially useful quantities and qualities comprising the protein itself and the way the molecules are packed to form the capsid.

Size, shape and symmetry. In an attempt to find criteria upon which viruses might be classified, Brandes & Wetter (1959) chose the dimensions of virus particles. Horne & Wildy (1961) have emphasized that the type of symmetry is often more basic than shape and suggested its use for classification. At present, however, our knowledge is so incomplete that we cannot afford to dismiss shape entirely. For example, where the symmetry is of a relatively low order, shape may be more informative, e.g. the bipyramidal prismatic capsid of the T-even phages. A further difficulty is that cubic and helical symmetry have only been discerned in about 30 strains of virus (for compilations of data see Bradley & Kay,

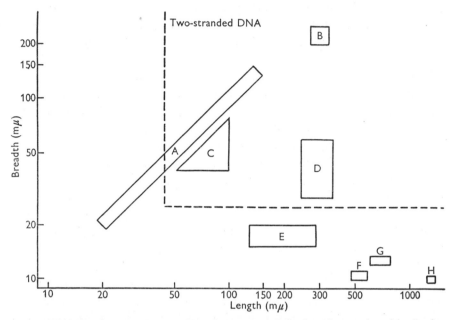

Fig. 1. The sizes of capsids from various viruses. Length is plotted versus breadth. Strains fall into the blocks shown (see text). Block A. Capsids with 'cubic symmetry'. Data quoted by Andrewes *et al.* (1961), Bradley & Kay (1960), Smith (1959), Williams *et al.* (1960), Loeb & Zinder (1961), and Klug & Caspar (1961). Blocks B, C and D. Elongated capsids. Data quoted by Andrewes *et al.* (1961), Bradley & Kay (1960) and Bergold (1953). Blocks E, F, G and H. Capsids with 'helical symmetry'. Data from Brandes & Wetter (1959) *Note.* All viruses falling into upper right-hand quadrant and none falling outside it have so far been found to contain two-stranded DNA.

1960; Klug & Caspar, 1961; Horne & Wildy, 1961). It is, however, probable that most spherical virus particles have capsids with cubic symmetry and that most of the thread-like virus particles have helical symmetry. Accordingly, we shall refer to three broad groups of capsids: those with 'cubic symmetry'; those with 'helical symmetry'; and elongated capsids.

Fig. 1 summarizes the geometrical features of capsids of a wide variety of viruses. In it the length is plotted against breadth and all strains fall in the eight blocks. It will be seen that these are quite distinct. The actual dimensions shown are approximate only, owing (a) to the fact that most of the available data refer to complete virus particles, (b) to differences and errors in techniques of measurement, and (c) to the technical difficulty of estimating length of thread-like particles (the dimension used here is the 'normal length' of Brandes & Wetter, 1959). The figure is useful in that it provides a good overall view of the sizes, shapes and symmetry of capsids from many species. It also provides a skeleton upon which further discussion may be based.

Capsids with 'cubic symmetry'. Block A of Fig. 1 shows the range of sizes of capsids with cubic symmetry. In general, the largest of these have DNA and the smaller RNA. Amongst the former we have *Tipula* iridescent virus (130 mμ), a number of bacteriophages including coliphages T1, T3, T5, several staphyloccal phages, typhoid phages S1BL and Vi1, a *Brucella* phage and *Pseudomonas* phages PC and PZ (50–90 mμ), Shope papilloma virus (50 mμ), polyoma virus (45 mμ) and the minute bacteriophages ϕX174 and S13 (25 mμ). Amongst the RNA viruses whose capsids have cubic symmetry, we find the enormous group of enteroviruses, several plant viruses, e.g. turnip yellow mosaic, bushy stunt virus and southern bean mosaic virus, and the minute RNA phage f2. These all fall in the size range 20–30 mμ diameter. The rather large group of arborviruses (30–100 mμ) may belong to this category, though the symmetry of their capsids is unknown.

Elongated capsids. In Fig. 1, blocks B, C and D represent virus particles with elongated capsids. These all appear to contain DNA. They fall in three well separated size groups, and their shapes are distinctive. The pox viruses comprise block B. Block C is composed entirely of bacteriophages with tails, and the capsids of many are polyhedral (Bradley & Kay, 1960). Block D is composed entirely of insect viruses. Some of these, the nuclear polyhedroses, are found to be variable in length.

Capsids with 'helical symmetry'. Blocks E, F, G and H comprise a number of viruses which probably all contain RNA and have helical symmetry. In E we find the shorter rigid rods including groups 1–3 of Brandes & Wetter (1959), i.e. the TMV complex, barley stripe mosaic virus, potato stem mottle virus, and some others. It is possible that the myxoviruses will fall within this grouping, for though the lengths of the capsids have not been estimated, the width (15–17 mμ) is of the right order. Block F comprises groups 4–6 of Brandes and Wetter, including somewhat longer flexible threads (e.g. potato virus X). Block G includes Brandes' and Wetter's groups 7–11, including two different serological groups, and a number of other strains, and block H is represented by the sinuous threads of beet yellows virus.

Packing arrangement of protein subunits in capsids. There are a number of ways in which protein subunits may be packed to give the various geometrical features of the capsid. Electron microscopy using negative staining has shown that the capsomeres (morphological subunits) are equivalent to the protein subunits of capsids such as that of TMV (Nixon & Woods, 1960). With capsids with cubic symmetry, this has not so far proved to be the case; the capsomeres are symmetrical and each probably consists of a number of chemical subunits (Wildy, Russell & Horne, 1960; Horne & Wildy, 1961). For reasons unknown, capsomeres have not been seen in capsids of all regular virus particles; it is quite possible that the protein subunits in such capsids are packed in some other way. For the moment, however, the packing of chemical subunits may be described for several viruses in terms of numbers of capsomeres. Although this information is at present restricted to only a few viruses (for list, see Horne & Wildy, 1961) there seems every reason to expect the list to increase rapidly in the near future. The numbers of capsomeres found in capsids with 5:3:2 symmetry can all be described by the formula $10x(n-1)^2+2$ (Horne & Wildy, 1961) where x may be 1 or 3, and n any whole number; this apparent homogeneity arises as a result of the 5:3:2 symmetry and is thus probably of no value for classification.

Aside from TMV we have as yet little knowledge of the packing arrangements of protein subunits in helical viruses. However, this is possibly reflected in the apparent rigidity of the threads. As a criterion this is objectionable because several degrees of rigidity may be discerned and it is arbitrary where lines should be drawn. Brandes & Wetter (1959) mention four categories: (1) rigid, e.g. TMV; (2) rigid to slightly flexible; (3) flexible; (4) very flexible, e.g. sugar beet yellow. Probably such features will serve as useful criteria until more is known of the packing of the protein subunits.

The packing arrangements in elongated capsids are not known; however, we have some idea of the way capsomeres are packed in aberrant elongated capsids of polyoma virus (Howatson & Almeida, 1960), and preliminary observations on vaccinia virus have led to the speculation that this may have a similar pattern (Horne & Wildy, 1961).

Nature of the protein subunit. Superficially the chemical nature of the protein subunit would seem to provide ideal criteria for classification. Its amino acid composition, its molecular weight and the nature of the end residues may all be characteristic for a strain of virus and show degrees of similarity between viruses (see Knight, 1959). The development of 'fingerprinting' and eventually determination of the total amino acid sequence will undoubtedly provide valuable information. Though a promising beginning has been made with the proteins of TMV (Tsugita *et al.* 1960) and turnip yellow mosaic virus (Harris & Hindley, 1961) the enormity of the task prevents this type of analysis being seriously considered at present. Aside from the laborious techniques which are employed for analysis, large quantities of highly purified virus are required and the difficulties increase with the size of the molecule.

(2) *The nucleic acid*

The properties of nucleic acid have suggested themselves as taxonomic criteria for various organisms (see Belozersky & Spirin, 1960; Sueoka, 1961). With viruses their importance is especially obvious, and they have several times been suggested as features for classification. The obvious basic categories are DNA-containing viruses and RNA-containing viruses. Cooper (1961) has already discussed the probability that this difference represents a fundamental division amongst viruses and the point requires no further stressing. Apart from this obvious criterion there are other possibilities. Most known examples of DNA are double-stranded, but that from the minute phage ϕX174 is single-stranded (Sinsheimer, 1960). Very possibly other examples will be found. Current opinion suggests that single-stranded and double-stranded nucleic acids may replicate in fundamentally different fashions, in which case 'strandedness' may be a worthwhile feature. Referring to Fig. 1, we find that all the virus particles known to contain double-stranded DNA are to be found in the quadrant enclosed by the dotted line.

The bases present in viral nucleic acids may form useful criteria for classification. Obvious examples are the occurrence of unusual bases such as 5-hydroxymethylcytosine in the DNA of the T-even coliphages. It is possible that uniqueness of this very obvious feature may render it of little use in classifying viruses.

A more universally applicable feature is the base constitution. With two-stranded DNAs it is only necessary to express the molar proportions of guanine plus cytosine (GC content) and since these may now readily be determined using small amounts of material it promises to be a useful feature. Belozersky & Spirin (1960) and Sueoka (1961) conclude that these values are characteristic for particular organisms and though this is not fully established, it may even reflect phylogenetic relationships. Wide variation in mean GC content occurs amongst different bacteria, but the average values for species are constant and for any strain the distribution of values amongst molecules and within molecules seems fairly uniform. Fig. 2 depicts the range of values found in a number of organisms against which are compared the values obtained for a few viruses. There is obviously too little evidence to draw useful conclusions yet, but it is plain that amongst different viruses there is sufficient scatter to suggest that the criterion may be useful.

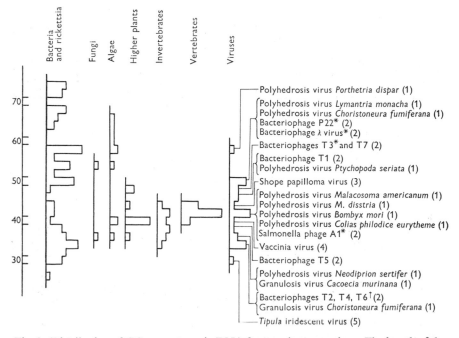

Fig. 2. Distribution of GC percentages in DNA from various organisms. The length of the blocks indicates numbers of strains. Data for bacteria and rickettsia, fungi, algae, higher plants, invertebrates and vertebrates, taken from Sueoka's compilation (1961). Data for viruses as follows: 1, Wyatt (1952); 2, compiled by Sinsheimer (1960); 3, Watson & Littlefield (1960); 4, Wyatt & Cohen (1953); 5, Thomas (1961). * indicates tentative data; † indicates T-even phages have 5-hydroxymethylcytosine in place of cytosine.

When RNA from different viruses is examined, wide differences in base composition are observed. Here it is necessary to express the molar proportions of all bases and this is shown in Fig. 3 for a number of viruses. It has previously been pointed out (Knight, 1959; Schuster, 1960) that related strains show similar patterns (as will be seen with the TMV group and the influenza group). Apart from this, considerable variation in pattern occurs (cf. turnip yellow mosaic virus with potato virus X, bacteriophage f2, or the influenza viruses). An unexpected similarity exists between the patterns of poliovirus and the TMV group. Again there is insufficient information to work with, but it seems worthwhile continuing to collect such data.

In times to come the base sequence in the nucleic acids may tell us all we want to know about a virus. Even when such data are available there is no guarantee that the patterns will make sense. Fortunately the solution of genetic codes is a popular quest, and we can expect a rapid expansion in knowledge about viral nucleic acids.

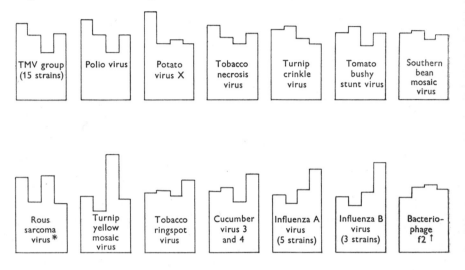

Fig. 3. Base composition reported for a number of RNA-containing viruses. The four columns in each block represent, from left to right, the molar proportions of adenine, guanine, cytosine and uracil. Note that related viruses have similar base composition. Data taken from compilations by Knight (1959), Markham (1959) and Schuster (1960). * = tentative results presented by Crawford & Crawford (1961); † = Loeb & Zinder (1961).

(3) *The nature of accessory components*

Besides the basic constituents nucleic acid and protein capsid, certain virus particles have been found embellished with tails, envelopes, enzymes and other materials. It is obviously important to ensure that such accessories are constitutive (see Pirie, 1957).

Tail structures. Bradley & Kay (1960) have compared the morphology of 22 different bacteriophages and their results show a striking variety of tail structures. These they group into three useful categories. *Group I. Contractile tail sheaths.* These are examples of evidently highly organized structures comprising a tail core surrounded by a contractile sheath which may show striations with negative staining. At the end of the tail core is a base plate which may or may not have prongs attached. Under appropriate stimulus the sheath contracts to approximately half its length revealing the tail core, and fibres may in some cases be seen attached to the plate. *Group II. Without contractile tail sheaths.* These tails appear to compose a core surrounded by an outer sheath which in some viruses terminates in a knob. Such tails often appear very flexible and have not been seen contracted. *Group III. Short tails.* These are short and wedge shaped. There is no clear evidence of a sheath.

Envelopes and other external structures. The polyhedrosis viruses and capsular viruses of insects are found embedded in large protein structures. These structures should not be considered a part of the virus for they may be removed by appropriate treatment releasing infective rod-shaped particles (Smith, 1959). On the other hand, the myxoviruses consist of helical structures contained in an outer envelope which certainly seems to be essential to the infective particle. This structure appears to contain the haemagglutinin part of the virus. It has a very characteristic appearance, in negatively stained preparations (Horne, Waterson, Wildy & Farnham, 1960). Other viruses such as herpes, vaccinia and *Tipula* iridescent virus have morphological membranes or envelopes constantly associated with them (Morgan, Ellison, Rose & Moore, 1954; Wildy *et al.* 1960; Smith & Hills, 1959). It is not at all certain that these structures are essential parts of infective virus particles. Obviously a distinction should be made between external structures which are a part of the virus particle and those which are not. Where it is uncertain the feature should not be scored.

The presence of lipid. It is well known that some groups of animal viruses are sensitive to ether which others are not (Andrewes & Horstmann, 1949). It is usually assumed that ether sensitivity indicates that lipid forms an essential and integral part of the infective particle. Franklin (1958) has drawn attention to the correlation between ether sensitivity and the way in which a virus matures in the cell, and both he and Cooper (1961) regard it as a basic property. It certainly serves as a useful criterion. However, the pox group is not homogeneous in this respect.

The presence of enzymes. The myxoviruses are unique in possessing neuraminidase and there is no doubt that this enzyme is an integral part of the virus particle. Other enzymes have been reported in viruses but it is not clear whether these are constitutive or not. With the exception of neuraminidase, it is therefore wise not to use the presence of enzymes as criteria for classification.

PRACTICABILITY OF CRITERIA AND THEIR APPLICATION

Many of the criteria we have discussed have not been seriously considered before and it may be objected that some of these are not practicable. Other features are, however, becoming increasingly easy to examine. Foremost among these are the morphological features of the capsids and accessory structures and the characteristics of nucleic acids. Not only have the techniques for examining these properties become simplified but the current interest in them appears to be sufficient to expect a lot of information on a wide front in the near future.

The important point at present is to provide enough features for making comparisons. Pirie (1955) pointed out that n differentiating features are sufficient to classify 2^n viruses; thus it should be sufficient to use between 10 and 20 valid features. Although at first sight, the criteria we have discussed cover rather few properties of virus particles, it should be remembered that each may contribute several features.

We have deliberately avoided trying to arrange viruses into groups and deciding how features are to be allocated amongst the various properties of virus particles. This is best left to an experienced taxonomist. It should be stressed that the blocks shown in Fig. 1 are not intended to imply that all strains falling in them are necessarily related. Block 7, for example, contains at least two separate serologically defined groups. Nevertheless, it is probably within these blocks that phylogenetically related groups are to be found. For the time being, we may adopt one or both of two courses. First, a plausible classification may be devised such as that of Cooper (1961) which has great utility. Secondly, we may continue collecting data about the groups of strains and plot these chessboard fashion, as is being done by Andrewes et al. (1961). Both are temporary expedients.

Finally, since Holmes's (1948) attempt at classification virologists have been reluctant to name viruses systematically. Despite the insistence that the binomials defined at Rome in 1953 were non-Linnean, there has been little inclination to adopt them. This is probably partly because everyone prefers to use common names for day-to-day purposes rather than bastard Latin, and partly because virologists are immensely aware of their extreme ignorance. There certainly seems to be little sense in even considering the introduction of new names at present. These remarks do not apply to names coined for convenience describing groups of viruses; their merit may be judged by the frequency with which they appear in the literature.

REFERENCES

ADAMS, M. H. (1959). *Bacteriophages*. New York: Interscience Publishers Inc.

ALLISON, A. C. & PERKINS, H. R. (1960). Presence of cell walls like those of bacteria in Rickettsia. *Nature, Lond.* **188**, 796.

ANDERSON, K. (1942). Dual infection of single cells. *Amer. J. Path.* **18**, 577.

ANDREWES, C. H. (1951). Viruses and Linnaeus. *Acta path. microbiol. scand.* **28**, 211.

ANDREWES, C. H. (1957). Factors in virus evolution. In *Advances in Virus Research*, **4**, 1–24. New York: Academic Press Inc.

ANDREWES, C. H. & HORSTMANN, D. (1949). The susceptibility of viruses to ethyl ether. *J. gen. Microbiol.* **3**, 290.

ANDREWES, C. H. & SNEATH, P. H. A. (1958). The species concept among viruses. *Nature, Lond.* **182**, 12.

ANDREWES, C. H., BURNET, F. M., ENDERS, J. F., GARD, S., HIRST, G. K., KAPLAN, N. M. & ZHDANOV, V. M. (1961). Taxonomy of viruses: present knowledge and ignorance. *Virology*, **15**, 52.

BAWDEN, F. C. (1955). The classification of viruses. *J. gen. Microbiol.* **12**, 362.

BELOZERSKY, A. N. & SPIRIN, A. S. (1960). Chemistry of the nucleic acids of microorganisms. In *The Nucleic Acids*, **3**, 147–185. New York: Academic Press Inc.

BENNETT, C. W. (1953). Interactions between viruses and virus strains. In *Advances in Virus Research*, **1**, 39–67. New York: Academic Press Inc.

BERGOLD, G. H. (1953). Insect viruses. In *Advances in Virus Research*, **1**, 91–139. New York: Academic Press Inc.

BRADLEY, D. E. & KAY, D. (1960). The fine structure of bacteriophages. *J. gen. Microbiol.* **23**, 553.

BRANDES, J. & WETTER, C. (1959). Classification of elongated plant viruses on the basis of particle morphology. *Virology*, **8**, 99.

BURNET, F. M. (1955). *Principles of Animal Virology*. New York: Academic Press Inc.

BURNET, F. M. (1959). Genetic interactions between animal viruses. In *The Viruses*, **3**, 275–306. New York: Academic Press Inc.

BURNET, F. M. & LIND, P. E. (1951). A genetic approach to variation in influenza viruses. 3. Recombination of characters in influenza strains used in mixed infections. *J. gen. Microbiol.* **5**, 59.

COLTER, J. S., BIRD, H. H. & BROWN, R. A. (1957). Infectivity of ribonucleic acid from Ehrlich ascites tumour cells infected with mengo encephalitis. *Nature, Lond.* **179**, 859.

COOPER, P. D. (1961). A chemical basis for the classification of animal viruses. *Nature, Lond.* **190**, 302.

COWAN, S. T. (1955). The philosophy of classification. *J. gen. Microbiol.* **12**, 314.

CRAWFORD, L. V. & CRAWFORD, E. M. (1961). The properties of Rous sarcoma virus purified by density gradient centrifugation. *Virology*, **13**, 153.

CRICK, F. H. C. & WATSON, J. D. (1956). Structure of small viruses. *Nature, Lond.* **177**, 473.

CRICK, F. H. C. & WATSON, J. D. (1957). Virus structure: general principles. In *The Nature of Viruses*, 5–18. pp. Ed. G. E. W. Wolstenholme and E. C. P. Millar. London: J. A. Churchill Ltd.

FENNER, F. & WOODROOFE, G. M. (1960). The reactivation of pox viruses II. The range of reactivating viruses. *Virology*, **11**, 185.

FRANCIS, T., Jr. (1959). Serological variation. In *The Viruses*, **3**, 251–73. New York: Academic Press Inc.

FRANKLIN, R. M. (1958). Hypothesis to explain the relation between the synthesis and release of animal viruses from infected cells and the lipid content of the viruses. *Experientia*, **14**, 346.

FRASER, K. B. (1953). Genetic interaction and interference between MEL and NWS strains of influenza virus. *Brit. J. exp. Path.* **34**, 319.

GIERER, A. & SCHRAMM, G. (1956). Infectivity of ribonucleic acid from tobacco mosaic virus. *Nature, Lond.* **177**, 702.

GOTTLIEB, T. & HIRST, G. K. (1954). Experimental production of combination forms of virus. III. The formation of doubly antigenic particles from influenza A and B virus and a study of the ability of individual particles of X virus to yield two separate strains. *J. exp. Med.* **99**, 307.

GRANOFF, A. & HIRST, G. K. (1954). Experimental production of combination forms of virus. IV. Mixed influenza A—Newcastle disease virus infections. *Proc. Soc. exp. Biol., N.Y.* **86**, 84.

GREEN, R. G. (1935). On the nature of filterable viruses. *Science*, **82**, 443.

HARRIS, J. I. & HINDLEY, J. (1961). The protein subunit of turnip yellow mosaic virus. *J. molec. Biol.* **3**, 117.

HENLE, W. & ROSENBERG, E. B. (1949). One step growth curves of various strains of influenza A and B viruses and their inhibition by inactivated virus of the homologous type. *J. exp. Med.* **89**, 279.

HIRST, G. K. (1959). Studies of mixed infections with NDV, poliovirus and influenza. In *Virus Growth and Variation*, pp. 82–101. London: Cambridge University Press.

HOLMES, F. O. (1948). Filterable viruses, in *Bergey's Manual of Determinative Bacteriology*, 6th ed. pp. 1125–86. Baltimore: Williams & Wilkins.

HORNE, R. W., WATERSON, A. P., WILDY, P. & FARNHAM, A. E. (1960). The structure and composition of myxoviruses. I. Electron microscope studies of myxovirus particles by negative staining techniques. *Virology*, **11**, 79.

HORNE, R. W. & WILDY, P. (1961). Symmetry in virus architecture. *Virology* (in the Press).

HOWATSON, A. F. & ALMEIDA, J. D. (1960). Observations on the fine structure of polyoma virus. *J. biophys. biochem. Cytol.* **8**, 828.

ISAACS, A. & LINDEMANN, J. (1957). Virus interference. I. The interferon. *Proc. roy. Soc.* B, **147**, 258.

ITOH, H. & MELNICK, J. L. (1959). Double infections of single cells with Echo 7 and Coxsackie A9 viruses. *J. exp. Med.* **109**, 393.

KLUG, A. & CASPAR, D. L. D. (1961). The structure of small viruses, in *Advances in Virus Research*, 225–325. New York: Academic Press Inc.

KNIGHT, C. A. (1959). Variation and its chemical correlates. In *The Viruses*, **2**, 127–156. New York: Academic Press Inc.

LAIDLAW, P. P. (1938). *Virus Diseases and Viruses*. Cambridge University Press.

LANDSTEINER, K. (1945). *The Specificity of Serological Reactions*. Cambridge, Mass.: Harvard University Press.

LE BOUVIER, G., SCHWERDT, C. E. & SCHAFFER, F. L. (1957). Specific precipitates in agar with purified poliovirus. *Virology*, **4**, 590.

LOEB, T. & ZINDER, N. D. (1961). A bacteriophage containing RNA. *Proc. nat. Acad. Sci., Wash.* **47**, 282.

LURIA, S. E. (1947). Reactivation of irradiated bacteriophage by transfer of self-reproducing units. *Proc. nat. Acad. Sci., Wash.* **33**, 253.

LWOFF, A. (1957). The concept of virus. *J. gen. Microbiol.* **17**, 239.

LWOFF, A., ANDERSON, T. F. & JACOB, F. (1959). Remarques sur les characteristiques de la particule virale infectieuse. *Ann. Inst. Pasteur*, **97**, 281.

MARKHAM, R. (1959). The biochemistry of plant viruses. In *The Viruses*, **2**, 35–125. New York: Academic Press Inc.

MARKHAM, R. & SMITH, K. M. (1949). Studies on the virus of turnip yellow mosaic. *Parasitology*, **39**, 330.

MORGAN, C., ELLISON, S. A., ROSE, H. M. & MOORE, D. H. (1954). Structure and development of viruses as observed with the electron microscope. I. Herpes simplex virus. *J. exp. Med.* **100**, 195.

NIXON, H. L. & WOODS, R. D. (1960). The structure of tobacco mosaic virus. *Virology*, **10**, 157.

PERRY, B. & BURNET, F. M. (1953). Recombination with two influenza virus B strains. *Aust. J. exp. Biol. med. Sci.* **31**, 319.

PIRIE, N. W. (1955). The principles of microbial classification. Summing up. *J. gen. Microbiol.* **12**, 382.

PIRIE, N. W. (1957). Material in virus preparations not necessary for the manifestation of characteristic properties. In *The Nature of Viruses*, 56–68. Ed. G. E. W. Wolstenholme and E. C. P. Millar. London: Churchill.

REISSIG, M. (1959). Double infection of cells in culture with measles and poliomyelitis viruses. *Ann. N.Y. Acad. Sci.* **81**, 17.

SCHUSTER, H. (1960). The ribonucleic acids of viruses. In *The Nucleic Acids*, **3**, 245–301. New York: Academic Press Inc.

SINSHEIMER, R. L. (1960). The nucleic acids of the bacterial viruses, in *The Nucleic Acids*, **3**, 187–244. New York: Academic Press Inc.

SMITH, K. M. (1959). The insect viruses. In *The Viruses*, **3**, 369–392. New York: Academic Press Inc.

SMITH, K. M. & HILLS, G. J. (1959). Further studies on the electron microscopy of the *Tipula* iridescent virus. *J. molec. Biol.* **1**, 277.

SNEATH, P. H. A. (1957*a*). Some thoughts on bacterial classification. *J. gen. Microbiol.* **17**, 184.

SNEATH, P. H. A. (1957*b*). The application of computers to taxonomy. *J. gen. Microbiol.* **17**, 201.

SPRUNT, K., MOUNTAIN, I. M., REDMAN, W. M. & ALEXANDER, H. E. (1955). Production of poliomyelitis virus with combined antigenic characteristics of Type I and Type II. *Virology*, **1**, 236.

STREISINGER, G. (1956). Phenotypic mixing of host range and serological specificities in bacteriophage T_2 and T_4. *Virology*, **2**, 388.

SUEOKA, N. (1961). Variation and heterogeneity of base composition of deoxyribonucleic acids: a compilation of old and new data. *J. molec. Biol.* **3**, 31.

SYVERTON, J. T. & BERRY, G. P. (1947). Multiple virus infection of single host cells. *J. exp. Med.* **86**, 145.

THOMAS, R. S. (1961). The chemical composition and particle weight of *Tipula* iridescent virus. *Virology*, **14**, 240.

TSUGITA, A., GISH, D. T., YOUNG, J., FRAENKEL-CONRAT, H., KNIGHT, C. A. & STANLEY, W. M. (1960). The complete amino acid sequence of the protein of tobacco mosaic virus. *Proc. nat. Acad. Sci., Wash.* **46**, 1463.

WATSON, J. D. & LITTLEFIELD, J. W. (1960). Some properties of DNA from Shope papilloma virus. *J. molec. Biol.* **3**, 161.

WILDY, P., RUSSELL, W. C. & HORNE, R. W. (1960). The morphology of herpes virus. *Virology*, **12**, 204.

WILLIAMS, R. C., KASS, S. J. & KNIGHT, C. A. (1960). Structure of Shope papilloma virus. *Virology*, **12**, 48.

WYATT, G. R. (1952). The nucleic acids of some insect viruses. *J. gen. Physiol.* **36**, 201.

WYATT, G. R. & COHEN, S. S. (1953). The bases of the nucleic acids of some bacterial and animal viruses. The occurrence of 5-hydroxymethyl cytosine. *Biochem. J.* **55**, 774.

COMPARATIVE BIOCHEMISTRY AND ENZYMOLOGY IN BACTERIAL CLASSIFICATION

J. DE LEY

Laboratory for Microbiology, Faculty of Sciences, State University, Ghent, Belgium

The ultimate aim of the natural classification of a group of living organisms is a taxonomy that is a reflection of their phylogenetic interrelationships. This has been broadly outlined for higher organisms during the last two centuries. However, this state has not yet been reached in bacterial classification, mainly because no evidence from comparative anatomy, comparative embryology or palaeontology is available.

The classification of bacteria is largely based on morphological and physiological data. The arrangement of the individual strains into species and higher taxa is quite often still a matter of personal preference. Therefore it is constantly changing, as exemplified by the different editions of *Bergey's Manual* (Breed, Murray & Smith, 1957).

The recent application of the Adansonian principle (Sneath, 1957 *a*, *b*) and the unbiased analysis by electronic computors of a large set of properties of as many strains as possible is a considerably improved approach for a better understanding of the natural relationships amongst bacteria. So far, this technique has only been applied with morphological, physiological and some biochemical and serological data (Sneath, 1957 *b*; Lysenko & Sneath, 1959; Sneath & Cowan, 1958; Hill, 1959; Cerbón & Bojalil, 1961; Gilardi, Hill, Turri & Silvestri (1960). However, the Adansonian principle requires that as many as possible properties of as many as possible strains are investigated. Otherwise a distorted picture of bacterial classification may again result. Therefore, the data on intermediary metabolism, enzymology and enzyme localization will also have to be included. The present review summarizes very briefly our information on the comparative biochemistry and enzymology of heterotrophic bacteria and it proposes some possible relationships of these organisms on this basis as a stimulus for further research in this field on Adansonian lines.

BACTERIA WITH THE ENTNER-DOUDOROFF PATHWAY*

In 1952–54 a third pathway for glucose dissimilation was discovered by Doudoroff and his associates in *Pseudomonas saccharophila*, the other two being the EM and the HMP mechanisms. The details of this pathway need not be discussed here, since they have been reviewed recently (De Ley, 1961). It is summarized in Fig. 1 *a*, and can be compared with the other two pathways shown in Fig. 1 *b* and *c*.

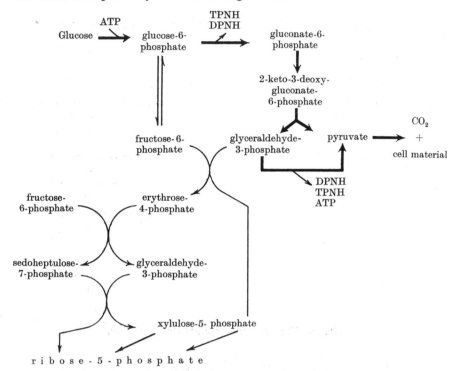

Fig. 1 *a*. Energy-producing (⟶) and biosynthetic (→) function of the Entner–Doudoroff pathway in *Pseudomonas saccharophila*.

The energy producing and biosynthetic role of the ED pathway

The essential difference between the EM and ED mechanisms resides in the production of glyceraldehyde-3-phosphate and pyruvate from glucose-6-phosphate. The overall equation in the EM pathway is:

$$glucose\text{-}6\text{-}phosphate + HPO_4^{--} + DPN^+ + ADP \rightarrow glyceraldehyde\text{-}3\text{-}phosphate + pyruvate + DPNH + H^+ + ATP.$$

* Abbreviations used: EM (Embden-Meyerhof pathway); HMP (hexose monophosphate pathway or shunt); ED (Entner-Doudoroff pathway); DPN, TPN⁺ (di- and triphosphopyridine nucleotide); DPNH, TPNH (reduced di- and triphosphopyridine nucleotide); ADP (adenosine diphosphate); ATP (adenosine triphosphate); CoA (coenzyme A).

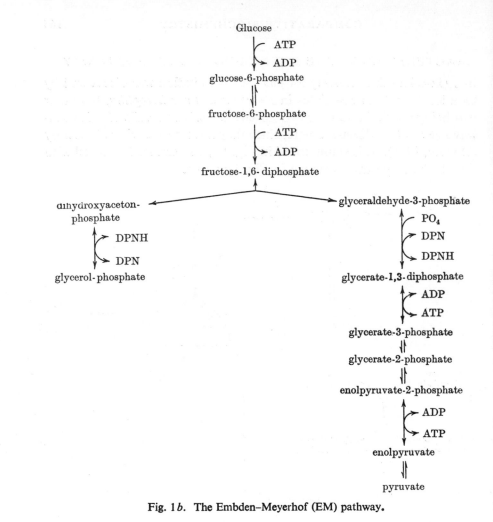

Fig. 1 b. The Embden–Meyerhof (EM) pathway.

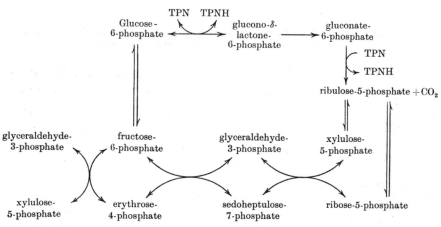

Fig. 1 c. The hexose monophosphate (HMP) pathway.

For the ED mechanism it is:

$$\text{glucose-6-phosphate} + \text{DPN}^+ \rightarrow \text{glyceraldehyde-3-phosphate} + \text{pyruvate} + \text{DPNH} + \text{H}^+.$$

The ED mechanism produces 1 mole of ATP per mole of glucose less than the EM pathway and therefore is less efficient. The results of labelling experiments and the absence of a gluconate-6-phosphate dehydrogenase showed that *Pseudomonas saccharophila* contains neither the EM nor the HMP mechanisms (Entner & Doudoroff, 1952). Ribose-5-phosphate, which is required for the biosynthesis of ribonucleic acid, (RNA) and several coenzymes, can thus not be formed through the decarboxylation of gluconate-6-phosphate. It could happen, however, through a reversal of the transaldolase-transketolase system. De Ley & Doudoroff (unpublished results) indeed detected the latter enzymes. Our results were later confirmed by Bernstein & Fossitt (1960) with labelled substrates. 94 % of the label of glucose-2-^{14}C was recovered as ribose-2-^{14}C and 92 % of glucose-1-^{14}C was present in ribose. The lack of gluconate-6-phosphate dehydrogenase explains the necessity for the ED mechanism. *P. saccharophila* synthesizes the pentose molecule by way of the transketolase and transaldolase enzymes and therefore glyceraldehyde-3-phosphate is required. The latter can be obtained solely through the ED pathway. *P. saccharophila* contains all the enzymes of the HMP pathway except the gluconate-6-phosphate dehydrogenase. If a bacterium, relying only on the HMP pathway, should lose the latter enzyme through mutation, it would become a lethal mutant. When the ED pathway is also present, the cell no longer requires this enzyme absolutely.

The occurrence of the ED pathway

Pseudomonas saccharophila is really a facultative autotrophic hydrogen bacterium. It would thus be very interesting to test for the presence of the ED and HMP pathways and the absence of gluconate-6-phosphate dehydrogenase in strains of *Hydrogenomonas*. It might be expected in *H. facilis*, *H. flava*, etc. The ED pathway has also been detected in some strains of *Pseudomonas* proper. Wood & Swerdt (1953a, b, 1954) and Kovachevich & Wood (1955a, b) found all the enzymes of the ED and HMP pathways in *P. fluorescens*. The EM pathway could not function because of the lack of phosphofructokinase. In all the pseudomonads investigated so far, the ED pathway seems to be the most important mechanism for glucose degradation (Wang *et al.* 1958; Wang, Gilmour

& Cheldelin, 1958; Lewis *et al.* 1955) since 50–88 % was catabolized this way. In some strains a weakly active EM pathway is present (Lewis *et al.* 1955). Katznelson (1958) detected ED enzymes in *P. angulata*, *P. coronafaciens*, *P. tabaci* and *P. syringae*, and Kovachevich & Wood (1955b) found them in *P. aeruginosa* and *P. fragi*. They were absent from *P. putrefaciens*. *Xanthomonas* also decomposes glucose according to the same pattern. Hochster & Katznelson (1958) proposed that the ED split may be part of a cyclic mechanism in bacteria which lack

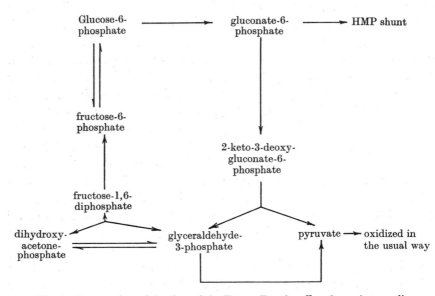

Fig. 2. Proposed participation of the Entner-Doudoroff pathway in a cyclic mechanism (Hochster & Katznelson, 1958).

phosphofructokinase and have only a weak shunt, such as in *Xanthomonas phaseoli* (Fig. 2). Other *Xanthomonas* species, such as *X. vesicatoria*, *X. pelargonii*, *X. malvacearum* and *X. begoniae*, also contain this mechanism, as well as *Agrobacterium rubi*, *A. tumefaciens* and *A. radiobacter* (Katznelson, 1958) and *Rhizobium* (Katznelson, 1955). It seems also to be present in *Gluconobacter melanogenus* and in *Azotobacter vinelandii* (quoted by Kovachevich & Wood, 1955b). Not only do the polarly flagellated facultative chemoautotrophs such as *Pseudomonas saccharophila* contain the ED pathway, but the corresponding photoautotrophs such as *Rhodopseudomonas spheroides* do so also (Szymona & Doudoroff, 1960).

Strictly anaerobic polarly flagellated bacteria can also contain the ED system. For example *Zymomonas mobilis* ferments glucose according to the equation:

1 mole glucose $\rightarrow$ 1·8 mole ethanol + 1·8 mole CO_2 + 0·2 mole lactic acid

Gibbs & DeMoss (1954) and Stern, Wang & Gilmour (1960) showed that this process proceeds exclusively via the ED mechanism. The general scheme, in which all the separate reactions have not yet been established, is represented in Fig. 3.

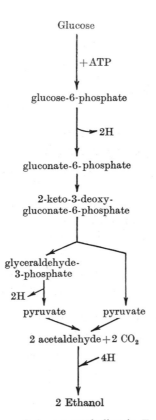

Fig. 3. Mechanism of glucose catabolism in *Zymomonas mobilis*.

Kovachevich & Wood (1955*b*) detected the 6-phosphogluconate dehydrase and the 2-keto-3-deoxy-6-phosphogluconate aldolase in *Escherichia coli*, although they appear to play no role in the overall carbohydrate breakdown by this organism. Several Enterobacteriaceae are able to produce a set of inducible enzymes which are operative in the catabolism of the uronic acids and which simulate the ED pathway. It is probably essential in the breakdown of pectins by the plant-pathogenic 'soft rot' bacteria *Erwinia*. These enzymes were also detected in *Aerobacter* and *Serratia* (for a review see Rabinowitz, 1959). Their activity can be represented as follows:

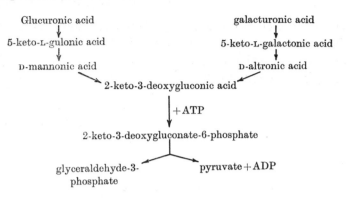

Possible relationships

The ED pathway is present only in a restricted group of micro-organisms. Direct enzymic tests have shown it to be absent in several bacteria listed in Table 1. Furthermore, the results on the breakdown of labelled glucose have shown that it is absent or ineffective in many organisms, such as homofermentative and heterofermentative lactic bacteria, clostridia, propionic acid bacteria, yeasts, plants and animals. The ED enzymes are present in Gram-negative bacteria, mainly strictly aerobic ones. In this group there is a variety of flagellated types. It would thus be worthwhile to look also for the presence of this pathway in related

Table 1. *Occurrence of the Entner–Doudoroff pathway in various bacteria*

Present	Absent
Bacteria with polar flagella	*Pseudomonas putrefaciens*
Strictly aerobic heterotrophs	*Proteus vulgaris*
Pseudomonas	*Leuconostoc mesenteroides*
Xanthomonas	*Corynebacterium creatinovorans, C.*
Gluconobacter	*michiganense, C. flaccumfaciens, C.*
Strictly anaerobic heterotrophs	*fascians*
Zymomonas	*Lactobacillus arabinosus*
Facultative heterotrophs	*Microbacterium lacticum*
Hydrogenomonas	*Erwinia amylovora, E. carotovora*
Rhodopseudomonas	Brewer's yeast.
Bacteria with lateral flagella	
Strictly aerobic	
Agrobacterium	
Bacteria with peritrichous flagella	
Azotobacter	
Rhizobium	
Escherichia	

genera such as *Protaminobacter*, *Vibrio*, *Chromobacterium*, *Flavobacterium*, *Achromobacter*, etc. The strictly anaerobic *Zymonomas* apparently lost its cytochrome system and acquired the ability to oxidize the reduced pyridine nucleotides with acetaldehyde and ethanol dehydrogenase. It is not excluded that the ED system might be active in other polarly flagellated anaerobic bacteria such as *Aeromonas*, *Lachnospira* (Bryant & Small, 1956), *Succinomonas* (Bryant, Small, Bouma & Chu, 1958) and *Succinovibrio* (Bryant & Small, 1956). Its presence in facultative autotrophs such as *Pseudomonas saccharophila* and *Rhodospeudomonas spheroides* suggests the study of other hydrogenomonads and the thiobacilli.

The presence of an inducible ED-like mechanism in Enterobacteria

Since the occurrence of the ED pathway is restricted to some bacterial genera, it seems tempting to speculate that these organisms are closely related phylogenetically and represent a separate evolutionary line. The presence of an inducible ED-like mechanism in the Enterobacteriaceae might point to a remote evolutionary link between the latter bacteria and the strict aerobes. There are two more indications in favour of this suggestion: *Aeromonas* is morphologically a pseudomonad but physiologically *Escherichia* or *Aerobacter*; the results of the electro-taxonomic analysis by Sneath & Cowan (1958). It would be interesting to confirm the observations of Sokatch & Gunsalus (1957), who reported on the only known case of an inducible ED pathway in a Gram-positive organism, *Streptococcus faecalis*.

THE ENTEROBACTERIACEAE

Innumerable strains of this family have been isolated. Their classification is in a constant state of flux. Adansonian analysis seems to be an absolute necessity to clarify the natural relationships within this family. The inclusion of the fermentation patterns and pathways will be required to settle the definitive classification, as will be shown below.

Intermediary carbohydrate metabolism

The catabolism of sugars occurs by both the EM and the HMP pathways, at least in the few strains which have been investigated in this respect. From the great similarity in their physiological behaviour and in the end products of their glucose fermentation it can be tentatively deduced that this will be a general rule. From many scattered papers, too numerous to review here, there is no doubt that all the enzymes of the EM pathway are present in *Escherichia coli* and in *Aerobacter*. Several of these enzymes have also been detected in *Serratia, Erwinia, Salmonella, Klebsiella* and *Paracolobactrum*. The enzymes of the HMP pathway were first detected in *E. coli* (McNair Scott & Cohen, 1953; Bergmann, Littauer & Volcani, 1954) and later in *Aerobacter, Paracolobactrum, Serratia, Klebsiella, Salmonella, Erwinia* and *Proteus* (De Ley, 1957). Further evidence for the participation of the transketolase-transaldolase system in the fermentation of pentoses in *E. coli* and *A. aerogenes* was supplied by Gibbs & Paege (1961 and see Simpson, Wolin & Wood, 1958). Cohen (1951) showed that EM is the major pathway for glucose dissimilation by *E. coli*. A concurrent result was obtained for *A. aerogenes* by Altermatt, Simpson & Neish (1955). The HMP pathway is apparently only active in aerobic conditions and as a biosynthetic mechanism for pentose.

Variations in the end products of the fermentation

Assuming that the intermediary metabolism of sugars is the same for all the enterobacteria, the difference in their fermentation pattern is due to variations in the enzymic outfit for the decomposition of pyruvate. Table 2 summarizes some of the published fermentation balances. Several types are clearly distinguishable. The basic type for the entire family is that of *Escherichia coli*. Pyruvate is mainly converted into acids and some ethanol. Lactic acid arises by reduction, acetic and formic acids by a thioclastic split and succinic acid by a preliminary CO_2 uptake with formation of oxaloacetate, followed by reduction. Part of the formic acid is decomposed by the complex 'hydrogenlyase' system with the formation of equal amounts of CO_2 and H_2. There are several variations on this theme.

Several genera (*Klebsiella, Cloaca, Aerobacter, Paracolobactrum,* some *Serratia* and *Hafnia* strains and some *Proteus mirabilis* strains) have an additional enzyme system that condenses pyruvate with the formation of acetylmethylcarbinol and CO_2. A considerable amount of pyruvate is withdrawn from the pyruvate pool and much less is left for the formation of acids. The pH drops less than with *Escherichia coli* and the methyl-red test is negative. There is also more CO_2 produced than H_2. Most of the acetylmethylcarbinol is used as H-acceptor for the formation of 2,3-butanediol.

A second variation is constituted by *Shigella*, some *Providencia* strains and some *Proteus rettgeri* isolates, which lack the 'formic hydrogenlyase' system. They do not form gas and accumulate formic acid instead.

A third variation is shown by the bacteria which produce trimethylene

Table 2. *The end products of glucose fermentation of some members of the* Enterobacteriaceae

(The results are expressed as mole of end product formed per mole of glucose fermented)

Organisms	Author	End products								
		Lactic acid	Acetic acid	Ethanol	CO_2	H_2	Butane-diol	Acetoin	Succinic acid	Formic acid
Escherichia coli	Harden (1906)	1–0·8	0·5–0·57	0·5	1–0·72	1	—	—	0·075	—
E. coli	Stokes (1949)	0·2	0·8	0·8	—	—	—	—	0·4	1·2
E. coli	Blackwood, Neish & Ledingham (1956)	0·70	0·39	0·51	0·02	0·0026	0·0026	0·0019	0·148	0·86
E. aurescens	Blackwood, Neish & Ledingham (1956)	0·76	0·39	0·40	0·02	0·0032	0·005	0·0029	0·093	0·75
Aerobacter aerogenes	Harden & Walpole (1906)	0·1	0·15	0·68	1·42	—	0·6	Present	0·05	—
A. indologenes	Reynolds & Werkman (1937)	0·03	0·05	0·70	1·72	0·36	0·665	—	0	0·18
A. aerogenes	Altermatt, Simpson & Neish (1955)	0·10	0·52	0·52	0·80	—	0·19	—	0·13	0·68
Erwinia carotovora	Kraght & Starr (1952)	0·23	0·64	0·64	0·13	—	0·15	—	0·11	1·34
Serratia plymuthicum	Neish *et al.* (1948)	0·27–0·34	0·04–0·08	0·46–0·5	1·45–1·5	0·6	0·47	0·01–0·03	0·06–0·07	0·02
S. marcescens	Neish *et al.* (1948)	0·10–0·28	0·04–0·16	0·36–0·53	0·86–1·2	0·0–0·08	0·51–0·64	0·02	0·08–0·11	0·48–0·55
S. kielensis	Neish *et al.* (1948)	1·03	0·50	0·46	1·0	0·9	0	0·02	0·02	0·02

glycol. *Escherichia freundii* apparently contains the same enzymes for the fermentation of glucose as *E. coli*, but in addition it has a set of enzymes for the reduction of glycerol to trimethylene glycol. There are also strains, related to *Aerobacter*, which carry out the same reaction (Mickelson & Werkman, 1940). The Bethesda-Ballerup group is—fermentatively speaking—almost *E. freundii* with a very weak β-galactosidase.

  Serratia, Erwinia, Klebsiella and *Paracolobactrum* have each a heterogeneous fermentation pattern; some strains ferment glucose in a way similar to *Escherichia coli* and others do so in a way similar to *Aerobacter*. We can illustrate this with *Serratia* (see Table 2). *S. plymuthicum* can be considered for present purposes as a pigmented *Aerobacter* because they make the same end products. *S. marcescens* lacks the 'formic hydrogenlyase' system. It is thus related to *S. plymuthicum* in the way *Shigella* is to *Salmonella*. *Serratia kielensis* is fermentatively almost *Escherichia coli*, but is pigmented. Other pigmented forms of *E. coli* are known, such as *E. aurescens*, which produces carotenoids. The sole basis for the existence of *Serratia* as a separate genus is its pigment production, which is a poor criterion. We would not be surprised if Adansonian analysis would show that *Serratia* as at present conceived is not a good genus and most forms would be best regarded as varieties of *E. coli* and *Aerobacter*.

Relationship with other micro-organisms

The similarity between the fermentation patterns of several aerobacilli and the Enterobacteriaceae will be pointed out below. *Aeromonas* strains can easily be mistaken for Enterobacteriaceae, because their glucose fermentation pattern is almost identical. *Aeromonas hydrophila* ferments glucose in a substantially identical manner to *Aerobacter aerogenes* (Stanier, 1943). *Aeromonas formicans* ferments like an anaerogenic *Escherichia coli* (Pivnick & Sabina, 1957). It remains quite possible that some strains, now relegated to the Enterobacteriaceae and on which no flagellar staining has been carried out, might turn out to be really strains of *Aeromonas*. *Photobacterium splendidum, P. sepiae, P. fischeri* and *P. phosphoreum* also yield fermentations similar to the enterobacteria (Doudoroff, 1942).

Possible phylogenetic relationships

This brief review of the fermentation patterns of the Enterobacteriaceae shows that they can be divided into three main groups:

(1) The *Escherichia coli* group and several of its minor variations, such as *Shigella dispar* and *S. alcalescens*. Here would also belong the pathogenic *Salmonella, Shigella* and *Arizona* strains.

(2) The trimethylene glycol producers such as *Escherichia freundii* and the Bethesda-Ballerup group.

(3) The 2, 3-butylene glycol producers such as *Aerobacter*.

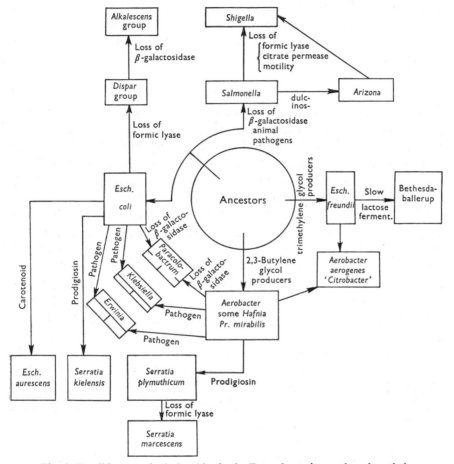

Fig. 4. Possible natural relationships in the Enterobacteriaceae, based on their comparative biochemistry.

There appear to be many intermediates between these main groups. The most striking are the genera, or so-called genera, *Serratia, Erwinia, Klebsiella* and *Paracolobactrum,* each one containing strains with the fermentation pattern of either *E. coli* or *Aerobacter*. It seems likely that each of them consists of a cluster of strains extending from the *E. coli* to the *Aerobacter* pattern. It seems likely that all these bacteria arose from a common pool of ancestors which divided during the course of evolution into three main branches and several intermediate groups. A first approximation of this opinion, based on carbohydrate metabolism mainly, is shown in Fig. 4. The most satisfying understanding of the natural relationship of the Enterobacteriaceae, *Photobacterium*, *Aeromonas* and the aerobacilli (and even the aerobic spore-formers) would result from the hypothesis that all these bacteria arose from a common phylogenetic origin, and slowly diverged into the different groups through loss and gain mutations during the course of their evolution.

THE AEROBIC SPORE-FORMERS

Smith, Gordon & Clark (1952) studied extensively 1134 strains of this group and they clarified considerably its classification. They used both morphological criteria (shape and location of the spore in the cell, shape of the sporangia, diameter of the cell, etc.) and physiological criteria (acid production from mannitol, formation of acetylmethylcarbinol, hydrolysis of gelatin, hydrolysis of starch, etc.). Of 175 species names previously proposed, the authors retained 19. Their classification was also a first attempt to introduce natural relationships amongst the species (Fig. 5). The main emphasis was on the morphology of the organisms. Within these arbitrary limits, species differentiation was based on the greatest number of commonly occurring properties. Since so much experimental material seems to be available from these investigations, it would be interesting to feed all this information into a computor (see Sneath in this Symposium). Here also fermentation patterns will have to be taken into account for an Adansonian analysis as will be shown below. Furthermore, the bacilli show a very striking division into strictly aerobic strains, such as *Bacillus subtilis* and *B. pumilus*, and facultative anaerobes such as *B. cereus*, *B. licheniformis*, *B. polymyxa*, *B. macerans*, etc.

The facultative aerobic sporeformers: Aerobacillus

Many strains of bacilli are able to grow anaerobically and to ferment sugars, particularly glucose, with the formation of a variety of end products. Donker (1926) proposed gathering all these strains into a separate genus *Aerobacillus*. The relationship between *Aerobacillus* and *Bacillus* could very well be the same as between the facultative aerobic *Aeromonas* and the strictly aerobic *Pseudomonas*. The end products of the fermentation of glucose by several strains of *Aerobacillus* are represented in Table 3. It will be seen that this group as a whole shows a fermentation pattern reminiscent of the Enterobacteriaceae. However, the variations between the fermentation patterns of the separate species of *Aerobacillus* are as great as between those of the genera of the Enterobacteriaceae. If uniform criteria for classification were used, then on fermentation pattern either many species of the aerobacilli

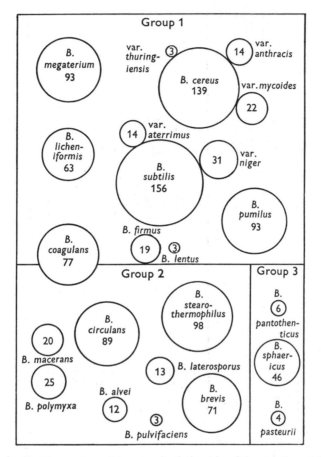

Fig. 5. The classification and possible natural relationship of the strictly and facultatively aerobic spore-formers, after Smith, Gordon & Clark (1952), slightly modified.

ought to be raised to genus level, or several genera of the Enterobacteriaceae would only be species. From the point of view of fermentation, there is hardly any difference between *Aerobacter aerogenes* and *Aerobacillus polymyxa*. One can calculate that nearly half of the pyruvate molecules are transformed into 2, 3-butanediol. *Aerobacillus megaterium* shows a fermentation more similar to *Escherichia coli* since it produces mainly lactic and acetic acids. *Aerobacillus macerans* makes

Table 3. *Anaerobic dissimilation of glucose by various aerobacilli*

Organism ...	macerans	polymyxa	subtilis (Ford strain)*	megaterium†	cereus	anthracis
Author ...	Donker (1926)	Donker (1926)	Blackwood et al. (1947)	Ehrlich & Segel (1959)	Puziss & Rittenberg (1957)	
Results expressed ...	mole/100 moles of glucose				mg./100 ml. medium	
Butanediol	1·2	43	36-54	1·9	12·2	8·3-17·1
Acetoin	Trace	Trace	0-16	1	3·6	1·7
Glycerol	n.d.	n.d.	31-57	6·2	1·6	1·4-2·8
Ethanol	121	88	7-21	0	n.d.	n.d.
Formic acid	10	0	1-19	0	3·1	5·0-6·5
Acetic acid	15	15	0·2-1·3	59·4	7·8	8·8-10·7
Lactic acid	Trace	Trace	17-62	107	6·1	3·1-8·0
Pyruvic acid	0	0	0	0·6	n.d.	n.d.
Succinic acid	n.d.	n.d.	0·2-1·7	0	6·3	5·6-9·6
CO_2	215	203	72-117	43	0	0
H_2	137	75	0-0·6	n.d.	0	0
Acetone	16	0·9	0	0	n.d.	n.d.
Cells (as mmole glucose)	n.d.	n.d.	n.d.	11·8	n.d.	n.d.

n.d.: not determined.   * *Bacillus licheniformis* according to Smith, Gordon & Clark (1952).   † Under intermittent aeration.

considerable amounts of ethanol and some acetone. It is known that *Aerobacillus macerans* resembles *E. coli* in exchanging formate rapidly with pyruvate and in possessing an active 'formic hydrogenlyase'. It also exhibits a CO_2-pyruvate exchange reaction closely similar to that of *Clostridium butyricum* (Hamilton & Wolfe, 1959). In the Ford strains of *Bacillus subtilis* (also called *B. licheniformis*) glycerol and butanediol are the main reduced end products. They appear to have no 'formic hydrogenlyase'. There is now ample evidence that the enzymes of both the EM and the HMP pathways are present in these bacteria. Neish (1953) showed with a strain of *B. subtilis* that the distribution of ^{14}C from $1-^{14}C$-glucose in lactic acid and glycerol agrees with their formation by glycolysis. Several enzymes of both mechanisms were detected in the Marburg strain of *B. subtilis* by Gary, Klausmeier & Bard (1954) and in *B. larvae* by Mylroie & Katznelson (1957). Spores appear not to be active glycolytically, but they metabolize glucose by way of the HMP pathway and a direct non-phosphorylative oxidation involving gluconate and 2-ketogluconate (Doi, Halvorson & Church, 1959). Wang *et al.* (1958) calculated from their radiorespirometric method that when the Marburg strain metabolizes glucose 65 % goes by way of the EM pathway and 35 % by way of the HMP shunt. Ehrlich & Segel (1959) showed that a facultative aerobic spore-former continues to ferment glucose under aerobic conditions. Beck & Lindstrom (1955) presented evidence for a Krebs cycle in *Aerobacillus cereus*.

The strictly aerobic spore-formers

Much less information is available concerning this group. Since they do not ferment glucose at all one is inclined to attribute this to a lack of one or more enzymes of the EM pathway, such as phosphofructokinase, as is the case in some pseudomonads. A very interesting observation was made by Gary *et al.* (1954). Cells of *Bacillus subtilis* grown on a complex tryptone-yeast extract-glucose medium were able both to ferment and to oxidize glucose vigorously and they contained the enzymes for both the EM and the HMP pathways. They lacked a CO-sensitive cytochrome oxidase. The same strain, grown in an inorganic nitrogen–salts–glucose medium exhibited oxidative activity and had nearly no fermentative abilities. This was explainable by a reduced activity of triose phosphate and lactate dehydrogenases. These cells contained a very active cytochrome oxidase. In several strains a glucose-6-phosphate and a gluconate-6-phosphate dehydrogenase as well as the transketolase have been detected (De Ley, unpublished).

THE CLOSTRIDIA AND RELATED ORGANISMS

The strict anaerobic spore-formers or clostridia can roughly be divided into four main groups, on the basis of their fermentative abilities: (1) the proteolytic; (2) the purinolytic; (3) the saccharolytic; and, (4) the incompletely saccharolytic clostridia.

The proteolytic clostridia

These are the strains which hydrolyse proteins rather easily and decompose amino acids. Most of these bacteria are unable to attack carbohydrates. Quite often they are pathogenic for man and animals and produce toxins. Apparently they constitute a group of anaerobic spore-formers which specialized wholly in the breakdown of a narrow range of nitrogenous substances and have lost their power to utilize carbohydrates. Typical examples are *Clostridium tetani* and *C. histolyticum*. All these bacteria are endowed with special enzymes for the breakdown of amino acids. A very well known example is the Stickland reaction, in which one amino acid serves as the H-donor and another as the H-acceptor. *C. sporogenes* has been particularly well studied in this respect. The general reaction is

$$R.CHNH_2.COOH + X.CHNH_2.COOH + H_2O \rightarrow R.CH_2.COOH + X.CO.COOH + 2NH_3.$$

At least fifteen species of clostridia can carry out this reaction (Nisman, 1954). Several other clostridia are able to grow at the expense of one single amino acid and to ferment it with the formation of a series of end products (Barker, 1956). *C. tetanomorphus*, for example, is particularly well adapted to the breakdown of glutamate and histidine. The latter compound is fermented with the formation of butyrate, acetate, CO_2, and H_2. These products suggest that the organism is indeed closely related to the true saccharolytic clostridia. *C. propionicum* is another example; e.g. it ferments alanine and threonine as follows:

$$3 \text{ alanine} + 2H_2O \rightarrow 2 \text{ propionate} + \text{acetate} + 3NH_3 + CO_2$$

and also

$$3 \text{ threonine} + 2H_2O \rightarrow 2 \text{ propionate} + \text{butyrate} + 3NH_3 + 2 CO_2.$$

The similarity with the real propionic acid fermentation is only coincidental, since in *C. propionicum* propionyl-CoA arises from acryl-CoA through reduction (Stadtman, 1956), while in the propionic acid bacteria it arises from succinyl-CoA.

Purinolytic clostridia

The purinolytic *Clostridium acidi-urici* and *C. cylindrosporum* decompose many purines with the formation of NH_3, CO_2, acetate and some formate. Both species attack neither carbohydrates nor amino acids, except glycine and serine. They represent apparently another slightly divergent phylogenetic line of bacteria, which specialized in the anaerobic decomposition of purines in nature.

The saccharolytic clostridia

This group can be subdivided into the butyric acid, the butanol-acetone and the isopropanol fermenters.

(*a*) *The butyric acid fermentation.* This is carried out by species such as *Clostridium saccharobutyricum*, *C. pectinovorum* and *C. aurantibutyricum*. The overall equation in its simplest form is the one by Donker (1926):

$$1 \text{ mole glucose} \rightarrow 0.75 \text{ mole butyric acid} + 0.43 \text{ mole acetic acid} + 1.96 \text{ mole } CO_2 + 2.33 \text{ mole } H_2.$$

Evidence is accumulating for the presence of both EM and HMP pathways in several saccharolytic clostridia. This is derived from both enzymic and tracer data, although the latter are not yet convincing. Also our knowledge on the enzymic mechanism of pyruvate decomposition in the saccharolytic clostridia is still far from complete and is derived mainly from the study of *C. kluyveri*. It can briefly be summarized as follows:

Glucose
|
EM ⊢→ 4H
↓
2 pyruvate
↓
2 acetyl-phosphate + 2CO$_2$ + 4H
↓
acetic acid ← 2 acetyl-CoA
↓
aceto-acetyl-CoA
+2H↓
β-hydroxybutyryl-CoA
↓
crotonyl-CoA
+2H↓
butyryl-CoA
↓
butyric acid

(b) *The butanol-acetone fermentation.* This is carried out by *Clostridium beijerinckii, C. acetobutylicum, C. felsineum,* etc. The basic equation is the one established by Van der Lek (1930):

1 mole glucose → 0·56 mole butanol + 0·22 mole acetone +
    0·09 mole ethanol + 0·04 mole butyric acid + 0·14 mole acetic acid
        + 0·06 mole acetoin + 2·2 mole CO_2 + 1·4 mole H_2.

These bacteria first produce butyric acid, probably in the same way as the previous group. At a certain moment a 'break' occurs during this fermentation and an additional set of enzymes becomes active. Acetoacetate is decomposed with the formation of acetone and CO_2. An H-acceptor is thus withdrawn and butyryl-phosphate is now used for this purpose, resulting in the formation of butanol.

(c) *The butanol-isopropanol fermentation.* This is carried out by *Clostridium butylicum.* This organism apparently contains one more enzyme than the previous group, namely an isopropanol dehydrogenase for the reduction of acetone.

All the saccharolytic clostridia contain a very active hydrogenase which facilitates the equilibration of the internal oxidation-reduction balance during the fermentation. The formation of free acetic acid from acetyl-CoA represents the loss of an H-acceptor. The excess H can be linked to the hydrogenase and liberated as H_2 gas. This is reflected in the equation of Donker as the extra 0·33 H_2 over and above the expected 2 moles. In many other bacteria this facility does not seem to be present and the H-pool has to be balanced by reaction of the excess H with substances like ethanol, lactic acid and 2, 3-butanediol (Enterobacteriaceae) or with ethanol, glycerol and mannitol (heterofermentative lactic acid bacteria). The reactions for the butyric acid bacteria could also be balanced by either one of the following equations:

$$\text{glucose} \rightarrow \text{butyric acid} + 2CO_2 + 2H_2$$
or $$\text{glucose} \rightarrow 2 \text{ acetic acid} + 2CO_2 + 4H_2.$$

Although no organisms are known which are able to carry out the above equations, it would not be so surprising if clostridia or related organisms (see below) were discovered with the above fermentation balances.

The incompletely saccharolytic clostridia

The classical example is *Clostridium kluyveri* which has been studied extensively by Barker (1956). When grown in the presence of both ethanol and acetate, it grows and ferments vigorously and produces either butyrate or caproate, depending on an excess of either acetate or ethanol. Ethanol serves as the H-donor for the reductive fermentation of acetyl-CoA to butyrate. For details of the enzymic mechanism, the original papers of Barker should be consulted (cited in Barker, 1956). Unlike the saccharolytic clostridia, *C. kluyveri* is unable to ferment sugars and pyruvate. It is thus enzymically less well equipped.

At a first glance it would appear that *Clostridium lactacetophilum* is an organism closely related to *C. kluyveri* because it requires both lactate and acetate for growth and fermentation, butyrate and CO_2 being produced. Lactate serves as the H-donor for the reduction of acetyl-CoA to butyrate. On the other hand, however, *C. lactacetophilum* is able to ferment glucose by a butyric acid fermentation. Barker has pointed out that the usual saccharolytic clostridia are likewise unable to grow on lactate alone. Therefore it seems that *C. lactacetophilum* is not an exceptional case but is a member of the saccharolytic clostridia.

These bacteria appear to possess still another mechanism of disposing of the internal H-pool. *Clostridium thermoaceticum* ferments glucose with the formation of 3 mole of acetic acid. Barker (1956) showed that CO_2 is used as the H-acceptor. The fermentation would occur in the following fashion:

$$\text{glucose} + H_2O \rightarrow 2 \text{ acetic acid} + 2CO_2 + 8H,$$
$$2CO_2 + 8H \rightarrow \text{acetic acid} + 2H_2O.$$

An extreme case again is *C. aceticum*, which is able to carry out the latter reaction by itself and converts CO_2 and H_2 to acetic acid.

Bacteria biochemically related to the clostridia

Butyribacteria are non-motile, non-spore-forming anaerobic rods which resemble morphologically the lactobacilli and present the fermentative characteristics of both the heterofermentative lactic acid bacteria and the clostridia. Glucose is fermented according to the following equation:

1 mole glucose $\rightarrow$ 1 mole lactic acid $+ 0.9$ mole acetic acid $+$
$\qquad\qquad 0.3$ mole butyric acid $+ 0.5$ mole $CO_2 + 0.74$ mole H_2.

Tracer experiments have shown that sugar decomposition mainly follows the EM pathway to pyruvate, which is oxidized to CO_2 and acetate. The latter is reduced to butyrate. CO_2 is reduced to acetate in a way resembling that in *Clostridium thermoaceticum* and *C. aceticum*.

Several other non-spore-forming Gram-positive bacteria are able to form butyric acid. If the enzymic mechanism is similar, this might point to a close phylogenetic relationship with the clostridia. The catenabacteria, ramibacteria, eubacteria and cillobacteria all show a mixed lactic-butyric acid fermentation. *Zymosarcina maxima* might be another link between the clostridia and the heterofermentative lactic bacteria, as may be seen from the fermentation equation:

1 mole glucose → 0·76 mole butyric acid + 0·30 mole acetic acid +
    0·04 mole formic acid + 0·21 mole lactic acid + 1·49 mole CO_2 +
                                                           2·33 mole H_2.

The anaerobic LC coccus, isolated by Elsden (see below), also shows some relationship with the clostridia and heterofermentative lactic acid bacteria. In Fig. 6 are shown the essential features of the metabolic maps of the clostridia and some biochemically related organisms.

THE LACTIC ACID BACTERIA

Morphologically, physiologically and biochemically speaking these are a heterogeneous group. The shape of the bacteria varies from small cocci to long slender rods. Some groups are aerobic, others anaerobic, some strains produce from glucose mainly lactic acid by one pathway (the homofermentative lactic acid bacteria) and others lactic acid and a variety of end products by an entirely different pathway (the hetero-fermentative lactic acid bacteria). Furthermore, there appear to be at least three mechanisms for the oxidation of the internal H-pool: (1) with an internal H-acceptor such as pyruvate or acetaldehyde; (2) by way of the cytochrome system; (3) by way of flavins. We shall discuss the homofermentative and heterofermentative lactic acid bacteria separately.

The homofermentative lactic acid bacteria

To the 'homolactic' acid bacteria belong the facultative anaerobic to micro-aerophilic genera *Diplococcus, Streptococcus, Pediococcus* and several lactobacilli and the aerobic *Microbacterium*. They all ferment glucose readily and quite often produce as much as 1·8 mole of lactic acid per mole of glucose fermented. Minor amounts of acetic and formic acids, ethanol and CO_2 are also formed.

It has been found for several strains that glucose is degraded almost solely by way of the EM scheme. Although several enzymes of this pathway have been studied separately, the best evidence for its overall activity comes from work with labelled glucose. Glucose-3, 4-^{14}C is converted by *Lactobacillus casei* to carboxyl-labelled lactate (Gibbs *et al.* 1950). *L. pentosus* and *Streptococcus faecalis* effect the same type of

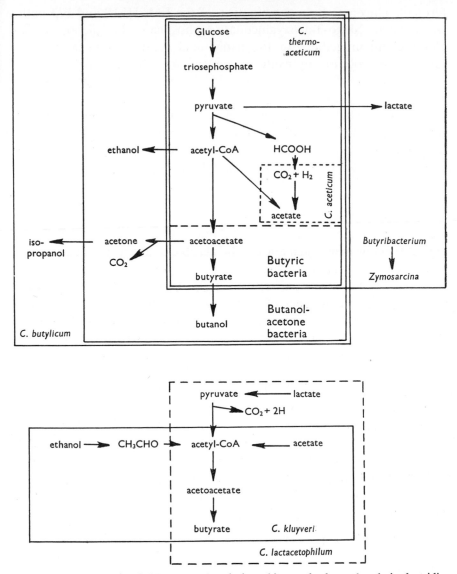

Fig. 6. The relationship of different saccharolytic and incompletely saccharolytic clostridia, as illustrated by the essential features of their metabolic maps.

decomposition (Gibbs, Sokatch & Gunsalus, 1955). The enzymic information is most complete for *Microbacterium lacticum* (Vandemark & Wood, 1956; Krichevsky & Wood, 1961), in which the enzymes for both the EM and HMP pathways were detected. No evidence was found for an ED mechanism. It would be interesting to confirm the results of Sokatch & Gunsalus (1957), according to which *S. faecalis* ferments gluconate by a combination of the EM, HMP and ED pathways, where 2-keto-3-deoxygluconate-6-phosphate aldolase and transaldolase are inducible. In the usual acid conditions in which this fermentation occurs, pyruvate is reduced by stereospecific lactic dehydrogenases to D, L or DL lactic acid. At neutral or slightly alkaline pH, however, pyruvate decomposition undergoes a change so that formic and acetic acids and ethanol are formed, approximately in the ratios 2:1:1. The mechanism of this type of 'heterolactic' fermentation has been elucidated by the well known studies of Gunsalus and his collaborators (see Gunsalus, Horecker & Wood, 1955).

The heterofermentative lactic acid bacteria

Heterolactic fermentations are carried out by the same range of morphological types as mentioned above: the aerobic to anaerobic *Leuconostoc* and some lactobacilli, the anaerobic peptostreptococci and the anaerobic eubacteria, catenabacteria, ramibacteria and bifidobacteria. There appear to be several types of 'heterolactic acid' fermentations. *Leuconostoc* and the heterofermentative lactobacilli produce about 0·8 mole lactic acid per mole glucose and they convert the rest of the substrate into acetate (*c.* 0·1–0·2 mole), about 0·9 mole CO_2, about 0·8 mole ethanol, and in some of them 0·2–0·4 mole of glycerol. The other genera have been less well studied. The peptostreptococci give a mixed lactic–propionic fermentation, while the remaining four genera give a mixed lactic–butyric fermentation. From the work of Buyze (1955) one obtains an interesting insight into the internal oxidation-reduction balance of these bacteria. At 24° *Lactobacillus brevis* ferments glucose very well with the formation of the usual 'heterolactic' end products. At 37° this no longer occurs and an external H-acceptor is required. For example, we may have

1 glucose + 2 fructose → 1 lactic acid + 1 acetic acid + 1CO_2 +

2 mannitol.

In principle then, at 37° the bacteria are ready to carry out the reaction

glucose + H_2O → lactic acid + acetic acid + CO_2 + 4H,

but are unable to couple the 4H with an internal H-acceptor. Furthermore, unlike the clostridia, they are unable to eliminate the H as H_2 gas. *Butyribacterium* is able to do so and, since it also produces some butyric acid and reduces CO_2, it is an intermediate stage between the clostridial and 'heterolactic' fermentations. Although an H_2-producing lactic acid bacterium has not yet been described and might seem to be a heresy, yet, in view of the above reaction it seems quite a possibility. The latter reaction also explains the common production of mannitol during the fermentation of fructose. In the usual 'heterolactic' fermentations, pyruvate, dihydroxyacetone phosphate or acetaldehyde serve as H-acceptor. In the eubacteria, catenabacteria, ramibacteria and bifidobacteria aceto-acetyl-CoA can apparently also serve this function. The intermediary metabolism of the heterofermentative lactic acid bacteria has not yet been studied extensively. DeMoss (1953) showed that in *Leuconostoc mesenteroides* the EM, the HMP and the ED pathways are absent. Subsequently a new pathway was discovered: the phosphoketolase mechanism (Heath, Hurwitz & Horecker, 1956; Hurwitz, 1958), which can be schematically summarized as follows:

$$Glucose$$
$$\downarrow$$
$$glucose\text{-}6\text{-}phosphate$$
$$\downarrow$$
$$gluconate\text{-}6\text{-}phosphate$$
$$\downarrow$$
$$ribulose\text{-}5\text{-}phosphate + CO_2$$
$$\downarrow$$
$$ribose\text{-}5\text{-}phosphate$$
$$\downarrow$$
$$xylulose\text{-}5\text{-}phosphate$$
$$\downarrow phosphoketolase$$

glycerol $\xleftarrow{+4H}$ glyceraldehyde- $+$ acetylphosphate $\xrightarrow{+4H}$ ethanol
$$3\text{-}phosphate$$
$$\downarrow \qquad\qquad\qquad \downarrow$$
$$lactate \qquad\qquad\qquad acetate$$

Metabolism of pentoses by homofermentative and heterofermentative lactic acid bacteria

It is quite interesting to note that both groups of bacteria ferment a variety of pentoses with the formation of acetic and lactic acids, in each case by way of the phosphoketolase. Fukui, Ôi, Ôbayashi & Kitahara (1957) found that several homofermentative lactic acid bacteria are able to ferment pentoses with the formation of lactic acid, roughly according to the equation

3 mole of pentose → 5 mole of lactic acid.

A combination of the EM and HMP pathways could allow the metabolism of xylulose-5-phosphate completely to lactate according to the scheme:

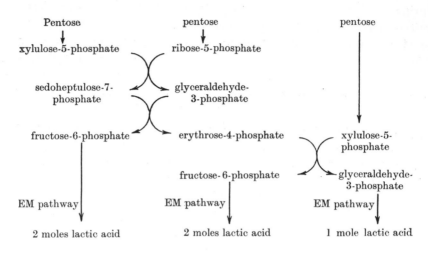

Possible relationship between the homofermentative and heterofermentative lactic acid bacteria

The 'homolactic' bacteria thus use the EM pathway for the formation of pyruvate. They also possess the HMP pathway, and it is likely that most of them also have the phosphoketolase pathway, used in the fermentation of pentoses. On the other hand, if one may generalize from the results with *Leuconostoc mesenteroides*, the phosphoketolase pathway would be the only effective one in the 'heterolactic' bacteria. The EM pathway cannot work in the latter bacteria because aldolase is lacking (Buyze, 1955). In *L. mesenteroides* the HMP pathway cannot be operative, since neither ribulose-5-phosphate nor ribose-5-phosphate are decomposed, indicating the absence of transketolase.

One can thus imagine that the 'heterolactic' bacteria could phylogenetically be derived from the 'homolactic' bacteria by the loss of aldolase and transketolase. Furthermore, there is some evidence that both groups also differ with respect to the mechanism of electron transport. It is well known that the homofermentative lactic acid bacteria on the whole grow poorly and form only very small colonies in aerobic conditions. The cytochrome system is not detectable in many streptococci (Farrell, 1935) or pediococci (Dobrogosz, 1960). Several of these bacteria on the other hand, such as *Lactobacillus delbrueckii*, contain very active flavoproteins. Aerobically H_2O_2 is formed and growth is arrested.

Heterofermentative lactic acid bacteria grow better aerobically, e.g. *Leuconostoc*. *L. cereale* behaves as a typical aerobe and it contains cytochromes. Unfortunately too little information on the cytochrome systems of the other bacteria from this group is available. It is an interesting subject for comparative biochemistry.

Summarizing, it is tempting to speculate that all the present lactic acid bacteria are derived from a common pool of ancestors very like the homofermentative lactic acid bacilli. One phylogenetic line might have persisted to yield the present-day cytochrome-lacking 'homolactic' rods and cocci. Another closely related line may have given the aerobic *Microbacterium* (which perhaps contains cytochromes). At some stage in the evolution aldolase and transketolase were lost, giving rise to a third line, the present-day heterolactic rods and cocci. It would be very interesting to study more extensively the fermentation patterns and the intermediary metabolism of the peptostreptococci, eubacteria, catena-bacteria, ramibacteria and bifidobacteria, in order to establish their relationship with the other heterofermentative lactic acid bacteria.

THE PROPIONIC ACID BACTERIA AND RELATED ORGANISMS

The propionic acid bacteria are short, Gram-positive, non-spore forming, non-motile rods. Morphologically they are intermediate between the lactic acid bacteria and the corynebacteria. In unfavourable conditions they have a tendency to form long branched swollen rods, much like the corynebacteria.

The propionic acid bacteria ferment glucose and some other sugars as well as lactate with the formation of *c.* 2 mole of propionic acid, *c.* 1 mole acetic acid, 1 mole CO_2 and some succinic acid. There is evidence that both the EM and HMP pathways are involved in the breakdown of sugars. The enzymic mechanism of the further breakdown of pyruvate is still partially unresolved. It is simplified in the scheme shown on the following page.

There are several groups of bacteria which appear to bear a more or less close relationship to the propionic acid bacteria. *Veillonella gazogenes*, a small Gram-negative coccus, ferments lactate in a similar fashion to the propionibacteria (Delwiche, Phares & Carson, 1956). In addition, it forms H_2. It is unable to ferment glucose. Several corynebacteria, *Actinomyces israelii* and a micromonospora are known to produce propionic acid. This strengthens the opinion that a close phylogenetic tie could exist amongst these micro-organisms. There are also intermediate groups between the lactic and the propionic acid bacteria, such as the peptostreptococci, which ferment glucose with the formation of lactic, propionic, acetic and formic acids. The propionic acid bacteria have the following scheme:

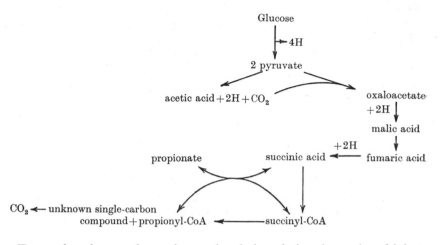

From the above scheme it can be deduced that bacteria which are unable to decarboxylate succinyl-CoA will accumulate succinate as a main end product of the fermentation, and therefore require CO_2. Such bacteria exist, and it is likely that their intermediary pyruvate metabolism might be closely related to the propionic acid bacteria. Most of them occur in the rumen. Several genera have been described: (1) *Bacteroides* sp. (Bryant *et al.* 1958), Gram-negative, strictly anaerobic non-motile rods or ovals, which are pleomorphic; (2) *Ruminococcus flavefaciens* (Sijpesteyn, 1951); (3) *Succinomonas amylolytica* (Bryant *et al.* 1958); (4) *Succinovibrio dextrinosolvens* (Bryant & Small, 1956) (the latter two genera are polarly flagellated and morphologically resemble pseudo-monads); (5) *Borrelia* sp. (Bryant, 1952); (6) *Cytophaga succinicans* (Anderson & Ordal, 1961). A different method of propionic acid formation was found in an unidentified anaerobic coccus, isolated by Elsden and called LC coccus. These cells are unable to attack glucose, but ferment lactate in the following fashion:

1 mole lactic acid → 0·98 mole CO_2 + 0·12 mole acetic acid +
0·07 mole propionic acid + 0·18 mole butyric acid + 0·3 mole
valeric acid + 0·03 mole H_2.

Ladd & Walker (1959) studied the fermentation with cell-free extracts, and the overall equation is approximately

2 lactate → 1 propionate + 1 acetate + 1CO_2 + 1H_2.

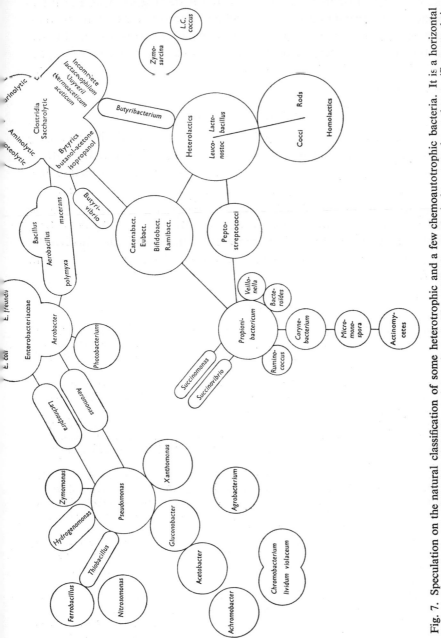

Fig. 7. Speculation on the natural classification of some heterotrophic and a few chemoautotrophic bacteria. It is a horizontal section at the present moment through the phylogenetic tree. The genera are tentatively arranged together to illustrate their morphological, physiological and biochemical kinship, based on the present fragmentary information. The closer they are, the closer the relationship is thought to be. It is realized that this model is temporary and will undergo many improvements when more data on the intermediary metabolism become available.

Evidence was presented that acrylate (or a derivative) was the intermediate between lactate and propionate. This shows that more than one mechanism is active in propionate formation. It is also an indication that the LC coccus is probably not as closely related to the propionibacteria and *Veillonella*, as might be suspected from its fermentation equation.

CONCLUSIONS

It can be seen from the above review that the comparative biochemistry and enzymology can give us a considerably better insight into the natural relationships amongst the bacteria. These data will have to be included in attempts at improved Adansonian analyses. At the present moment it is possible to see dimly the natural relationships of part of the bacterial world. It is a horizontal section through the phylogenetic tree, where the vertical dimension represents time and the horizontal dimension represents relationship. A first crude attempt is made in Fig. 7.

REFERENCES

ALTERMATT, H. A., SIMPSON, F. J. & NEISH, A. C. (1955). The fermentation of D-allose and D-glucose by *Aerobacter aerogenes*. *Canad. J. Microbiol.* **1**, 473.

ANDERSON, R. L. & ORDAL, E. J. (1961). *Cytophaga succinicans* sp.n., a facultatively anaerobic, aquatic myxobacterium. *J. Bact.* **81**, 130.

BARKER, H. A. (1956). *Bacterial Fermentations*. New York: John Wiley and Sons.

BECK, E. S. & LINDSTROM, E. S. (1955). The oxidative metabolism of *Bacillus cereus*. *J. Bact.* **70**, 335.

BERGMANN, E. D., LITTAUER, U. Z. & VOLCANI, B. E. (1954). Breakdown of pentose phosphates in *Escherichia coli*. *Biochim. biophys. Acta*, **13**, 288.

BERNSTEIN, I. A. & FOSSITT, D. (1960). Biosynthesis of ribose and desoxyribose by *Pseudomonas saccharophila*. *Bact. Proc.* 182.

BLACKWOOD, A. C., NEISH, A. C., BROWN, W. E. & LEDINGHAM, G. A. (1947). Fermentation of glucose by strains of *Bacillus subtilis*. *Canad. J. Res.* B, **25**, 56.

BLACKWOOD, A. C., NEISH, A. C. & LEDINGHAM, G. A. (1956). Dissimilation of glucose at controlled pH values by pigmented and non-pigmented strains of *Escherichia coli*. *J. Bact.* **72**, 497.

BREED, R. S., MURRAY, E. G. D. & SMITH, N. R. (1957). *Bergey's Manual of Determinative Bacteriology*, 7th ed. Baltimore: Williams and Wilkins Co.

BRYANT, M. P. (1952). The isolation and characteristics of a spirochete from the bovine rumen. *J. Bact.* **64**, 325.

BRYANT, M. P. & SMALL, N. (1956). Characteristics of two new genera of anaerobic curved rods isolated from the rumen of cattle. *J. Bact.* **72**, 22.

BRYANT, M. P., SMALL, N., BOUMA, C. & CHU, H. (1958). *Bacteroides ruminicola* n.sp. and *Succinomonas amylolytica* the new genus and species. *J. Bact.* **76**, 15.

BUYZE, G. (1955). *De Koolhydraatstofwisseling van* Lactobacillus brevis. Thesis, Utrecht.

CERBÓN, J. & BOJALIL, L. F. (1961). Physiological relationships of rapidly growing mycobacteria. *J. gen. Microbiol.* **25**, 7.

COHEN, S. S. (1951). Utilisation of gluconate and glucose in growing and virus-infected *Escherichia coli*. *Nature, Lond.* **168**, 746.

DE LEY, J. (1957). The hexose monophosphate oxidative route in *Aerobacter cloacae*. *Enzymologia*, **18**, 33.

DE LEY, J. (1961). Comparative carbohydrate metabolism and localisation of enzymes in *Pseudomonas* and related bacteria. *J. appl. Bact.* **23**, 400.

DELWICHE, E. A., PHARES, E. F. & CARSON, S. F. (1956). Succinic acid decarboxylation system in *Propionibacterium pentosaceum* and *Veillonella gazogenes*. *J. Bact.* **71**, 598.

DEMOSS, R. D. (1953). Routes of ethanol formation in bacteria. *J. cell. comp. Physiol.* **41**, suppl. 207.

DOBROGOSZ, W. (1960). *Studies on the development and utility of oxidative activities in* Pediococcus cerevisiae. Thesis, Pennsylvania State University.

DOI, R., HALVORSON, H. & CHURCH, B. (1959). The mechanism of glucose and hexose phosphate oxidation in extracts of *Bacillus cereus* spores. *J. Bact.* **77**, 43.

DONKER, H. J. L. (1926). *Bijdrage tot de Kennis der Boterzuur-, Butyl-alcohol en Acetongistingen*. Thesis, Delft.

DOUDOROFF, M. (1942). Some observations on the anaerobic metabolism of facultatively anaerobic species. *J. Bact.* **44**, 461.

EHRLICH, H. L. & SEGEL, I. H. (1959). Carbon balance for *Bacillus megaterium* growing in a glucose-mineral medium. *J. Bact.* **77**, 110.

ENTNER, N. & DOUDOROFF, M. (1952). Glucose and gluconic acid oxidation of *Pseudomonas saccharophila*. *J. biol. Chem.* **196**, 853.

FARRELL, M. A. (1935). Studies on the respiratory mechanism of the streptococci. *J. Bact.* **29**, 411.

FUKUI, S., ÔI, A., ÔBAYASHI, A. & KITAHARA, K. (1957). A new type-lactic acid fermentation of pentoses by lactic acid bacteria. *J. gen. appl. Microbiol.* **3**, 258.

GARY, N. D., KLAUSMEIER, R. E. & BARD, R. C. (1954). Metabolic patterns of nutritionally differentiated cell types of *Bacillus subtilis*. *J. Bact.* **68**, 437.

GIBBS, M. & DEMOSS, R. (1954). Anaerobic dissimilation of C^{14}-labelled glucose and fructose by *Pseudomonas lindneri*. *J. biol. Chem.* **207**, 689.

GIBBS, M., DUMROSE, R., BENNETT, F. A. & BUBECK, M. R. (1950). On the mechanism of bacterial fermentation of glucose to lactic acid studied with C^{14} glucose. *J. biol. Chem.* **184**, 545.

GIBBS, M. & PAEGE, L. M. (1961). The anaerobic dissimilation of D-xylose-1-C^{14}, D-arabinose-1-C^{14} and L-arabinose-1-C^{14} by *Escherichia coli*. *J. biol. Chem.* **236**, 6.

GIBBS, M., SOKATCH, J. T. & GUNSALUS, I. C. (1955). Product labelling of glucose-1-C^{14} fermentation by homofermentative and heterofermentative lactic acid bacteria. *J. Bact.* **70**, 572.

GILARDI, E., HILL, L. R., TURRI, M. & SILVESTRI, L. G. (1960). Quantitative methods in the systematics of actinomycetales. I. *G. Microbiol.* **8**, 203.

GUNSALUS, I. C., HORECKER, B. L. & WOOD, W. A. (1955). Pathways of carbohydrate metabolism in microorganisms. *Bact. Rev.* **19**, 79.

HAMILTON, R. D. & WOLFE, R. S. (1959). Pyruvate exchange reactions in *Bacillus macerans*. *J. Bact.* **78**, 253.

HARDEN, A. (1901). The chemical action of *Bacillus coli communis* and similar organisms on carbohydrates and allied compounds. *J. chem. Soc.* **79**, 612.

HARDEN, A. & WALPOLE, G. S. (1906). The chemical action of *B. lactis aerogenes* (Escherich) on glucose and mannitol. Production of 2-3-butylene glycol and acetylmethylcarbinol. *Proc. roy. Soc.* B, **77**, 399.

HEATH, E. C., HURWITZ, J. & HORECKER, B. L. (1956). Acetyl phosphate formation in the phosphorolytic cleavage of pentose phosphate. *J. Amer. chem. Soc.* **78**, 5449.

HILL, L. R. (1959). The Adansonian classification of the staphylococci. *J. gen. Microbiol.* **20**, 277.

HOCHSTER, R. M. & KATZNELSON, H. (1958). On the mechanism of glucose-6-phosphate oxidation in cell-free extracts of *Xanthomonas phaseoli* (XP 8). *Canad. J. Biochem. Physiol.* **36**, 669.

HURWITZ, J. (1958). Pentose phosphate cleavage by *Leuconostoc mesenteroides*. *Biochim. biophys. Acta*, **28**, 599.

KATZNELSON, H. (1955). Production of pyruvate from 6-phosphogluconate by bacterial plant pathogens and legume bacteria. *Nature, Lond.* **175**, 551.

KATZNELSON, H. (1958). Metabolism of phytopathogenic bacteria. II. Metabolism of carbohydrates by cell-free extracts. *J. Bact.* **75**, 541.

KOVACHEVICH, R. & WOOD, W. A. (1955 *a*). Carbohydrate metabolism by *Pseudomonas fluorescens*. III. Purification and properties of a 6-phosphogluconate dehydrase. *J. biol. Chem.* **213**, 745.

KOVACHEVICH, R. & WOOD, W. A. (1955 *b*). Carbohydrate metabolism by *Pseudomonas fluorescens*. IV. Purification and properties of 2-keto-3-deoxy-6-phosphogluconate aldolase. *J. biol. Chem.* **213**, 757.

KRAGHT, A. J. & STARR, M. P. (1952). Fermentation of galacturonic acid and glucose by a strain of *Erwinia carotovora*. *J. Bact.* **64**, 259.

KRICHEVSKY, M. I. & WOOD, W. A. (1961). Pathway of ribose-5-phosphate utilization in *Microbacterium lacticum*. *J. Bact.* **81**, 246.

LADD, J. N. & WALKER, D. J. (1959). The fermentation of lactate and acrylate by the rumen micro-organism LC. *Biochem. J.* **71**, 364.

LEWIS, K. F., BLUMENTHAL, H. J., WEINRACK, R. S. & WEINHOUSE, S. (1955). An isotope tracer study of glucose catabolism in *Pseudomonas fluorescens*. *J. biol. Chem.* **216**, 273.

LYSENKO, O. & SNEATH, P. H. A. (1959). The use of models in bacterial classification. *J. gen. Microbiol.* **20**, 284.

McNAIR SCOTT, D. B. & COHEN, S. S. (1953). The oxidative pathway of carbohydrate metabolism in *Escherichia coli*. *Biochem. J.* **55**, 23.

MICKELSON, M. & WERKMAN, C. H. (1940). Formation of trimethyleneglycol from glycerol by *Aerobacter*. *Enzymologia*, **8**, 252.

MYLROIE, R. L. & KATZNELSON, H. (1957). Carbohydrate metabolism of *Bacillus larvae*. *J. Bact.* **74**, 217.

NEISH, A. C. (1953). Studies on the anaerobic dissimilation of glucose by *Bacillus subtilis* (Ford's type). *Canad. J. Bot.* **31**, 265.

NEISH, A. C., BLACKWOOD, A. C., ROBERTSON, F. M. & LEDINGHAM, G. A. (1948). Dissimilation of glucose by bacteria of the genus *Serratia*. *Canad. J. Res. B*, **26**, 335.

NISMAN, B. (1954). The Stickland reaction. *Bact. Rev.* **18**, 16.

PIVNICK, H. & SABINA, L. R. (1957). Studies of *Aeromonas formicans* Crawford comb.nov. from soluble oil emulsions. *J. Bact.* **73**, 247.

PUZISS, M. & RITTENBERG, S. C. (1957). Studies on the anaerobic metabolism of *Bacillus anthracis* and *Bacillus cereus*. *J. Bact.* **73**, 48.

RABINOWITZ, J. C. (1959). Fermentative metabolism. *Annu. Rev. Microbiol.* **13**, 441.

REYNOLDS, H. & WERKMAN, C. H. (1937). The intermediate dissimilation of glucose by *Aerobacter indologenes*. *J. Bact.* **33**, 603.

SIJPESTEYN, A. (1951). On *Ruminococcus flavefaciens*, a cellulose-decomposing bacterium from the rumen of sheep and cattle. *J. gen. Microbiol.* **5**, 869.

SIMPSON, F. J., WOLIN, M. J. & WOOD, W. A. (1958). Degradation of L-arabinose by *Aerobacter aerogenes*. *J. biol. Chem.* **230**, 457.

SMITH, N. R., GORDON, R. E. & CLARK, F. E. (1952). Aerobic sporeforming bacteria. *Agric. Monogr. U.S. Dept. Agric.* No. 16.

SNEATH, P. H. A. (1957a). Some thoughts on bacterial classification. *J. gen. Microbiol.* **17**, 184.

SNEATH, P. H. A. (1957b). The application of computers to taxonomy. *J. gen. Microbiol.* **17**, 201.

SNEATH, P. H. A. & COWAN, S. T. (1958). An electro-taxonomic survey of bacteria. *J. gen. Microbiol.* **19**, 551.

SOKATCH, J. T. & GUNSALUS, I. C. (1957). Aldonic acid metabolism. I. Pathway of carbon in an inducible gluconate fermentation by *Streptococcus faecalis. J. Bact.* **73**, 452.

STADTMAN, E. R. (1956). Propionate oxidation by cell-free extracts of *Clostridium propionicum. Fed. Proc.* **15**, 360.

STANIER, R. Y. (1943). A note on the taxonomy of *Proteus hydrophilus. J. Bact.* **46**, 213.

STERN, I. J., WANG, C. H. & GILMOUR, C. M. (1960). Comparative catabolism of carbohydrates in *Pseudomonas* species. *J. Bact.* **79**, 601.

STOKES, J. L. (1949). Fermentation of glucose by suspensions of *Escherichia coli. J. Bact.* **57**, 147.

SZYMONA, M. & DOUDOROFF, M. (1960). Carbohydrate metabolism in *Rhodopseudomonas spheroides. J. gen. Microbiol.* **22**, 167.

VANDEMARK, P. J. & WOOD, W. A. (1956). The pathways of glucose dissimilation by *Microbacterium lacticum. J. Bact.* **71**, 385.

VAN DER LEK, J. B. (1930). *Onderzoekingen over de Butylalkoholgisting.* Thesis, Delft.

WANG, C. H., GILMOUR, C. M. & CHELDELIN, V. H. (1958). Comparative study of glucose catabolism in microorganisms. *VII Intern. Congr. Microbiol., Stockholm, Abstracts*, p. 146.

WANG, C. H., STERN, I., GILMOUR, C. M., KLUNGSOYR, S., REED, D. J., BIALY, J. J., CHRISTENSEN, B. E. & CHELDELIN, V. H. (1958). Comparative study of glucose catabolism by the radiorespirometric method. *J. Bact.* **76**, 207.

WOOD, W. A. & SWERDT, R. F. (1953a). Alternate pathways of hexose oxidation in *Pseudomonas fluorescens. J. cell. comp. Physiol.* **41**, Suppl. 1, 165.

WOOD, W. A. & SWERDT, R. F. (1953b). Carbohydrate oxidation by *Pseudomonas fluorescens.* I. The mechanism of glucose and gluconate oxidation. *J. biol. Chem.* **201**, 501.

WOOD, W. A. & SWERDT, R. F. (1954). Carbohydrate oxidation by *Pseudomonas fluorescens.* II. Mechanism of hexose phosphate oxidation. *J. biol. Chem.* **206**, 625.

THE USE OF BIOCHEMICAL CRITERIA IN THE TAXONOMY OF YEASTS

NELLY J. W. KREGER-VAN RIJ

Centraalbureau voor Schimmelcultures, Yeast Division, Delft, Netherlands

INTRODUCTION

A discussion of biochemical criteria for the taxonomy of yeasts requires an introduction into the general principles of the classification of these fungi. First we may recall the definition of yeasts, a definition which is neither precise nor binding. Yeasts have been defined as fungi in which the unicellular form is predominant and in which vegetative reproduction is usually by budding. They do not constitute a natural taxonomic unit, though many of them are closely related. The historical developments which have led to the collection of these organisms under one heading have largely been governed by practical considerations.

The yeasts are distributed in three major taxonomic groups. The ascosporogenous yeasts may be placed in one or two families of Ascomycetes, the ballistosporogenous yeasts probably belong to the Basidiomycetes, and the asporogenous yeasts are classified as a single family, Cryptococcaceae, Fungi Imperfecti.

It was probably in the first instance the unicellular condition of the yeasts which promoted the use of uniform criteria for their classification, though the value attached to the criteria varies in the three groups. The limited number of morphological criteria made it inevitable that physiological properties would play an important part in the classification. Moreover, the earliest described yeasts, from beer and wine, possessed a conspicuous physiological property, namely the ability to ferment sugars.

Differences in the fermentation of a number of sugars were recorded and used for the differentiation of the yeasts at an early date. From that time it has been generally accepted that physiological properties should be used to distinguish species. Physiological characters as well as morphological ones are also used to define genera.

We may illustrate this by noting the original descriptions of the genera *Saccharomyces*, *Pichia* and *Hansenula*. *Saccharomyces* was the first genus to be described. It comprised budding sporogenous yeasts which did not form true mycelium (Reess, 1870). Hansen (1883) included physiological properties in his description of the species *S. cerevisiae,* *S. ellipsoideus* and *S. pastorianus,* namely fermentation of the sugars glucose, sucrose and maltose. Originally several species of yeast were placed in *Saccharomyces* which were later transferred to other genera. Thus *S. membranaefaciens* became *Pichia membranaefaciens* (Hansen, 1904). The new genus *Pichia* differed from *Saccharomyces* in the shape of the spores, in the absence of fermentation, and in the abundant formation of 'mycelium'. Another species, *S. anomalus,* became *Willia* (later *Hansenula*) *anomala.* Hansen (1904) gave the following diagnosis of this genus: formation of a dry pellicle on liquid media, spores hat-shaped or lemon-shaped with a prominent ledge, esters are formed by most species, a few species do not ferment sugars.

These genera, *Saccharomyces, Pichia* and *Hansenula,* were thus characterized by a combination of morphological and physiological properties.

Since the description of the first species, yeasts have been studied from various points of view, and knowledge of their properties has increased considerably. At the same time many new forms have come to light. The integration of these forms into a system which is considered to express natural relationships and which is also practicable is often very difficult.

Morphological characters determine the classification of the sporogenous yeasts into the main groups, i.e. families, subfamilies and tribes. These morphological characters are taken from both vegetative and sexual states. The distinction between fission and unipolar, bipolar and multilateral budding is of importance in vegetative reproduction. In the sexual states the formation of the ascus and the shape of the ascospores and ballistospores may be typical of certain taxa.

In the last few decades investigations of the sexual reproduction have led to a better insight into the life cycle of yeasts. We have grown familiar with the alternation of haploid and diploid phases, with homo- and heterothallism and with the occurrence of heterozygotes. Basic information on these subjects has been provided by the studies of Winge, Lindegren and others. Since the characteristics of the life cycle are highly valued in taxonomy this knowledge is of fundamental importance in yeast taxonomy.

As an illustration one may mention the realization that asporogenous strains may simply be one of the mating types of a heterothallic species, and this may lead to the search for the other mating type. Thus Wickerham & Burton (1952) have found strains of opposite mating type in asporogenous species. When two strains of opposite mating type are mixed, conjugation and ascus formation may occur and thus allow the classification of the strains as sporogenous species.

Sporogenous yeasts of which the life cycle is completely known probably yield the best opportunities for classification in a natural system because important morphological properties (such as spore shape) may be studied. The classification of the asporogenous yeasts is necessarily more artificial because these important characteristics are lacking. Thus the genera *Candida* and *Torulopsis* contain imperfect states of species of diverging genera. The differentiation of *Candida* from *Torulopsis* on the basis of the presence or absence of pseudomycelium is probably merely of practical convenience.

As mentioned above, physiological properties are largely used for the differentiation at species level. In the sporogenous yeasts the genera are partly defined biochemically. In the asporogenous yeasts biochemical criteria are still more important because of the lack of the morphological criteria of the sexual stages: for instance, *Cryptococcus* and *Rhodotorula* are mainly characterized biochemically.

BIOCHEMICAL CRITERIA

Of the biochemical criteria used in the taxonomy of yeasts sugar fermentation and the assimilation of carbon compounds and of nitrate nitrogen are the most important. Fermentation was introduced for the differentiation of species at an early stage. The utilization of nitrate as a source of nitrogen was extensively used as a criterion by Stelling-Dekker (1931). Auxanographic assimilation tests for sugars were employed systematically by Lodder (1934), and assimilation of other carbon compounds was studied by several authors. Wickerham & Burton (1948) described a standardized method for the assimilation tests, which has found general acceptance. Special tests have been devised for the splitting of the β-glucosides aesculin and arbutin, based on a colour reaction of the resulting aglucon.

Some other reactions, occasionally derived from bacteriology, are also used as criteria, e.g. liquefaction of gelatin, coagulation and peptonization of milk, the urease reaction, and the splitting of fat. Moreover, metabolites may be formed which are typical of a genus or species, e.g. acetic acid in *Brettanomyces*, ethyl acetate in *Hansenula*. Many biochemical tests have been devised, but because the design of these tests has great influence on the results obtained, strict standardization of the test procedures is necessary. These standardized tests are generally rather simple. On the one hand, this makes them easy to perform. On the other hand, the biochemical information obtained from such tests is restricted. However, practice has shown that the results obtained are generally sufficient for characterizing species.

In the following sections the principal biochemical criteria, fermentation and assimilation will be discussed. For a detailed description of them the reader is referred to Wickerham (1951) and the Delft yeast monographs (Stelling-Dekker, 1931; Lodder, 1934; Diddens & Lodder, 1942; Lodder & Kreger-van Rij, 1952).

FERMENTATION

Fermentation of sugars by yeasts results in the production of alcohol and carbon dioxide. For the fermentation of a sugar an enzyme system is required. This is controlled by various genes, and both biochemical and genetic studies have been made of such enzymes and genes. These studies concern the fermentation pathways of glucose and galactose, and the enzymes and genes which control the splitting of disaccharides, trisaccharides and polysaccharides. An example is the occurrence of six different genes responsible for the fermentation of maltose as demonstrated by Winge & Roberts (1948, 1950, 1956) and Gilliland (1953); the presence of any of them in a yeast strain allows the fermentation of this sugar. Three genes are known to control the hydrolysis of raffinose to fructose and melibiose. An example of the study of an enzyme is the recent investigation of inulase, a β-fructosidase, by Snyder & Phaff (1960). It is present in strains of *Saccharomyces fragilis*, and it catalyses the splitting off of fructose from inulin, sucrose and raffinose. It appeared to be distinct from invertase, another β-fructosidase.

Stability of the fermentative pattern

The ability to ferment a given sugar has proved to be rather constant in yeast strains. The fermentation pattern is one of the important characteristics of a species. For the definition of genera the fermentation rate is generally less important, but often helpful. For instance *Saccharomyces* is characterized by vigorous fermentation of one or more sugars, while the species of *Cryptococcus* and *Rhodotorula* are non-fermentative. In *Hansenula*, however, every gradation from non-fermentation to good fermentation is found.

There are a few exceptions to the constancy of the fermentation pattern of a strain. A very striking example of such an exception is a mutation in the species *Saccharomyces capensis* described by van der Walt & Tscheuschner (1956). When first isolated this yeast did not ferment maltose. However, when the strain was plated out on malt agar, after 10–17 days papillae were visible on the surface of the colonies. These papillae consisted of cells which fermented maltose readily. When the strain was maintained on malt agar for a longer time the maltose fermenting cells outgrew the cells which did not ferment maltose. The maltose-fermenting strain cannot be distinguished from *S. oviformis* by the usual criteria. Roberts & van der Walt (1960) made a genetical study of *S. capensis* and the maltose-fermenting mutant, and found that a single gene was involved. A similar case may be the change in the strain of *Torulopsis colliculosa*, isolated and described by Hartmann (1903). The author mentioned that young cultures of this strain on malt agar did not ferment maltose, while the cells of the papillae (which formed after some time on the colonies) were maltose positive. When Lodder (1934) studied a strain of this species she only found maltose positive cells, even in the young colonies. A third case in which the ability to ferment maltose was acquired by a culture is mentioned by Kudriavzev (1938) in *S. paradoxus* Batschinskaia. Kudriavzev describes this change as an 'experimental modification'. He obtained maltose positive cells from the maltose negative *S. paradoxus* by growing this species in malt extract for a long period. The strain of this species, studied by Stelling-Dekker (1931), obtained from Guilliermond, was maltose positive. Kudriavzev (1960) mentions *S. tetrasporus* as a synonym of *S. paradoxus*. Both species have been isolated from exudate of an oak tree. Stelling-Dekker (1931) found that *S. tetrasporus* did not ferment maltose and classified it as *S. mangini* var. *tetrasporus*. Lodder & Kreger-van Rij (1952) studied this strain and found it to be maltose positive. Phaff, Miller & Shifrine (1956) isolated from *Drosophila* 22 strains which they designated *S. cerevisiae* var. *tetrasporus*. The strains differed from *S. cerevisiae* in the smaller size of the cells in malt extract. A delayed fermentation of maltose was frequently found among these strains. It is possible that these cases of the acquiring of maltose fermentation are all based on mutation and subsequent selection of the maltose positive cells by the malt agar medium, as was shown for *S. capensis* by Roberts & van der Walt (1960).

Another phenomenon influencing the fermentation of a special sugar is adaptation. Galactose is notable in this respect, but the fermentation of sucrose, maltose and melibiose may also be adaptive.

The transport of a sugar into the interior of a yeast cell is an important factor in the fermentation of the sugar. Douglas & Condie

(1954), as a result of genetical studies on galactose fermentation in *Saccharomyces*, have suggested the presence of a mechanism for this transport which they found to be controlled by one gene.

Methods of testing for fermentation

There are several methods by which the fermentation may be observed. Usually it is the production of carbon dioxide that is observed and for this purpose both closed and open test systems are of use. In the former case (where the amount of available oxygen is limited) growth of the yeast in the sugar-containing solution may be restricted, and the inoculum should be heavy. If the yeast can ferment the sugar, gas production usually occurs early. Quantitative determination of gas is possible in some apparatus of this type. In an open system (where oxygen is more readily available) good growth is possible. These conditions have been found favourable for the fermentation of sugars which require adaptation. The conditions in an open system are complex. The carbon dioxide which is collected in a closed part of the vessel diffuses through the liquid to the open surface. In Durham tubes and Einhorn tubes, which are examples of open vessels, a weak or slow fermentation may be unnoticed if the carbon dioxide diffuses out as quickly as it is formed. Thus the closed vessels have the advantage of giving quick results and retaining all carbon dioxide produced. Their disadvantage is that adaptation is not favoured.

The medium used in the fermentation tests is of importance, especially if growth should occur. Yeast water or yeast extract, which provide nitrogen as well as necessary vitamins, are often used. Wickerham (1951) adds peptone and, as indicator, bromthymol blue to this medium. Bouthilet, Neilson, Mrak & Phaff (1949) have pointed out that yeast water prepared from baker's yeast may contain trehalose, and yeast strains which ferment this sugar may give a very weak fermentation reaction in Durham tubes containing yeast water alone. The authors advocate the use of yeast autolysate, during the preparation of which the trehalose has been destroyed, in a 1 in 10 dilution. Fermentation of trehalose in yeast water is conspicuously shown by *Torulopsis glabrata*. In Durham tubes containing either galactose, sucrose, maltose or lactose (sugars which are not fermented by this species) a bubble of gas may be formed from the trehalose in the yeast water.

The sugars which are commonly used in fermentation tests are glucose, galactose, sucrose, maltose, lactose, raffinose and melibiose. van der Walt & van Kerken (1959) have added melezitose, cellobiose and trehalose for the study of *Brettanomyces*. Polysaccharides, like inulin and soluble starch, may also be used. Gilliland (1956) has suggested the use of maltotriose (which can be prepared from wort) for the differentiation of certain species. True brewers' yeasts are expected to ferment this sugar. He found that a number of strains of *Saccharomyces cerevisiae* and its variety *ellipsoideus* reacted differently with maltotriose, some fermenting it and others not. Gilliland proposes that strains fermenting this sugar should be regarded as *S. cerevisiae*, while the nonfermenting strains should be regarded as a separate species. He found that the fermentation of maltotriose is governed by a single gene. Kudriavzev (1960) also distinguishes between yeasts fermenting maltotriose and those not fermenting it. *S. cerevisiae* and *S. vini* differ in this respect. The latter species (of which most of the strains have been isolated from wine) does not ferment maltotriose. A similar distinction is made between *S. carlsbergensis* and *S. uvarum*.

The fermentation of raffinose

Some details of the fermentation of raffinose will be discussed because it has received the attention of a number of authors. In the splitting of this trisaccharide several enzymes may be involved. In the first place it may be split into fructose and melibiose by invertase, a β-fructosidase. Secondly, it may be split into galactose and sucrose by melibiase, an α-galactosidase. A combination of both enzymes leads to the total fermentation of raffinose, that is if glucose, fructose and galactose can all be fermented by the strain.

The taxonomic difference between the species *Saccharomyces cerevisiae* and *S. carlsbergensis* lies in the presence of melibiase in the latter and the absence of it in the former, while both species contain invertase. The species *S. oleaceus* (Santa Maria, 1958) contains melibiase, but does not split sucrose. It therefore ferments only one-third of the raffinose namely only the galactose part. Another yeast, *S. italicus* var. *melibiosi* described by van Uden & Assis-Lopes (1957), also contains melibiase, but in addition it possesses a sucrose-splitting enzyme, which, however, does not attack the raffinose molecule. Sucrose is slowly fermented by this variety. It is identical with the species *S. oleaginosus* (Santa Maria, 1958).

It has been the hope of taxonomists that they might obtain information on the enzymes involved in the splitting of raffinose with few simple tests, and without the use of melibiose, mainly because the latter sugar is very expensive. In these tests raffinose is fermented in a Durham tube.

When this fermentation has finished the presence or absence of melibiose is determined by a subsequent fermentation with *Saccharomyces carlsbergensis* (Wickerham, 1943) or by a reduction test (Domercq, 1956; van Uden, 1956). These tests did not take into account the fermentation of raffinose in the presence of melibiase alone. Therefore, after the description of *S. italicus* var. *melibiosi* (which contains melibiase but no invertase) van Uden & Assis-Lopes (1957) extended the tests. After the initial fermentation of raffinose, the sucrose left could be detected by inoculation with *Candida tropicalis* which ferments sucrose but not raffinose. Since in *S. italicus* var. *melibiosi* the action of the sucrose-splitting enzyme is quite marked, though rather slow and incomplete, gas formation after subinoculation with *C. tropicalis* will always be found. Therefore this method is not reliable. In a van Iterson-Kluyver fermentometer strains of *S. italicus* var. *melibiosi* were found to ferment about one-half of the raffinose.

Losada (1957) has demonstrated the complementary action of the genes *Me* (α-galactosidase) and *M*1 (α-glucosidase) in a hybrid strain which was capable of fermenting raffinose completely. Melibiase acted first and the resulting sucrose was hydrolysed by the α-glucosidase. It appeared that the action of the latter enzyme was influenced by the medium on which the cells had been grown. *S. italicus* var. *melibiosi* shows a resemblance to the hybrid studied by Losada. Ramirez Gomez (1959) has also contributed to the literature on raffinose fermentation. He deduced the presence or absence of invertase and melibiase from the auxanographic assimilation tests of raffinose and melibiose. Apart from the fact that raffinose and melibiose often give negative results in these tests because the possibilities for adaptation are small, Ramirez Gomez does not take account of the type of yeast which contains only melibiase and no invertase. A simple method to avoid the complication mentioned above is the use of a melibiose solution for the fermentation test. The solution can be prepared by partially fermenting raffinose with a strain of *S. cerevisiae*. A description for this preparation has been given by Skinner & Bouthilet (1947).

Standardization of fermentation tests

As mentioned above the characteristics studied cannot be dissociated from the methods used to detect them. Therefore, in fermentation the use of a standard method for comparative study is of great importance. Allowance for adaptation, by using a suitable vessel such as the Durham tube, has been found advantageous since it increases the number of properties useful in taxonomy. The tests in these tubes may yield a clear-cut result when the fermentation is vigorous, or when it is delayed but still reasonably vigorous. However, it is also possible that the results are better expressed as: fermentation positive, weak, or negative. Skinner & Fletcher (1960) have objected to the crudeness of this terminology since they consider the difference between fermentation and non-fermentation to be fundamental. Even if this is so it may be difficult to find a method which gives satisfactory results. Lodder (1934) and Diddens & Lodder (1942) have pointed out that with less crude methods (for example the Warburg manometric technique) a weak fermentation may be observed in yeast species which show no fermentation in Einhorn and Durham tubes. On the other hand, the presence of adaptive enzymes in the yeast may not be detected using the Warburg apparatus. Though more accurate methods will doubtless give a better insight in the biochemistry of yeasts, the taxonomic value of the data obtained by them remains still to be established.

ASSIMILATION

Assimilation of carbon compounds

The assimilation of carbon compounds by a yeast can be detected by observing growth, i.e. an increase in the number of yeast cells in a complete medium containing this compound as sole source of carbon. Both fermentation and respiration may be responsible for this growth.

Five sugars—glucose, galactose, sucrose, maltose and lactose—have been used extensively for differentiating species. Besides the sugars used in the fermentation tests other compounds, namely pentoses, alcohols and acids, may be used. Wickerham & Burton (1948) have made preliminary tests with some 70 compounds, and have selected 38 of them for use in the description of strains. A smaller number of these may suffice for routine classification tests in a given genus. Before deciding whether a compound is suitable for differentiating the species in a genus, a large number of strains should be studied. After a general survey the species may be defined, often on a combination of morphological and physiological criteria.

In the genus *Hansenula*, extensively studied by Wickerham (1951), the species are marked off rather clearly from one another on these principles. The role of the assimilation tests in this classification may be illustrated by the fact that of the 38 carbon compounds used for the description of the species 8 are of considerable importance for their differentiation. However, variations in reactions to one compound among the strains of one species are also frequent and are noted for 21 compounds. A secondary but very important help for the delimitation of the species in *Hansenula* is that hybridization does not occur between them (Wickerham & Burton, 1956). This is not the case in all other genera. *Rhodotorula* is an example of a genus in which assimilation reactions are of limited value, since variation is considerable (Skinner & Huxley, 1956). The choice of compounds to be used for the differentiation is here very difficult, while the morphology of this asporogenous genus offers little assistance.

Assimilation reactions may be of importance not only for the characterization of species, but also for genera. Thus the genus *Dekkeromyces*, named by Wickerham (1955) and Wickerham & Burton (1956) but not yet formally proposed, according to these authors differs from *Saccharomyces* (from which it is to be segregated) in the assimilation of a greater number of carbon compounds among other features.

Barnett & Kornberg (1960) distinguished between K+ and K− yeasts, the former capable of utilizing intermediates of the tricarboxylic acid cycle when exogenously supplied with them, the latter not. *Saccharomyces cerevisiae* strains appeared to be the K− type. However, this difference did not apply to cell-free extracts. It was suggested by the authors that the difference does not lie in the presence or absence of the enzyme system, but in the permeability of the intact cells.

Among carbon compounds tested, the assimilation of two, cellobiose and salicin, may indicate the presence of β-glucosidases. In addition the splitting of the β-glucosides arbutin and aesculin can be detected in special tests in which the presence of the free aglucon is shown by a colour reaction with ferric chloride. Assimilation of one compound does not necessarily mean that the others are split as well, though very often there is agreement. Barnett, Ingram & Swain (1956) made a careful study of the action on β-glucosides of a number of yeast strains. They suggested that yeasts may contain different β-glucosidases. They also pointed out the influence of the medium on the production of enzymes. Apart from the assimilation tests for cellobiose and salicin, we have found that among the routine tests for the identification of a yeast testing for the splitting of arbutin is very helpful.

Standardization of assimilation tests

Several types of assimilation tests are available. They cannot be detailed here, but the main aspects of some must be noted because the results obtained largely depend on the technique employed. In one test growth is tested in a liquid basal medium to which a single carbon compound has been added. In a second test a solid medium of the same composition is used, and the yeast is inoculated on the agar as a streak or dot. In a third the yeast inoculum is mixed in a basal medium with agar and poured into a dish, and after solidification of the agar a small amount of the carbon compound is placed on the surface.

The first method has been standardized by Wickerham & Burton (1948). By this method adaptation is possible since the test may be extended over a long period. The use of a blank consisting of the basal medium alone was found useful for avoiding erroneous results. Aeration of the medium by using shaken cultures gives a quicker result (Barnett & Ingram, 1955; Ahearn, Roth, Fell & Meyers, 1960) but complicates the test.

In the analogous test on a solid medium a blank is indispensable since very often some growth is seen on the medium containing a nonassimilable compound. Shifrine, Phaff & Demain (1954) used this type of test for screening a great number of yeasts on one plate. With Lederberg's replica method, from the same inoculum on glucose-containing agar a series of plates, each containing a different carbon compound, could be inoculated.

The third method mentioned above, the familiar auxanographic test, which is read after 2–4 days' incubation, has the disadvantage that compounds requiring adaptation may not give a satisfactory result because of the drying out of the agar. Nevertheless, this method may be very satisfactory for routine tests. Up to seven compounds may be tested on one plate and those giving a negative result can be retested in liquid medium. Aerobic species especially often give good results in the auxanogram.

Another type of method for assimilation tests has been described by Kocková-Kratochvílová, Vojtková-Lepšíková & Fischerová (1959) and Minárik, Laho & Navara (1959). The test consists of paper chromatographic analysis of a solution containing one or more sugars in which a yeast strain has been grown for some time. When the sugar has been completely utilized the corresponding spot will be absent.

The pH of the medium may influence the results of the assimilation tests. This holds especially for the acids tested. Thus we found in a strain of *Pichia robertsii* (CBS 4288) by the auxanographic method good growth with succinic acid, but no growth with succinate. In the liquid medium test at pH 3·5 and 6·7 no growth or very little growth was observed, but at pH 4·9 growth was very good. Wickerham & Burton (1948) adjust the tenfold concentrated medium (including the carbon compound) to a pH of 5·2.

Assimilation of nitrogen compounds

The assimilation tests for nitrogen compounds are restricted to nitrate and nitrite. Other compounds which were formerly tested are ammonium sulphate, asparagine and urea. Wickerham (1946) found that the utilization of the latter N-compounds by all strains tested by him depends on the presence of the required vitamins in the medium. The utilization of nitrate is rated highly in yeast taxonomy, and in the sporogenous yeasts it serves to characterize genera. At present three nitrate positive genera are known, *Hansenula, Pachysolen* and *Citeromyces.* Morphologically they differ in the shape of the ascus and of the spores.

The assimilation reactions of nitrate are usually good in the auxanogram. In a few cases the response is very weak, e.g. by *Candida melinii* and *Hansenula capsulata.* The liquid medium test may be used for them. This is performed in two steps. The first tube is read after one week; this is often positive, even when nitrate cannot be assimilated, due to nitrogenous substances excreted by the cells of the inoculum. A second tube is inoculated from the first one and read after one week's incubation.

Wickerham (1957) found nitrite assimilation by *Debaryomyces* strains isolated from lunch meat. We have studied nitrite assimilation in a number of strains of *D. hansenii, D. kloeckeri, D. subglobosus* and *D. nicotianae,* and found variable results in each species. The tests can be made both in the auxanogram and in liquid medium. As may be expected the pH is also of great importance here.

CONCLUSIONS

It is seen that the physiological criteria mentioned are selected merely for their differentiating value even though a detailed knowledge of their biochemical and genetical background is often lacking. For a practical system there is no objection to this, provided the methods for checking the reactions are standardized and the limitations thus implied are kept in mind. However, it is clear that a thorough knowledge of the mechanisms involved is very desirable since it may allow a better taxonomic evaluation of the criteria. This has recently again been pointed out by Barnett (1960, 1961) in a discussion on the biochemical classification of yeasts. Roberts & Thorne (1960) have indicated the value of the genetical background of both biochemical and morphological properties.

The study of more properties leads to improved knowledge of the organisms, while the examination of more strains gives an insight into the variation of properties within one species. The delimitation of species depends on the number of strains studied, and the taxonomist's selection of the criteria. As mentioned earlier, the strains considered to belong to one genus may be divided into species after one has made a general survey and with special reference to the peculiarities of the genus. For instance in *Saccharomyces* the presence or absence of one hydrolysing enzyme is sufficient to differentiate a number of species. In other genera, e.g. *Pichia*, the difference between species may depend on both morphological and physiological properties.

With a few exceptions genera as well as species are characterized by a combination of properties. Therefore, it is possible to use various keys to the genera and species. Usually the keys follow the scheme of the taxonomic system, but this is not necessary. Thus the keys given to *Hansenula* begin with the shape of the spores, after which assimilation and fermentation reactions are mentioned, but the reverse of this is also feasible. A combined key for sporogenous and asporogenous nitrate-positive strains is possible in this way.

This brings us to the identification of yeasts. The number of properties which have to be checked for this purpose is generally less than the number of properties used for the description of a species, while they may vary for the different genera. A basic knowledge of the system and of the characteristics and methods is, however, necessary, and only then can a limited number of routine tests be employed. In cases of doubt more properties must be studied and comparisons with authentic strains can be made. The latter procedure is especially advisable when the description of a new species is considered.

So far, I have discussed the biochemical criteria chiefly from a practical point of view, and not phylogenetically. Indeed, they are used in the first place for the differentiation of species. Their value for the characterization of higher taxa, i.e. their function in constructing a natural system—if the realization of such a system is considered to be attainable—is still a matter for discussion. Uncertainty regarding the taxonomic value of biochemical criteria may be illustrated by the tentative classification of the asporogenous yeasts, where they are used without the guidance of important morphological characteristics. As mentioned earlier, the classification of these yeasts is not satisfactory as a natural system, and must be considered to be provisional.

A re-evaluation of criteria is sometimes necessary, as is shown by the following example. Recently van der Walt & van Kerken (1961) have described a new species, *Torulopsis capsuligenus*, with capsulated cells, forming no pseudomycelium, producing 'starch', and fermenting glucose and maltose weakly in Durham tubes. Another strain of this species was previously isolated by Beech. The formation of 'starch' is typical of *Cryptococcus* and does not occur in the genus *Torulopsis*. On the other hand, fermentation was hitherto not observed in *Cryptococcus*, while *Torulopsis* contains both fermenting and non-fermenting species. In this case a re-definition of the genera seems necessary. The question arises which property, 'starch'-formation or fermentation, is of more importance for the differentiation of *Cryptococcus* from *Torulopsis*? van der Walt & van Kerken have chosen fermentation, and provisionally classified their strain in the genus *Torulopsis*.

Summarizing we may say that the taxonomy of yeasts is in a relatively primitive stage. The relationships of yeasts to other fungi and with each other are still the subject of speculation and discussion. There is, however, no doubt that biochemical criteria must play an important part in the classification of yeasts. The development of biochemistry and the interest of chemists and biochemists in yeasts will help the taxonomist in his attempts to construct an improved system of yeast classification.

REFERENCES

AHEARN, D. G., ROTH, F. J., FELL, J. W. & MEYERS, S. P. (1960). Use of shaken cultures in the assimilation test for yeast identification. *J. Bact.* **79**, 369.

BARNETT, J. A. (1960). Comparative studies of yeasts. *Nature, Lond.* **186**, 449.

BARNETT, J. A. (1961). Biochemical classification of yeasts. *Nature, Lond.* **189**, 76.

BARNETT, J. A. & INGRAM, M. (1955). Technique in the study of yeast assimilation reactions. *J. appl. Bact.* **18**, 131.

BARNETT J. A., INGRAM, M. & SWAIN, T. (1956). The use of β-glucosides in classifying yeasts. *J. gen. Microbiol.* **15**, 529.

BARNETT, J. A. & KORNBERG, H. L. (1960). The utilization by yeasts of acids of the tricarboxylic acid cycle. *J. gen. Microbiol.* **23**, 65.

BOUTHILET, R. J., NEILSON, N. E., MRAK, E. M. & PHAFF, H. J. (1949). The fermentation of trehalose by yeasts and its taxonomic implications. *J. gen. Microbiol.* **3**, 282.

DIDDENS, H. A. & LODDER, J. (1942). *Die anaskosporogenen Hefen, II Hälfte.* Amsterdam: North Holland Publishing Co.

DOMERCQ, S. (1956). *Étude et classification des levures de vin de la Gironde.* Thèse, Bordeaux.

DOUGLAS, H. C. & CONDIE, F. (1954). The genetic control of galactose utilization in *Saccharomyces*. *J. Bact.* **68**, 662.

GILLILAND, R. B. (1953). The genetics of super-attenuation. *European Brewery Conv. Proc. 4th Congr. Nice*, p. 121.

GILLILAND, R. B. (1956). Maltotriose fermentation in the species differentiation of *Saccharomyces*. *C.R. Lab. Carlsberg*, **26**, 139.

HANSEN, E. C. (1883). Recherches sur la physiologie et la morphologie des ferments alcooliques. II. Les ascospores chez le genre *Saccharomyces*. *C.R. Lab. Carlsberg*, **2**, 13.

HANSEN, E. C. (1904). Grundlinien zur Systematik der Saccharomyceten. *Zbl. Bakt.* (2 *Abt.*), 12, 529.

HARTMANN, M. (1903). Eine rassenspaltige *Torula*-Art, welche nur zeitweise Maltose zu vergären vermag. (*Torula colliculosa* n.sp.). *Wschr. Brau.* 20, 113.

KOCKOVÁ-KRATOCHVÍLOVÁ, A., VOJTKOVÁ-LEPŠÍKOVÁ, A. & FISCHEROVÁ, M. (1959). Die Art der Zuckerverwertung durch die Hefe und hefeartigen Mikroorganismen. *Brauwissenschaft,* 12, 110. (Review in: *Wallerstein, Labs. Commun.* (1960) 23 227).

KUDRIAVZEV, V. I. (1938). Experimental change in the physiological properties of yeast. *C.R. Acad. Sci., U.R.S.S.* 19, 513.

[KUDRIAVZEV, V. I.] KUDRJAWZEW, W. I. (1960). *Die Systematik der Hefen.* Berlin: Akademie Verlag. (Translation of the Russian edition (1954), Moscow: Acad. Sci. U.S.S.R.).

LODDER, J. (1934). Die anaskosporogenen Hefen, I. Hälfte. *Verh. Akad. Wet. Amst., Afd. Natuurkunde,* sect. II, 32, 1.

LODDER, J. & KREGER-VAN RIJ, N. J. W. (1952). *The Yeasts.* Amsterdam: North Holland Publishing Co.

LOSADA, M. (1957). The hydrolysis of raffinose by yeast melibiase and the fermentation of raffinose by complementary gene action. *C.R. Lab. Carlsberg,* 25, 460.

MINÁRIK, E., LAHO, L. & NAVARA, A. (1959). Contribution to an objective method of determination of sugar assimilation by wine yeasts by means of paper chromatography. (English summary.) *Biológia, Bratislava,* 14, 597.

PHAFF, H. J., MILLER, M. W. & SHIFRINE, M. (1956). The taxomony of yeasts isolated from *Drosophila* in the Yosemite region of California. *Leeuwenhoek ned. Tijdschr.* 22, 145.

RAMIREZ GOMEZ, C. (1959). Méthode rapide et simple pour déterminer le degré de fermentation du raffinose par les levures. *Leeuwenhoek ned. Tijdschr.* 25, 445.

REESS, M. (1870). *Botanische Untersuchungen über die Alkoholgärungspilze.* Leipzig: A. Felix.

ROBERTS, C. & THORNE, R. S. W. (1960). Biochemical classification of yeasts. *Nature, Lond.* 188, 872.

ROBERTS, C. & WALT, J. P. VAN DER (1960). Investigations on maltose utilization in *Saccharomyces* I. The acquisition of maltose fermentative ability by *S. capensis. C.R. Lab. Carlsberg,* 32, 19.

SANTA MARIA, J. (1958). Ecología de las levaduras. I. Nuevas especies aisladas de alpechín. *Bol. Inst. Invest. agron. Madr.* No. 38, p. 301.

SHIFRINE, M., PHAFF, H. J. & DEMAIN, A. L. (1954). Determination of carbon assimilation patterns of yeasts by replica plating. *J. Bact.* 68, 28.

SKINNER, C. E. & BOUTHILET, R. (1947). Melibiose broth for classifying yeasts. *J. Bact.* 53, 37.

SKINNER, C. E. & FLETCHER, D. W. (1960). A review of the genus *Candida. Bact. Rev.* 24, 397.

SKINNER, E. E. & HUXLEY, M. J. (1956). *Rhodotorula glutinis. Mycologia,* 48, 371.

SNYDER, E. H. & PHAFF, H. J. (1960). Studies on a beta-fructosidase (inulinase) produced by *Saccharomyces fragilis. Leeuwenhoek ned. Tijdschr.* 26, 433.

STELLING-DEKKER, N. M. (1931). Die sporogenen Hefen. *Verh. Akad. Wet. Amst. Afd. Natuurkunde,* sect. II, 28, 1.

UDEN, N. VAN (1956). Rapid method for testing raffinose fermentation by yeasts. *J. Bact.* 72, 793.

UDEN, N. VAN & ASSIS-LOPES, L. (1957). Fermentation of raffinose in the absence of invertase by *Saccharomyces italicus* Castelli var. *melibiosi* nov.var. *Portug. acta biol.,* Série A, 4, 323.

WALT, J. P. VAN DER & KERKEN, A. E. VAN (1959). The wine yeasts of the Cape. II. The occurrence of *Brettanomyces intermedius* and *Brettanomyces schanderlii* in South African table wines. *Leeuwenhoek ned. Tijdschr.* **25**, 145.

WALT, J. P. VAN DER & KERKEN, A. E. VAN (1961). Three new anascosporogenous yeasts. *Leeuwenhoek ned. Tijdschr.* **27**, 206.

WALT, J. P. VAN DER & TSCHEUSCHNER, T. T. (1956). *Saccharomyces capensis* nov. spec. a new yeast from South African grape must. *Leeuwenhoek ned. Tijdschr.* **22**, 257.

WICKERHAM, L. J. (1943). A simple technique for the detection of melibiose-fermenting yeasts. *J. Bact.* **46**, 501.

WICKERHAM, L. J. (1946). A critical evaluation of the nitrogen assimilation tests commonly used in the classification of yeasts. *J. Bact.* **52**, 293

WICKERHAM, L. J. (1951). Taxonomy of yeasts. *Tech. Bull. U.S. Dep. Agric.* No. 1029.

WICKERHAM, L. J. (1955). New materials and procedures for genetic studies of yeasts. *Nature, Lond.* **176**, 22.

WICKERHAM, L. J. (1957). Presence of nitrite-assimilating species of *Debaryomyces* in lunch meats. *J. Bact.* **74**, 832.

WICKERHAM, L. J. & BURTON, K. A. (1948). Carbon assimilation tests for the classification of yeasts. *J. Bact.* **56**, 363.

WICKERHAM, L. J. & BURTON, K. A. (1952). Occurrence of yeast mating types in nature. *J. Bact.* **63**, 449.

WICKERHAM, L. J. & BURTON, K. A. (1956). Hybridization studies involving *Saccharomyces lactis* and *Zygosaccharomyces ashbyi*. *J. Bact.* **71**, 290.

WINGE, Ö. & ROBERTS, C. (1948). Inheritance of enzymatic characters in yeasts, and the phenomenon of long-term adaptation. *C.R. Lab. Carlsberg*, **24**, 263.

WINGE, Ö. & ROBERTS, C. (1950). The polymeric genes for maltose fermentation in yeasts, and their mutability. *C.R. Lab. Carlsberg*, **25**, 35.

WINGE, Ö. & ROBERTS, C. (1956). Complementary action of melibiase and galacto-zymase on raffinose fermentation. *Nature, Lond.* **177**, 383.

IMMUNOCHEMICAL SPECIFICITY AND THE LOCATION OF ANTIGENS IN THE BACTERIAL CELL

C. S. CUMMINS

Department of Bacteriology, London Hospital Medical College, London, E. 1

INTRODUCTION

The various anatomical elements which can be recognized in bacteria by electron microscopy have been thoroughly described in recent years (e.g. Spooner & Stocker, 1956; Gunsalus & Stanier, 1960). The principal structural elements of the bacterial cell are *flagella, fimbriae, cell-walls, cytoplasmic membranes, chromatin bodies* and *cytoplasmic granules,* to which one must add *spores* in the genera *Bacillus* and *Clostridium*.

Capsules, microcapsules, slime layers and other highly hydrated and viscous polymers so frequently found on the surface of bacteria are omitted from the list, because they cannot be considered structural in the sense of being organized insoluble material of definite dimensions. These outer layers can of course be very important if agglutination tests are being performed, since they form the effective antigenic surface of the cell and prevent detection of the antigens in the outer layer of the cell-wall. They are very largely polysaccharide in nature (with a few notable exceptions such as the polypeptide capsules of some *Bacillus* strains) and their properties have recently been reviewed by Wilkinson (1958).

It is proposed in this article to consider in the main the *somatic* or *structural antigens,* as opposed to *soluble* ones such as toxins, haemolysins or enzymes which cannot normally be regarded as structural features of the cell, even though they may be elaborated at particular locations in it. It is perhaps better to use the word *structural* rather than *somatic* since the latter term usually excludes surface structures such as flagella. It must be remembered that in abnormal circumstances such as occur in old and autolysed cultures, or in the presence of lytic enzymes, even the most firmly bound antigen may appear in soluble form. Structural antigens may also of course be obtained in solution by various extraction procedures, but the fact that such methods are necessary to liberate them merely emphasizes their normally insoluble state.

No attempt will be made to treat the subject extensively from the chemical point of view, although recent work by Westphal and his colleagues is described in some detail to show the further development which can be expected in correlating the specificity of bacterial antigens with their chemical structure. The question of the chemical basis of immunological specificity has been dealt with in a number of recent articles and reviews (see for example Heidelberger, 1956a, b; Stacey & Barker, 1960). Nor is it proposed to give exhaustive lists of antigenic formulae for organisms of different types. This would, I imagine, rapidly kill all interest in the subject of immunochemical criteria in classification. I hope merely to show in a general way that it is important to try and locate antigens correctly in the cell if antigenic specificity is to be of value in taxonomy.

There is one final point to be made in the introduction, concerning the use of the word *antigen*. It often seems to be implied when talking about the various antigenic specificities which can be identified in bacterial products that each represents a separate substance at the molecular level, so that in the case of a bacterium showing two antigenic specificities, A and B, a sufficiently skilful chemist could ultimately place two bottles on his shelf, labelled *antigen A* and *antigen B*, each containing chemically different pure material. This is misleading. Immunochemical analysis, especially in the last ten years, has given some idea of the size of the specific groupings with which antibodies combine. For example, in the case of some polysaccharide antigens the antibody-combining site is probably not larger than six sugar residues and may be smaller (Kabat, 1958). Such a unit may be only one of several, each of which is repeated many times in a large polymer. It is perhaps better therefore, as far as possible, to speak of 'specific groupings', 'antigenic determinants', or 'determinant groups' when referring to the individual specificities concerned and to reserve as far as possible the word 'antigen' for the higher molecular weight complexes which cause animals injected with them to produce antibodies to the different determinants in the complex. It is difficult to avoid referring to single specificities as antigens in groups such as *Salmonella* where a well established antigenic classification has been in general use for a considerable time.

TECHNICAL METHODS

Practical details of the techniques of immunochemistry are outside the scope of this article: for them, reference may be made in particular to Kabat & Mayer (1961). Some aspects of technical methods must be considered briefly, however, because of their bearing on the use of immunochemical criteria in classification.

Sensitivity of serological methods

The most commonly used techniques for demonstrating the reactions of bacterial antigens with antisera are still the agglutination reaction with suspensions of killed or living bacteria and the precipitin test with extracted antigens; complement fixation is used less frequently. Two more recent methods are haemosensitization with adsorbed antigens (passive haemagglutination) and the use of immunofluorescent staining.

Grabar (1953) has published figures showing the relative sensitivities (in terms of antibody nitrogen detected) of different methods, from which it is clear that agglutination is 5–10 times more sensitive than qualitative precipitin tests (ring tests, or precipitation in gels) and about equal in sensitivity to complement fixation. On the other hand, the haemosensitization method (Middlebrook & Dubos, 1948; Boyden, 1951) is about 100 times as sensitive as agglutination, and except for some techniques involving anaphylactic reactions is far the most sensitive method known. It has, however, so far largely been used for soluble antigens found in culture filtrates, and not for studies of structural antigens.

The most recent technique is immunofluorescent staining. This is essentially the method of Coons, Creech, Jones & Berliner (1942) applied to bacteria in smears, and obviously is largely a staining procedure for surface materials or cell-wall antigens, using fluorochrome-labelled antibody to visualize them. Its sensitivity appears to be about equal to that of the complement-fixation test, and perhaps rather less than that of agglutination (Beutner, 1961).

One of the things which emerges from a study of this scale of sensitivities is that precipitin tests in capillary tubes, which are so frequently used in serological studies involving large numbers of organisms, probably represent the least sensitive technique which could be used, and will tend to give positive results only with major antigen-antibody reactions. This is certainly no bad thing especially in preliminary surveys involving large numbers of strains, but it does mean that a re-examination of the same material by a more sensitive method will demonstrate considerably more cross-reactions. This is well illustrated by the findings of Moody, Ellis & Updyke (1958) who used the immuno-fluorescent technique to stain streptococci of various Lancefield groups. They found that whereas groups A and C did not cross-react in precipitin tests, there was quite marked cross-reaction between them with fluorescent antibody, and the sera had to be absorbed with the heterologous group to achieve specificity. The same thing has been found in cell-wall agglutination tests with cell-wall suspensions from various streptococcal groups (Cummins & Slade, 1961, and see Table 1).

Tomcsik has described a method of detecting capsular and surface cell-wall antigens depending on the visible alteration under phase-contrast microscopy when such materials react with their antisera. The capsule and the cell-wall of *Bacillus megaterium* can readily be shown to be distinct by this technique, although some cell-wall-reacting material occurs in the capsule in the form of bands opposite the site of cross-walls in the chain of bacilli (Tomcsik, 1956; Baumann-Grace & Tomcsik, 1957). This method may give a valuable demonstration of the position of surface antigens under favourable conditions.

Extraction of antigens

Since the site of antigens in the cell is important, and has often been neglected, all extraction procedures must be viewed with suspicion. Obviously the detailed chemical structure of antigenic material cannot be worked out unless it is prepared in sufficient amount, and freed from other cell constituents, and for this some extraction method is often essential. The possible fallacies of the method from the point of view of classification come from assuming that similar extracts from related (or assumedly related) organisms actually consist of anatomically similar material. In the Enterobacteriaceae most extraction procedures have given polysaccharide antigens whose specificity is demonstrably the same as that of the cell surface, so that at least one of the original sites of the antigen is known, even though its complete distribution is not certain. In the case of Gram-positive organisms the evidence suggests that most cell-wall polysaccharide antigens cannot be detected at the cell surface by agglutination, so that when extracted there is little or no clue as to their position in the cell (see the section on cell-wall antigens).

Heat stable and heat labile antigens

In an attempt to determine the nature of the surface antigens of bacteria, the reactions of heated and unheated bacteria have often been compared. A frequent method has been to prepare sera against heated and unheated organisms, and then to compare the reaction of each type of suspension against each serum. When this is done it is often found that the heated bacterial suspension (which may have been boiled for 2 hr., or even autoclaved at 120°) does not react against a serum to the unheated organisms, but will agglutinate to high titre with its own serum. Broadly speaking, of the two major classes of antigenic components in bacteria, polysaccharides are heat stable and do not alter in serological specificity on heating for long periods at neutral pH. On the other hand, the effect of heat on proteins is to denature them; this is accompanied by a great change in serological specificity and in particular the serological activity of flagella is usually destroyed.

MacPherson and his co-workers showed that denatured hen-egg albumin cross-reacted less with antiserum to native hen-egg albumin than did native duck-egg albumin (MacPherson & Heidelberger, 1945a, b; MacPherson, Heidelberger & Moore, 1945). The important practical point for the antigenic classification of bacteria is that heat-denaturation of proteins alters their serological specificity greatly, but does not necessarily abolish their antigenicity. Heating a suspension of a bacterium whose superficial antigens are protein will therefore destroy the original specificity of the suspension and coat the organisms with a layer of denatured protein. Antisera to such heated bacteria will often agglutinate the heated suspension to high titre, and this seems often in the past to have been misinterpreted as the 'uncovering' of a heat-stable antigen by heating. Since a series of related proteins may cross-react more when all of them are heat denatured (Rothen & Landsteiner, 1942), the effect of comparing the reactions of heated and unheated suspensions with sera prepared against each may be to suggest the false picture of a 'heat-stable' antigen which is normally 'hidden' by one of a series of 'heat-labile' antigens.

This type of misinterpretation is most likely to occur in Gram-positive organisms where protein surface antigens appear to be common. It obviously does not cause errors where the surface antigens are heat-stable material like the O-antigens of *Salmonella*, which are traditionally distinguished from the heat-labile flagellar proteins by heating the suspension. It would appear safer to use only sera which have been prepared against unheated bacteria, and to test the heat lability or stability of various materials by comparing their reactions with these sera before and after heating.

SITE OF ANTIGENS IN THE BACTERIAL CELL

Flagella and fimbriae

Fimbriae and flagella are definite structures with characteristic dimensions, and in most cases they are either present in normal amount or completely absent, depending on the strain. The multiplicity of H-antigen specificities associated with flagella in the Enterobacteriaceae is too well known to need further discussion. The flagellar antigens of other motile groups such as *Bacillus* and *Clostridium* have not been studied to anything like the same degree, but wherever a group of strains from these genera have been fairly thoroughly examined, a similar kind of antigenic complexicity appears to be present (e.g. in *Bacillus polymyxa*, Davies, 1951).

While flagella have been known in motile bacteria from the early days of bacteriology, fimbriae were not identified until recently (Houwink & van Iterson, 1950) since they can only be seen in the electron microscope. They are rod-like structures of varying length, unconnected with motility, which appear in electron micrographs of shadowed preparations to stick out perpendicularly from the cell surface, but which may presumably form a closer layer in the living cell. They have been found in most genera of Gram-negative bacilli, but have not been reported in Gram-positive bacteria. These structures have also been referred to as *pili* (e.g. by Brinton, 1959).

Both chemically and immunologically fimbriae seem to be quite distinct from flagella. Their presence makes fimbriate bacteria unusually adhesive, so that such organisms will cause red cell suspensions to agglutinate. However Gillies & Duguid (1958) have shown that fimbriae can also cause bacterial agglutination, which resembles flagellar agglutination in giving rapid loose floccules, and that where fimbriate bacilli were tested against unabsorbed homologous serum, fimbrial agglutination was dominant and interfered with recognition of the O-antigen at the cell surface. Fimbrial antigens do not seem to be subject to the degree of variation usually found in flagella, since all strains of *Shigella flexneri* tested, irrespective of O-serotype, had fimbriae of identical antigenic composition. There was some cross-reaction between the fimbrial antigens of *S. flexneri* and those of *Escherichia coli*: this was usually at low titre, although one fimbriate strain of *E. coli* was able to remove all antibodies from an *S. flexneri* antifimbrial serum. There appeared to be no cross-reaction between fimbriate strains of *S. flexneri* and fimbriate strains of *Salmonella* or *Proteus*, and it seems possible therefore that the antigens associated with fimbriae will be useful in taxonomy.

Cell-wall antigens

Assuming that no interfering substances such as capsules or slime are present, agglutination tests will identify the presence of an antigen in the cell-wall only if that antigen is close enough to the surface of the intact cell to bind sufficient antibody. It seems surprising that purified cell-wall fractions have been relatively little used in systematic studies of cell-wall antigens, although the ability of such fractions to react satis-factorily in agglutination tests (Tomcsik & Geux-Holzer, 1954; Cummins, 1954) or by complement-fixation or slide agglutination (Salton, 1956) has been reported. Disintegration of the cell, and the breaking of the cell-wall into fragments, will not only create artificial surfaces at the broken edges but will also expose the inner layers, so that compared with the original intact cell at least 50 % of the surface of any fragment of wall will be composed of previously unexposed material. The difference which this exposure of the inner surface of the wall can make may be judged to some extent by comparing the effect of absorbing samples of the same serum with intact bacteria or with cell-walls from the same strain. An experiment of this kind is illustrated in Table 1. It is obviously much more efficient to absorb the serum with the cell-walls from 20 mg. of bacteria than with 20 mg. of intact cells under the same conditions (these are dry weights/2 ml. of serum diluted 1/20; the actual dry weight of cell-walls would be 3 mg., assuming a 15 % yield). The strain used in this experiment was a group D streptococcus, but the antigen in question is a cell-wall polysaccharide unconnected with the group D substance, which is largely or entirely cytoplasmic in this group (see below).

Table 1. *Availability of cell-wall antigens to antibody: a comparison of absorption with intact cells and with cell-walls*

A cell-wall suspension of *Streptococcus zymogenes* NCTC 8176 and the corresponding antiserum were used as test materials. Crude cell-wall was the deposit after disintegratio.. in the Mickle shaker, centrifuging and washing once in 0·9 % saline. Absorption was done as follows: 2 ml. amounts of serum diluted 1/20 were absorbed with the amounts of material shown, for 1 hr. at 37°, followed by 4° overnight. The antigen responsible for the agglutina-tion is *not* the group antigen of group D streptococci (see text). + + indicates strong agglutination; + indicates moderate agglutination; − indicates no agglutination.

	Serum dilutions							
Treatment of serum ...	1/80	1/160	1/320	1/640	1/1280	1/2560	1/5120	Saline
Unabsorbed	+ +	+ +	+ +	+ +	+ +	+ +	+	−
Absorbed with 20 mg. of intact bacteria	+ +	+ +	+ +	+ +	+	−	−	−
Absorbed with crude cell-wall from 20 mg. of bacteria	−	−	−	−	−	−	−	−

Salton (1953) found that the cell-walls of group A streptococci, pre-pared by disruption in the Mickle Shaker followed by repeated washing, still retained the M-protein. This could be removed from the walls by tryptic digestion, as would be expected from the known effects of trypsin on intact streptococci (Lancefield, 1943). It has also been clearly demonstrated that the group polysaccharide in group A streptococci is the carbohydrate moiety of the basic cell-wall skeleton (Salton, 1953; McCarty, 1952), and the same is almost certainly true in other Lancefield groups except group D (Elliott, 1960; Jones & Shattock, 1960; Cummins & Slade, 1961). There is clear evidence, then, that in group A streptococci the cell-wall contains antigenic material of two different kinds, protein and polysaccharide, and since suspensions of intact streptococci agglutinate by virtue of the M protein (or the T protein antigens, where these are present) this is presumably at the surface of the intact cell. So far as is known it is not possible to detect streptococcal group antigens by agglutination whether or not the M or other proteins have been removed by trypsin (Lancefield, 1941) although these group antigens are sufficiently available to bind antibody if antisera are absorbed with suspensions of intact bacteria. However, if suspensions of cell-wall fragments are used as antigens in agglutination tests, these group antigens are easily demonstrable. Table 2 gives the results of a series of tests using this technique, and shows that each cell-wall suspension reacts with sera of the corresponding group, although there are a number of cross-reactions at considerably lower titre.

Table 2. *Cell-wall agglutination tests showing cross-reactions between streptococci of different Lancefield groups*

Titre with cell-wall suspension from group

Antisera against group	A	A variant (strain K43)	B	C	E	F	K	L	O
A	640	320	—	40	20	20	—	20	—
A variant (K 43)	640	2560	—	320	—	—	20	40	—
B	—	—	80	—	—	—	—	—	—
C	40	80	—	160	—	—	—	—	20
E	40	—	—	—	320	—	—	—	—
F	—	—	—	—	—	320	—	—	—
K	40	20	—	20	20	80	5120	—	—
L	—	—	—	—	—	—	—	160	—
O	—	—	—	—	—	—	—	—	80

— Means no reaction in serum diluted 1/20.

Another interesting observation is that multiple specificities can be demonstrated by the use of cell-wall agglutination tests. This is evident from the results illustrated in Table 3. The only explanation of these results which seems feasible is that strain 8176 contains both '8176' and '8213' specificities, hence antibodies to both are present in 8176 antiserum. However, 8176 cell-wall suspensions can only agglutinate by virtue of '8176', and not because of '8213' specificity (negative result in the second column). The rabbit which was immunized presumably responded to specific groupings which are occluded in some way in the native material but became available after partial breakdown in the animal's tissues.

Table 3. *Demonstration of multiple antigenic specificities in cell-walls by agglutination*

The strains were *Streptococcus faecium* NCTC 7379, *S. liquefaciens* NCTC 8175, *S. zymogenes* NCTC 8176 and *S. faecalis* NCTC 8213. The absorbed serum was not tested at a dilution lower than 1/40.

	Titres with antisera		
Cell-wall suspension from strain	8176 unabsorbed	8213 unabsorbed	8176 absorbed with 8213 cell-wall
7379	320	640	< 40
8175	320	640	< 40
8176	2560	< 20	2560
8213	320	640	< 40

In a purely mechanical way, therefore, cell-wall antigens can be revealed by exposing surfaces which are normally hidden. The only other method, short of extraction, which seems likely to demonstrate these antigens satisfactorily is that of using fluorescent antibody. This might be expected, since, if the antigens are sufficiently close to the surface to be capable of binding antibody in absorption, it is not unreasonable to suppose that they will hold it firmly enough to be outlined by immunofluorescence.

A situation similar to that found in the streptococci also appears to exist in *Corynebacterium diphtheriae* (Cummins, 1954). In the 'mitis' strain examined the surface antigen responsible for the agglutination of intact suspensions was almost certainly protein, since it was relatively heat-labile, was resistant to periodate oxidation and was destroyed by pepsin (though not by trypsin). Suspensions of intact bacteria of the 'mitis' strain did not agglutinate with antiserum to a 'gravis' strain. However, if suspensions of cell-wall fragments were used, these agglutinated equally well both with the homologous serum and with the 'gravis' antiserum. This suggested that the cell-wall contained a superficial specific protein antigen, and a more deeply situated antigen which occurred also in the 'gravis' strain. Absorption experiments using intact suspensions of both 'gravis' and 'intermedius' strains supported this hypothesis, since both of them were able to remove antibodies to the group antigen while leaving the titre to the specific protein unaltered (Table 4).

The results of these experiments indicate that both in streptococci and in corynebacteria there exist antigenic specificities in the deeper parts of the cell-wall which cannot readily be detected by ordinary agglutination techniques using intact suspensions. In the streptococci, these deeper antigens correspond to the well known group antigens of the Lancefield antigenic scheme, which are normally identified by the precipitin technique after having been extracted by heating with dilute acid.

Table 4. *Distinction between the group (polysaccharide) and specific (protein) antigens in the cell-wall of a strain of* Corynebacterium diphtheriae *var.* mitis *(modified from Cummins, 1954)*

The '*Mitis*' antiserum used was prepared against '*Mitis*' cell-walls treated with trypsin but not pepsin, and therefore contained antibodies to both protein and polysaccharide antigens.

	Titre against	
'*Mitis*' antiserum absorbed with	'*Mitis*' intact cell suspension (only specific antigen exposed)	'*Mitis*' cell-wall suspension, pepsin treated (both group and specific antigens exposed)
'*Gravis*' suspension	320	< 40
'*Intermedius*' suspension	320	< 40
Unabsorbed	320	320

A considerable amount is now known about the qualitative composition of the cell wall in Gram-positive bacteria (Cummins & Harris, 1956 a, b, 1958, 1959). Broadly speaking, the basic skeleton of the wall in these organisms is a complex of sugars, amino sugars and amino acids (the latter few in number, generally three or four). What information there is suggests that this basic material is antigenic and that its determinant groups are polysaccharide (e.g. the group antigens of streptococci). The actual surface material of the wall in Gram-positive bacteria is probably protein, although it must be admitted that direct evidence for this seems only to be available for strains in three genera: *Streptococcus*, *Corynebacterium* (mentioned above), and *Staphylococcus*, where Pillet, Rouyer & Orta (1955) found that treatment with papain appeared to destroy surface antigens. In many other cases a proper investigation of the nature of the surface material has been vitiated by using boiled or autoclaved suspensions; a not-too-thorough search of the literature reveals that this has been done in investigations on strains of *Corynebacterium*, *Staphylococcus*, *Bacillus* and *Clostridium*. The probable fallacies of this procedure have already been stressed.

If one may generalize then, on the rather scanty evidence presented, it seems likely that in Gram-positive bacteria the bulk of the cell-wall is the so-called 'mucocomplex' composed of amino sugars, sugars, and amino acids: this is antigenic and its determinants are carbohydrate. At the surface is a protein layer, which is normally responsible for the serological reactions of intact suspensions (in the absence of interference from surface structures such as flagella or capsules). The mucocomplex is sufficiently submerged to be unable to participate in the agglutination of intact cells, but can bind antibody to some extent and hence can be detected at the surface by absorption. On the other hand, if suspensions of cell-wall fragments are used, the specificities of the mucocomplex are dominant, and the cell-wall suspensions agglutinate mainly by virtue of them and not the original surface protein, e.g. results with *Corynebacterium diphtheriae* (Cummins, 1954).

The situation in typical Gram-negative bacteria is apparently rather different. Comparison of the serological reactions of the lipo-protein-polysaccharide complexes which can be extracted from enterobacteria with the antigens revealed on the surface of the cell-wall by agglutination, shows that the same antigenic specificities are responsible for both. These determinants are polysaccharide (the 'somatic' O-antigens). However, in the few cases tested, it appears that suspensions of cell-wall fragments from these organisms did not show any new specificity. For example, Shafa (1958) found that the isolated cell-walls of *Salmonella gallinarum* and *Vibrio metchnikovi* reacted as though the surfaces of the cell-wall fragments were serologically identical with the O-antigen at the surface of the intact cell. A similar situation was found in a strain of *Shigella* 'Shiga' (Cummins, unpublished observations). These findings suggest that although the wall of Gram-negative bacteria is more complex chemically than that of Gram-positive bacteria (Salton, 1960; Weidel, Frank & Martin, 1960), turning it inside out, so to speak, does not reveal any new antigen.

Teichoic acids

In considering antigens in bacterial cell-walls the possible presence of teichoic acids must also be remembered (Armstrong *et al.* 1958; Armstrong, Baddiley & Buchanan, 1960). These are polymers of glycerol or ribitol phosphate, with D-alanine residues ester-linked to hydroxyl groups of the polymer, and have so far largely been studied in the walls of *Lactobacillus* and *Bacillus*.

The role of these compounds in the structural make-up of the wall is not yet certain, since they seem to be completely absent from the walls of some lactobacilli although forming up to 40 % or more of the dry weight of the walls of others (Baddiley & Davison, 1961). They are also found in the cytoplasm. Baddiley & Davison suggest that they are at least potentially antigenic because of their resemblance to the antigenic glycerophosphate polymer found in a number of Gram-positive species by McCarty (1959).

Antigens in the cytoplasmic membrane

Removal of the cell-wall from bacteria while allowing the cytoplasm to continue at least for a time as a functioning unit has been accomplished in two principal ways: either by removing the cell-wall by some lytic or autolytic system, or by interfering with cell-wall synthesis (see Weibull, 1958; McQuillen, 1960). In either case the process must take place in media of suitable osmotic tension (e.g. $0\cdot1$–$0\cdot2$M sucrose, 7% (w/v) NaCl, etc.). Once the wall has been removed it is possible, by diluting the medium with water, to lyse the osmotically sensitive spherical body which results. The centrifuged deposit from such a diluted lysate is found to contain thin membranes which are assumed to be largely if not entirely the cytoplasmic membranes of the original bacteria.

Antigenic analysis of these fractions is not of much value unless it can be shown that all cell-wall substance is gone. The most general usage (see McQuillen, 1960) is to apply the term *protoplast* to these spherical bodies if no cell-wall material can be demonstrated, but to call them *spheroplasts* when it appears that the cell-wall structure has only been modified, but is not completely absent. In these terms, and with present techniques protoplasts have been prepared from Gram-positive bacteria, but not yet from Gram-negative bacteria.

Protoplast membranes which seem to be free from cell-wall material have been examined serologically in the case of *Bacillus megaterium* (Tomcsik & Geux-Holzer, 1954; Baumann-Grace & Tomcsik, 1957; Vennes & Gerhardt, 1956), and *Streptococcus pyogenes* (Freimer & Krause, 1960). In each case the protoplast membranes (i.e. the cytoplasmic membranes of the original organisms) were antigenic, and were serologically distinct from the cell-wall. These serological tests were done either by agglutination of membrane suspensions (*B. megaterium*) or by precipitin tests with extracts of the membranes (*S. pyogenes*). It would be very interesting to see how much variation, if any, there is in the antigenic specificity of such membranes from a series of species in one genus. Protoplasts which appeared to be free from all cell-wall material (since no rhamnose could be detected) have also been prepared from *S. faecalis*, but were apparently not examined serologically (Bleiweis & Zimmerman, 1960).

In *Streptococcus*, at least, it seems possible to produce cytoplasmic membrane fractions free from cell-wall material either by removing the wall with a phage-associated lysin, by preventing cell-wall synthesis by penicillin, or mechanically by disintegration and differential centrifugation (Freimer, Krause & McCarty, 1959; Freimer & Krause, 1961). However, in Gram-negative organisms no lytic system yet described gives the clearcut removal of the cell wall obtained with, for example, lysozyme acting on *Bacillus megaterium*. The commonest method of obtaining osmotically sensitive forms has been to interfere with cell-wall synthesis by penicillin (Lederberg, 1956), but the spherical bodies produced are *spheroplasts*, and still show, by evidence of several kinds, that some wall material is present. Thus it appears that they may still adsorb phage, and can take part in mating with compatible strains (Lederberg & St Clair, 1958). It is not surprising therefore to find that these bodies still show the serological specificity of the O-antigen from the cell-wall of the parent strain. For example in *Shigella dysenteriae*, Cooper & Pillow (1960) found that spheroplasts prepared by the penicillin method had the same serological specificity as that of the isolated cell-wall of the same strain, and similar results were obtained by Carey & Baron (1959) with *Salmonella typhi*, using essentially the same technique.

It is possible that the cytoplasmic membrane of Gram-negative bacilli is more closely bound to the inner surface of the cell-wall than is the case in Gram-positive organisms, which could account for the difficulty in removing all cell-wall material without complete disruption of the cell. Still, the ease with which Gram-negative bacilli are said to plasmolyse (see Murray, 1960) suggests that it should be possible to obtain true protoplasts (and hence pure cytoplasmic membranes) from Gram-negative bacilli if a suitable lytic agent could be found, or if the penicillin method can be modified or adapted to produce total loss of cell-wall.

It is interesting to note that if protoplasts are prepared from motile organisms, the flagella, although no longer functional, remain attached and can be a cause of serological cross-reaction between intact cells and antiprotoplast sera (Baumann-Grace & Tomcsik, 1957).

Chromatin bodies and cytoplasmic granules

The bacterial cytoplasm differs from that of animal and plant cells in that it does not contain mitochondria or endoplasmic reticulum, nor is there a membrane protecting the nuclear material. Nevertheless, apart from the cytoplasmic membrane at least two organized structures can be regularly detected. These are the nuclear or chromatin bodies, and the cytoplasmic granules of diameter *c*. 200 Å. (Bradfield, 1956; Murray, 1960).

Chromatin bodies in a more or less purified state were prepared from *Bacillus megaterium* by Spiegelman, Aronson & FitzJames (1958), using lysozyme to prepare protoplasts from the bacilli, and lipase to disrupt the protoplast membrane under suitable osmotic conditions. After this dual enzyme attack the nuclear bodies could be collected as a separate layer after centrifuging for 5 min. at 10,000*g*. The purified chromatin body fraction was composed of deoxyribonucleic acid, ribonucleic acid and protein in the proportions $1:1:3$. Among other tests used to determine the degree of purity of their fractions, these authors compared the serological reaction of the chromatin bodies with those of protoplast membranes, by testing both against an antiprotoplast serum. Although both reacted to about the same extent in direct tests, cross-absorption showed that antibodies specific for each were present. Speigelman *et al.* (1958) found that these nuclear bodies from *B. megaterium* appear to consist of a non-chromatinic core on which lies the chromatin material proper. If this is so these two elements should ultimately be susceptible of separate antigenic analysis.

The preparation of chromatin bodies as a separate fraction must be largely confined at present to organisms whose cell-walls can be stripped off by enzymes. Apart from *Bacillus megaterium* and *Micrococcus lysodeikticus*, which are very sensitive to lysozyme, the streptococci would seem to be suitable for investigating this problem, since a number of cell-wall lytic agents are available for them (e.g. phage lysin and streptomyces enzyme).

No antigenic work seems to have been done on the cytoplasmic granules. However, as it is possible to concentrate them by ultracentri-fugation and separate them from the soluble cytoplasmic constituents, it seems technically feasible to examine them as a separate entity. They would be expected to be antigenic, as they are composed of RNA and protein.

These cytoplasmic structures, and also soluble cytoplasmic antigens, are likely to be contaminated with pieces of cell-wall or cytoplasmic membrane when mechanical breakage of the cell is used, since prolonged disruption times will shred the cell-wall into very small pieces of varying size and reduce some of it to a completely soluble state (see Slade & Vetter, 1956; Marr & Cota-Robles, 1957). This effect is particularly marked with disruption by sonic oscillation.

Spore antigens

Heat-resistant spores are characteristic morphological features of *Bacillus* and *Clostridium*, although similar forms appear to occur also in some other genera (see Robinow, 1960). The work of Lamanna (Lamanna, 1940 *a*, *b*; Doak & Lamanna, 1948; Lamanna & Eisler, 1960) and of Davies (1951), both of whom used spore suspensions in agglutinations tests, shows clearly that the surface antigens of the spores of *Bacillus* are quite different from those of the vegetative cell. From the taxonomic point of view the earlier results of Lamanna (1940 *a*, *b*) who found three serological spore groups among four 'species' of *Bacillus* seemed somewhat confusing, but from the biochemical reactions of the strains it seems possible (Davies, 1951) that the three serological groups may represent in fact *B. licheniformis*, *B. subtilis* and *B. pumilus*, as defined by Smith, Gordon & Clark (1952). Davies (1951), who examined the spore, flagellar and 'somatic' antigens of 38 strains of *B. polymyxa*, found a very homogeneous picture so far as agglutination of spore suspensions was concerned, since the spores of all 38 strains reacted identically with each of 7 anti-spore sera. Moreover, no cross-reactions were found with spore suspensions of 81 other strains of *Bacillus*, representing 15 different species. In contrast to these clear-cut results with spores, the flagellar antigens of *B. polymyxa* showed biphasic variation, and in the group phase cross-reacted with motile strains from other species. Similar cross-reactions were found with 'somatic' antigens, but since the suspensions used had been steamed for 30 min. the results must be interpreted with caution (see section on heat stable and heat labile antigens).

Tomcsik and his colleagues have examined the serological reactions of spores of *Bacillus cereus* and *B. anthracis* (Tomcsik, Bouille & Baumann-Grace, 1959) and of *B. megaterium* (Tomcsik & Baumann-Grace, 1959) by agglutination and by observing the reactions under phase contrast. It appeared that the spores of 35 strains of *B. cereus* all belonged to the same serological type, and that *B. anthracis* spores also agglutinated with *B. cereus* spore antiserum. In *B. megaterium* spores, however, a number of distinct specificities could be detected and at least five different groups were found. A close relationship has also recently been demonstrated by Lamanna & Eisler (1960) between the spores of *B. cereus* and those of *B. anthracis*, although not all spore suspensions agglutinated with each type of antispore serum. Similar results were found by Dowdle & Hansen (1961) using fluorescent antispore sera.

Almost all these investigations into spore antigens have used agglutination, and have therefore dealt only with the spore surface, although Doak & Lamanna (1948) reported that formamide or acid extracts of spores will give a positive precipitin test with antispore sera, which may represent a reaction to an interior antigen. In view of the detailed morphological studies of spore structure which have been made recently, especially by Robinow (see Robinow, 1960), which show the presence of several different spore coats, it seems possible that a combined immunological and anatomical attack on spores of different species of *Bacillus* and *Clostridium* might give results of use in classification. Gerhardt, Bannan & Ribi (1961) have recently reported the preparation of a highly purified exosporium fraction from the spores of *B. cereus* var. *terminalis*. The serological properties of this material should be of considerable interest. So far, little or no serological work seems to have been done with spores of *Clostridium*, although presumably they are just as distinct antigenically from their sporangia as are the spores of *Bacillus*.

COMPOSITION OF BACTERIAL ANTIGENS: RELATION OF STRUCTURE TO IMMUNOCHEMICAL SPECIFICITY

Although I have stressed earlier in this article that it is not a review of the present state of structural immunochemistry of bacterial antigens, some reference to recent work in this field must be included. It is usual to regard the substances in bacteria which can give rise to specific antibodies when injected into animals as being either lipid, protein or polysaccharide. Of these three classes of substance, virtually nothing is yet known about the chemical nature of the antigenic determinants in either proteins or lipids. In fact there seems to be some doubt as to whether lipids are truly antigenic, or can themselves react with antibody. Heidelberger (1956a) has stated that in his opinion antibodies to lipids have never been rigorously demonstrated. The use of the term 'lipid antigen' in bacteriology frequently implies no more than that the material in question can be extracted by lipid solvents: however this may also be true of lipoproteins or lipopolysaccharides, in which case the antigenic specificities of the complex may well be determined by the non-lipid part of the molecule.

Polysaccharide antigens

With polysaccharides, however, structural investigations are relatively easier, and it seems not unlikely that in a few years time it will be possible to explain the specificity of quite a number of polysaccharide antigens in terms of specific chemical linkages between the sugar residues they contain. The pneumococcal capsular substances are the classical field of study in the immunochemistry of bacterial polysaccharides (Heidelberger & Avery, 1923, Heidelberger, 1926–27) and they are still being actively investigated (e.g. Goodman & Kabat, 1960 *a*, *b*). This is perhaps not surprising since there are over 70 different types of capsular substance and in only one (Type III) is the structure known in anything like full detail. Nevertheless, it is frequently possible to say with a good deal of confidence which sugars are involved in reactions or cross-reactions. For example Type II pneumococcus polysaccharide, which contains glucuronic acid, glucose and rhamnose, cross-precipitates with gum arabic and lung galactan by virtue of its glucuronic acid, but with dextrans and tamarind seed polysaccharide by virtue of linkages involving glucose. It also seems probable that the rhamnose units of Type II polysaccharide are responsible for cross-reaction with karaya gum, which contains rhamnose (Heidelberger & Adams, 1956). These multiple specificities in a single polymer show how difficult it is to talk satisfactorily about 'the capsular antigen' of the Type II pneumococcus, if the word antigen is used in a narrow sense.

More recently, considerable attention has been paid to the chemical structure of the polysaccharides of Gram-negative bacilli, and in a series of papers Westphal and Kauffmann and their colleagues have begun to correlate structure and antigenic specificities in these substances. From the strictly taxonomic point of view, this work is probably of more interest than that with the pneumococcal capsular substances, since it is concerned with a wider range of organisms representing different species and genera, and also since the polysaccharides concerned are more strictly 'structural'. It represents a logical extension of the work of Kauffmann and White which laid the foundation of the well-known antigenic scheme for classification of the Enterobacteriaceae (see Kauffmann, 1954).

Westphal, Kauffmann and their co-workers have been systematically examining the sugar components of the O-antigens of various serological groups of salmonellas in the Kauffmann-White scheme, and also of strains of *Escherichia coli* and of the Arizona group. Two tables, Tables 5 and 6, show some data from their papers (Westphal & Lüderitz, 1960; Kauffmann *et al.* 1960; Lüderitz *et al.* 1960; Westphal *et al.* 1960; Lüderitz, O'Neill & Westphal, 1960) and illustrate the type of relationship which exists between qualitative composition and the different O-antigenic specificities present.

Table 5 shows the sugar components of the O-antigens of salmonellas

Table 5. *Sugar components of O-antigens in* Salmonella *groups A, B, C_1, C_2, C_3, D_1, D_2, O and Z, taken from Kauffmann, Lüderitz, Stierlein & Westphal* (1960)

Serotype	Group	O-antigen	Galactosamine	Glucosamine	Heptose	Galactose	Glucose	Mannose	Fucose	Rhamnose	Abequose	Colitose	Paratose	Tyvelose
S. paratyphi A	A	1, 2, 12	−	+	+	+	+	+	−	+	−	−	+	−
S. paratyphi A var. durazzo		2, 12	−	+	+	+	+	+	−	+	−	−	+	−
S. kiel		1, 2, 12	−	+	+	+	+	+	−	+	−	−	+	−
S. abortus equi	B	4, 12	−	+	+	+	+	+	−	+	+	−	−	−
S. paratyphi B		4, 5, 12	−	+	+	+	+	+	−	+	+	−	−	−
S. java		4, 5, 12	−	+	+	+	+	+	−	+	+	−	−	−
S. schleissheim		4, 12, 27	−	+	+	+	+	+	−	+	+	−	−	−
S. typhi murium		4, 5, 12	−	+	+	+	+	+	−	+	+	−	−	−
S. paratyphi C	C₁	6, 7	−	+	+	+	+	+	−	−	−	−	−	−
S. paratyphi C (Vi)		6, 7	−	+	+	+	+	+	−	−	−	−	−	−
S. cholerae suis		6, 7	−	+	+	+	+	+	−	−	−	−	−	−
S. decatur		6, 7	−	+	+	+	+	+	−	−	−	−	−	−
S. isangi		6, 7	−	+	+	+	+	+	−	−	−	−	−	−
S. montevideo		6, 7	−	+	+	+	+	+	−	−	−	−	−	−
S. thompson*		6, 7	−	+	+	+	+	+	−	−	−	−	−	−
S. bareilly		6, 7	−	+	+	+	+	+	−	−	−	−	−	−
S. muenchen	C₂	6, 8	−	+	+	+	±	+	−	+	+	−	−	−
S. newport		6, 8	−	+	+	+	+	+	−	+	+	−	−	−
S. virginia	C₃	(8),	−	+	+	+	±	+	−	+	+	−	−	−
S. kentucky		(8), 20	−	+	+	+	+	+	−	+	+	−	−	−
S. sendai	D₁	1, 9, 12	−	+	+	+	+	+	−	+	−	−	−	+
S. miami		1, 9, 12	−	+	+	+	+	+	−	+	−	−	−	+
S. onarimon		1, 9, 12	−	+	+	+	+	+	−	+	−	−	−	+
S. typhi		9, 12	−	+	+	+	+	+	−	+	−	−	−	+
S. typhi (Vi)		9, 12	−	+	+	+	+	+	−	+	−	−	−	+
S. ndolo		9, 12	−	+	+	+	+	+	−	+	−	−	−	+
S. enteritidis		1, 9, 12	−	+	+	+	+	+	−	+	−	−	−	+
S. dublin		1, 9, 12	−	+	+	+	+	+	−	+	−	−	−	+
S. gallinarum		1, 9, 12	−	+	+	+	+	+	−	+	−	−	−	+
S. strasbourg	D₂	(9), 46	−	+	+	+	±	+	−	+	−	−	−	+
S. haarlem		(9), 46	−	+	+	+	+	+	−	+	−	−	−	+
S. fresno		(9), 46	−	+	+	+	+	+	−	+	−	−	−	+
S. adelaide	O	35	−	+	+	+	+	−	−	−	−	+	−	−
S. monshaui		35	−	+	+	+	+	−	−	−	−	+	−	−
S. greenside	Z	50	+	+	+	+	+	−	−	−	−	+	−	−

* Antigen obtained from cultures grown in broth.

in groups A, B, C_1, C_2, C_3, D_1, D_2, O and Z. It is evident that while A, D, O and Z could be distinguished readily in terms simply of the sugars present (subgroups could not be differentiated) groups B and C_2 plus C_3 show the same overall sugar composition but differ widely in their serological specificities.

In the antigenic groups included in Table 5 it is noticeable that all except C_1 have one or more deoxyhexoses (fucose, rhamnose) or dideoxyhexoses (abequose, colitose, paratose, tyvelose). These deoxy sugars are not present in the polysaccharides of all the O-antigenic groups. For example, they are absent also from strains of group H, J, K and a number of others (Kauffmann *et al.* 1960). Wherever they do occur, they seem to have a powerful effect in determining serological specificity, and they appear to be characteristic of smooth and freshly isolated cultures. Staub & Tinelli (1956) investigated the ability of pure sugars of this kind to inhibit precipitin reactions with salmonella polysaccharides. From this work, they concluded that antigen 9 specificity (in *Salmonella typhi*) was probably associated with the presence of tyvelose, while antigen 12 specificity (in *S. paratyphi* B) was probably due to rhamnose. In other similar work (Staub *et al.* 1959), evidence was obtained of various other associations of antigenic specificities with particular sugars (e.g. abequose with antigen 4, paratose with antigen 2, etc.). The evidence is still largely circumstantial, but the technique of preparing artificial antigens (see Lüderitz *et al.* 1960*b*) with a given sugar as the determinant should be most useful in trying to unravel this very complicated piece of taxonomic immunochemistry.

Cross-reactions between O-antigens from some strains of *Salmonella* and strains of *Escherichia coli* have long been known, and investigations of the kind described above indicate a possible chemical basis for them. Table 6, which is taken from a paper by Westphal *et al.* (1960), shows a number of such organisms grouped according to cross-reactions, together with the sugars found on hydrolysis of their polysaccharides. In general each cross-reacting group possesses the same distinctive pattern of sugar components, i.e. the same *chemotype* (Kauffmann *et al.* 1960), although this is not true in all cases. For example, the two groups Salmonella adelaide (35) Arizona (20) *Escherichia coli* (111:B4) and S. greenside (50) Arizona (9) *E. coli* (55:B5) appear to be broadly similar, in particular in their possession of the dideoxy-sugar colitose, yet the organisms comprising them cross-react only within the group, not outside it. This must indicate that in neither case is colitose involved in that part of the structure producing the cross-reaction. The whole subject is still very much in the experimental stage, but one general

Table 6. *Component sugars of the O-antigens (lipopolysaccharide) of various cross-reactive Gram-negative bacteria, taken from Westphal, Kauffmann, Lüderitz & Stierlein* (1960)

Organism	O-antigen	Galactosamine	Glucosamine	Heptose(s)	Galactose	Glucose	Mannose	Fucose	Rhamnose	Colitose	Abequose
Salmonella hvittingfoss	16	+	+	+	+	+	+	+	−	−	−
Arizona	25	+	+	+	+	+	+	+	−	−	−
Escherichia coli	11	+	+	+	±	+	+	+	−	−	−
S. onderstepoort	(1), 6, 14, 25	−	+	+	+	+	+	−	−	−	−
E. coli	73	−	+	+	−	+	+	−	−	−	−
S. weslaco	42	−	+	+	+	+	−	−	+	−	−
Arizona	15	−	+	+	+	+	−	−	+	−	−
E. coli	31	−	+	+	+	+	−	−	+	−	−
S. inverness	38	+	+	+	+	+	−	−	−	−	−
Arizona	16	+	+	+	+	+	−	−	−	−	−
E. coli	21	+	+	+	+	+	−	−	−	−	−
S. aberdeen	11	−	+	+	+	+	+	−	+	−	−
Arizona	17	−	+	+	+	±	+	−	+	−	−
E. coli	75	−	+	+	+	+	+	−	+	−	−
S. adelaide	35	−	+	+	+	+	−	−	−	+	−
Arizona	20	−	+	+	+	+	−	−	−	+	−
E. coli	111:B4	−	+	+	+	+	−'	−	−	+	−
S. greenside	50	+	+	+	+	+	−	−	−	+	−
Arizona	9	−	+	+	+	+	−	+	−	+	−
E. coli	55:B5	+	+	+	+	+	−	−	−	+	−
S. milwaukee	43	+	+	+	+	+	−	+	−	−	−
Arizona	21	+	+	+	+	+	−	+	−	−	−
E. coli	86:B7	+	+	+	+	+	−	+	−	−	−
S. paratyphi B	4, 5, 12	−	+	+	+	+	+	−	+	−	+
Citrobacter	(4, 5)	−	+	+	+	+	+	−	−	−	+
S. dakar	28	+	+	+	+	+	−	−	−	+	−
Citrobacter	(28)	+	+	+	+	+	−	−	+	−	−
S. djakarta	48	−	+	+	+	+	−	(Colominic acid)			
Citrobacter	(48)	−	+	+	+	+	−	(Colominic acid)			

The substance colominic acid, indicated as being present in *S. djakarta* and *Citrobacter* (48) is a polymer of *N*-acetyl-neuraminic acid and confers O-inagglutinability. It is not a component of the polysaccharide from the O-antigen.

principal which seems to emerge is that deoxy sugars are associated with the polysaccharides from smooth strains, and are absent from those of rough strain. This is so in *Salmonella* (Westphal & Lüderitz, 1960; Kauffmann *et al.* 1961), in *Escherichia* (Westphal & Lüderitz, 1953) and in *Shigella* (Davies, 1957), although in the latter genus the position is complicated by the fact that the rough form, while having 'lost' the deoxy sugar, now contains a heptose. However, it seems fairly clear the deoxy sugars are characteristic of smooth strains and that when present they tend to be major antigenic determinants.

The 'smooth' to 'rough' variation

This work also throws some light on the changes underlying the S → R variation. This is usually represented as being the 'loss' of a 'Smooth' surface antigen which 'uncovers' the 'Rough' antigen underlying it, an explanation which presupposes the existence of the 'Rough' antigen in the smooth strain. However, Davies (1957) investigated this point in a smooth strain of *Shigella dysenteriae* and could not extract any 'Rough' antigen from it. Moreover, diethylene glycol, which will extract the 'Smooth' somatic antigen, will not extract 'Rough' antigen from the rough strain, a process which needs phenol or 7 M urea. All this suggests that the S → R variation is the expression in colonial form of the switch from the synthesis of one type of polymer to another. Westphal and his collaborators (Westphal, personal communication) have recently made the very interesting observation that 'Rough' specificity can be detected in 'Smooth' polysaccharides after mild hydrolysis which splits off the side chains determining the 'Smooth' specificity. This means that 'Rough' specificity is part of the intrinsic structure of the 'Smooth' polysaccharide, although that part of the molecule responsible for it is normally covered or prevented from reacting by the side chains which determine 'Smooth' reactivity. It is interesting to see that the classical explanation of the 'Smooth' antigen covering the 'Rough' and preventing its detection is perfectly correct when reinterpreted in terms of chemical groupings on a single polymer, but that it would be misleading to talk of the 'Smooth' and 'Rough' antigens as though they were separate and distinct substances which stood in a fixed anatomical relationship to each other. The constitution of a large number of polysaccharides from Gram-negative bacteria has recently been reviewed by Davies (1960).

DISCUSSION

First, it seems obvious that single antigenic specificities, considered without relation to any other property of the organism, have little or no significance in classification. If they had, we would have to look for some subtle phylogenetic relationship between *Homo sapiens* and *Escherichia coli* O 86, whose O-antigens cross-react with human group B blood cells. However, if these antigenic specificities are associated with a polymer of a particular kind, which is characteristic of a certain type of structure in some kinds of bacteria, then they may become useful indicators. It seems to me therefore that our approach to the problems of immunochemical criteria in bacterial taxonomy should be as far as possible an anatomical one, since it is cells which have the same kinds of polymers in the same anatomical position that are likely to be related. It would be useful to think primarily in terms of cell-wall proteins or cytoplasmic polysaccharides, for example, before we start thinking in terms of 'group' or 'type' antigens.

Of the various anatomical features of bacteria listed at the beginning of the article, some are probably of better taxonomic value than others. For example, the presence of flagella, fimbriae and spores is very unevenly distributed throughout Eubacteriales, and therefore the antigens associated with these features cannot be used for comparative purposes over a wide field. The same argument applies to capsules and other surface polymers, whose presence is also very variable. On the other hand, the cell-wall and the cytoplasmic membrane, and presumably also the chromatin bodies, are invariable structural features of the bacterial cell and a comparison of their properties over the whole field of microbiology is possible.

Cell-wall antigens have been quite widely used in taxonomy for a considerable time, although not always recognized as such. Agglutination tests using intact bacteria will detect surface cell-wall antigens, but almost certainly not the major carbohydrate antigens in the walls of Gram-positive bacteria, which need either to be extracted in soluble form, or detected by the agglutination of cell-wall suspensions. However there are difficulties inherent in using only extracted antigens in classification, which are illustrated by the present position of Group D streptococci. The polysaccharide antigen of this group is a polyglucose which occurs largely in the cytoplasm although some of it may be present also at the cell surface (Elliott, 1960; Jones & Shattock, 1960). Since all other Lancefield groups appear to depend on polysaccharide antigens representing the carbohydrate part of the cell-wall mucopeptide, the use of a cytoplasmic polysaccharide antigen in group D seems illogical. To see whether cell-wall antigens in group D corresponded in any way to the various subgroups normally recognized, a small number of strains was examined by cell-wall agglutination tests (Cummins & Slade, unpublished). No clear-cut correlation appeared to exist, but most strains showed evidence of at least two antigenic components (see, for example, Table 3). It might be better to arrange all streptococci (including 'viridans' and 'ungroupable' strains) as far as possible in

groups based solely on cell-wall polysaccharide antigens, although from
the results of cell-wall agglutination (see Table 2), this would probably
mean ultimately giving each group an antigenic formula explicable
largely or completely in chemical terms. The work of McCarty has
illustrated how this may be done with group A and a series of group A
variant strains (McCarty & Lancefield, 1955; McCarty, 1956). It may
be noted in passing that if their origin were not known these variant
strains would surely have been regarded as belonging to a separate
group.

Despite the present rather illogical position of group D strains, the
Lancefield classification of streptococci is a very successful example of
the subdivision on primarily antigenic grounds of a large group of
organisms. It may be noted also that these groups are often (although
not always) given specific rank (e.g. *Streptococcus pyogenes, S. agalactiae,
S. lactis*, etc.). Group D is again something of an exception in this
respect. It is interesting to compare this streptococcal antigenic scheme
with results recently obtained by analysis of cell-wall antigens in quite
a different group of organisms, namely, strains of corynebacteria,
mycobacteria and nocardia.

An examination of cell-wall compositions in strains of Actinomycetales (Cummins & Harris, 1958) showed that the strains of mycobacteria and most of the strains of nocardia examined had a pattern of
components which was the same as that previously found for most
strains of corynebacteria (Cummins & Harris, 1956a). All the strains
in question had arabinose and galactose as the principal cell-wall sugars,
and alanine, glutamic acid and DL-diaminopimelic acid (DAP) as amino
acids. A rather larger collection of strains of corynebacteria, mycobacteria and nocardia has now been examined to compare cell-wall
composition with the cell-wall agglutination reaction in the same strains.
This will be published in detail elsewhere (Cummins, 1961), but some of
the results with corynebacteria appear in condensed form in Table 7.
It can be noticed first that in terms of cell-wall composition the strains
are heterogeneous, and fall into three groups. One of these contains
strains which have the wall composition mentioned above (arabinose,
galactose, alanine, glutamic acid and DAP). The second consists of four
strains of *Corynebacterium pyogenes*, which resemble streptococci in
cell-wall composition (Cummins & Harris, 1956a). The third group,
made up of plant pathogenic corynebacteria, is itself heterogeneous,
but bears no resemblance to either of the others. The serological reactions of the cell-wall suspensions from these strains have been examined
against a number of sera prepared against mycobacteria and coryne-

Table 7. *Cell-wall composition and cell-wall antigens in corynebacteria (from Cummins, 1961)*

| Name of strain | Principal cell-wall components | | | Serological reactions. Cell-wall agglutination tests with antisera to | |
	Sugars	Amino sugars	Amino acids	C. diphtheriae	C. pyogenes
C. diphtheriae var. mitis 2764 C. ulcerans NCTC 7910 C. renale NCTC 7448 C. equi NCTC 1621 C. hofmanii L.H. C. fascians NCPPB 188	Arabinose and galactose (some strains have glucose or mannose or both in addition)	Glucosamine and muramic acid (galactosamine also in C. hofmanii)	Alanine, glutamic acid and diaminopimelic acid	Positive	Negative
C. pyogenes Wye 1 C. pyogenes Wye 2 C. pyogenes Wye 3 C. pyogenes NCTC 5224	Rhamnose and glucose	Glucosamine, galactosamine and muramic acid	Alanine, glutamic acid and lysine	Negative	Positive
C. tritici NCPPB 471 C. betae NCPPB 373 C. poinsettiae NCPPB 177 C. flaccumfacians var. auranticum NCPPB 558	Variable	Glucosamine and muramic acid	Variable	Negative	Negative

bacteria, the results with two of which are given in the table to illustrate the correspondence between overall cell-wall composition and the presence or absence of certain antigenic specificities. All six strains of corynebacteria which have the arabinose-galactose pattern of components (including the plant pathogen *C. fascians*) reacted with *C. diphtheriae* antiserum but not with *C. pyogenes* antiserum, and all four strains of *C. pyogenes* reacted with the *pyogenes* antiserum but not with the *diphtheriae* antiserum, while the heterogeneous group of plant pathogens reacted with neither. The results cannot be given in greater detail here for lack of space, but it was found that all organisms (with two partial exceptions) which had the arabinose-galactose pattern of cell-wall components reacted with sera prepared against *Mycobacterium smegmatis*, *C. diphtheriae* and *C. ovis* (which themselves have this pattern), but not against other sera. The titres showed considerable variation, but wherever absorption tests were done, all antibody was removed for the homologous suspension.

This widespread antigenic cross-reaction between the cell-walls of mycobacteria, corynebacteria and nocardia seems to be additional evidence that these groups are closely related, which has already been argued on grounds of cell-wall composition (Cummins & Harris, 1958). It was particularly interesting to find the three strains of *Nocardia pelletieri*, which had a pattern of cell-wall components resembling *Streptomyces*, did not contain the cross-reacting antigen. It is assumed that the serological specificities involved are polysaccharide, and therefore are presumably equivalent taxonomically to the major polysaccharide antigens of the streptococcal scheme. This would result in a considerable number of strains at present in *Mycobacterium*, *Corynebacterium* and *Nocardia* being placed at least in a single genus and possibly in a single species. Such a degree of 'lumping' might need a considerable re-assessment of present ideas about the value of morphology in bacterial classification, but it would merely be using the chemical anatomy of the cell in a logical way.

There is probably at least one other group in which cell-wall polysaccharide antigens have been used in classification, although not definitely identified as such. This is in *Lactobacillus*, where Sharpe (1955) was able to classify 70 % of 442 strains into a number of groups by precipitin tests using HCl extracts. The groups found agreed well with those defined by physiological tests (Briggs, 1953).

In this article I have been frankly partisan and have devoted a good deal more time to antigens of cell-walls than to those in other parts of the bacterium. I think this emphasis is not entirely unjustified. The cell-wall is the main structural feature of the cell, making up about 15–20 % (or sometimes more) of the cell dry weight. Cell-wall composition also seems to be a very constant character (Cummins & Harris, 1956a). It may change under certain conditions (e.g. in *Streptococcus pyogenes* when inoculated into animals; Wilson, 1945; McCarty & Lancefield, 1955), but these changes seem to be infrequent, and once established seem to be as permanent as the original strain. There are other reasons also why the cell-wall deserves particular consideration in bacterial taxonomy. There is a good deal of evidence that the basic cell-wall material (mucopeptide) is synthesized by a system distinct from the general metabolism of the cell: its synthesis is, for example, inhibited by penicillin but unaffected by chloramphenicol, while the reverse is the case with protein synthesis (Mandelstam & Rogers, 1958; Hancock & Park, 1958). It might perhaps be argued from this that if simple and unchanging physical properties are needed for the basic structure of the cell-wall, this is less likely to be subject to evolutionary pressures than are those parts of the cell which must adapt to changing external conditions. If this is so, cell-wall structure (including its antigenic specificities) should indicate phylogenetic relationships more accurately than some other properties of the cell.

ACKNOWLEDGEMENTS

This article was written during a year as visiting investigator in the laboratory of Dr Hutton D. Slade, Department of Microbiology, Northwestern University Medical School, Chicago, U.S.A. I am very grateful to Dr Slade and to the Chairman of the Department, Dr Guy P. Youmans, for facilities during the preparation of the manuscript. I must also thank Dr R. Parlett for reading the typescript.

REFERENCES

ARMSTRONG, J. J., BADDILEY, J. & BUCHANAN, J. G. (1960). Structure of the ribitol teichoic acids from the walls of *Bacillus subtilis. Biochem. J.* 76, 610.

ARMSTRONG, J. J., BADDILEY, J., BUCHANAN, J. G., CARSS, B. & GRENNBERG, G. R. (1958). Isolation and structure of ribitol phosphate derivatives (teichoic acids) from bacterial cell walls. *J. chem. Soc.* p. 4344.

BADDILEY, J. & DAVISON, A. L. (1961). The occurrence and location of teichoic acids in lactobacilli. *J. gen. Microbiol.* 24, 295.

BAUMANN-GRACE, J. B. & TOMCSIK, J. (1957). The surface structure and serological typing of *Bacillus megaterium. J. gen. Microbiol.* 17, 227.

BEUTNER, E. H. (1961). Immunofluorescent staining; the fluorescent antibody method. *Bact. Rev.* 25, 49.

BLEIWEIS, A. S. & ZIMMERMAN, L. N. (1960). Protoplasts of *Streptococcus faecalis* var. *liquefaciens. Bact. Proc.* p. 62.

BOYDEN, S. V. (1951). The adsorption of proteins on erythrocytes treated with tannic acid and subsequent haemagglutination by antiprotein sera. *J. exp. Med.* **93**, 107.

BRADFIELD, J. R. G. (1956). Organization of bacterial cytoplasm. *Symp. Soc. gen. Microbiol.* **6**, 269.

BRIGGS, M. (1953). The classification of lactobacilli by means of physiological tests. *J. gen. Microbiol.* **9**, 234.

BRINTON, C. C. (1959). Non-flagellar appendages of bacteria. *Nature, Lond.* **183**, 782.

CAREY, W. F. & BARON, L. S. (1959). Comparative immunologic studies of cell structures isolated from *Salmonella typhosa. J. Immunol.* **83**, 517.

COONS, A. H., CREECH, H. J., JONES, R. N. & BERLINER, E. (1942). The demonstration of pneumococcal antigen in tissues by the use of fluorescent antibody. *J. Immunol.* **45**, 157.

COOPER, G. N. & PILLOW, J. A. (1960). An immunological comparison of cell components of *Shigella dysenteriae* type 2. *J. Immunol.* **84**, 135.

CUMMINS, C. S. (1954). Some observation on the nature of the antigens in the cell wall of *Corynebacterium diphtheriae. Brit. J. exp. Path.* **35**, 166.

CUMMINS, C. S. (1962). Chemical composition and antigenic structure in cell-walls of *Corynebacterium, Mycobacterium, Nocardia, Actinomyces* and *Arthrobacter. J. gen. Microbiol.* (in the Press).

CUMMINS, C. S. & HARRIS, H. (1956a). The chemical composition of the cell-wall in some Gram positive bacteria and its possible value as a taxonomic character. *J. gen. Microbiol.* **14**, 583.

CUMMINS, C. S. & HARRIS, H. (1956b). The relationship between certain members of the staphylococcus-micrococcus group as shown by their cell wall composition. *Int. Bull. bact. Nomen. Taxon.* **6**, 111.

CUMMINS, C. S. & HARRIS, H. (1958). Studies on the cell-wall composition and taxonomy of Actinomycetales and related groups. *J. gen. Microbiol.* **18**, 173.

CUMMINS, C. S. & HARRIS, H. (1959). Taxonomic position of *Arthrobacter. Nature, Lond.* **184**, 831.

CUMMINS, C. S. & SLADE, H. D. (1961). Cell wall agglutination and precipitation tests on streptococci of different serological groups. *Bact. Proc.* p. 94.

DAVIES, D. A. L. (1957). Isolation of a 'Rough' somatic antigen from *Shigella dysenteriae. Biochim. biophys. Acta*, **26**, 151.

DAVIES, D. A. L. (1960). Polysaccharides of Gram-negative bacteria. *Advanc. Carbohyd. Chem.* **15**, 271.

DAVIES, S. N. (1951). The serology of *Bacillus polymyxa. J. gen. Microbiol.* **5**, 807.

DOAK, B. W. & LAMANNA, C. (1948). On the antigenic structure of the bacterial spore. *J. Bact.* **55**, 373.

DOWDLE, W. R. & HANSEN, P. A. (1961). A phage-fluorescent antiphage staining system for *Bacillus anthracis. J. infect. Dis.* **108**, 125.

ELLIOTT, S. D. (1960). Type and group polysaccharides of group D streptococci. *J. exp. Med.* **111**, 621.

FREIMER, E. H. & KRAUSE, R. M. (1960). Chemical and immunological studies of protoplast membranes of group A streptococci. *Fed. Proc.* **19**, 244.

FREIMER, E. H. & KRAUSE, R. M. (1961). The isolation of membranes from mechanically disrupted haemolytic streptococci. *Fed. Proc.* **20**, 29.

FREIMER, E. H., KRAUSE, R. M. & MCCARTY, M. (1959). Studies on L-forms and protoplasts of group A streptococci. I. Isolation, growth and bacteriologic characteristics. *J. exp. Med.* **110**, 853.

GERHARDT, P., BANNAN, E. A. & RIBI, E. (1961). Selective disruption of spores and isolation of exosporium. *Bact. Proc.* p. 77.

GILLIES, R. R. & DUGUID, J. P. (1958). The fimbrial antigens of *Shigella flexneri*. *J. Hyg., Camb.* **56**, 303.

GOODMAN, J. W. & KABAT, E. A. (1960*a*). Immunochemical studies on cross-reactions of antipneumococcal sera. I. Cross-reactions of Types II and XX antipneumococcal sera with dextran, and of Type II antipneumococcal serum with glycogen and Friedlander type B polysaccharide. *J. Immunol.* **84**, 333.

GOODMAN, J. W. & KABAT, E. A. (1960*b*). Immunochemical studies on cross-reactions of antipneumococcal sera. II. Cross-reactions of types IX and XII antipneumococcal sera with dextran. *J. Immunol.* **84**, 347.

GRABAR, P. (1953). Comparaison entre les methods immunologique quantitative et bilan de leurs application. *Atti VI Congr. int. Microbiol., Rome* **2**, 169.

GUNSALUS, I. C. & STANIER, R. Y. (1960). *The Bacteria*. Vol. 1. New York: Academic Press.

HANCOCK, R. & PARK, J. T. (1958). Cell-wall synthesis by *Staphylococcus aureus* in the presence of chloramphenicol. *Nature, Lond.* **181**, 1050.

HEIDELBERGER, M. (1926–27). Immunologically specific polysaccharides. *Chem. Rev.* **3**, 403.

HEIDELBERGER, M. (1956*a*). *Lectures in Immunochemistry*. New York: Academic Press.

HEIDELBERGER, M. (1956*b*). Chemical constitution and immunological specificity. *Annu. Rev. Biochem.* **25**, 641.

HEIDELBERGER, M. & ADAMS, J. (1956). The immunological specificity of Type II pneumococcus and its separation into partial specificities. *J. exp. Med.* **103**, 189.

HEIDELBERGER, M. & AVERY, O. T. (1923). The soluble specific substance of the pneumococcus. *J. exp. Med.* **38**, 73.

HOUWINK, A. L. & VAN ITERSON, W. (1950). Electron microscopical observations on bacterial cytology. II. A study on flagellation. *Biochim. biophys. Acta*, **5**, 10.

JONES, D. & SHATTOCK, P. M. F. (1960). The location of the group antigen of group D streptococci. *J. gen. Microbiol.* **23**, 235.

KABAT, E. A. (1958). Immunochemical approaches to p. iysaccharide and muco-polysaccharide structure. In *Chemistry and Biology of Mucopolysaccharides*. London: Churchill.

KABAT, E. A. & MAYER, M. M. (1961). *Experimental Immunochemistry*. 2nd edition. Springfield: Thomas.

KAUFFMANN, F. (1954). *Enterobacteriaceae*, 2nd ed. Copenhagen: E. Munksgaard.

KAUFFMANN, F., LÜDERITZ, O., STIERLEIN, H. & WESTPHAL, O. (1960). Zur Immunchemie der O-antigene von Enterobacteriaceae. I. Analyse der Zuckerbausteine von Salmonella-O-antigenen. *Zbl. Bakt.* (1 *Abt. Orig.*), **178**, 442.

KAUFFMANN, F., KRÜGER, L., LÜDERITZ, O. & WESTPHAL, O. (1961). Zur Immunchemie der O-antigene von Enterobacteriaceae. VI. Vergleich der Zuckerbausteine von Polysacchariden aus Salmonella-S-und R-Formen. *Zbl. Bakt.* (1. *Abt. Orig.*), **182**, 57.

LAMANNA, C. (1940*a*). The taxonomy of the genus *Bacillus*. II. Differentiation of small-celled species by means of spore antigens. *J. infect. Dis.* **67**, 193.

LAMANNA, C. (1940*b*). The taxonomy of the genus *Bacillus*. II. Differentiation of the large-celled species by means of spore antigens. *J. infect. Dis.* **67**, 205.

LAMANNA, C. & EISLER, D. (1960). Comparative study of the agglutinogens of the endospores of *Bacillus anthracis* and *Bacillus cereus*. *J. Bact.* **79**, 435.

LANCEFIELD, R. C. (1941). Specific relationship of cell composition to biological activity of haemolytic streptococci. *Harvey Lect.*, ser. 36, 251.

LANCEFIELD, R. C. (1943). Studies on the antigenic composition of group A haemolytic streptococci. I. The effect of proteolytic enzymes on streptococcal cells. *J. exp. Med.* **78**, 465.

LEDERBERG, J. (1956). Bacterial protoplasts induced by penicillin. *Proc. nat. Acad. Sci., Wash.* **42**, 574.

LEDERBERG, J. & ST CLAIR, J. (1958). Protoplasts and L-type growth of *Escherichia coli. J. Bact.* **75**, 143.

LÜDERITZ, O., O'NEILL, G. & WESTPHAL, O. (1960). Zur Immunchemie der O-antigene von Enterobacteriaceae. V. Die Antigenfaktoren in isolierten Salmonella-O-antigenen. *Biochem. Z.* **333**, 136.

LÜDERITZ, O., KAUFFMANN, F., STIERLIN, H. & WESTPHAL, O. (1960). Zur Immunchemie der O-antigene von Enterobacteriaceae. II. Vergleich der Zuckerbausteine von Salmonella, S-, R- and T-formen. *Zbl. Bakt.* (1. *Abt. Orig.*), **179**, 180.

McCARTY, M. (1952). The lysis of group A haemolytic streptococci by extracellular enzymes of *Streptomyces albus*. II. Nature of the cellular substance attacked by the lytic enzymes. *J. exp. Med.* **96**, 569.

McCARTY, M. (1956). Variation in the group specific carbohydrate of group A streptococci. II. Studies on the chemical basis for serological specificity of the carbohydrates. *J. exp. Med.* **104**, 629.

McCARTY, M. (1959). The occurrence of polyglycerophosphate as an antigenic component of various Gram-positive bacterial species. *J. exp. Med.* **109**, 361.

McCARTY, M. & LANCEFIELD, R. C. (1955). Variation in the group specific carbohydrate of group A streptococci. I. Immunochemical studies on the carbohydrates of variant strains. *J. exp. Med.* **102**, 11.

MACPHERSON, C. F. C. & HEIDELBERGER, M. (1945*a*). Denatured egg albumin. I. The preparations and purification of crystalline egg albumin denatured in various ways. *J. Amer. chem. Soc.* **67**, 574.

MACPHERSON, C. F. C. & HEIDELBERGER, M. (1945*b*). Denatured egg albumin. III. Quantitative immunochemical studies on crystalline egg albumin denatured in various ways. *J. Amer. chem. Soc.* **67**, 585.

MACPHERSON, C. F. C., HEIDELBERGER, M. & MOORE, D. H. (1945). Denatured egg albumin. II. Viscosities, particle weights and electrophoretic mobilities of crystalline egg albumin denatured in various ways. *J. Amer. chem. Soc.* **67**, 578.

McQUILLEN, K. (1960). Bacterial protoplasts. In *The Bacteria*, vol. 1, p. 249. New York: Academic Press.

MANDELSTAM, J. & ROGERS, H. J. (1958). Chloramphenicol resistant incorporation of amino acids into staphylococci and cell wall synthesis. *Nature, Lond.* **181**, 956.

MARR, A. G. & COTA-ROBLES, E. H. (1957). Sonic disruption of *Azotobacter vinelandii. J. Bact.* **74**, 79.

MIDDLEBROOK, G. & DUBOS, R. J. (1948). Specific serum agglutination of erythrocytes sensitized with extracts of tubercle bacilli. *J. exp. Med.* **88**, 521.

MOODY, M. D., ELLIS, E. C. & UPDYKE, E. L. (1958). Staining bacterial smears with fluorescent antibody. IV. Grouping streptococci with fluorescent antibody. *J. Bact.* **75**, 553.

MURRAY, R. G. E. (1960). The internal structure of the cell. In *The Bacteria*, Vol. 1, p. 35. New York: Academic Press.

PILLET, J., ROUYER, M. & ORTA, B. (1955). Recherches sur la nature chimique des agglutinogènes staphylococciques. *Ann. Inst. Pasteur*, **88**, 662.

ROBINOW, C. F. (1960). Morphology of bacterial spores, their development and germination. In *The Bacteria*, vol. 1, p. 207. New York: Academic Press.

ROTHEN, A. & LANDSTEINER, K. (1942). Serological reactions of protein films and denatured protein. *J. exp. Med.* **76**, 437.

SALTON, M. R. J. (1953). Studies of the bacterial cell wall. IV. The composition of the cell walls of some Gram positive and Gram negative bacteria. *Biochim. biophys. Acta*, **10**, 512.

SALTON, M. R. J. (1956). Bacterial cell walls. *Symp. Soc. gen. Microbiol.* **6**, 81.

SALTON, M. R. J. (1960). Surface layers of the bacterial cell. In *The Bacteria,* vol. 1, p. 97. New York: Academic Press.

SHAFA, F. (1958). *A study of the surface structure of some bacteria.* Ph.D. Thesis, University of Manchester. (Quoted by Salton, 1960.)

SHARPE, M. E. (1955). A serological classification of lactobacilli. *J. gen. Microbiol.* **12**, 107.

SLADE, H. D. & VETTER, J. K. (1956). Studies on *Streptococcus pyogenes.* II. Observations on the microscopical and biological aspects of the disintegration and solubilization of a type 6 strain by sonic oscillation. *J. Bact.* **71**, 236.

SMITH, N. R., GORDON, R. E. & CLARK, F. E. (1952). Aerobic sporeforming bacteria. *Agric. Monogr.* no. 16.

SPIEGELMAN, S., ARONSON, A. I. & FITZJAMES, P. C. (1958). Isolation and characterization of nuclear bodies from protoplasts of *Bacillus megaterium. J. Bact.* **75**, 102.

SPOONER, E. T. C. & STOCKER, B. A. D. (1956) (editors). Bacterial anatomy. *Symp. Soc. gen. Microbiol.* **6**.

STACEY, M. & BARKER, S. A. (1960). *Polysaccharides of Microorganisms.* Oxford: Clarendon Press.

STAUB, A. M. & TINELLI, R. (1956). Essai d'identification des antigènes O des salmonelles au moyen de l'oxidation periodique du polyoside spécifique. *C.R. Acad. Sci., Paris,* **243**, 1460.

STAUB, A. M., TINELLI, R., LÜDERITZ, O. & WESTPHAL, O. (1959). Étude immunochimique sur les Salmonella. V. Role de quelques sucres, et en particulier des 3–6 didésoxyhexoses, dans la spécificité des antigènes O du tableau de Kauffmann-White. *Ann. Inst. Pasteur,* **96**, 303.

TOMCSIK, J. (1956). Antibodies as indicators for bacterial surface structures. *Annu. Rev. Microbiol.* **10**, 213.

TOMCSIK, J. & BAUMANN-GRACE, J. B. (1959). Specific exosporium reaction of *Bacillus megaterium. J. gen. Microbiol.* **21**, 666.

TOMCSIK, J., BOUILLE, M. & BAUMANN-GRACE, J. B. (1959). Réaction spécifique de l'exosporium chez *Bacillus cereus* et *Bacillus anthracis. Schweiz. Z. allg. Path.* **22**, 630.

TOMCSIK, J. & GEUX-HOLZER, S. (1954). Antikorperproduktion mit isolierter Bakterienzellwand und mit Protoplasten. *Experientia,* **10**, 484.

VENNES, J. W. & GERHARDT, P. (1956). Immunological comparison of isolated surface membranes of *Bacillus megaterium. Science,* **124**, 535.

WEIBULL, C. (1958). Bacterial protoplasts. *Annu. Rev. Microbiol.* **12**, 1.

WEIDEL, W., FRANK, H. & MARTIN, H. H. (1960). The rigid layer of the cell-wall of *Escherichia coli* strain B. *J. gen. Microbiol.* **22**, 158.

WESTPHAL, O. & LÜDERITZ, O. (1953). Zur chemischen Analyse von Lipopolysacchariden gramnegativer bakterien: neue Desoxyzucker sowie einbetrag zur chemischen Differenzierung einiger O-glatt- und O-rauh-formen. *Atti VI int. Congr. Microbiol.,* Rome, **2**, 22.

WESTPHAL, O. & LÜDERITZ, O. (1960). 3, 6-Dideoxy-hexosen. Chemie und Biologie. *Angew. Chem.* **72**, 881.

WESTPHAL, O., KAUFFMANN, F., LÜDERITZ, O. & STIERLEIN, H. (1960). Zur Immunochemie der O-antigene von Enterobacteriaceae. III. Analyse der Zuckerbausteine kreuzreagierender Salmonella-Arizona- und Escherichia-O-antigene. *Zbl. Bakt.* (1 *Abt. Orig.*), **179**, 336.

WILKINSON, J. F. (1958). The extracellular polysaccharides of bacteria. *Bact. Rev.* **22**, 46.

WILSON, A. T. (1945). Loss of group carbohydrate during mouse passages of a group A haemolytic streptococcus. *J. exp. Med.* **81**, 593.

SOLUBLE BACTERIAL ANTIGENS AS DISCRIMINANTS IN CLASSIFICATION

C. L. OAKLEY

Bacteriology Department, University of Leeds

When, in 1955, this Society last discussed bacteriological classification I was asked to deal with the same discriminants (the bacterial toxins) as I am now expected to review. Having re-read the paper I gave on that occasion (Oakley, 1955), I find myself in entire agreement with the conclusions I then came to, that bacterial toxins are useful for dividing species into types, but of little value in delimiting larger groups, and that questions of convenience in referring to bacterial toxins might occasionally justify retention of rather aberrant forms in a species if they produced one of the toxins characteristic of the more typical forms. Of course, I might repeat what I then said in other words, and hope that no one would notice the resemblance; but I prefer to be honest with you, and confess that I have nothing new to say. In the circumstances I hope you will bear with a few general platitudes on classification that may seem new to the youngest among you; I shall try to illustrate them here and there with the bacterial toxins.

The first thing to remember about classifications of living things is that they are made by man; bacteria have, so far as we know, little interest in the subject. Moreover, when man devises classifications, he nearly always has some practical object in mind, and the developments of his classification will reflect the development of his own purposes. Primitively, classifications are applied to real or imaginary objects so that they can be given names; every student of magic knows that in primitive, and even in some not-so-primitive communities, to know a man's name is to have power over him, and men will carefully conceal their real names and be known by false ones to counteract this magic. If we wish to summon devils or call upon angels we must know their names; and by extension this principle is readily applied to other organisms. It does not matter whether the power desired is real or imaginary; controlled experiments are in my limited experience hardly popular with magicians; but it is worth while remembering that even today when we name a bacterium we may (if we have named it rightly) know also the antibiotic with which to attack it. But whether we wish to call upon angels, call up devils or cast them out of the sick, or possess powers against bacteria, we must, if we argue magically, know their right names, otherwise we shall gain nothing. Only the right name for the purpose will do; and here comes the real puzzle of classification. The numbers of angels and demons of *serious* importance is probably limited and might reasonably be learned during his apprenticeship by any competent student of witchcraft; but dangerous living things are very numerous and become much more so the more refined your methods of observation become, so that it really is a very serious problem if you have to deal with them as individuals. So as usual we compromise and allow a range of variation round a node for a particular category and call all the individuals included in that category by the same name, hoping, even believing, that our incantations or our treatment or reference will be good enough for our present purpose against any or all of them.

This process provides an obvious economy, for if we are to deal with lions, it is very useful to have a name for lions in general rather than to have to depend on a probably imperfect knowledge of the names of particular individuals.

It is quite common, I find, for people to laugh at the medieval disputations between the nominalists and the realists, possibly because these are so poorly represented by our terms, but these philosophers were dealing with exactly the same problem that faced the first classifiers: the nominalists held that groups of individuals, like 'man', '*Clostridium welchii*' were merely words, and that only individuals—individual men and *C. welchii* existed; no species for them!—whereas the realists accepted, though to varying degrees, that species existed, and had some relation to reality. Convenience has made it easier for us to adopt both attitudes; so that when, for example, men are to be saved, they are treated as individuals, but when they appear in statistical tables or in armies, their reality is wholly or partly specific in character.

Larger and larger groups may obviously be devised by treating the first aggregates as members of larger groups, which we discriminate from one another by differences we consider more important than those by which we distinguish the smaller constituent groups. What we mean by 'important' I leave for a while. Hogben, I think, once suggested that the pyramidal character of early classifications reflected the pyramidal character of society at the time, and one might suggest that the use of Latin reflects not only its status as a universal language, but its magical value; when Horatio and the guard meet Hamlet's father's ghost on the battlements of Elsinore, the unlettered soldiers say to him 'Thou art a scholar, speak to it, Horatio' because, as a scholar, he can speak to it in Latin, which all ghosts used to understand.

Evidently as long as we are dealing with organisms with a long generation time and we know little about them, and particularly when we have no theory of evolution to worry us, the easiest discriminatory system is a dichotomous key, in which easily observed and reasonably consistent characters are used to divide organisms into groups of nearly equal size, so that by the smallest number of repetitions of the process we can put the organism in its proper place and give it its right name. Thus it is possible to divide spiders into two main categories, black and coloured, and then divide each of these groups into large and small spiders; this is not a classification found in any treatise on spiders known to me, but it's a good start in practice. Now classifications of this kind are always being improved upon by the discovery of new discriminants, and there is always the hope that our standard of naming will get better and better, for the best name is clearly that which tells us the most about the organism we are dealing with. But when we realize that living organisms have evolved from earlier forms, and are therefore related, however distantly, to one another, and we have this capacity for evolution forced on our notice by the mutations appearing in organisms with a short generation time, like bacteria, we have another basis for classification—the closeness of phylogenetic relationships between forms. In many cases we can be fairly certain what these are, though we may be in difficulties about details, and a classification that emphasizes the relationship between birds and dinosaurs may be regarded as of greater value than one that groups them with bats, pterodactyls, and perhaps dragons and angels. But bacteria have little morphology to assist us in classification, and a phylogenetic classification based on it, or indeed on any other character, is at present something of a mirage. So we are forced back on 'useful' classifications, and the natural question is 'What is a useful discriminant'. Early bacteriology is inextricably mixed up with medicine, and once you show that some bacteria are responsible for infectious disease, and you want to know how the infectious disease arises, how it spreads and how to cure it, you must know the attributes of the infective organism if you are to have any power over it. So that the best name will be the one that tells you most about the organisms, and the very best would be the one that told you everything; perhaps this would be a name in a phylogenetic classification—I am not sure. It is therefore hardly surprising that classification has been pushed to very extreme limits with pathogenic bacteria. As our knowledge advances we bring in biochemical differences, somatic and flagellar antigenic analysis, capsular antigenic analysis, toxigenicity and phage-typing. The last is an excellent example of an extremely fine discriminant used for a particular purpose. Epidemics of a particular disease are often due to a single strain of an organism, which closely resembles the other members of its species except in its susceptibility to particular bacteriophages; knowledge of the phage-type of such an organism may then tell us something of its spread in the community or even about the origins of the epidemic. It is natural enough that phage-typing should be applied in the main to organisms that spread rapidly from patient to patient, or to many patients from a common source—staphylococci, *Salmonella typhi*, *Pseudomonas aeruginosa*; as far as I know, no one has applied phage-typing to *Bacillus circulans* or to *Nitrobacter*; nobody has yet found anything useful in the degree of discrimination it might provide.

Pragmatic classifications of this kind can equally well be applied to diseases, where associations of particular characters are considered adequate justification for separating diseases into categories, even when their causes are unknown. It is obviously convenient that in diseases caused by organisms the categories of disease should as far as possible be associated with particular categories of organism; and indeed in medical and veterinary bacteriology categories of bacteria that do not cut across disease categories are usually preferred. True there are exceptions. Streptococci, meningococci, pneumococci can all cause a purulent meningitis; but then we can easily lump them together as pyogenic cocci.

But let us take actual examples. *Clostridium welchii* may, by a consideration of the toxins it produces, be divided into 5 types, A–E; these types are closely associated with certain diseases of man and his domestic animals. Moreover, as some of these toxins are directly responsible for the disease and largely determine its outcome and the means used for its prevention or treatment, classifications based on toxins (and significantly enough on lethal toxins) are preferred to those based on somatic antigens, which cut clearly across groups based on toxigenicity. In other groups, e.g. the salmonellas, somatic and flagellar antigenic analysis is preferred; in *C. welchii* toxigenic analysis is troublesome enough, but it is still easier than somatic antigenic analysis, and what is more important it is felt that the information it provides is more useful.

Those of you who are familiar with *Clostridium welchii* will realize that I have left out Type F. I did this deliberately, as this is the one type that is not discriminated by its toxin production; its toxin pattern is like that of Type C. Why then do we not put it in this type? The main reason for this is that it has one property that, when it was first described, separated it from all other *C. welchii* strains—its spores were far more heat-resistant. Moreover, it was associated with a disease in man in which ordinary heat-sensitive Type C strains never seemed to occur—enteritis necroticans. So Zeissler naturally wanted to separate it out, and called it Type F; no doubt it was better than calling it *Bacillus enterotoxicus* as he had first intended. Later on Miss Hobbs and her colleagues found other heat-resistant *C. welchii* in some cases of food-poisoning in man; as the toxigenicity of these organisms was limited to alpha-toxin production, they called them heat-resistant *C. welchii* Type A. I expect that Zeissler would say that they ought to be called Type F; it all depends on what you think important. Which do you prefer?

This dependence of the classification of bacteria on disease production is well shown by *Clostridium septicum* and *C. chauvoei*; the differences between them are in my opinion very small, and I should prefer to regard them as types of *C. septicum*, especially since the haemolysins, hyaluronidases and deoxyribonucleases produced by *C. chauvoei* all seem to bear some relationship to the corresponding antigens of *C. septicum*. But the diseases they produce—braxy and black-quarter— are different, and for many years attempts have been made to find characters that will readily allow discrimination between the two pathogens; it has not been easy. Similar troubles arise with *C. bifermentans* and *C. sordellii*; they admittedly differ in colonial character and in urease production, and some strains of *C. sordellii* produce a potent lethal toxin and are pathogenic, whereas *C. bifermentans* never produces a lethal toxin and is not pathogenic. Admittedly there are non-pathogenic strains of *C. sordellii*, but these produce urease, whereas *C. bifermentans* does not. But both *C. bifermentans* and *C. sordellii* produce lecithinases and these lecithinases are antigenically indistinguishable, and only remotely related to the lecithinase of *C. welchii*. How we discriminate here is largely a question of our preoccupations; for my purpose it is more convenient to lump them; Huang (1959) felt the same; Brooks & Epps (1959) preferred to separate them.

Now it is evident that, as bacterial toxins are often the means by which bacteria display their pathogenicity, medical and veterinary workers are likely to be extremely interested in them; indeed they may regard pathogenicity, and consequently toxicity, as characteristic of a species, and reject from a species its non-toxigenic and non-pathogenic forms. DeSpain Smith (1955), for instance, once said that forms having all the characteristics of a particular species except that they did not produce the characteristic toxin, should be regarded as 'unidentified'; I am not in direct medical practice, and the distinction means less to me, and it probably means even less to those of you who are concerned with bacteria of no immediate medical or veterinary interest. I was rather amused to find, when this subject was last discussed, that those in favour of pathogenicity as a discriminant were mainly medical bacteriologists; those who rejected it were not. I voted with the latter group (defying my own natural classification!) but I did so in the knowledge that non-toxigenic non-pathogenic variants of originally toxigenic strains are common enough, and it seemed to me impossible not to regard members of a clone as the same species. But it must not be forgotten that from the practical point of view the medical supporters of pathogenicity had something on their side; non-toxigenic variants of *Clostridium tetani* are very unlikely to produce tetanus, and the distinction is of obvious medical importance.

But if we look at toxigenicity from another point of view, and loftily ignore the unfortunate cases of tetanus, botulism and other diseases due to bacterial toxins, we may feel that such diseases have little to do with the 'normal' life of the bacterium—by which I suppose that we mean either that very little of the time of a toxigenic bacterium is spent in producing pathological changes, or that these pathological propensities are of little value to the general survival of the species. A short time ago van Heyningen said to me that he felt that a bacterial toxin must have *some* value to the bacterium, but that its value could hardly be the gift of pathogenicty. His example at the time was tetanus toxin, which he felt must have some affinity for a substance resembling a ganglioside in the gut, where, he supposed, the tetanus bacillus normally spent the more active parts of its normal existence—and that the property of tetanus toxin of combining with ganglioside in nerves and central nervous system, with its deplorable sequelae, was a regrettable accident, of no value to tetanus bacilli at all. I go a certain distance with him here, especially as the idea may give practical leads in the problems van Heyningen likes to tackle, but not all the way. *Clostridium welchii*, for instance, will metabolize dead animal tissue with equal effectiveness whether the whole animal is alive or dead, and it seems reasonable enough that the various types of *C. welchii* should produce toxic substances to kill off tissues or whole animals, and afterwards use the dead tissue or the corpses for nutriment. Obviously the arguments will be different in different cases, and in the world outside laboratories organisms that have little to do with killing animals may often assist in their disposal; *C. tetani* and *C. botulinum* are no doubt of great value in maintaining populations of hyaenas, jackals, vultures and, in our own realm, of *C. sporogenes* and *C. histolyticum*.

Now, as is perhaps proper enough, I have wandered very discursively over the field of classification, but perhaps I may leave with you the idea that until an ideal classification that subsumes all the possible information is devised, we shall have to put up with practical classifications that are useful to us. They may be, of course, as ephemeral as the practical requirements they serve, and there is a great deal to be said for not enshrining them in official Latin sets of binomials. The more we know, the better our classifications can be, but we may still find, while we are still so ignorant, that for different purposes different classifications are necessary, and we may even be inclined to relegate to earthly paradises and other non-existent Utopias classifications in which all the properties of an organism are regarded as equally important. Now we are back again to the real question—important to whom?—to classifiers? and the mulberry bush has turned full circle.

REFERENCES

BROOKS, M. E. & EPPS, H. B. G. (1959). Taxonomic studies of the genus *Clostridium*: *Clostridium bifermentans* and *Cl. sordellii*. *J. gen. Microbiol.* **21**, 144.
HUANG, C.-T. (1959). *A comparison of* Clostridium bifermentans *and* Clostridium sordellii. Thesis, University of Leeds.
OAKLEY, C. L. (1955). Bacterial toxins and classification. *J. gen. Microbiol.* **12**, 344.
SMITH, L. DS. (1955). *An Introduction to the Pathogenic Anaerobes*, p. 21. Chicago.

PATHOGENICITY AND THE TAXONOMY OF FUNGI

G. C. AINSWORTH

Commonwealth Mycological Institute, Kew, Surrey

Pathogenicity, with its economic overtones, has profoundly affected both the development and practice of microbial taxonomy. First, pathogenicity has been a major factor in isolating taxonomists from one another. Students of bacteria pathogenic for man have had few contacts with bacteriologists interested in bacteria pathogenic for plants while non-pathogenic bacteria—the majority of bacteria—have been neglected by both groups. Mycologists have tended to approach the systematics of fungi pathogenic for plants on a somewhat wider front and students of plant diseases have made major orthodox contributions to taxonomic mycology, but fungi pathogenic for man and higher animals were for long treated in isolation; their taxonomy is notoriously confused. For protozoa similar generalizations could be made, but for algae and viruses the situations are rather different. Pathogenic algae are great rarities ('red rust' of tea (*Cephaleuros*), the one major economically important algal infection of crop plants, is frequently referred to the mycologist) and though, as Bawden (1960) has recalled, 'pathogenicity is ...what makes viruses economically important', and 'is also the feature that usually first brings their existence to notice and provides the means for their assay in most kinds of work' the isolation of plant virologists from animal virologists has had little effect on taxonomic problems, plant and animal viruses having, apparently, little more in common than an arbitrarily imposed and not generally accepted binomial nomenclature.

For microbial taxonomy in general a major current trend is the realization that rational and stable basic classifications result only by treating pathogens and non-pathogens, parasites and saprophytes, on an equal footing and assessing their overall similarities and dissimilarities. This does not imply that pathogenicity will not continue to be used, as it has been widely used in the past, as a taxonomic criterion. It does imply that pathogenicity will influence taxonomic practice less as a taxonomic criterion than by affecting taxonomic categories, for the second major effect of pathogenicity on microbial taxonomy is due to the insistence by students of the aetiology, epidemiology, and control of infectious disease that the disease-inducing micro-organisms shall be precisely named. Such taxa are frequently not referable to the traditional taxonomic categories and they have posed problems which both taxonomists and the codes of international nomenclature have yet to solve. The basic theme of this contribution to the Symposium is a consideration of some such taxa with special reference to fungi.

Parasitism and pathogenicity

First the distinction between parasitism and pathogenicity must be noted. According to the *Oxford Dictionary* 'parasitic' was first used in Britain in the biological sense in 1731, 'pathogenic' in 1852 (with a medical connotation; pathogen and pathogenic were not used in relation to plant diseases until the second decade of the twentieth century when they were probably introduced by Whetzel and his students in the United States (Horsfall & Dimond, 1960)). These are outside dates for the concepts of parasite (an organism living in or upon another organism (its host) from which it obtains its nutriment) and pathogen (a disease-inducing agent) for parasite was first, mistakenly, applied to ivy and the lesson that micro-organisms may be pathogenic was slowly learnt between 1807 and 1846 from the studies of Prevost on wheat bunt, Bassi on the aetiology of muscardine of silkworms, the elucidation of the causes of thrush and ringworm in man by Gruby and others, and finally the Rev. M. J. Berkeley's conclusions on potato blight. Bacterial pathogens were a later discovery. Just as the distinction between saprophyte and parasite is blurred so is that between parasitic and pathogenic micro-organisms. Though many parasites are also pathogens, many are not. Parasitic micro-organisms show all gradations from symbiosis ('negative pathogenicity') through commensalism ('zero pathogenicity') to widely varying degrees of pathogenicity and, though not without exceptions, there is some truth in the generalization that the most successful highly specialized parasites are the least pathogenic. For example, *Microsporum gypseum*, a common soil fungus, has a wider host range and is more pathogenic as a cause of ringworm than *M. audouinii* which characteristically causes head ringworm in children. The point of this digression is that parasitism and pathogenicity, parasite and pathogen, are not interchangeable terms although frequently used as if they were. It could be argued that it is parasitism not pathogenicity that is really the taxonomic criterion. This may be true. It is, however, pathogenicity which has given the edge to parasitism as a taxonomic differential.

SPECIATION

Species being designated by binomials comprised of generic names coupled with specific epithets, a consideration of specific epithets might, it was thought, give objective clues to criteria used in speciation. And this they appear to do. A random sampling of the specific epithets in Persoon's, *Synopsis methodica fungorum*, 1801 (the starting-point of modern taxonomic mycology) showed, in round numbers, 40 % of the epithets to be based on morphological features, 25 % on colour terminology, and 10 % on the names of higher plants. Similar examinations of Saccardo's *Sylloge fungorum*, vol. **12**, 1897 (the index to the first eleven volumes of that major compilation) and of the first volume of the *Index of Fungi* covering 1940–49 showed the distribution of the three categories of epithets to be approximately similar in these two works: between one-quarter and one-third are based on morphological characters, approximately 10 % on colour, and 30 % on the names of host plants. The predominance of morphology for distinguishing species (more for purposes of identification than classification) is very evident. The greater use of colour distinctions by early mycologists was clearly determined by their indifferent optical equipment and by the fewer forms with which they had to deal while the popularity of the host as a 'spot' character in recent mycology is well brought out. This last usage could be emphasized even more by an examination of obligate parasites, such as rusts and powdery mildews, and of other genera composed entirely of plant pathogens in which up to 50–80 % of the specific epithets are derived from host names.

Another statistical effect of parasitism among fungi is that the number of species per genus is higher in parasitic groups than in saprophytic groups (Ainsworth, 1955), an increase which is probably not to be adequately accounted for merely by the greater attention which such groups have often received because of their pathogenicity.

As has been constantly reiterated in this Symposium, the approach to the speciation of micro-organisms is largely subjective. It has also been recalled that the temperament of the taxonomist is an important determining factor in speciation. Some taxonomists have a happy knack of synthesis, of seeing things in black and white; they can quickly refer any specimen to a taxon and so are invaluable members of any identification service. For others, who are more analytical perhaps, all is reduced to shades of grey, one taxon fades into another, and there is a tendency for such systematists to give the intermediates they recognize the prestige of specific rank. When such a taxonomist approaches a parasitic genus the result can be devastating. A much quoted example, because typical if rather extreme, is Gäumann's (1923) monograph on *Peronospora*, a genus of downy mildews. In this work 267 species are distinguished. Of these, 146 were proposed by Gäumann himself and the downy mildew of brassicas (*P. parasitica*) is divided into no less than 54 species. This excessive subdivision resulted from detailed biometrical studies on spore size which showed the different forms to exhibit closely overlapping ranges of conidial dimensions (differences too small to be of much practical value, as Butler (1929) pointed out) and from experimental studies on parasitic specialization. The treatment is logical and the monograph monumental if not utilitarian.

Another example of a genus in which the host plant plays a domineering role in speciation is *Cercospora*, a genus of leaf-spotting fungi of world-wide distribution and wide host range, monographed by Chupp (1954). *Cercospora* has a relatively complicated morphology and many of the species which have been proposed are readily distinguished from one another. Other species are very similar, and throughout the genus host specialization (proved or assumed) has been a major factor in speciation. As a result the more than 1270 species catalogued and described in Chupp's monograph are arranged in one series under families of the plant hosts, from Acanthaceae (*Acanthus*) to Zingiberaceae (*Zingiber*). Specific keys are provided when several species occur in one host family, but the chances of identifying a specimen of *Cercospora* from an unidentified or a wrongly identified host or from a culture in the absence of a host are small—which is humiliating for the mycologist. Every year additional species of *Cercospora* are proposed. The genus would appear to be ripe for computor analysis.

The examples so far considered illustrate the use as specific criteria of (in Ciferri's terminology) 'specialization characteristics' to which in an interesting analysis of the criteria for the definition of species in mycology he (Ciferri, 1932) added two other categories of 'matrical characteristics' (criteria based on parasite/host relationships): (1) 'ecological characteristics', based on the study of the localization of the fungus in or on definite organs of the host, and (2) 'pathographic characteristics', based on the study of the effect of the fungus in the host, an effect which is usually a host response. While both these last two categories of criteria have been used, neither have been popular. At the generic level the main distinction between *Phyllosticta* and *Phoma* is that the first typically attacks leaves (and not stems), the second stems (and not leaves), a distinction of convenience for cataloguing a multitude of species (Dennis, 1946), while at the lower levels it is varieties more often than species which have been distinguished by spatial host-parasite relationships. That host response has played its part is shown by the specific epithets of such pathogens as the peach leaf curl fungus (*Taphrina deformans*) and the bacterial agent of crown gall (*Agrobacterium tumefaciens*).

A current approach to speciation in fungi which is still considered to be a modern development is to delimit parasitic species on morphological rather than physiological grounds as did Salmon at the turn of the century, in a monograph (Salmon, 1900) which is still influential, when he reduced to 49 the 160 species of the Erysiphaceae (powdery mildews) compiled in Saccardo's *Sylloge*. Similarly, Yerkes & Shaw (1959), in contrast to Gäumann's approach, list over eighty synonyms of *Peronospora parasitica*, the downy mildew of brassicas.

Major consolidations on these lines have been made during recent years in the Ustilaginales (smuts) in which host specialization is such a prominent feature. Although not the first to make the suggestions, Fischer (1943) forcefully advocated the consolidation of various well known morphologically indistinguishable cereal and grass smuts specialized for different hosts and so generally accepted as different species. This approach he further developed in his admirable monograph on the North American smuts (Fischer, 1953) where he brought together morphologically similar smuts unless they attacked hosts of different families. Fischer's lead has been widely followed, in spite of the reluctance of some pathologists to designate the covered smut of oats (*Avena*) *Ustilago hordei* because the first description of this smut was on barley (*Hordeum*).

Fischer has now further increased his reputation by a monograph on the smut genus *Tilletia* (Duran & Fischer, 1961). Over a 6-year period several thousand specimens of *Tilletia* drawn from more than sixty herbaria were examined and described in a standard manner. The details of each collection were recorded on punched cards which were then mechanically sorted, the groups of similar collections forming the basis of the specific descriptions and the synonymies detailed in the monograph. By this means the 200 previously described species of *Tilletia* were reduced to 72 and only three additional species had to be proposed. It is, however, a pity, because of the current interest in quantitative taxonomy, that the statistical scaffolding has been carefully removed from the monograph.

The Rusts

An account of speciation of fungi in a context of pathogenicity must include a consideration of the rusts, an order (Uredinales) of obligate parasites of major world-wide importance as pathogens. Rusts possess five sorts of spores and their life cycles are often complex; in one series (autoecious rusts) a single host is involved, in another (heteroecious) two or more hosts. The most familiar rust is black rust of wheat and other cereals, *Puccinia graminis*, the life cycle of which is retailed to every student of elementary botany, although over much of its geographical range some of its spore forms are very rare and are of even greater rarity in the fresh state in classrooms. In *P. graminis* if haploid *basidiospores* of two mating types infect barberry (*Berberis*) + and − *pycniospores* (spermatia) are developed on the leaves which later bear dikaryotic *aeciospores* developed from dikaryotic mycelium resulting from the fusion of a pycniospore (spermatium) with a hypha of opposite mating type. Infection of the alternate host, say wheat, is effected by the airborne aeciospores. Subsequently dikaryotic *urediospores* are produced on the alternate host and finally diploid perfect spores (*teliospores*) which on germination undergo meiosis and give rise to haploid basidiospores, and so the cycle restarts. In this example the greater part of the dikaryophase is found on different cereals (wheat, oats, rye), the haplophase is confined to *Berberis vulgaris*. In the crown rust of cereals the aecidial state (haplophase) occurs on several different species of *Rhamnus* while a species of *Melampsora* on aspen has aecidial states on larch, pine, dogs mercury, and other hosts. This has led to much confusion in speciation. A common practice has been to separate as distinct species rusts with indistinguishable urediospore and teliospore states which have aecidial states on different hosts, e.g. the rusts of *Populus tremula* have been distinguished as *Melampsora larici-tremulae*, *M. pinitorqua*, *M. rostrupii* according to whether the aecidial host was *Larix*, *Pinus*, or *Mercurialis*. As with one-host specialization there is now a tendency to group such collections of taxa with similar teliospore (perfect) states under one name, e.g. to consolidate the *Populus tremula* rusts, as advocated by Hylander, Jørstad & Nannfeldt (1953), as one species under the earliest name, *Melampsora populnea*. Another difficulty with rusts is that for many only the aecidial or the urediospore state is known (or the connexion between known aecidial and uredial states is unrecognized) and many species have been described according to their hosts in the form genera *Aecidium* and *Uredo*. For a more detailed consideration of speciation in rusts the reviews by Dennis (1952) and Johnson (1953) may be consulted.

Perfect and imperfect states

Before considering infraspecific taxonomy attention must be drawn to a taxonomic and nomenclatural peculiarity of speciation in fungi. Many fungi occur in two states: (1) the 'imperfect' state characterized by the absence of spores or by asexually produced spores (e.g. conidia), and (2) the 'perfect' state characterized by sexual spores (e.g. ascospores, basidiospores, teliospores). The imperfect and the perfect states may be given different specific names (as is permissible under the Botanical Code) but the binomial assigned to the perfect state takes precedence over one given to the imperfect state. For example, the name *Venturia inaequalis* of the perfect (ascospore) state of the apple scab fungus may be used, as it frequently is, to cover the imperfect (conidial) state which is also known as *Fuscicladium dendriticum*. Names of imperfect states may, however, be used legitimately in works referring to such states (Botanical Code, Art. 59; for comments on this Article see Deighton, 1960). By analogy with animals having larval stages, that a fungus in which the connexion between perfect and imperfect states is proved should bear two legitimate binomials may seem peculiar and very undesirable. It also appears undesirable to some taxonomic mycologists but a major difficulty is that though in some fungi the succession of imperfect and perfect states is regular (when to refer to the imperfect and perfect states as 'stages' does not mislead) the imperfect state is often indefinitely prolonged and the occurrence of the perfect state an event of extreme rarity. Furthermore, an imperfect fungus having a known perfect state may have to be distinguished from other imperfect fungi of the same 'form genus', some of which have and some of which have not perfect states, e.g. the imperfect state (*Aspergillus nidulans*) of *Diplostephanus nidulans* is regularly accompanied by the perfect state while for *A. niger* no perfect state is known. Formerly it was believed that it was only a matter of time before the perfect state of every imperfect fungus would be known. This now appears to be most unlikely. Some fungi (e.g. *A. niger*) have probably lost the ability to form ascospores. By heterokaryosis resulting from hyphal fusions new phenotypes can arise in imperfect fungi, although in the absence of a sexual phase expression of the potential variation inherent in the gene complement is limited. The recent discovery of the parasexual cycle (see p. 275), in which recombination and segregation is associated with the mitotic cycle, relieves imperfect fungi of this disability and in effect makes them perfectly imperfect.

The relevance of all this to pathogenicity is that for most fungi which are facultative parasites the pathogenic phase is the imperfect state and in groups such as the 'dermatophytes' which cause ringworm in man and animals and species of *Fusarium* which are major pathogens of plants the perfect states are in general sporadic and rare and the practical convenience of approaching these pathogens as imperfect fungi very considerable. Much more could be written on this confused taxonomic and legal problem. It must be sufficient to note that once the viewpoints of the taxonomist and the applied worker are appreciated and the technicalities of the situation understood it is quite possible to provide a practical taxonomic monograph on a group of pathogenic fungi without offending the susceptibilities of the taxonomic purist.

INFRASPECIFIC TAXA

Formae speciales

Puccinia graminis also provides a convenient example by which to introduce complexities of the infraspecific taxonomy of parasitic fungi. Cross-inoculation experiments with isolates of *P. graminis* from cereals show that three series can be distinguished: (1) isolates from wheat which infect barley but not oats or rye; (2) isolates from oats which do not attack rye or wheat; and (3) isolates from rye to which barley but not wheat is susceptible. All these isolates also attack various wild grasses but examination of isolations of black rust from grasses reveal three additional series of forms: (4) that from Timothy grass (*Phleum pratense*), which has the distinction of not attacking barberry; and those specialized for (5) species of *Agrostis* and (6) species of *Poa*. It is customary to distinguish these six taxa, which show minor morphological differences, by the epithets *tritici, avenae, secalis, phlei-pratensis, agrostidis,* and *poae,* respectively.

There has been much divergence in the ranks to which these six epithets have been assigned. Black rust of Timothy was at one time given specific rank as *Puccinia phlei-pratensis* but now it is more usually considered to be of varietal status and Stakman (see Stakman & Harrar, 1957) consider that all six epithets should be used at this rank, i.e. as *P. graminis* var. *tritici,* etc. This is in line with the general botanical practice of distinguishing varieties by morphological criteria. Others while recognizing the morphological differences as taxonomically significant consider them to be too small for making varietal distinctions and rank the taxa as 'forms' (e.g. *P. graminis* f. *tritici*), a rank below variety under the *International Code of Botanical Nomenclature,* but still one based on morphology. Another treatment is to use the epithets to make trinomials (as does Arthur, 1934) of the form *P. graminis tritici*; a usage not recognized by the Botanical Code, though permissible under the Zoological. Finally there is the practice of workers 'who do not give specific value to taxa characterized from a physiological standpoint but scarcely or not at all from a morphological standpoint' and who follow Recommendation 4A of the Botanical Code and 'distinguish within the species special forms (*formae speciales*) characterized by their adaptation to different hosts'; e.g. *P. graminis* f.sp. *tritici*. All these usages occur in the current literature.

As should be evident from the preceding section on speciation, host specialization is a characteristic of many pathogenic fungi and a rank or ranks for such categories are needed by those who are not able to accept taxonomic treatments such as Gäumann's of *Peronospora* but who wish to give precision to host-limited taxa. The concept of *formae speciales* is now widely accepted, but it may be noted that the rank is introduced into the Botanical Code as a Recommendation and it is not clear whether the publication of a forma specialis should be accompanied by a Latin diagnosis and whether it should have a type specimen (which would not give much essential diagnostic information unless living). Some authors provide these, others do not.

The nomenclature of infraspecific subdivisions

Many other points are not clear about infraspecific subdivisions and their use, particularly for reflecting the variation in cultural characteristics shown by many pathogenic fungi which are not, like the rusts, obligate parasites, and another digression may be permissible.

Different authors only too frequently use the same subdivisional name in very different senses and this lack of uniformity must at least in part be attributed to the lack of official guidance. The specific subdivisions officially listed by the Botanical Code (Art. 4) are subspecies, variety, subvariety, form, and subform—all presumably intended for morphologically distinguishable categories—together with, as an afterthought in the accompanying Recommendation, forma specialis. Under the recent Bacteriological Code, devised because bacteriologists found the Botanical Code unsatisfactory, subspecies and variety are treated as synonymous (Rule 7) as are form and special form (Rec. 8a(5); in the sense of the forma specialis of the Botanical Code) while in addition strain, serotype (serological type), biotype (physiological type), phagotype (phage type), morphotype (morphological type), group, phase, and state (stage) are defined. The *International Code of Nomenclature for Cultivated Plants* contributes the infraspecific category cultivar but this far from exhausts the vocabulary available and the senses in which even the terms noticed by the Codes are employed (see the Glossary, p. 264).

The basic unit for taxonomizing cultures is the single isolation or *isolate*, a term frequently also used to cover successive subcultures from an original single culture isolated from say, morbid material—a convenient usage and one free from ambiguity if the first (original) culture is distinguished as the *primary isolate*, a distinction frequently needed because, for example, while primary isolates of some dermatophytes are taxonomized (or identified) without difficulty, to do this from subsequent cultures is difficult or impossible. In this sense isolate is synonymous with the Bacteriological Code's strain, 'the descendants of a single isolation in pure culture' but the practice among mycologists to refer two different but indistinguishable isolates to one strain introduces a second meaning and the Bacteriological Code ruling (Rec. 8*a* (1)) that 'strain' may also be used to designate cultures 'which correspond to cultivated "varieties" (cultivars) of higher plants in having some special economic significance' introduces a third.

On the other hand, diversity in usage also results from taking over terms clearly defined in one field for use in another. An example of this is the cultivar concept. The designation of horticultural and agricultural varieties of plants by fancy names is familiar to everyone and the recently introduced *International Code of Nomenclature for Cultivated Plants* should do much to regularize this long-standing practice. There has always been ambiguity, though usually of little inconvenience in practice, between a botanical variety subject to the Botanical Code and receiving a scientific name and a horticultural variety not covered by the Botanical Code and designated by a fancy name. To obviate this the Code for Cultivated Plants introduced the term *cultivar* for 'an assemblage of cultivated individuals...significant for the purposes of agriculture, forestry, or horticulture', cultivated plants which are essential to civilization. The coining of the term cultivar, like the coining of the term taxon, clearly filled a need, and provided a term which could fill the same need in other fields. Microbiology has its equivalents of horticultural varieties, and to classify commercial strains of mushrooms as cultivars or to designate a well known economically important micro-organism '*Penicillium chrysogenum* cultivar NRRL 1951' seems only helpful. But Snyder & Hansen (1954) would go further. They argue that by planting crops man in effect cultivates pathogenic fungi and induces variation in them similar to that shown by cultivated plants. They advocate the application of the cultivar terminology to the genus *Fusarium* on which they are authorities (Snyder, Hansen & Oswald, 1957). Similarly, one of their colleagues in the Department of Plant Pathology of the University of California has applied the same principle to the variation within one species of plant pathogen, *Sclerotinia sclerotiorum* (Purdy, 1955). Many taxa of *Fusarium* which occur naturally (or 'in cultivation', fide Snyder & Hansen) have been described and named as species and diverse infra-specific categories and what Snyder & Hansen propose is that a number of well known specific epithets should be treated as cultivar names, e.g. that *Fusarium caeruleum*, the cause of a rot of potato tubers should be named *F. solani* cultivar 'Caeruleum' with the description as provided for *F. caeruleum*, and they further propose that within *F. roseum* cultivars may be named on the pattern '*F. roseum* "Graminearum"' when no pathogenesis is indicated or when pathogenesis is indicated as '*F. roseum* f. *cerealis* "Graminearum"' ('f.' in this case standing for forma specialis). While many aspects of the consolidation of species within the genus *Fusarium* by Snyder & Hansen can only be welcomed it is difficult to see how the 'adoption of cultivar names in fungi is a step towards the simplification of fungus identification', particularly in such a 'difficult' genus as *Fusarium*. The procedure is more what C. G. Lloyd called 'name juggling' and the debasing of a useful terminology which becomes even more confused by the use by Stover (1959) and Waite & Stover (1960) in their treatment of cultivars of *F. oxysporum* f. *cubense* (the cause of Panama disease of banana) of 'clones' as a subdivision of 'cultivar' although under the *Code for Cultivated Plants* a clone is one sort of cultivar. The Bacteriological Code's recommendation to use strain as synonymous (or analogous) with cultivar when wild micro-organisms are unintentionally 'cultivated' might commend itself, as might Hoare's (1955, 1956) suggestions on the use of the deme terminology (see Glossary, p. 265).

Physiologic races

In returning to the main theme at the next subdivision *Puccinia graminis* again affords the introductory example. *P. graminis* f.sp. *tritici* can be subdivided according to differences in pathogenicity shown to different cultivars of wheat into a number of groups or *physiologic races*, which, like formae speciales, may also show minor morphological differences too small to be of taxonomic use. Attention was first drawn to this phenomenon by Stakman & Piemeisel (1917) in the United States and the techniques devised by Stakman and his colleagues (Stakman & Levine, 1922) for distinguishing physiologic races have remained virtually un-changed throughout forty years of world-wide use.

Briefly, the method employed is to inoculate with urediospores seedlings of twelve carefully chosen and precisely particularized pure-bred wheat cultivars ('differential varieties' or 'differentials') in the greenhouse under approximately optimum conditions of humidity, temperature, and light for infection. The type of infection and the varietal reaction after one to two weeks is scored on an arbitrary agreed numerical scale: 0, immune (no rust pustules); 1, very resistant (pustules very small); 2, moderately resistant (pustules small to medium); 3, moderately susceptible (pustules medium); 4, very susceptible (pustules large and often confluent); x, heterogeneous (mesothetic) (pustules variable, sometimes Types 1–4 on one plant). For identifying races (which are designated by numbers) the five types of varietal reaction can be reduced to three: resistant (R), infection types 0, 1, 2; susceptible (S), infection types 3, 4; mesothetic (M), infection type x. For example, all twelve differential varieties are susceptible to race 189; all but one (cultivar Khapli C.I. 4013) are susceptible to race 15; six are susceptible and six resistant to race 56, etc. Data are available on the range of infection types given by different races and many races have been subdivided into what Stakman previously called biotypes but now prefers to term *subraces* (designated by letters (Stakman & Stewart, 1957)), either on minor differences in infection type on one or more of the differential varieties or by the reaction of additional differential varieties, e.g. subrace 59 A is distinguished from race 59 by inducing infection type 2 instead of type 0 reaction on the cultivar Reliance; race 15 and the subrace 15 B by the reaction of a thirteenth cultivar, Lee. But as with all detailed taxonomic studies the more intensive the study the greater the nomenclatural refinement required. Recently, subdivisions of subraces have been distinguished as *lines* designated by a second number, e.g. race 15 B–1, 15 B–2 (Stakman & Stewart, 1957).

While the general pattern is basically simple in practice it is very complex because of the size of the problem. More than 250 physiologic races of *Puccinia graminis* from wheat have been distinguished, and smaller numbers of the formae speciales from oats and barley, and as it is the physiologic races which interest plant pathologists, plant breeders, and others concerned with the control and prevention of cereal rusts the literature on the topic is vast. Much detail can be filled in by consulting the well documented reviews by Stakman & Harrar (1957), Stakman & Christensen (1960) and Johnson (1953, 1961).

Physiologic races have also been distinguished for other rusts, smuts, and many other pathogenic fungi including *Phytophthora infestans*, the agent of late blight of potato, *Venturia inaequalis*, the cause of apple scab, and species of *Fusarium*. For all these pathogens the number of races is, in general, fewer than for the cereal rusts. The general taxonomic problems are however similar if the pressure to solve them is less.

The incidence of the physiologic races of black rust of wheat, like that of many pathogenic micro-organisms, is ever fluctuating. The races found in any wheat-growing region vary from one year to another by changes in the proportions of the different races which make up the population, by the introduction of races previously known in other geographical areas and by the appearance of new races, while a race that is common or predominant at one time may disappear, sometimes to reappear after a decade or more in the same or another locality. These variations are in part due to the movement of airborne spores, particularly urediospores, mass movements of which occur regularly in parts of North America, Europe and India. For example, the outbreaks of black rust on cereals in summer in Britain are derived from outbreaks which originated some months previously in North Africa. They are in part due to the hybridization which can be effected during the sexual phase of *Puccinia graminis* on barberry but genetic variation can occur in the absence of barberry by heterokaryosis resulting from hyphal fusions between mycelia of different races in one host plant (an effect which has been reproduced experimentally, e.g. Bridgmon (1957)) and perhaps a parasexual cycle is also involved.

On the other side of the equation is the host plant. For *Puccinia graminis* f.sp. *tritici*, man made selections from more than 14,000 wheat cultivars and the novelties continuously being introduced by plant breeders to suit the local soil, climatic conditions, or market and to resist infection by the predominating rust races. It was formerly thought that the host was a more or less passive recipient of the rust. It now appears that the pathogen/host interaction is more complicated and more intimate.

Gene-for-gene relationships. Since the classical researches by Biffen at the beginning of the century it has been known that the resistance of cereals to fungal infection is genetically determined, and on this knowledge the multifarious contributions of plant breeders in developing cultivars of crop plants immune or resistant to pathogens have been based. The discovery of sex in rusts by Craigie in 1927 (see Craigie (1931) for a review) made experimental hybridization between rust races possible and from this work it soon became clear that pathogenicity in rusts, like resistance in the host is gene determined and segregates in a Mendelian manner. In flax, immunity to rust (*Melampsora lini*) is dominant to susceptibility and is determined according to the cultivar by one, two, or three pairs of genes. Flor, in a brilliant and extended investigation, showed that where the host had one pair of rust-condition-ing factors the rust had one pair of pathogenicity factors and that there was similar correspondence for flax cultivars in which rust reaction was determined by two and three pairs of genes. Further, by identifying twenty or so genes in flax and a similar number in the flax rust he was able to show by experiments with hosts and rust races of known gene complements that the correspondence of the host genes controlling sus-ceptibility and the rust genes controlling pathogenicity is specific. Each rust gene has its counterpart in the host. Infection only occurs when the gene complements of host and pathogen are correctly matched.

This is not an occasion to consider in detail the complexities of this 'gene-for-gene' relationship which have been described by Flor (1940–56), discussed theoretically by Person (1959), and reviewed by Johnson (1960, 1961). A similar relationship has been detected for potato blight (*Phytophthora infestans: Solanum tuberosum*) and may well be of general occurrence. The implications are clear. The cultivars of crop plants select appropriate genotypes from the ever-varying populations of pathogens and to this extent man guides, if unintentionally, the evolution of the pathogens.

CONCLUSIONS

The conclusions that can be drawn from a brief survey of some general aspects of the taxonomy of pathogenic fungi tend, in this, the twelfth, contribution to the Symposium, to the platitudinous. Different groups of pathogens have clearly been approached in different ways and their taxonomic treatments have been determined by convenience and by the taxonomic usages of dominant specialist workers. This is as true for *Puccinia* and *Fusarium* as for *Salmonella* and *Plasmodium* and also for non-pathogenic genera like *Chlamydomonas* and *Euglena*. Two aspects of the uniformity within these diverse taxonomies perhaps merit comment.

First, many of the taxa into which pathogens are classified belong to categories for which the nomenclature is not subject to the legislation of the international codes of nomenclature. At the specific and varietal levels the codes give detailed guidance and lay down rigid requirements on the proposal and publication of names by which subsequent workers can ascertain whether a name is in line with the codes and whether its use or consideration is obligatory (see Appendix I, p. 456). Below variety the Codes may suggest and define categories for which the nomen-clature is not closely regulated. Also in passing it may be noted that binomial nomenclature, as recently pointed out by Donk (1960), has been applied both to 'natural' taxa and to what Donk calls 'conventional' taxa such as states of those imperfect fungi which have perfect states and to lichens composed of two distinct micro-organisms. In other words, binomial nomenclature under the Botanical Code is used without distinction for complete organisms, parts of organisms, and pairs of organisms with implications not always appreciated (Donk, 1960).

While the codes regulate the form and publication of names no code requires that new names should be registered or even reported to any central authority or authorities. Subsequent workers must search the literature for new names and because of the wide scatter of publication, and in spite of the current interest in documentation, it will be the best part of a decade before all the new names published this year are compiled in the various sectional indexes. This is inconvenient, but for all micro-organisms most groups are receiving very little attention at any one time. For pathogenic micro-organisms interest is more continuous, more intense, and nomenclatural confusion more inconvenient. These pressures should, and have, made registration of taxa easier. For the cereal rusts, to return to *Puccinia graminis* for the last time, the authority of the work of Professor Stakman and his colleagues made his laboratory at the University of Minnesota, St Paul, Minn., the centre to which workers in all parts of the world reported their races of cereal rusts and from which numbers have been allocated for new races. Periodically complete lists of the physiologic races of wheat rust with details of their reactions on the differential varieties have been issued from St Paul. The St Paul laboratory has been officially recognized by the United States Department of Agriculture and, together with the Dominion Rust Laboratory at Winnipeg, acts as a clearing house for data on the races of the cereal rusts. There are other agreements or understandings between specialists in various groups but more might be done in this way, and on a permanent basis for pathogens are so mutable.

Secondly, it is clear that in designating the categories of taxa of pathogens microbiologists have taken over for their own ends terms from other branches of taxonomy with little thought as to original or current meanings. This borrowing and adaptation began with 'species' and even if, as Dr Cowan would have it, microbial species are a macro-myth the binomial nomenclature which accompanied this category has proved and is likely to continue to prove invaluable for the everyday labelling of different kinds of microbes. Intraspecific borrowings, as this contribution and its glossary show, have often been less satisfactory and while there seems to be no prospect of a uniform terminology for taxonomic categories throughout microbiology, microbiologists would do well to consider carefully exactly what it is they need before coining new terms or deciding on takeovers.

GLOSSARY OF INTRASPECIFIC TERMINOLOGY

This glossary lists and defines the terms for intraspecific categories of micro-organisms mentioned in the foregoing contribution, together with some others found in the literature. Whenever possible definitions based on those given by the international codes of nomenclature are included and a number of special usages are documented. The glossary of Darlington & Mather (1949) was consulted as a standard for genetical usage.

This glossary is by no means complete either for terms or senses but it does illustrate the wide divergences in the senses in which some of the terms are used. The use of 'intraspecific' rather than 'infraspecific' in the title is intentional, for many of the subdivisional categories cannot be arranged in definite hierarchical order of rank as are infraspecific categories under the Botanical Code.

Note: The form and proposal of names for categories marked with an asterisk (*) are subject to the provisions of the international code (or codes) of nomenclature indicated.

Terms in definitions in *italics* are defined elsewhere in the glossary.

Abbreviations: *Bact. Code, Bot. Code, Cult. Code, Zool. Code*, International Codes of Nomenclature for Bacteriology, Botany, Cultivated Plants, and Zoology, respectively (for details see Appendix I, p. 462).

biologic (biological) form. See biological race.

biological race. A general term for a group of micro-organisms morphologically similar to the other groups from which it is distinguished by differences in host-parasite relationships (Hoare, 1955, 1956); biologic (biological) form; biological strain; *physiologic race*; if of specific rank, biological species (Cholodkovsky, 1895, see Hoare, 1955).

biological strain. *See* biological race.

biotype. (1) A group of organisms occurring in nature assumed to be genotypically almost identical (Johannsen, 1903, see Darlington & Mather, 1949); a population of genetically identical individuals (Stakman & Harrar, 1957). (2) 'A subdivision of a species, subspecies or serotype which may be distinguished from other subdivisions of the species by possession of some special or usefully diagnostic physiological character' (*Bact. Code*, Rec. 8a (2) annot.). (3) A subdivision of a *physiologic race*; *subrace*.

clone. (1) A group of organisms descended by mitosis from a common ancestor (Webber, 1903, see Darlington & Mather, 1949); a genetically uniform assemblage of individuals derived originally from a single individual by vegetative propagation and constituting a *cultivar* (*Cult. Code*, Art. 11a). (2) Isolates with the same genotype which are distinguishable from others on the basis of morphological and/or physiological traits including pathogenicity; a *cultivar* or a division of a *cultivar*; a *race* or a division of a *race* (Stover, 1959).

cultivar*. (1) 'An assemblage of cultivated individuals which is distinguished by any characters (morphological, physiological, cytological, chemical, or others) significant for the purposes of agriculture, forestry, or horticulture, and which, when reproduced (sexually or asexually), retains its distinguishing features; *variety* (2) (*Cult. Code*, Art. 5); *Strain* (3); example: barley 'Balder'. A cultivar may be a *clone* (*Solanum tuberosum* 'King Edward') or a *line* (*Triticum aestivum* 'Marquis'). (2) 'A distinct group of isolates that have some common morphological or physiological characteristics but which may consist of one or more clones or races' (Stover, 1959); example: *Fusarium oxysporum* [cultivar] 'Inodoratum' [clone] B.

culture. A general term for a growth of a micro-organism *in vitro* or *in vivo*; often used in the sense of *isolate* or *strain* (2).

Dauermodification. A lasting heritable change, presumably cytoplasmic, induced by the environment or experimental treatment (Jollos, 1913, see Darlington & Mather, 1949; Hoare, 1955); *relapse strain.*

deme terminology was introduced for natural populations within a specified taxon of flowering plants by Gilmour & Gregor (1939), but is a concept of general application (see p. 33). Hoare (1955, 1956) has proposed the use of this terminology in protozoology and advocated its use in other branches of microbiology. **nosodeme,** a clinical variant, e.g. *Leishmania donovani* nosodeme Indian; *L. tropica* nosodeme rural. **serodeme,** an immunologically distinct strain, e.g. the geographical races of *Plasmodium falciparum* and *P. vivax.* **xenodeme,** a biological race characterized by host specificity, e.g. *Trypanosoma evansi* xenodeme equine.

form (Latin, **forma**)*. (1) A subdivision of a species below the rank of variety (*Bot. Code*, Art. 4). (2) 'A subdivision of a species of a parasitic or symbiotic micro-organism distinguished primarily by adaptation to a particular host'; *forma specialis* (*Bact. Code*, Rec. 8a (5)).

forma specialis. A taxon characterized from a physiological standpoint (especially host adaptation) but scarcely or not at all from a morphological (*Bot. Code*, Rec. 4A).

group. (1) Any taxonomic group; taxon. (2) An assemblage of similar cultivars within a species or interspecific hybrid (*Cult. Code*, Art. 13). (3) 'Congeries of organisms having common characteristics', e.g. assemblages of related serotypes (*Bact. Code*, Rec. 8a (3)).

isolate. A single pure culture made by direct isolation from fresh material and any subcultures derived from it (Brierley, 1931); *strain* (3); *line.* (The first culture of the series may be distinguished as a **primary isolate**).

jordanon. A term coined by Lotsy in 1916 for the microspecies described for *Draba verna* [*Erophila verna*] by Jordan (in contrast to **linneon** for species in the Linnean sense) and use for which in mycology was suggested by Brierley (1919, 1931) a suggestion, more often quoted than adopted.

line. (1) An inbred homozygous strain (Darlington & Mather, 1949). (2) 'An assemblage of sexually reproducing individuals of uniform appearance, propagated by seeds or by spores, its stability maintained by selection to a standard', and constituting a cultivar (*Cult. Code*, Art. 11b). (3) *isolate*. (4) A subdivision of a *physiologic race* (see p. 260).

linneon. *See* jordanon.

modification. Non-transmissible effects of external conditions (Brierley, 1919).

morpha (pl. **morphae**). A transient population which is environmentally induced (Semenov-Tian-Shansky, 1910, see Hoare, 1955, 1956); cf. *relapse strain*.

morphotype. 'A subdivision of a species, distinguished by possession of some special or unusual morphological character which may or may not be associated with a change in serological state'; morphological type (*Bact. Code*, Rec. 8a (2), annot.).

nomenclatural type. *See* type.

nosodeme. *See* deme.

phage type. *See* phagotype.

phagotype. 'A subdivision of a species which is distinguished by its sensitivity to a particular bacteriophage or by a distinctive pattern of sensitivity to a set of specific bacteriophages'; phage type (*Bact. Code*, Rec. 8a (2) annot.).

phase. A well defined *stage* of a naturally occurring alternating variation (*Bact. Code* Rec. 8a (4)).

physiologic form. *See* physiologic race.

physiologic race. A taxon of parasites (particularly fungi) characterized by specialization to different cultivars of one host species. (The 6th International Botanical Congress, Amsterdam, 1935, recommended that physiologic race be substituted for physiologic form. Other synonyms are physiological form (or race), biological (or biologic) form (or race), and often *race*.)

physiological type. *See* biotype.

primary isolate. *See* isolate.

race. (1) A genetically, and as a rule geographically, distinct mating group within a species (Darlington & Mather, 1949). (2) *Physiologic race*. (3) *Strain* (3), *jordanon*; *forma*.

relapse strain (of pathogenic trypanosomes). A transient immunologically distinct population adapted to successive antibodies produced by the host in the course of an infection (Ritz, 1916, see Hoare, 1955, 1956); *morpha*.

saltant (in mycology and bacteriology). A discontinuous variation of unknown origin, e.g. a mutant unconfirmed by cytological evidence.

serodeme. *See* deme.

serotype. (1) 'A subdivision (infrasubspecific) of a species or subspecies distinguished from other strains of the same species on the basis of its antigenic structure' (*Bact. Code*, Rec. 8a (2) annot.). (2) (Of plant viruses), a group of viruses sharing only a few of its antigens in common with another group (serotype) (Kassanis, 1961), cf. *strain* (5b).

special form. *See* forma specialis.

stage. Frequently a synonym of *state* but, for fungi at least, better reserved for circumstances where the succession of two or more states is regular; cf. *phase*.

state. (1) (Of fungi) one phase of a pleomorphic fungus, e.g. the imperfect state characterized by asexual spores, the perfect state characterized by sexual spores. (2) (Of bacteria) 'the name given to the rough, smooth, mucoid and similar variants which arise in cultures of many species of bacteria' (*Bact. Code*, Rec. 8a (6)).

strain. (1) A group of similar *isolates*; *race*; *forma*; *jordanon* (Brierley, 1931). (2) The descendants of a single isolation in pure culture (*Bact. Code*, Rec. 8a (1)); *isolate*. (3) A culture of bacteria which corresponds to a cultivated variety (*cultivar*) of higher plants in having some special economic significance (*Bact. Code*, Rec. 8a (1)). (4) Biological strain, see *biological race*. (5) (of plant viruses) (*a*) 'a virus that is serologically or immunologically related to type strain virus, or to other demonstrable strains' (Terminology Committee of the Canadian Phytopathological Society, see Kassanis, 1961); (*b*) a group of viruses having most of its antigens in common with that of another group (strain) (Kassanis, 1961); cf. *serotype* (2).

subrace. *See* biotype.

subspecies.* A primary subdivision of a species (*Bot. Code*, Art. 4, *Bact.* and *Zool. Codes*); *variety* (*Bact.* and *Zool. Codes*).

type. (1) (In nomenclature) 'that constituent element of a taxon to which the name of the taxon is permanently attached'; nomenclatural type (*Bot. Code*, Art. 7; *Bact. Code*, Principle 11). (2) An infraspecific group of micro-organisms characterized by pathological and immunological manifestations (Hoare, 1955). This use has not the approval of the *Bact. Code* (Rec. 8a (2)); see *biotype* (2), *morphotype*, *phagotype*, *serotype*, and cf. *wild type*.

variant. A general term for any variation from the typical; cf. *saltant*.

variety.* (1) A subdivision of a species below the rank of subspecies and above the rank of form (*Bot. Code*, Art. 4); *subspecies* (*Bact. Code*, and *Zool. Code*). (2) *Cultivar* (1).

wild type. Of an organism or gene predominating in the wild population (Darlington & Mather, 1949).

xenodeme. *See* deme.

REFERENCES

AINSWORTH, G. C. (1955). Host-parasite relationships. *J. gen. Microbiol.* **12**, 352.

ARTHUR, J. C. (1934). *Manual of the Rusts in United States and Canada*. Lafayette, Indiana: Purdue Research Foundation.

BAWDEN, F. C. (1960). A trilogy of virology. *Nature, Lond.* **188**, 882.

BRIDGMON, G. H. (1957). The production of new races of *Puccinia graminis* var. *tritici* by hyphal fusion on wheat. *Phytopathology*, **47**, 517 (abstract).

BRIERLEY, W. B. (1919). Some concepts in mycology—an attempt at synthesis. *Trans. Brit. mycol. Soc.* **6**, 204.

BRIERLEY, W. B. (1931). Biological races in fungi and their significance in evolution. *Ann. appl. Biol.* **18**, 420.

BUTLER, E. J. (1929). The delimitation of species of fungi on physiological grounds. *Proc. int. Congr. Pl. Sci.* **2**, 1590.

CHUPP, C. (1954). *A Monograph of the Fungus Genus* Cercospora. Ithaca, N.Y.: author.

CIFERRI, R. (1932). The criteria for definition of species in mycology. *Ann. mycol., Berl.* **30**, 122.

CRAIGIE, J. H. (1931). An experimental investigation of sex in the rust fungi. *Phytopathology*, **21**, 1001.

DARLINGTON, C. D. & MATHER, K. (1949). *The Elements of Genetics*. London: Allen and Unwin.

DEIGHTON, F. C. (1960). Article 59. *Taxon*, **9**, 231.

DENNIS, R. W. G. (1946). Notes on some British fungi ascribed to *Phoma* and related genera. *Trans. Brit. mycol. Soc.* **29**, 11.

DENNIS, R. W. G. (1952). Biological races and their taxonomic treatment by mycologists. *Proc. Linn. Soc., Lond.* **163**, 47.

DONK, M. A. (1960). Nomenclature of conventional systems. *Taxon*, **9**, 103.

DURAN, R. & FISCHER, G. W. (1961). *The Genus* Tilletia. Pullman, Washington: Washington State University.

FISCHER, G. W. (1943). Some evident synonymous relationships in certain graminicolous smut fungi. *Mycologia*, **35**, 610.

FISCHER, G. W. (1953). *Manual of the North American smut fungi*. New York: Ronald Press.

FLOR, H. H. (1940). New physiologic races of flax rust. *J. agric. Res.* **60**, 575.

FLOR, H. H. (1942). Inheritance of pathogenicity in *Melampsora lini*. *Phytopathology*, **32**, 653.

FLOR, H. H. (1946). Genetics of pathogenicity in *Melampsora lini*. *J. agric. Res.* **73**, 335.

FLOR, H. H. (1947). Inheritance of reaction to rust of flax. *J. agric. Res.* **74**, 241.

FLOR, H. H. (1954). Identification of races of flax rust by lines with single rust-conditioning genes. *Tech. Bull. U.S. Dep. Agric.* no. 1087.

FLOR, H. H. (1955). Host-parasite interactions in flax rust—its genetics and other complications. *Phytopathology*, **45**, 680.

FLOR, H. H. (1956). The complementary genetic systems in flax and flax rust. *Adv. Genet.* **8**, 29.

GÄUMANN, E. (1923). Beiträge zu einer Monographie der Gattung *Peronospora* Corda. *Beitr. KryptFlora Schweis.* **5** (4), 360 pp.

GILMOUR, J. S. L. & GREGOR, J. W. (1939). Demes: a suggested new terminology. *Nature, Lond.* **144**, 333.

HOARE, C. A. (1955). Intraspecific biological groups in pathogenic protozoa. *Refualh Veterinarith*, **12**, 263.

HOARE, C. A. (1956). Intraspecific ecological categories in pathogenic protozoa. *Zoologitsheskij J.* **8**, 1113 [Russian; English summary, p. 3.]

HORSFALL, J. G. & DIMOND, A. E. (1960). *Plant Pathology*, **2**, *The Pathogen;* **3**, *The Diseased Population, Epidemics and Control.* N.Y. and London: Academic Press.

HYLANDER, N., JØRSTAD, I. & NANNFELDT, J. A. (1953). Enumeratio Uredinearum scandinavicarum. *Opera bot., Soc. bot. Lund.* **1** (1), 102 pp.

JOHNSON, T. (1953). Variation in the rusts of cereals. *Biol. Rev.* **28**, 105.

JOHNSON, T. (1960). Genetics of pathogenicity. In Horsfall & Dimond (1960), **2**, 407.

JOHNSON, T. (1961). Man-guided evolution in the plant rusts. *Science*, **133**, 357.

KASSANIS, B. (1961). Potato paracrinkle virus. *Europ. Potato J.* **4**, 14.

PERSON, C. (1959). Gene-for-gene relationships in host: parasite systems. *Canad. J. Bot.* **37**, 1101.

PURDY, L. H. (1955). A broader concept of the species *Sclerotinia sclerotiorum* based on variability. *Phytopathology*, **45**, 421.

SALMON, E. S. (1900). The Erysiphaceae. *Mem. Torrey bot. Cl.* **9**, 292 pp.

SNYDER, W. C. & HANSEN, H. N. (1954). Variation and speciation in the genus *Fusarium. Ann. N.Y. Acad. Sci.* **60**, 16.

SNYDER, W. C., HANSEN, H. N. & OSWALD, J. W. (1957). Cultivars of the fungus, *Fusarium. J. Madras Univ.* B, **27**, 185.

STAKMAN, E. C. & CHRISTENSEN, J. J. (1960). The problem of breeding resistant varieties. In Horsfall & Dimond (1960), **3**, 567.

STAKMAN, E. C. & HARRAR, J. G. (1957). *Principles of Plant Pathology.* New York: Ronald Press.

STAKMAN, E. C. & LEVINE, M. N. (1922). The determination of biologic forms of *Puccinia graminis* on *Triticum* spp. *Tech. Bull. Minn. agric. Exp. Sta.*, no. 8, 10 pp.

STAKMAN, E. C. & PIEMEISEL, F. J. (1917). Biologic forms of *Puccinia graminis* on cereals and grasses. *J. agric. Res.* **10**, 429.

STAKMAN, E. C. & STEWART, D. M. (1957). *Memorandum Regarding Taxonomy of Physiologic Races of* Puccinia graminis *var.* tritici. 10 pp. Co-operative Rust Lab., St Paul, Minn. [Mimeographed.]

STOVER, R. H. (1959). Studies on *Fusarium* wilt of bananas. IV. Clonal differentiation among wild type isolates of *F. oxysporum* f. *cubense. Canad. J. Bot.* **37**, 245.

WAITE, B. H. & STOVER, R. H. (1960). Studies on *Fusarium* wilt of bananas. VI. Variability and the cultivar concept in *Fusarium oxysporum* f. *cubense. Canad. J. Bot.* **38**, 985.

YERKES, W. D. & SHAW, C. G. (1959). Taxonomy of the *Peronospora* species on Cruciferae and Chenopodiaceae. *Phytopathology*, **49**, 499.

GENETICS AND MICROBIAL CLASSIFICATION

J. A. ROPER

Department of Genetics, University of Sheffield

Genetics has so far played no direct role in microbial systematics. The reasons for this can be seen in the requirements of *The New Systematics* (Huxley, 1940) which introduces the ideas of genetics and evolution in aiming at a natural classification. Such a classification is based on the concept of common ancestry and a potential common posterity. A species is defined as that group of individuals who are potentially able to contribute to, or share in, a common gene pool. Intraspecific variation, variation in time and space and borderline cases are welcomed.

No group of micro-organisms is yet ripe for the attack required in such a classification. Indeed, micro-organisms present a formidable challenge to any system devised for their classification. The essence of these difficulties, as seen by a geneticist, can be summarized in the following four points:

(1) Most microbial species have a simple morphology. The morphological criteria which can be applied with substantial success to higher forms are generally not available.

(2) The rate of evolutionary change in higher forms is limited by, among other things, mutation rates and the selection pressure which a population can withstand. To some extent the maximum tolerable selection pressure is determined by population size and density. The number of individuals in a microbial population may be astronomical and such populations carry a wide range of mutants. Since the rate of multiplication may be high, micro-organisms are especially susceptible to rapid variation in time.

(3) The cytology of most microbial groups—certain fungi provide a notable exception—is extremely difficult and unrewarding compared with the cytology of many plants. Unless new and revolutionary techniques are devised it can hardly be hoped that the cytotaxonomic approach, so fruitful in some higher forms, will find much successful application.

(4) A concerted study of the genetic systems of micro-organisms began less than twenty years ago. Most species of bacteria and many fungi are provisionally classified as asexual since they are not known to possess any means for genetic recombination.

Powerful tools are now available to search for the products of rare events of recombination or to detect stages in the recombination processes. The most important tool derives from the studies of Beadle &

Tatum (1941) on nutritional mutants of *Neurospora*. From crosses of two different mutants it is possible to select extremely rare recombinants by the use of media which permit growth of recombinant, but not parental, classes. The studies of recombination by transduction and conjugation in bacteria, and via the parasexual cycle in fungi, have been especially dependent on selective techniques. It is almost inconceivable that these processes should have been detected by observable events in the life cycles. For instance, pairing in *Escherichia coli* (Lederberg, 1956; Anderson, Wollman & Jacob, 1957) was observed only as a result of carefully planned experiments *after* recombination had been discovered.

Despite these advances there remain groups for which new techniques may be needed to detect recombination. For reasons of growth habit or nutrition these groups may not be readily amenable to the now classical techniques used originally for *Escherichia coli*. In some instances the detection of recombination may have to await the chance association of appropriate mating types. Ecological studies are needed to supplement the genetical studies. Only in this way will it be possible to distinguish between potential and actual contributions of related types to a common gene pool.

In a discussion of classification, and particularly so for micro-organisms, the geneticist may appear to be adopting the role of destructive critic. No aspect of the organism is immune from gene-determined variation, either potential or expressed. Nutritional requirements, enzyme complement, all aspects of morphology, resistance to physical and chemical agents, virulence, antigenic constitution, pigmentation and so on are all subject to change through single gene mutations, and such simple phenotypic differences must clearly be used with caution in classification. Luria (1947) pointed out that certain bacterial tribes, genera and species are separated on the basis of phenotypic differences that could well be brought about, in each case, by a single mutation.

Nevertheless, descriptive classification is a necessary preliminary to any rationally planned attempt at a natural classification. Indeed, but for the labours of classical taxonomists, microbial genetics would be much less advanced than it is. It is well to remember that in only a few groups of higher organisms have the various complementary approaches to a natural classification been attempted. This provides perspective for the statement that no microbial group is yet ready for such a classification. Nevertheless, enormous advances are being made in the elucidation of microbial genetic systems and in the formal genetics of some species. The way to a natural classification will be open only when this spade work has been done in a well described group.

The purpose of this paper is to discuss the standard mechanism and briefly survey some of the newly discovered non-standard mechanisms of recombination in micro-organisms. This may provide a measure of how far we are along one of the paths which will provide the basis for a natural classification in microbiology.

RECOMBINATION IN MICRO-ORGANISMS

In the following survey of recombination a subdivision is made on the basis of the details of zygote formation and subsequent recombination. These processes represent only one facet of the whole genetic system of a species. A subdivision based on, for example, mating-type systems would have high-lighted similarities and differences which will not be apparent in this account. However, the present criterion for subdivision appears not only convenient but may also reflect, to some extent, a natural division between groups.

The standard sexual cycle

The standard sexual cycle consists, in essence, of an alternation of nuclear fusion and meiosis. Fusion involves a complete haploid genome from each parent. At meiosis, recombination results from two co-ordinated processes; members of non-homologous chromosome pairs segregate independently and, by crossing-over, homologous segments are exchanged between members of a chromosome pair. A sexual cycle of this standard kind is found in certain fungi, unicellular algae and protozoa.

The mating-type systems of these groups show great variation in their complexity, and a full discussion of them is beyond the scope of this article. Recent reviews are provided by Sonneborn (1957) for protozoa, Raper (1954) for fungi, Papazian (1958) for basidiomycetes, and Lewin (1954) for unicellular algae. Formal genetic studies have been undertaken mainly in certain basidiomycetes and ascomycetes. In these cases mating-type systems range from that determined by two genes in certain basidiomycetes, through the single gene (A/a) system of *Neurospora* and heterothallic yeasts to the homothallic situation obtaining in certain other yeasts and filamentous fungi.

Neurospora tetrasperma is a representative of the group showing secondary homothallism. Fertile crosses are achieved only in cultures containing nuclei of both mating types. However, the mechanics of nuclear division at ascus formation are such that each ascospore is normally binucleate and contains a nucleus of each mating type (Dodge, 1927;

Shear & Dodge, 1927). Thus a culture derived from a single ascospore is self-fertile.

Homothallism, as opposed to heterothallism, may be expected to favour a high degree of inbreeding. In many instances the haploid fusion nuclei, in a homothallic species, will be genetically identical and no recombinants will be formed. Nevertheless, as Raper (1954) has pointed out '...the widespread occurrence of homothallism in fungi...is eloquent testimony of the evolutionary success of this pattern of sexuality among these forms'.

Several well studied instances show that the breeding system and pattern of sexuality, at least in some cases, can be modified by simple genetic changes. Dodge, Singleton & Rolnick (1950) showed that a single gene, in heterozygous state, could determine 8- instead of 4-spored asci in *Neurospora tetrasperma*. This resulted in a change from secondary homothallism to heterothallism since each ascospore was now uninucleate and belonged to only one of the two mating types. In a cross between the homothallic yeast *Saccharomyces chevalieri* and the heterothallic *S. cerevisiae*, Winge & Roberts (1949) demonstrated a single gene difference controlling heterothallism *versus* homothallism. 'Relative heterothallism' (Hemmons, Pontecorvo & Bufton, 1953), in the normally homothallic ascomycete *Aspergillus nidulans*, is a less well elucidated phenomenon. However, it provides an example of the evolution in the laboratory, of a mechanism leading to outbreeding. In this case, the strains showing relative heterothallism are usually self-sterile; crosses between two such strains may produce abundant perithecia of which most, or all, are hybrid in origin.

The most definitive cytological studies of micro-organisms have been made in those groups with a standard sexual cycle. One might mention in particular the outstanding cytotaxonomic studies by Emerson & Wilson (1954) of the *Euallomyces* and the cytological studies of *Neurospora* (McClintock, 1945; Dodge *et al.* 1950; Singleton, 1953) and *Aspergillus* (Elliott, 1960).

Extensive genetic mapping has been carried out in a few microbial species which have a standard sexual cycle. In *Aspergillus nidulans* more than 40 loci have been mapped in eight linkage groups (Pontecorvo *et al.* 1953b; Käfer, 1958) and in *Neurospora crassa* more than 75 loci have been mapped in seven linkage groups (Barratt, Newmeyer, Perkins & Garnjobst, 1954). No group of related species has yet been studied to the point where extensive homologies might be sought from linkage data. An important step in this direction has been taken by Fincham (1951) who made a comparative study of the mating-type chromosomes of

N. crassa and *N. sitophila* including interspecific crosses. Interspecific crosses had low fertility but serial backcrosses to *crassa* or *sitophila* produced fully fertile strains like *crassa* or *sitophila*, respectively. However, these fertile strains carried a portion of 'alien' chromosome and it was deduced that the mating type chromosomes in these two species are probably largely homologous.

Heterokaryosis

Heterokaryosis is the occurrence of nuclei of two or more different genotypes in a common cytoplasm. Multinucleate bacteria are briefly heterokaryotic following mutation in one nucleus. Certain yeasts show a brief heterokaryotic phase following cell fusion and prior to nuclear fusion. However, heterokaryosis has been studied mainly in the filamentous fungi. In these cases the heterokaryotic state may, under appropriate conditions, be indefinitely prolonged.

Heterokaryons are formed by mutation in a pure culture or by anastomoses occurring between hyphae or cells carrying genetically different nuclei. Stable or 'balanced' heterokaryons are readily synthesized and maintained in many fungal species by using parents which differ in their nutritional requirements; the heterokaryon is maintained on a selective medium lacking the parental growth requirements (see Beadle & Coonradt (1944) and Pontecorvo (1947) for early references).

Heterokaryotic vigour (Dodge, 1942) is directly comparable to hybrid vigour in diploid organisms. Heterokaryosis is as efficient as heterozygosis for the storing of genetic variation. As suggested by Pontecorvo (1947), and amply demonstrated by Jinks (1952), heterokaryons, with their flexible nuclear ratios, provide a plastic system for natural adaptation under changing conditions.

Apart from the above consideration, heterokaryosis is implicated, in one or other way, in the following recombination processes:

(1) It is the essential first step in inter-strain crosses of homothallic fungi (Pontecorvo, 1949) and in the perfect (sexual) state of basidiomycetes.

(2) It is the first step in the parasexual cycle of filamentous fungi (see below).

(3) Recombinants have been obtained from heterokaryons of basidiomycetes (Buller (1931); for later references see Crowe (1960)) by a mechanism not yet fully elucidated.

(4) In the actinomycetes, heterokaryosis may be implicated in the recombination process (Sermonti & Spada-Sermonti (1955); for later references see Hopwood (1959) and Bradley (1960)). The recombination process in actinomycetes is by no means fully elucidated. Most of the studies have been made with the heterogeneous group *Streptomyces coelicolour* and, as Hopwood has

pointed out, strain differences may be responsible for different results of the various workers.

Homologies between strains may be explored through attempts at heterokaryon formation. For instance, Bradley, Anderson & Jones (1959) and Uchida, Ishitani, Ikeda & Sakaguchi (1958) have obtained interspecific anastomoses in *Streptomyces* and *Aspergillus*. Taschdjian & Muskatblitt (1955) have used anastomosis in *Trichophyton* as an indication of specific relationship. Lack of hyphal fusion between strains and inability to form heterokaryons is, by itself, insufficient evidence of species difference. Apart from the obstacle which may arise from mating type differences, Garnjobst (1953) and Holloway (1955a) showed that simple genetic differences between pairs of strains may determine, in *Neurospora crassa*, their ability or inability to form a heterokaryon.

When fungal heterokaryons are formed by anastomosis the homo-karyotic parents contribute both nuclei and cytoplasm. The nuclei are eventually segregated out into conidia. This can result in what is most simply described as the recombination, between strains, of nuclear and cytoplasmic determinants; in fact, the situation may often be more complex than this statement implies. A temporary heterokaryotic association can produce profound hereditary changes in a strain (see Jinks, 1957, 1958; Roper, 1958). Srb (1958) undertook a deliberate and successful search for cytoplasmic differences among strains of *Neurospora crassa* and *N. sitophila* on the presumption that certain cytoplasmic genetic systems may participate in evolution. In Srb's experiments recombination of nuclear and cytoplasmic elements was achieved through the more conventional method of crosses in which the maternal parent supplies most or all of the cytoplasm to the progeny. The interpretation of cases of 'cytoplasmic inheritance' is far from agreed (see Nanney, 1958a, b). Whatever the final interpretation, the approaches outlined above offer promise for the study of divergences within species and, in some cases, between related species.

The parasexual cycle in fungi

This cycle of events, called by Pontecorvo (1954) 'parasexual', was first discovered in *Aspergillus nidulans* where it exists side by side with a standard sexual cycle. Comparative genetic analyses via both cycles has made it possible to fully elucidate the steps of the parasexual cycle which are as follows:

(1) The formation of a heterokaryon.
(2) The rare but regular fusion, in the heterokaryon, of pairs of unlike

haploid nuclei (Roper, 1952). Of the newly discovered recombination mechanisms, the parasexual cycle is the only one which appears to invariably involve a zygote containing complete parental genomes. The heterozygous diploid nuclei formed by these fusions are relatively stable and a very small proportion of conidia carrying them (1 in 10^5 to 10^7) are produced by the heterokaryon. In laboratory studies the parental haploids carry different nutritional and conidial colour markers; thus, the heterozygous diploids can be detected and isolated visually or by selective plating.

(3) As a result of rare but regular 'accidents' of mitosis the heterozygotes produce new recombinant types which may be recognized and isolated by various means (see Roper & Käfer, 1957; Pontecorvo, 1958).

Three independent processes are known to give rise to recombinants:

(1) *Mitotic non-disjunction*, which results in nuclei homozygous for one pair of homologous chromosomes but still heterozygous for the other chromosome pairs (Pontecorvo & Käfer, 1958).

(2) *Mitotic crossing-over*, which occurs according to the modalities first indicated by Stern (1936) for *Drosophila*. Mitotic crossing-over occurs at the 4-strand stage and is exactly reciprocal (Roper & Pritchard, 1955). At any one event, crossing-over is almost invariably confined to one chromosome arm out of the whole chromosome complement (Pontecorvo & Käfer, 1958). The subsequent division of the centromeres and segregation of strands is mitotic in form. Crossing-over, followed by appropriate segregation of strands, gives homozygosis for all alleles linked in coupling and distal to the point of crossover. Markers which are proximal to the exchange or on other chromosome arms usually remain heterozygous. Mitotic crossing-over can also produce new phenotypes by an alteration of the *cis-trans* arrangement of mutant alleles which show a position effect (Roper & Pritchard, 1955).

(3) The third mechanism is *haploidization*. Haploids arise by infrequent breakdown of the diploid nuclei. The process rarely, if ever, involves coincident crossing-over (Pontecorvo, Tarr Gloor & Forbes, 1954). The haploids arise mainly through aneuploidy by the successive loss of chromosomes until the stable haploid state is reached (Käfer, 1957, 1960). Haploidization results, then, in reassortment of whole chromosomes.

Following discovery of the parasexual cycle in *Aspergillus nidulans* a successful search was made for similar processes in some of the imperfect fungi. Although the full details are not yet unequivocally established in certain cases, it is known that the essential features of the cycle occur in *A. niger* (Pontecorvo, 1952; Pontecorvo, Roper & Forbes, 1953*a*), *Penicillium chrysogenum* (Pontecorvo & Sermonti, 1954), *A. oryzae* and *A. sojae* (Ishitani *et al.* 1956) and *Fusarium oxysporum* (Buxton, 1956). The cycle will doubtless be found in many other imperfect fungi.

Pontecorvo (1954, 1956) has discussed some aspects of the possible role of parasexual processes in nature including their place, if any, in the variation of imperfect fungal pathogens. Tentative calculations, based on *Aspergillus nidulans*, suggest that recombination via the parasexual cycle may be of the order of 500-fold less than that occurring in the sexual cycle (Pontecorvo, 1958). However, in the asexual *A. niger* and *Penicillium chrysogenum*, both the frequency of diploid nuclei and the frequency of recombination appear to be higher than in *A. nidulans*. The role, in nature, of parasexual processes may be slight in the case of fungi with a perfect stage. But, in the imperfect fungi, the parasexual cycle, regardless of its inefficiency, offers the only known means for gene recombination. As Pontecorvo (1956) has pointed out '. . .it would be surprising if a system with potentialities as great as that of sexual reproduction were merely a laboratory curiosity'.

Uchida *et al.* (1958) have attempted to produce interspecific diploids between *Aspergillus oryzae* and *A. sojae*. Their results are promising but not decisive. Clearly, there are several possible barriers to interspecific recombination via the parasexual cycle. Difficulties might be met at heterokaryosis, nuclear fusion or recombination. However, any success along these lines would open immense possibilities for the study of homologies in the imperfect fungi and perhaps even in some species with sexual reproduction.

Conjugation in bacteria

Recombination in bacteria was first reported by Lederberg & Tatum (1946) in *Escherichia coli* K-12. Pairs of mutant strains which differed in their nutritional requirements were plated on selective media which allowed growth of recombinant types only. Unselected markers segregated and provided unequivocal evidence of recombination (Lederberg, 1947). The elegant studies by Lederberg and subsequent workers towards an understanding of the recombination process may be summarized as follows.

Hayes (1952) showed that, at conjugation, there is unidirectional transfer of genetic markers and this implied a sexual differentiation between the parents. The sexual differentiation is determined by the presence or absence of an infective fertility factor F. Donor (male, or F^+) strains possess the factor and recipient (female, or F^-) strains do not (Cavalli, Lederberg & Lederberg, 1953; Hayes, 1953a). Crosses of $F^- \times F^-$ strains are sterile, $F^+ \times F^+$ crosses show low fertility, while $F^- \times F^+$ crosses show considerably greater fertility.

Crosses, reciprocal with regard to sex, showed that most recombinants carried genes derived mainly from the F^- parents, and it was suggested (Hayes, 1953a, b) that sometimes only part of the donor genome is transferred at conjugation.

The fertility factor has been described as an 'episome' (for a review, see Jacob, Schaeffer & Wollman, 1960). The factor is not essential to the cell; when it is present, it can exist either as an autonomous unit independent of the chromosome or it may be integrated as an element attached to and replicating with the chromosome. The unintegrated factor is infective and may be transferred to F^- cells by cell contact without the transfer of chromosomal markers. In F^+ strains there arise, with low frequency, *Hfr* (high frequency of recombination) variants. *Hfr* variants, mated to F^- strains, transfer the sex factor with low efficiency (Hayes, 1953 b) but transfer certain of their chromosomal markers with high efficiency. It is possible that, in $F^+ \times F^-$ crosses, recombinants arise from the mating of F^- cells with rare *Hfr* variants in the F^+ population but the evidence is not quite conclusive (see Hayes, 1960).

In each *Hfr* strain the donor markers enter the recipient in a fixed sequence but this sequence differs in independently arising *Hfr* strains (Wollman & Jacob, 1955; Jacob & Wollman, 1958 a, b). These workers interpret *Hfr* strains as representing the integrated state of the sex factor. The bacterial chromosome is formally represented as a closed ring; at integration of the sex factor the ring is opened at one of many possible sites and the sex factor becomes attached to one end. The other end, the origin, is the first point to enter the recipient at conjugation. Mating may be interrupted spontaneously or experimentally before the whole of the donor chromosome is transferred to the recipient. Thus the zygotes are often incomplete and the greater the distance of a locus from the origin, in a particular *Hfr* strain, the less its chance of inclusion in the zygote. The integrated sex factor is included only in the comparatively rare, complete zygotes.

The reality of the bacterial zygote was demonstrated by Lederberg (1949) and Zelle & Lederberg (1951) who isolated unstable heterozygotes. The mechanism of segregation from the zygote is complex. Pedigree analyses by micromanipulation have been undertaken by Lederberg (1956, 1957) and Anderson (1958). In Anderson's pedigrees some recombinants segregated out after as many as nine cell divisions following zygote formation.

Conjugation has been reported in other bacterial species including *Pseudomonas aeruginosa* (Holloway, 1955 b; Holloway & Jennings, 1958; Holloway & Fargie, 1960) and *Vibrio cholerae* (Bhaskaran & Iyer, 1961). In both of these cases there are similarities with the *Escherichia coli* system.

Particularly relevant here is the recombination obtained between *Escherichia* and *Shigella* (Luria & Burrous, 1957) and *Escherichia* and

Salmonella (Miyake & Demerec, 1959). In both cases *E. coli* K-12, *Hfr* or F$^+$, was used as donor and the *Shigella* and *Salmonella* strains behaved as F$^-$. The results show substantial homologies and point to a close phylogenetic relationship among these three genera.

Clearly, conjugation, especially when coupled with other mechanisms of bacterial recombination, will prove a very powerful tool in bacterial classification. Already some progress is being made in the Enterobacteriaceae.

Bacterial transformation

Bacterial transformation was first demonstrated by Griffith (1928) in pneumococci. The chemical nature of the transforming principle was determined by Avery, Macleod & McCarty (1944) who found it to be DNA. Deoxyribonucleic acid (DNA) from one strain (the donor), when applied to another, phenotypically distinct strain (the recipient), may effect permanent hereditary changes in some of the recipient cells. In the classical example, the DNA of a smooth, encapsulated strain of pneumococcus has the ability to transform cells of a rough, unencapsulated strain. With the exception of rare mutations the transformed cells produce only smooth encapsulated progeny.

Transformation has been observed in a number of other bacterial species including *Haemophilus influenzae* (Alexander & Leidy, 1951, 1953), *Salmonella typhimurium* (Demerec *et al.* 1958) and *Bacillus subtilis* (Spizizen, 1958). Other instances of transformation, some of which require confirmation, are reviewed by Hartman & Goodgal (1959). Transformations have now been observed for a variety of properties and it seems reasonable to suppose that, in those species which show transformation, any gene-determined potentiality might be transferred between compatible strains.

In transformation an incomplete zygote is formed and eventually there is genetic integration which probably involves only a limited length of the absorbed DNA (Hotchkiss & Evans, 1958). Details of the integration process are not yet fully elucidated (Ephrussi-Taylor, 1960).

Transformation of single properties, presumably determined by single genes, is formally equivalent to a high frequency of mutation in a single gene. Recombination to produce new non-parental transformants was first demonstrated by Ephrussi-Taylor (1951) in pneumococci. Recombinant, fully encapsulated transformants were obtained from a 'cross' in which both parents had a small capsule. A comparable situation has been described for sulphonamide resistance in pneumococci by Hotchkiss & Evans (1958). Linked transformation of two distinct properties, mannitol utilization and streptomycin resistance, was demonstrated by Hotchkiss & Marmur (1954). In 'crosses' involving both markers, double transformants were far more frequent than could be expected on the basis of the coincidence of two single marker transformations. Thus, the transforming DNA molecules, while small compared with the whole bacterial genome, may be sufficient in size to carry more than one locus.

Of a number of cases of reported interspecific transformations (reviewed by Hartman & Goodgal, 1959), the most thoroughly analysed is that found in *Haemophilus* (see Schaeffer, 1958). In *Haemophilus* there appears to be no barrier to uptake of DNA from another species but interspecific transformation is invariably less frequent than intraspecific transformation.

The occurrence of transformation in nature is not yet established, but Ottolenghi & Hotchkiss (1960) have shown that growing cultures of pneumococci accumulate extracellular transforming principle and they suggest that '. . . transformation may not be a phenomenon restricted to laboratory conditions'. Indeed, Griffiths pioneering work was done *in vivo*.

Transduction in bacteria

Bacterial transduction may be considered as essentially a phage-mediated transformation. Phage particles may carry a chromosome fragment from the donor strain, on which they were grown, to recipient strains in which the fragment may be incorporated. Zinder & Lederberg (1952) first reported transduction in a system using *Salmonella typhimurium* and phage P22.

The first step in transduction is the preparation of a phage lysate of the donor strain; the lysate is produced either by infecting the donor under conditions favouring lysis or by inducing lysis in a lysogenic donor strain. Recipient, usually mutant, cells are infected under conditions favouring lysogeny. Of the recipient cells which survive infection, a small proportion possess hereditary properties previously associated with the donor but not the recipient. Transduced cells are detected by selective techniques based on nutrition or drug resistance or, in the case of flagellar transformations, motility (Stocker, Zinder & Lederberg, 1953).

As is usual in conjugation and invariable in transformation, the zygote of the transduction process is incomplete. The phage carries a fragment which represents about 1 % of the donor chromosome (see Clowes, 1960). Simultaneous transduction for more than one marker is dependent on close linkage and this imposes a restriction on the range of recombinants from a single transduction event. Nevertheless, extremely elegant and important genetic analysis have been carried out in *Salmonella*, particularly by Demerec and his colleagues (Demerec *et al*. 1956, 1958).

The P22–*Salmonella* system has been termed 'general transduction' in that the phage-carried fragments represent, collectively, all or most of the donor chromosome. General transduction has been reported also in an *Escherichia coli*–phage P1 system (Lennox, 1955). Transduction has also been demonstrated in other species including *Pseudomonas aeruginosa* (Loutit, 1958; Holloway & Monk, 1959), *Vibrio cholerae* (Bhaskaran, 1958) and *Proteus mirabilis* (Coetzee & Sacks, 1960). It is not yet known how many of these systems permit general transduction.

Restricted transduction is typified by the *Escherichia coli*–phage λ system (Morse, Lederberg & Lederberg, 1956a, b; E. M. Lederberg, 1960). The transducing phage must be derived by induction of lysis in a lysogenic strain. The donor strain carries the prophage as an integrated element at a specific chromosomal site. At lysis the liberated phage is able to carry a fragment of the donor chromosome but is limited to a segment adjacent to the prophage locus. Thus the phage can transduce only those genes carried in that particular segment. The vectors in restricted transduction are not limited to those elements which may assume a typical viral form. Other episomes such as the sex factor in *E. coli* may also be responsible for restricted transduction (Jacob & Adelberg, 1959). Interspecific transduction between *Escherichia* and *Shigella* has been reported by Adams & Luria (1958).

Recombination in viruses

The only extensive genetic analyses so far made of viruses have been confined to bacteriophages, in particular the T phages of *Escherichia coli* B. Viral markers used in early crosses were host range (Luria, 1945) and plaque morphology (Hershey & Rotman, 1949; Doermann & Hill, 1953). Crosses are made by infecting bacteria with two or more genetically different phage types, of the same strain or of related strains, so that mixed infection occurs in individual cells. Single bacteria, so infected, produce recombinant as well as parental phage types. This result was first observed by Delbrück & Bailey (1946) and analysed in genetic terms by Hershey & Rotman (1948, 1949).

The phage cross is a problem in population genetics since several rounds of mating occur between infection and lysis (Visconti & Delbrück, 1953). However, this has not prevented standard genetic analysis.

Linkages have been detected and Benzer (1957) has made an extremely fine analysis of one region of the phage T4 chromosome.

Jacob & Wollman (1954) have undertaken genetic analysis of the λ phage of *Escherichia coli*. As mentioned previously, λ is an episomic element which may occupy a chromosomal site and, as such, could be considered a constituent of the bacterial cell. Other infectious elements such as Kappa in *Paramecium* (Sonneborn, 1939), the sex factor in *E. coli* and colicinogenic factors (for a review see Frédericq, 1958) have certain of the essential properties of viruses in that they can invade cells and multiply within them. These facts emphasize a primary difficulty in virus classification. As Luria (1959) has pointed out 'Viruses are grouped together taxonomically on methodological rather than biological criteria. There is no reason to assume that they represent a naturally related group. The ability to invade living cells from outside and to multiply within them...may well be common to a variety of unrelated elements.'

To share in a common gene pool viruses must be able to multiply in the same host. Genetic approaches such as that used for the T phages may well be revealing. They may even be applied to animal viruses (Burnet, 1959), but here the technical difficulties are substantial. This approach, valuable as it may be, would leave vital questions unanswered. Luria (1959) has suggested that 'We are not stretching our imagination too far if we consider the phage DNA as a transmissible fragment of bacterial DNA. Some of the RNA viruses...may ultimately prove related to or homologous to cell microsomes....' Perhaps the ultimate classification of many viruses and virus-like agents will be primarily in relation to 'normal' cell constituents. Secondary relationships of one virus 'species' to another will then be apparent.

DISCUSSION AND CONCLUSIONS

In the above account an attempt has been made to survey some of the recombination mechanisms which operate in micro-organisms. A bewildering array of processes is known. These processes include the standard sexual cycle, the parasexual cycle of fungi, conjugation, transformation and transduction in bacteria, and recombination in viruses. It would be unwise to suggest that no further mechanisms will be found.

Certain species of fungi and bacteria possess more than one recombination mechanism. The diversity of mechanisms and their multiplicity in certain single species poses important questions relevant to the major problem of the evolution of genetic systems themselves.

Despite the advances implied in this survey it is clear that no group is yet fully ripe for an attempted natural classification based on genetic studies. Most groups are far from ready. Nevertheless, significant advances are being made. Aside from the genetic systems themselves, formal genetic analysis is revealing what appear to be important differences between, for example, bacteria and other micro-organisms. Pontecorvo (1950) discussed reasons which might lead us to expect, in certain cases, close linkage of genes with related biochemical functions. Instances of this have now been found in *Escherichia* and *Salmonella* (see reviews by Demerec & Hartman (1959) and Clowes (1960)), but no conspicuous examples are yet available in fungi. The reason for the grouping of certain genes with related biochemical functions is not yet known, but on present knowledge appears to represent an important distinction between groups. Such differences are genetically gross. However, it can hardly be hoped that more subtle homologies and divergences will be apparent until the formal genetics of related species has been thoroughly worked out.

There is still room for more useful descriptive work coupled with the 'old' systematics. Indeed, this is an essential preliminary to an attempted natural classification. New and promising approaches may be included in this work. For instance, Vogel (1961) has shown that lysine synthesis may be a useful character to explore phylogenetic links. Lysine synthesis follows different routes in different fungal groups, and Vogel believes that 'the two sets of enzymes represent a considerable period of evolution'.

When the necessary spade work has been done in a well described group the way will be open to a genetic classification. The rewards will be substantial for genetics and microbiology. Hartman & Goodgal (1959) have said: 'The ultimate solution to an enduring and stable taxonomic system would appear to reside only in thorough analysis at the genetic level; there is no reason to believe that such analysis is not possible in any group of bacteria if looked for thoroughly. . . .' The viruses may pose special problems of their own, but the above quotation could well be extended to include the fungi.

REFERENCES

ADAMS, J. N. & LURIA, S. E. (1958). Transduction by bacteriophage P1: abnormal phage function of the transducing particles. *Proc. nat. Acad. Sci., Wash.* **44**, 590.

ALEXANDER, H. E. & LEIDY, G. (1951). Determination of inherited traits of *H. influenzae* by desoxyribonucleic acid fractions isolated from type-specific cells. *J. exp. Med.* **93**, 345.

ALEXANDER, H. E. & LEIDY, G. (1953). Induction of streptomycin resistance in sensitive *Haemophilus influenzae* by extracts containing deoxyribonucleic acid from resistant *Haemophilus influenzae*. *J. exp. Med.* **97**, 17.

ANDERSON, T. F. (1958). Recombination and segregation in *Escherichia coli*. *Cold Spr. Harb. Symp. quant. Biol.* **23**, 47.

ANDERSON, T. F., WOLLMAN, E. L. & JACOB, F. (1957). Sur les processus de conjugaison et de recombinaison chez *Escherichia coli:* III. Aspects morphologiques en microscopie électronique. *Ann. Inst. Pasteur*, **93**, 450.

AVERY, O. T., MACLEOD, C. M. & MCCARTY, M. (1944). Studies on the chemical nature of the substance inducing transformation of pneumococcal types. Induction of transformation by a desoxyribosenucleic acid fraction from pneumococcus type III. *J. exp. Med.* **79**, 137.

BARRATT, R. W., NEWMEYER, D., PERKINS, D. D. & GARNJOBST, L. (1954). Map construction in *Neurospora crassa*. *Advanc. Genet.* **6**, 1.

BEADLE, G. W. & COONRADT, V. L. (1944). Heterokaryosis in *Neurospora crassa*. *Genetics*, **29**, 291.

BEADLE, G. W. & TATUM, E. L. (1941). Genetical control of biochemical reactions in *Neurospora*. *Proc. nat. Acad. Sci., Wash.* **27**, 499.

BENZER, S. (1957). The elementary units of heredity. In *The Chemical Basis of Heredity*. Baltimore: Johns Hopkins Press.

BHASKARAN, K. (1958). Genetic recombination in *Vibrio cholerae*. *J. gen. Microbiol.* **19**, 71.

BHASKARAN, K. & IYER, S. S. (1961). Genetic recombination in *Vibrio cholerae*. *Nature, Lond.* **189**, 1030.

BRADLEY, S. G. (1960). Reciprocal crosses in *Streptomyces coelicolor*. *Genetics*, **45**, 613.

BRADLEY, S. G., ANDERSON, D. L. & JONES, L. A. (1959). Genetic interactions within heterokaryons of streptomycetes. *Ann. N.Y. Acad. Sci.* **81**, 811.

BULLER, A. H. R. (1931). *Researches on Fungi*, **4**. London: Longmans, Green and Co.

BURNET, F. M. (1959). Genetic interactions between animal viruses. In *The Viruses*, **3**. New York: Academic Press.

BUXTON, E. W. (1956). Heterokaryosis and parasexual recombination in pathogenic strains of *Fusarium oxysporum*. *J. gen. Microbiol.* **15**, 133.

CAVALLI, L. L., LEDERBERG, J. & LEDERBERG, E. M. (1953). An infective factor controlling sex compatibility in *Bacterium coli*. *J. gen. Microbiol.* **8**, 89.

CLOWES, R. C. (1960). Fine genetic structure as revealed by transduction. In *Microbial Genetics. Symp. Soc. gen. Microbiol.* **10**, 92.

COETZEE, J. N. & SACKS, T. G. (1960). Transduction of streptomycin resistance in *Proteus mirabilis*. *J. gen. Microbiol.* **23**, 445.

CROWE, L. K. (1960). The exchange of genes between nuclei of a dikaryon. *Heredity*, **15**, 397.

DELBRÜCK, M. & BAILEY, W. T. (1946). Induced mutations in bacterial viruses. *Cold Spr. Harb. Symp. quant. Biol.* **11**, 33.

DEMEREC, M. & HARTMAN, P. E. (1959). Complex loci in microorganisms. *Annu. Rev. Microbiol.* **13**, 377.

DEMEREC, M., HARTMAN, Z., HARTMAN, P. E., YURA, T., GOTS, J. S., OZEKI, H. & GLOVER, S. W. (1956). Genetic studies with bacteria. *Publ. Carneg. Instn*, no. 612.

DEMEREC, M., LAHR, E. L., MIYAKE, T., GOLDMAN, I., BALBINDER, E., BANIC, S., HASHIMOTO, K., GLANVILLE, E. V. & GROSS, J. D. (1958). Bacterial genetics. *Yearb. Carneg. Instn*, **57**, 390.

DODGE, B. O. (1927). Nuclear phenomena associated with heterothallism and homothallism in the Ascomycete *Neurospora*. *J. agric. Res.* **35**, 289.

DODGE, B. O. (1942). Heterocaryotic vigor in *Neurospora*. *Bull. Torrey bot. Cl.* **69**, 75.

DODGE, B. O., SINGLETON, J. R. & ROLNICK, A. (1950). Studies on lethal E gene in *Neurospora tetrasperma*, including chromosome counts also in races of *N. sitophila*. *Proc. Amer. phil. Soc.* **94**, 38.

DOERMANN, A. H. & HILL, M. B. (1953). Genetic structure of bacteriophage T4 as described by recombination studies of factors influencing plaque morphology. *Genetics*, **38**, 79.

ELLIOTT, C. G. (1960). The cytology of *Aspergillus nidulans*. *Genet. Res.* **1**, 462.

EMERSON, R. & WILSON, C. M. (1954). Interspecific hybrids and the cytogenetics and cytotaxonomy of *Euallomyces*. *Mycologia*, **46**, 393.

EPHRUSSI-TAYLOR, H. (1951). Transformations allogènes du Pneumocoque. *Exp. Cell Res.* **2**, 589.

EPHRUSSI-TAYLOR, H. (1960). On the biological functions of deoxyribonucleic acid. In *Microbial Genetics. Symp. Soc. gen. Microbiol.* **10**, 132.

FINCHAM, J. R. S. (1951). A comparative genetic study of the mating-type chromosomes of two species of *Neurospora*. *J. Genet.* **50**, 221.

FREDERICQ, P. (1958). Colicins and colicinogenic factors. In *The Biological Replication of Macromolecules. Symp. Soc. exp. Biol.* **12**, 104.

GARNJOBST, L. (1953). Genetic control of heterocaryosis in *Neurospora crassa*. *Amer. J. Bot.* **40**, 607.

GRIFFITH, F. (1928). The significance of pneumococcal types. *J. Hyg., Camb.* **27**, 113.

HARTMAN, P. E. & GOODGAL, S. H. (1959). Bacterial genetics (with particular reference to genetic transfer). *Annu. Rev. Microbiol.* **13**, 465.

HAYES, W. (1952). Recombination in *Bacterium coli* K-12: unidirectional transfer of genetic material. *Nature, Lond.* **169**, 118.

HAYES, W. (1953a). Observations on a transmissible agent determining sexual differentiation in *Bacterium coli*. *J. gen. Microbiol.* **8**, 72.

HAYES, W. (1953b). The mechanism of genetic recombination in *Escherichia coli*. *Cold Spr. Harb. Symp. quant. Biol.* **18**, 75.

HAYES, W. (1960). The bacterial chromosome. In *Microbial Genetics. Symp. Soc. gen. Microbiol.* **10**, 67.

HEMMONS, L. M., PONTECORVO, G. & BUFTON, A. W. J. (1953). Perithecium analysis and relative heterothallism. *Advanc. Genet.* **5**, 194.

HERSHEY, A. D. & ROTMAN, R. (1948). Linkage among genes controlling inhibition of lysis in a bacterial virus. *Proc. nat. Acad. Sci., Wash.* **34**, 89.

HERSHEY, A. D. & ROTMAN, R. (1949). Genetic recombination between host range and plaque type mutants of bacteriophage in single bacterial cells. *Genetics*, **34**, 44.

HOLLOWAY, B. W. (1955a). Genetic control of heterocaryosis in *Neurospora crassa*. *Genetics*, **40**, 117.

HOLLOWAY, B. W. (1955b). Genetic recombination in *Pseudomonas aeruginosa*. *J. gen. Microbiol.* **13**, 572.

HOLLOWAY, B. W. & FARGIE, B. (1960). Fertility factors and genetic linkage in *Pseudomonas aeruginosa*. *J. Bact.* **80**, 362.

HOLLOWAY, B. W. & JENNINGS, P. A. (1958). An infectious fertility factor for *Pseudomonas aeruginosa*. *Nature, Lond.* **181**, 855.

HOLLOWAY, B. W. & MONK, M. (1959). Transduction in *Pseudomonas aeruginosa*. *Nature, Lond.* **184**, 1426.

HOPWOOD, D. A. (1959). Linkage and the mechanism of recombination in *Streptomyces coelicolor*. *Ann. N.Y. Acad. Sci.* **81**, 887.

HOTCHKISS, R. D. & EVANS, A. H. (1958). Analysis of the complex sulfonamide resistance locus of *Pneumococcus*. *Cold Spr. Harb. Symp. quant. Biol.* **23**, 85.

HOTCHKISS, R. D. & MARMUR, J. (1954). Double marker transformations as evidence of linked factors in desoxyribonucleate transforming agents. *Proc. nat. Acad. Sci., Wash.* **40**, 55.

HUXLEY, J. (editor) (1940). *The New Systematics.* Oxford: Clarendon Press.

ISHITANI, C., IKEDA, Y. & SAKAGUCHI, K. (1956). Hereditary variation and genetic recombination in Koji-molds (*Aspergillus oryzae* and *Aspergillus sojae*). VI. Genetic recombination in heterozygous diploids. *J. gen. appl. Microbiol.* (*Japan*), **2**, 401.

JACOB, F. & ADELBERG, E. A. (1959). Transfert de caractères génétiques par inporation au facteur sexuel d'*Escherichia coli*. *C.R. Acad. Sci., Paris,* **249**, 189.

JACOB, F., SCHAEFFER, P. & WOLLMAN, E. L. (1960). Episomic elements in bacteria. In *Microbial Genetics. Symp. Soc. gen. Microbiol.* **10**, 67.

JACOB, F. & WOLLMAN, E. L. (1954). Etude génétique d'un bactériophage tempéré d'*Escherichia coli*. I. Le système génétique du bactériophage lambda. *Ann. Inst. Pasteur,* **87**, 653.

JACOB, F. & WOLLMAN, E. L. (1958a). Genetic and physical determination of chromosomal segments in *Escherichia coli*. In *The biological replication of macromolecules. Symp. Soc. exp. Biol.* **12**, 75.

JACOB, F. & WOLLMAN, E. L. (1958b). Les épisomes, éléments génétique ajoutés. *C.R. Acad. Sci., Paris,* **247**, 154.

JINKS, J. L. (1952). Heterokaryosis: a system of adaptation in wild fungi. *Proc. roy. Soc.* B, **140**, 83.

JINKS, J. L. (1957). Selection for cytoplasmic differences. *Proc. roy. Soc.* B, **146**, 527.

JINKS, J. L. (1958). Cytoplasmic differentiation in fungi. *Proc. roy. Soc.* B, **148**, 314.

KÄFER, E. (1957). Genetics of *Aspergillus*. *Yearb. Carneg. Instn,* **56**, 376.

KÄFER, E. (1958). An 8-chromosome map of *Aspergillus nidulans*. *Advanc. Genet.* **9**, 105.

KÄFER, E. (1960). High frequency of spontaneous and induced somatic segregation in *Aspergillus nidulans*. *Nature, Lond.* **186**, 619.

LEDERBERG, E. M. (1960). Genetic and functional aspects of galactose metabolism in *Escherichia coli* K-12. In *Microbial Genetics. Symp. Soc. gen. Microbiol.* **10**, 115.

LEDERBERG, J. (1947). Gene recombination and linked segregations in *Escherichia coli*. *Genetics,* **32**, 505.

LEDERBERG, J. (1949). Aberrant heterozygotes in *Escherichia coli*. *Proc. nat. Acad. Sci., Wash.* **35**, 178.

LEDERBERG, J. (1956). Conjugal pairing in *Escherichia coli*. *J. Bact.* **71**, 497.

LEDERBERG, J. (1957). Sibling recombinants in zygote pedigrees of *Escherichia coli*. *Proc. nat. Acad. Sci., Wash.* **43**, 1060.

LEDERBERG, J. & TATUM, E. L. (1946). Novel genotypes in mixed cultures of biochemical mutants of bacteria. *Cold Spr. Harb. Symp. quant. Biol.* **11**, 113.

LENNOX, E. S. (1955). Transduction of linked genetic characters of the host by bacteriophage Pl. *Virology,* **1**, 190.

LEWIN, R. A. (1954). Sex in unicellular algae. In D. H. Wenrich (editor), *Sex in Microorganisms,* p. 100. *Symp. Amer. Ass. Advanc. Sci., Wash.*

LOUTIT, J. S. (1958). A transduction-like process within a single strain of *Pseudomonas aeruginosa*. *J. gen. Microbiol.* **18**, 315.

LURIA, S. E. (1945). Mutations of bacterial viruses affecting their host range. *Genetics,* **30**, 84.

LURIA, S. E. (1947). Recent advances in bacterial genetics. *Bact. Rev.* **11**, 1.

LURIA, S. E. (1959). The reproduction of viruses: a comparative survey. In *The Viruses,* **3**. New York: Academic Press.

LURIA, S. E. & BURROUS, J. W. (1957). Hybridization between *Escherichia coli* and *Shigella*. *J. Bact.* **74**, 461.

McCLINTOCK, B. (1945). *Neurospora*. I. Preliminary observations on the chromosomes of *Neurospora crassa*. *Amer. J. Bot.* **32**, 671.

MIYAKE, T. & DEMEREC, M. (1959). *Salmonella–Escherichia* hybrids. *Nature, Lond.* **183**, 1586.

MORSE, M. L., LEDERBERG, E. M. & LEDERBERG, J. (1956a). Transduction in *Escherichia coli* K-12. *Genetics*, **41**, 142.

MORSE, M. L., LEDERBERG, E. M. & LEDERBERG, J. (1956b). Transductional heterogenotes in *Escherichia coli*. *Genetics*, **41**, 758.

NANNEY, D. L. (1958a). Epigenetic control systems. *Proc. nat. Acad. Sci., Wash.* **44**, 712.

NANNEY, D. L. (1958b). Epigenetic factors affecting mating type expression in certain ciliates. *Cold Spr. Harb. Symp. quant. Biol.* **23**, 327.

OTTOLENGHI, E. & HOTCHKISS, R. D. (1960). Appearance of genetic transforming activity in pneumococcal cultures. *Science*, **132**, 1257.

PAPAZIAN, H. P. (1958). The genetics of basidiomycetes. *Advanc. Genet.* **9**, 41.

PONTECORVO, G. (1947). Genetic systems based on heterokaryosis. *Cold Spr. Harb. Symp. quant. Biol.* **11**, 193.

PONTECORVO, G. (1949). Genetical techniques for self-fertile (homothallic) species. *Proc. 8th int. Congr. Genet.* 642.

PONTECORVO, G. (1950). New fields in the biochemical genetics of microorganisms. *Biochem. Soc. Symp.* **4**, 40.

PONTECORVO, G. (1952). Non-random distribution of multiple mitotic crossing-over among nuclei of heterozygous diploid *Aspergillus*. *Nature, Lond.* **170**, 204.

PONTECORVO, G. (1954). Mitotic recombination in the genetic systems of filamentous fungi. *Caryologia*, **6** (suppl.), 192.

PONTECORVO, G. (1956). The parasexual cycle in fungi. *Annu. Rev. Microbiol.* **10**, 393.

PONTECORVO, G. (1958). *Trends in Genetic Analysis*. New York: Columbia University Press.

PONTECORVO, G. & KÄFER, E. (1958). Genetic analysis based on mitotic recombination. *Advanc. Genet.* **9**, 71.

PONTECORVO, G., ROPER, J. A. & FORBES, E. (1953a). Genetic recombination without sexual reproduction in *Aspergillus niger*. *J. gen. Microbiol.* **8**, 198.

PONTECORVO, G., ROPER, J. A., HEMMONS, L. M., MACDONALD, K. D. & BUFTON, A. W. J. (1953b). The genetics of *Aspergillus nidulans*. *Advanc. Genet.* **5**, 141.

PONTECORVO, G. & SERMONTI, G. (1954). Parasexual recombination in *Penicillium chrysogenum*. *J. gen. Microbiol.* **11**, 94.

PONTECORVO, G., TARR GLOOR, E. & FORBES, E. (1954). Analysis of mitotic recombination in *Aspergillus nidulans*. *J. Genet.* **52**, 226.

RAPER, J. R. (1954). Life cycles, sexuality, and sexual mechanisms in the fungi. In D. H. Wenrich (editor), *Sex in Microorganisms*, p. 42. *Symp. Amer. Ass. Advanc. Sci., Washington*.

ROPER, J. A. (1952). Production of heterozygous diploids in filamentous fungi. *Experientia*, **8**, 14.

ROPER, J. A. (1958). Nucleo-cytoplasmic interactions in *Aspergillus nidulans*. *Cold Spr. Harb. Symp. quant. Biol.* **23**, 141.

ROPER, J. A. & KÄFER, E. (1957). Acriflavine resistant mutants of *Aspergillus nidulans*. *J. gen. Microbiol.* **16**, 660.

ROPER, J. A. & PRITCHARD, R. H. (1955). Recovery of the complementary products of mitotic crossing-over. *Nature, Lond.* **175**, 639.

SCHAEFFER, P. (1958). Interspecific reactions in bacterial transformation. In *The Biological Replication of Macromolecules*. *Symp. Soc. exp. Biol.* 12, 60.

SERMONTI, G. & SPADA-SERMONTI, I. (1955). Genetic recombination in Strepto-myces. *Nature, Lond.* 176, 121.

SHEAR, C. L. & DODGE, B. O. (1927). Life histories and heterothallism of the red bread-mold fungi of the *Monilia sitophila* group. *J. agric. Res.* 34, 1019.

SINGLETON, J. R. (1953). Chromosome morphology and the chromosome cycle in the ascus of *Neurospora crassa*. *Amer. J. Bot.* 40, 124.

SONNEBORN, T. M. (1939). *Paramecium aurelia:* Mating types and groups; lethal interactions; determination and inheritance. *Amer. Nat.* 73, 390.

SONNEBORN, T. M. (1957). Breeding systems, reproductive methods, and species problems in Protozoa. In E. Mayr (editor), *The Species Problem*, p. 155. *Symp. Amer. Ass. Advanc. Sci., Washington*.

SPIZIZEN, J. (1958). Transformation of biochemically deficient strain of *Bacillus subtilis* by deoxyribonucleate. *Proc. nat. Acad. Sci. Wash.* 44, 1072.

SRB, A. M. (1958). Some consequences of nuclear-cytoplasmic recombinations among various Neurosporas. *Cold Spr. Harb. Symp. quant. Biol.* 23, 269.

STERN, C. (1936). Somatic crossing over and segregation in *Drosophila melano-gaster*. *Genetics*, 21, 625.

STOCKER, B. A. D., ZINDER, N. D. & LEDERBERG, J. (1953). Transduction of flagellar characters in *Salmonella*. *J. gen. Microbiol.* 9, 410.

TASCHDJIAN, C. L. & MUSKATBLITT, E. (1955). Hyphal fusions between *Trichophyton tonsurans* variants as an indication of species relationships. *Mycologia*, 47, 339.

UCHIDA, K., ISHITANI, C., IKEDA, Y. & SAKAGUCHI, K. (1958). An attempt to pro-duce interspecific hybrids between *Aspergillus oryzae* and *A. sojae*. *J. gen. appl. Microbiol. (Japan)*, 4, 31.

VISCONTI, N. & DELBRÜCK, M. (1953). The mechanism of genetic recombination in phage. *Genetics*, 38, 5.

VOGEL, H. J. (1961). Lysine synthesis and phylogeny of lower fungi: some chytrids versus *Hyphochytrium*. *Nature, Lond.* 189, 1026.

WINGE, Ø. & ROBERTS, C. (1949). A gene for diploidisation in yeast. *C.R. Lab. Carlsberg*, série physiologique, 24, 341.

WOLLMAN, E. L. & JACOB, F. (1955). Sur le mécanisme du transfert de matériel génétique au cours de la recombinaison chez *Escherichia coli*. *C.R. Acad. Sci., Paris*, 240, 2449.

ZELLE, M. R. & LEDERBERG, J. (1951). Single cell isolations of diploid heterozygous *Escherichia coli*. *J. Bact.* 61, 351.

ZINDER, N. D. & LEDERBERG, J. (1952). Genetic exchange in *Salmonella*. *J. Bact.* 64, 679.

THE CONSTRUCTION OF TAXONOMIC GROUPS

P. H. A. SNEATH

National Institute for Medical Research, Mill Hill, London, N.W. 7

INTRODUCTION

Whenever a biologist wishes to make generalizations about the organisms he studies he is forced to arrange them in groups of some kind. The intuitive and commonly unconscious nature of this process obscures the fact that it is a distinct logical operation which has its own rules and conventions. Elsewhere in this Symposium are papers on the different sorts of character which can be found in micro-organisms and on their value in classification. This contribution deals with the problem of how to arrange micro-organisms into taxonomic groups if one is provided with an adequate body of data upon them (a problem for which one rarely finds any explicit instructions given, as if it were too simple to need any). When this is done one may proceed to describe the taxa and to construct schemes for identification and other purposes. Although these steps may be carried out *pari passu* as one examines a group of organisms, the construction of taxonomic groups logically follows the observation of the characters and precedes identification or nomenclature.

It is now becoming generally recognized that taxonomic groups are constructions of the taxonomist (e.g. Cowan, 1956), for however nearly they may correspond to entities in nature, yet the taxa are formed operationally by placing together individual organisms and assuming that these represent reasonably well the populations from which they are drawn. Whether we say that the taxa are the populations themselves or the concepts of the populations, our knowledge comes from the sample of individuals and our arrangement of these into taxonomic groupings.

Most of this contribution discusses the sort of groupings which we loosely call 'natural' and which are based on overall similarity. This is because of the pre-eminent usefulness of 'natural' classifications in biology compared with those based on Aristotelian logic, well discussed by Cain in this Symposium (see also Cain, 1958). Much of the recent work on the topic has been discussed elsewhere (Sneath, 1957a, 1958, 1961; Cowan, 1959; Floodgate, 1962; Sneath & Sokal, 1962) and the logical arguments will not be repeated here in detail. Mathematical techniques for constructing taxonomic groupings have recently been added to these theoretical developments; this has led to what has been called 'numerical taxonomy', which will be treated comprehensively in a forthcoming publication (Sokal & Sneath, unpublished). In addition, the opportunity has been taken of making uniform the symbolism in different branches of numerical taxonomy, leading to several changes in the earlier conventions.

THE NATURE OF TAXONOMIC GROUPS

Natural taxa

Taxonomic groups can be of many kinds. This is often overlooked, yet there are many ways of grouping things which are never seriously proposed as scientific classifications. We must therefore ask what sort of criteria are used for constructing groups which we find useful, or which we call 'good' taxonomies.

The usual answer is to say that good taxonomies are natural ones. The term 'natural' has itself many meanings in taxonomy (as can be seen from various contributions in this Symposium and cf. Bather (1927)). Most commonly it is taken to mean phylogenetic, as if this were self-evident. However, as pointed out by Pirie in this Symposium, in viruses the idea of a phylogenetic classification is practically useless, yet we recognize groups of viruses which we feel are 'natural' in the sense of being very similar overall. The distinction between natural in the phylogenetic sense and in this second sense may be made plain by two examples. First, if we have four geometric shapes, two identical circles and two identical triangles, the circles form one natural group based on similarity and the triangles form another. Obviously there can be no meaning to a phylogenetic classification here. Secondly, if two phyletic lineages converged so closely that they became identical they would be two phyletic groups but only one natural group based on similarity. This second sense of 'natural' follows the usage of Gilmour (1951) and is distinguished here by the term *phenetic*, introduced by Cain & Harrison (1960) to mean the relation based not on ancestry but on overall similarity or affinity. Classification is used here in the wide sense of any kind of arrangement, not in the restricted sense of placing entities into distinct classes, nor in the sense of 'artificial' classification as used by Ciferri (1959).

Special and general classifications. Gilmour (1937, 1940, 1951) has emphasized that the nature of a classification depends on the purpose for which it is constructed (further discussed by Sneath (1958) and Floodgate (1962)). Gilmour draws the useful distinction between general classifications, such as phenetic ones, and special classifications intended for special purposes. The latter have also been called artificial or arbitrary classifications, or catalogues (Sneath, 1957a). Gilmour (1937) made an important contribution by showing that the basic idea of a general classification—that is one intended for general purposes—was that the resultant groups allowed one to make the greatest number of generalizations about their members. This is one way of saying that the groups contain much information. For example, the concept of *mammal* allows one to predict many characters which will (with high probability) be found in each individual mammal. The concept *black creatures* (a group in a special classification) only allows one to predict that the members are black. Intermediate situations occur, of course, and it may happen that an artificial classification happens also to be close to a natural one, but the logical concepts of the two are quite different.

Monothetic and polythetic taxa. Special classifications are usually based on single characters, or on a series of single characters, such that the possession of a unique set of these is both sufficient and necessary for membership in the group which is thus defined. For example, the group of black limbless animals comprises all animals which are black and limbless, and no others. Beckner (1959, pp. 14–31) calls such groups monotypic, because the defining set of features is unique, but since monotypic has other meanings, *monothetic* is a better term (from Greek *mono* 'one' and *thetos* 'arrangement'). Phenetic groups, on the other hand, are composed of organisms with the highest overall similarity, and this means that no single feature is either essential to group membership or is sufficient to make an organism a member of the group. The organisms 1, 2, 3 and 4, possessing respectively the features A, B, C; A, B, D; A, C, D and B, C, D might form a phenetic group, where each organism possesses three of the four features A, B, C and D; however, none of the four is found in all four organisms. Such groups, in which several sets of characters occur, are called 'polytypic' by Beckner, but are better called *polythetic*. Phenetic taxa are always in theory polythetic. In practice it is usually possible to find some characters which are constant, but there is always the possibility that an individual will be found which is aberrant in one or more of these respects. This is why any monothetic system (such as that suggested by Maccacaro (1958), or the subdivision techniques used by Brisbane & Rovira (1961), or, in ecology, by Williams & Lambert (1959)) will always carry the risk of serious mis-classification; an organism which is aberrant in the feature used to make the primary division will be inevitably moved to a category far from its phenetic position.

The contribution of Adanson. The first taxonomist to attempt to discover the logical basis of what we call 'natural' groups was probably Michel Adanson. He described a new method of classification in his work on molluscs (Adanson, 1757, coquillages, pp. x–xiii), and developed this in detail in his famous botanical text-book (Adanson, 1763, préface, pp. cliv *et seq.*) as 'la méthode naturelle'. The important point he made was that creatures should be grouped together on the greatest number of features in common, and that there is no justification for deciding *a priori* on the relative importance of characters in making a natural taxonomy. This was of course a direct argument for equal weighting of characters (see below), and it was on this point that he was attacked by his contemporaries. Yet, as shown by Cain (1959*a*, *b*), they were making classifications which were largely based on Adanson's principles, although they did so intuitively, without recognizing this. Adanson's ideas could not show their value until the statistical procedures which they required could be handled by modern electronic computing machines, but this is now practicable, and the following section will deal with methods which have been called Adansonian (Sneath, 1957*b*) and which are part of the wider development of numerical taxonomy. Adansonian classifications may be briefly summarized as follows:

(1) The ideal 'natural' taxonomy is that in which the taxa have the greatest content of information and which are based on as many features as possible.
(2) Every feature is of equal weight in constructing 'natural' taxa.
(3) Overall similarity (affinity) is a function of the proportion of features in common.
(4) Distinct taxa are based on correlated features.
(5) Affinity is treated as independent of phylogeny, i.e. as an independent taxonomic dimension, and is therefore phenetic.

The first and last of these points have been discussed earlier, and the second is discussed in a separate section below. The third point is of importance because it allows us to measure affinity in a quantitative manner, and this is one of the main contributions of numerical taxonomy: the statistical procedures are discussed in the section on Methods. The fourth point needs brief mention here.

Correlation between characters. When we say that two groups of organisms are distinct, this implies that one does not find all possible combinations of their characters. If this did indeed occur it would give a chain of intermediate forms in which any division would be quite arbitrary. Possibly such chains are more common in bacteria than in most organisms, and Cowan (1955) has referred to these as a spectrum of merging forms, but there are usually places in the chain where there are fewer individuals. Divisions at these places will be reasonably satis-factory, and can be found by looking for correlations between characters —partial if not absolute correlations. It is not satisfactory, however, to try to create taxonomies on a large scale by using character correlations. The highly correlated characters may be found, but if they are used to subdivide the collection of organisms the resulting groups are mono-thetic with the attendant disadvantages of this. In addition, very high and significant correlations between features in a given pair of taxa may be swamped and rendered unrecognizable by poor correlation in the members of other taxa in the same study. Since we cannot recognize the taxa at this stage, we cannot extract from the rest the relevant pair of taxa, and are unable to clarify the situation. Correlations between characters, therefore, are by themselves of little value in constructing taxonomies, but are important in distinguishing between taxa taken two at a time. Since Adansonian methods use many characters, it will seldom occur that only one character separates the resulting taxa, so that correlations will usually be present. These will reveal themselves in abrupt changes in similarity values, although a good deal of theoretical work is needed on this aspect of the subject.

The a priori hierarchy of characters

Microbiology is one of the last strongholds of the assumption that certain functional classes of characters are *a priori* appropriate to the definition of certain 'natural' taxonomic categories of rank. This assumes that there is a hierarchy of characters paralleling the hierarchy of taxa. For example, Prévot (1933) states that morphological characters define genera, physiological characters define species, and serological characters define varieties; van Niel (1955) has shrewdly discussed this example. The theory has a considerable influence on the current taxo-nomy of yeasts. The origin of this theory, sometimes called *subordination of characters*, and its development by the De Jussieus, De Candolle and Cuvier, in particular, is lucidly discussed by Cain (1959a).

If the theory were generally true, then constructing a 'natural' taxo-nomy would be a simple matter. Unfortunately it is not. It may be pos-sible to select examples which purport to prove the theory, but only *a posteriori* from a previous taxonomic study. Even then it is usually simple to find characters of the 'forbidden' classes which had been over-looked. Mammals, for example, show peculiarities in morphology, physiology, biochemistry, cytology, etc. This means that whether mor-phological or physiological or other types of features are to be used for the definition depends on which kinds one ignores or upon how one defines these terms. It is now becoming realized that only 'artificial' groups can be constructed on these principles. Aberrant organisms which do not fit the schemes are constantly being found (for example the motile and catalase-positive lactobacilli described by Harrison & Hansen (1950), Dacre & Sharpe (1956) and Vaňková (1957), to cite but one instance).

The hierarchy of characters is one form of differential weighting; it is therefore invalid if equal weight is to be given to all characters, whether for constructing phenetic or phyletic taxa. It would indeed be curious if evolution, which is responsible for the natural hierarchy, should be so obliging as to operate only on certain classes of characters at specified taxonomic ranks.

The history of bacterial classification

The history of bacterial classification well illustrates some of the points made above (the reader may be referred for details to *Bergey's Manual*, 1923, pp. 1–22; 1948, pp. 5–38; Bulloch, 1938; Stanier & van Niel, 1941; and van Niel, 1946, 1955). The classification of Cohn (1872) was the basis of the early attempts to classify bacteria, and he recognized several genera based on morphology. As Bulloch (1938) and van Niel (1946, 1955) have emphasized, Cohn was aware that the 'naturalness' of these genera was open to doubt, and he regarded them mainly as 'form genera'. The limited morphological differentiation among bacteria and their importance in producing disease and fermentations encouraged attempts to define bacterial genera on physiological criteria. Bergonzini (1879) employed pigmentation to subdivide Cohn's genera, and this trend culminated in the classification of Orla-Jensen (1909), in which most of the genera were defined on biochemical criteria, although the highest ranks were based on morphology. It was at once seen that the 'morphological' and 'physiological' genera did not agree very well, and whichever scheme was adopted there were many obvious misfits. The attempts of Kluyver & van Niel (1936) and Stanier & van Niel (1941) to reconcile these schemes were not very successful, and van Niel (1946) suggested that until a great deal more work had been done it was best to make a number of different and overlapping diagnostic keys which were avowedly artificial, rather than to attempt a natural taxonomy of bacteria.

These classifications were basically monothetic, and the dilemma of choosing between morphological and physiological criteria was therefore insoluble so long as the theory of an *a priori* hierarchy of characters lingered on (at least insofar as creating 'natural' taxa went). The attempt to resolve the dilemma by using phylogenetic criteria, as has been done by Bisset (1950, 1952, 1957), has not been satisfactory since one cannot decide *a priori* which features are good guides to phylogeny and which are not: such classifications are therefore based on phylogenetic speculations, and are themselves speculative (Floodgate, 1961). They may indeed be phenetic taxonomies which probably represent more or less closely the phylogeny, but in the absence of a good fossil record (see Pia, 1928) we cannot be sure of this. Other criteria, such as pathogenicity, serology, etc., meet the same difficulties.

Another line of thought may be traced in works such as those of Winslow & Rogers (1906), Rogers, Clark & Davis (1914), Levine (1918), Topley & Wilson (1929, p. 202) and White (1937), and an interesting example of their application is that of Dible (1921). In these there is no preoccupation with *a priori* hierarchies of characters, but rather with the correlations between features whatever their kind, and they are therefore in the Adansonian tradition. It is perhaps worth noting that many of the findings of these early workers have stood the test of time, and this general plan is now usually employed in taxonomic work (e.g. Cowan, Steel, Shaw & Duguid, 1960). There is no longer a conflict between morphological and physiological criteria, since equal-weighting has cut the Gordian knot. All kinds of features are found *a posteriori* to contribute to the definition of all kinds of taxa.

Catalogues

Special classifications, or catalogues, are ones which are devised for special purposes. An example is the arrangement of books alphabetically by the authors' names; it is good for the purpose of finding the book if you know the author's name, but it is no guide to the size, shape, colour or subject-matter. Such classifications are commonly called 'artificial'. They are also monothetic. In contrast, a general classification may be exemplified by an arrangement by subject-matter, where many criteria are employed and no single one is either sufficient or necessary. For example, there is no single attribute both necessary and sufficient to define a book as a book on chemistry; the concept *chemistry* is polythetic. Such arrangements are useful for many purposes, since most of the questions we ask will deal with the contents of the book. A 'natural' (i.e. phenetic) classification is thus a general classification, useful for general purposes, but perfect for none.

Catalogues are exceedingly useful devices which are by no means to be despised. Their value depends on their suitability for the purpose for which they were made, and they can be entirely suited to this purpose. Their construction presents no great difficulty if this purpose can be clearly specified, and if the appropriate technical methods are available for observing the characters to be used.

The weighting of characters

A consequence of the views expressed above is that every character has equal weight in constructing 'natural' (i.e. phenetic) taxa. This follows from several considerations.

First, if the aim is to make taxa of the greatest content of information this is measured by the number of statements which can be made about its members, and the importance of the statements is irrelevant because importance is related to the purpose in hand. For general purposes all statements are equally important. If this were not so, if for example chemical features were given great importance, the classification would be predominantly a chemical one and not a general one. The concept of importance has no exact meaning in taxonomy and usually it only means 'important to me because I am interested in it'.

Secondly, there is no way of allocating an exact numerical value for importance on rational grounds, nor would the systematist have the patience to do so. In particular it is not possible to score importance on grounds of phylogeny (since we do not know the phylogenies before we make our classifications, but deduce them from the phenetic affinities), nor on grounds of constancy in taxa (since we have not yet recognized these taxa).

Thirdly, characters have no fixed genetic, evolutionary or selective importance, since this will depend on the environment, which is constantly changing.

Fourthly, the use of large numbers of characters has an 'evening-up' effect such that weighted features are effectively given approximately equal weight.

These points have been dealt with at greater length elsewhere (Sneath, 1958; Sneath & Sokal, 1962; Cain & Harrison, 1960). Paradoxically, repeated revisions of a group (which seem to be necessary using traditional taxonomic methods) result in the progressive removal of excessive weight which had been given to some features, and hence lead to more equal weighting.

Classification from above and classification from below

It is now possible to see the relation between 'classification from above' (analytic) and 'classification from below' (synthetic) discussed by White (1937). This refers to the usual practice of taxonomists, for machines can work from above or below indifferently. At the start of a study it is necessary to divide organisms into manageable groups—no one, for instance, can classify all micro-organisms in one study—and this can only be done by employing arbitrary characters, since one cannot hope to recognize many of the affinities and character correlations before one has made the study. In this way one separates a group of high rank but of manageable size, such as the actinomycetes, using certain criteria which will need revision at a later date. In practice it is important not to apply the criteria too rigidly for fear of excluding near relatives which are aberrant in these respects. Repeated classification from above will not yield natural taxa, for by their monothetic construction they depend on 'key features' (which cannot define phenetic groups) and will only approach naturalness by chance or intuition. They are therefore special classifications and are 'artificial', and need extensive revision if they are to be made 'natural'. They are, nevertheless, essential in the early stages of taxonomy. Like other arbitrary schemes they are easy to set up and it is easy to identify an unknown organism as belonging to one of the 'artificial' taxa.

Classification from below, i.e. grouping individuals into species, species into genera, etc., can also be monothetic and artificial, although this is less likely, since the systematist has a better chance of realizing intuitively if the taxa of low rank are natural or not. He will therefore correct his scheme repeatedly as he builds it, and it will be based largely on the over-all similarities between the organisms. If it is formally monothetic some revision will be needed, and the usual process is for a group to be revised repeatedly until it is acceptably phenetic. The advantage of numerical taxonomy is that the phenetic taxa are constructed in one operation by the successive steps of recording characters, estimating overall similarity between organisms and grouping the organisms into taxa on these similarities.

THE METHODS OF NUMERICAL TAXONOMY

The successive steps in a numerical taxonomic analysis (each of which is treated in a separate section, and which are illustrated by Tables 1 and 2 and figs. 2–4), may be summarized as follows:

(1) *Characters and operational taxonomic units.* A group of organ-

isms is chosen for study. Of necessity this is largely by arbitrary criteria, unless the group is already fairly well known. The taxonomic entities of lowest rank (such as strains) are called the operational taxonomic units (OTUs). Numerous characters of the OTUs are recorded and coded for numerical analysis.

(2) *Similarity*. The overall similarity (affinity, or phenetic similarity) between each OTU is calculated.

(3) *Cluster analysis*. The OTUs are grouped into clusters of high mutual similarity, which are called *phenons*, and which approximate to natural taxonomic groups (the term phenon has been used in quite another sense by Camp & Gilly (1943), but this does not seem to have come into general use). The phenons can be arranged to form the desired taxonomic hierarchy.

(4) *Keys*. The characters can now be re-examined, in order to list the characters of the taxa recognized, prepare descriptions, and in particular to find the characters most useful in making diagnostic keys.

Some basic hypotheses of numerical taxonomy, in addition to the theoretical points mentioned earlier, are discussed in detail elsewhere (Sneath & Sokal, 1962; Sokal & Sneath, unpublished). One of these is directly pertinent here, the 'matches hypothesis'. This assumes that it is possible to obtain a meaningful parametric value for the proportion of matches to mis-matches when computing the characters of two organisms. If this is so (and it seems to be founded on sound theoretical principles, taxonomic, genetic and statistical) then the observed value for the proportion of matches will tend toward the parametric value (i.e. that which one would obtain if one could compare all characters) as the number of characters is increased. The deviation from the parametric value will be approximately that due to sampling error. Since a second independent estimate will tend toward the same value, this implies that different estimates will tend to agree, or in other words that different studies will yield in general the same taxonomies. Numerical taxonomic studies should therefore be self-consistent. This is born out in practice, and Haltenorth (1937) found agreement between affinities based on measures of length and measures of breadth. In addition different methods of estimating affinity and of cluster analysis are statistically robust, by which is meant that different methods give very much the same end-result despite minor variations. This is well shown by the papers of Silvestri and his colleagues (Gilardi, Hill, Turri & Silvestri, 1960; Hill, Turri, Gilardi & Silvestri, 1961; and see Silvestri, Turri, Hill & Gilardi in this Symposium, p. 333). In these, two different affinity indices and several methods of cluster analysis were employed on the same data with results which were surprisingly similar (see, for example, spheres VII and XV in this Symposium and the corresponding groups II and E in the earlier papers).

Characters and operational taxonomic units

Operational taxonomic units. The taxonomic entities in a numerical taxonomic study (OTUs) may be of various kinds. In microbiology they will usually be individual strains, sometimes simply strains as such, sometimes as representatives of a species or other taxon. When they are intended as exemplars of taxa some care should be taken with their choice. They should if possible be typical of the taxa they represent, although this may not be known. Some advantages lie in using the nomenclatural type strains (that is, the name-bearers, or nomenifers, to use the term of Schopf, 1960); this will help to keep the nomenclature straightforward, though nomenifers are not necessarily typical. In other cases the operational taxonomic units may be species or genera represented, not by exemplars, but by taxon descriptions, and here one must decide what to do about characters which vary in the taxon. The simplest course is to score the commonest state of a variable character, but this raises some ambiguities, for a taxon may be subdivided into a number of others and the term 'commonest' can then mean several things (e.g. commonest among the taxa, commonest among strains, etc.). It is probably wisest to employ actual strains as exemplars where possible, and also to include nomenifers where possible. Two or three exemplars for each taxon will greatly increase our confidence in the results, for they should emerge as tight clusters in the analysis. As mentioned earlier, our selection of OTUs will perforce be largely an artificial group, and organisms should not be too readily excluded if they seem to be closely related, whatever their 'key' characters are.

Characters. The kinds of character which may be employed for classification are discussed in detail in other papers in this Symposium. Characters which are obtained in large numbers by the application of a simple testing procedure will become increasingly important in microbial classification since they yield much information for little effort. Examples are infra-red spectroscopy (see Norris, 1959) and methods for studying metabolic changes and components of cell-walls and of cell extracts (Proom & Woiwod, 1949; Cummins & Harris, 1956, 1958; Mattick, Cheeseman, Berridge & Bottazzi, 1956).

What sorts of characters should we employ in constructing natural taxonomic groups? It has been argued above that all characters are *a priori* of equal importance for this purpose, so we can employ any kind of character provided they are valid taxonomic ones. Some attributes are not characters which we consider pertinent to taxonomy, such as the strain number in a culture collection, which does not express any property inherent in the strain. Geographical distribution is another attribute whose validity may here be doubtful.

Characters must also be reliable ones, that is, the experimental error of determining them must not be so great as to render the result more a matter of chance than of the properties of the strain. This does not exclude mutable characters, since the mutability itself, and the characteristic mutation rate, are perfectly valid taxonomic characters provided they can be accurately determined. The criteria for deciding whether a character is reliable are not primarily taxonomic, but depend on scientific judgement.

We should try to choose as varied a selection of characters as possible, morphological, physiological, fermentative, nutritional and so on. Attempts to obtain a varied selection will assist in getting what we want, i.e. a random selection of the characters of the genome, and the larger the number of characters and the more varied they are the closer we will come to this ideal. By the matches hypothesis we would expect that if the number chosen is large the selection will approach a random selection. We should, however, attempt to randomize the selection deliberately since there is always the possibility of bias, either conscious or unconscious. It would, for example, be possible to get almost any taxonomic result by choosing only characters which agree with a preconceived theory, just as one could get almost any figure for the mean height of the population by choosing only certain individuals to measure. Accidental bias may also occur; if, for example, we chose only carbohydrate fermentation results for our taxonomy, a block in glucose metabolism might prevent any other fermentation, and this might well give a biased result. In the same way we might get a biased result for height if we measured only the occupants of one omnibus—it might be a school bus! But an attempt to randomize the characters should overcome most of this bias. To carry our analogy further, we would expect to get a fair estimate of the mean height of the population if we chose some occupants of omnibuses, some from trains, some from bathing beaches and some listed in the electoral rolls and telephone directory.

How many characters do we need? At least forty or fifty characters (or character states, mentioned below) are needed and preferably several hundred. It is not easy to obtain such large numbers of characters in micro-organisms, but if we wish to make natural taxonomies we must do so. The distribution of variation of similarity coefficients is not yet well understood, but we may assume for the present that the standard error of a similarity coefficient S is approximately $\sqrt{[S(1-S)/n]}$, where n is the number of features. A more exact estimate is probably that given by the binomial distribution, since the sampling error is skewed for values of S

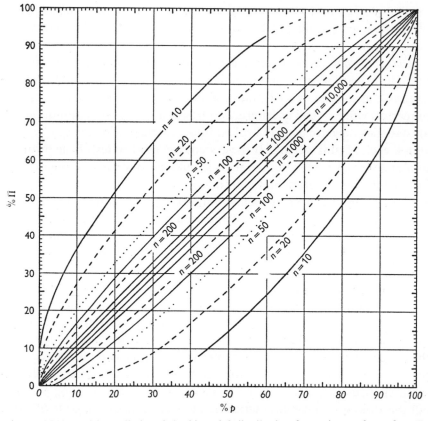

Fig. 1. 95 % confidence limits of the binomial distribution for various values of n. For example, if the proportion, Π, of positive values in a large population is 70 % and one takes repeated samples of size $n = 20$, then in 95 % of cases the observed proportion of positives, p, will lie between $45 \cdot 7$ and $88 \cdot 1$ %.

near 0 or 1. Fig. 1 is a diagram of the 95 % confidence limits of sampling. It can be seen that very little reliance can be placed on an S value which is based on fewer than fifty characters.

Unit characters. Unit weight is given to a unit character. If characters are multiple they should be broken down into unit characters. It is possible to interpret and define unit characters in several ways, for example in terms of the genetic code of deoxyribonucleic acid (Watson & Crick,

1953) or in terms of information theory. In practice they can be defined as follows: *a unit character is a taxonomic character of two or more states which within the study at hand cannot be further subdivided logically (except for subdivision brought about by changes in the method of coding).* The ruling idea is that each character state should contribute one new item of information. A number of redundancies are to be excluded (see Sneath, 1957*b*), and wherever known, logical or necessary consequences of a character should not be counted as independent characters. The next section describes how characters are reduced to units.

Coding of characters. Characters require coding in a standard fashion. Straightforward positive and negative characters can be recorded directly as plus and minus, or as 1 and 0. With some statistics characters with numerical values, such as length, can be employed as they stand, but for all statistics they are usually broken into a number of steps, or *character states*, each of unit weight. If these steps are not too few, little information or accuracy is lost, but the steps should not of course be finer than is justified by the experimental methods.

The scaling of characters is also important. This is the conversion of the quantitative value to a new value used in the analysis, and breaking up a continuous variable into steps of unit weight is one example. The important point is to prevent any single character assuming excessive weight in the analysis. For example it would not be proper to use the crude values for the number of molecules of glucose catabolized per cell, since this would give millions of character states, far outweighing all the other data. In order to prevent this it is wise to restrict the character states on any one attribute to ten or less, and in much work only two or three states will be justified. The common 'one plus, two plus, three plus' scoring system will often serve admirably as it stands. It is inevitable that small changes in weight will be produced by different scaling systems, but this does not make impracticable the Adansonian principle of equal weight even if it cannot always be rigorously applied, for the use of a large number of characters has an equalizing effect.

Provision is necessary for entries which are missing, unscorable or inapplicable. Such entities should not be employed in a comparison, and can be marked NC, as in Table 1, for 'no comparison with this entry'. Inapplicable characters are those where a feature cannot be manifested in any form because some necessary condition is missing. For example, 'spores smooth or rough' is inapplicable in non-sporing bacteria. Unscorable features include those where one feature masks another: e.g. we could not score pink pigment in a colony which was black.

Care must be taken to break down into logical components any complex test. A test like 'litmus milk' demonstrates many different things, e.g. fermentation of lactose, digestion of casein, reduction of litmus, all of these possibly affected by the semi-anaerobic conditions. These should be scored as separate characters. If this is done, one should not then score acid from lactose or casein hydrolysis from other tests.

Table 1. *Example of a coded data table (t × n table)*

Character states	Operational taxonomic units (strains)			
	A	B	C	D
1	+	+	−	NC
2	+	+	+	+
3	+	+	+	−
4	−	+	NC	NC
5	+	+	+	+
6	+	+	−	+
7	+	+	−	NC
8	NC	−	+	+
9	+	+	+	+
10	+	+	+	−
11	+	NC	−	NC
12	+	+	+	−

The details of the scoring system suggested earlier (Sneath, 1957b) seem in retrospect to be unnecessarily complicated. They dealt at some length with the logic of coding since it was felt that with the small numbers of characters usually available in micro-organisms it was important to make the best use of them. If we omit as redundant any character which is constant in all the OTUs, we can dispense with the scoring scheme there labelled B (Beers & Lockhart, 1962; Beers, Fisher, Megraw & Lockhart, 1962).

A character may either be coded 1, 2, 3, 4, etc. (multistate coding) or + and − (two-state coding). The latter are required for simple coefficients of association, and multistate values can be converted into two-state values in several ways. The simplest is to give a separate entry for each of the states. In the above example state 1 would be coded + − − −, state 2 would be + + − −, and so on.

Quantitative features may be scored additively or non-additively. In the former the scoring of three strains A, B and C, for four character states 1, 2, 3, 4 would be:

Character states ...	1	2	3	4
A (strong positive)	+	+	+	+
B (weak positive)	+	−	−	−
C (negative)	−	−	−	−

The similarity of A to B would here be 1/4. Non-additive scoring omits certain entries, as below:

Character states ...	1	2	3	4
A (strong positive)	+	NC	NC	+
B (weak positive)	+	−	−	−
C (negative)	−	NC	NC	NC

Here the similarity of A to B is 1/2. C is scored in the manner shown because of a logical bar: if the first state represents the attribute responsible for the smallest degree of the reaction, then when it is scored as negative it is meaningless to score the others since they could not be positive.

Additive characters have one major defect: they exaggerate dissimilarities due to different growth rates in different strains. A slow-growing strain will usually give delayed reactions in chemical tests. Sometimes the delay will be great enough for the test to be scored as negative at the standard time of observation, but more commonly it will be scored as a weak positive. In the latter event additive scoring will usually give a lower similarity than non-additive scoring, where the similarity will be 1/2 on this character whatever the degree of difference. On the other hand, the non-additive method loses information on the degree of difference in the character. Where large numbers of features are employed it is likely that the two methods will give much the same result, but we need additional work on the effect of growth rates, which is analogous to a general size factor in the morphology of higher organisms. Until more is known the non-additive method may be the safer one.

Having scored the characters in the OTUs, one now makes up the data table for analysis, consisting of t OTUs scored for n characters. A hypothetical example is shown in Table 1. This is a $t \times n$ data table (the $i \times m$ table in Sneath, 1957b).

The measurement of similarity

The methods used for estimating overall similarity may be divided into three groups, correlation coefficients, measures of distance and coefficients of association. The first two are particularly convenient for quantitative characters, but though they may be useful on occasion in microbiology the most generally useful are coefficients of association, which are well suited to data expressed in plus and minus form. By suitable coding any of the statistics can be used with any data. Correlation coefficients have been used by Michener & Sokal (1957) and Morishima

& Oka (1960), and distance measures by Haltenorth (1937), Cain & Harrison (1958) and Sokal (1961); the reader may be referred to these papers and to Sokal & Sneath (unpublished) for detailed discussions.

Two of the many possible association coefficients have been used in microbial systematics. These are shown below in terms of the four entries a, b, c, d, in a 2×2 table:

		First strain: number of attributes	
		+	−
Second strain:	$\{+$	a	b
number of attributes	$\{-$	c	d

The similarity coefficient employed by Sneath (1957 b and there called S) is

$$S_J = \frac{a}{a+b+c}.$$

This does not take into account the negative matches (entry d), that is two negatives do not count as a similarity. The coefficient varies from 0 (complete dissimilarity) to 1 (complete identity), and was first used at the beginning of the century in ecology (Jacquard, 1908).

The matching coefficient suggested by Sokal & Michener (1958), in which negative matches count toward the similarity, is:

$$S_S = \frac{a+d}{a+b+c+d}.$$

It has been employed by Brisbane & Rovira (1961) under the name of the 'affinity index', and by Hill et al. (1961) and Silvestri et al. (p. 333).

Whether to allow two negatives to count as a similarity in estimating overall similarity is a vexed question. Originally it was suggested that one should not (Sneath, 1957 b), but it has been pointed out that the scoring of a character as negative may be an arbitrary matter (e.g. with resistance tests) and also that there are logical grounds for allowing two absences to count as a similarity (Hill et al. 1961). The difficulty is that we are particularly liable in microbiology to confuse a negative result with a result which is inapplicable. We would not, for instance, let the absence of wing-veins in two wingless insects count as similarities, since if wingless they could not express the wing-veins. But if a bacterium does not ferment glucose it may be unable to ferment any carbohydrate, and these other fermentation reactions, though negative, should properly be scored as NC. In many instances we shall be in doubt as to the proper course. It is therefore heartening to see that when a large number of features is employed we do get, by and large, the same sort of end result

Table 2. *Similarity matrix obtained from Table* 1 *on comparing each strain with every other*

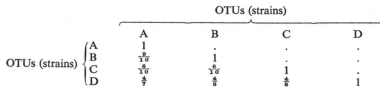

		A	B	C	D
	A	1	.	.	.
OTUs (strains)	B	$\frac{9}{10}$	1	.	.
	C	$\frac{6}{10}$	$\frac{6}{10}$	1	.
	D	$\frac{4}{7}$	$\frac{4}{8}$	$\frac{4}{8}$	1

whether we count negative matches or not (see Gilardi *et al.* 1960; Hill *et al.* 1961). This is what we would expect on general statistical grounds, since if it is arbitrary whether a given character state is scored + or − then in the long run we will tend to find them scored as + or − in a more-or-less random manner. One may note, however, that in the study

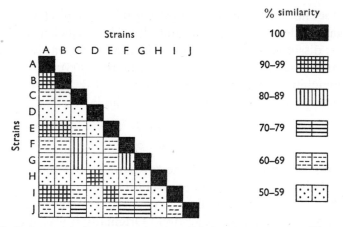

Fig. 2. Similarity matrix between strains A to J before rearrangement. The squares are shaded to represent the degree of similarity between strains.

of Hill *et al.* the relation between *Mycobacterium phlei* and *Escherichia coli* is surprisingly high when negative matches are used, and possibly this is due to inapplicable features being counted as similarities. We can conclude that we may employ negative matches, but it is well to be on the watch for aberrant results (particularly in very different organisms, where inapplicability is likely to be more of a problem than in very similar organisms; see also Beers *et al.* 1962).

One next calculates the similarity between every OTU and every other, and tabulates this in a $t \times t$ table (the $i \times i$ table in Sneath, 1957*b*). Since the upper right-hand part is a mirror image of the lower left-hand part, we may omit one half of the complete matrix. An example is shown in

Table 2, where the similarity is expressed as the fraction of matches between the character states. Fig. 2 is a diagram in which the squares have been shaded to represent similarity values. The strains may be originally in a haphazard order, as in this figure, and the next step is to examine the similarity matrix for phenons and to rearrange the strains so that very similar strains are adjacent. When this is done the matrix will contain areas of high similarity which show in the shaded figure as dark

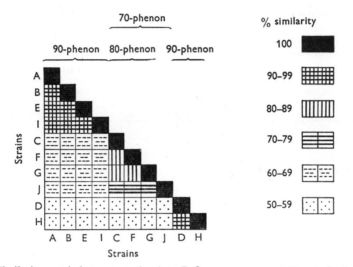

Fig. 3. Similarity matrix between strains A to J after rearrangement. The strains have been placed in the new order by cluster analysis, as described in the text. The phenons of different value are indicated by brackets.

triangles (Fig. 3). These shaded diagrams are useful for identifying the main phenons; this can be done by eye in simple instances, but more objective methods, described below, are preferable.

Cluster analysis

Methods for identifying the phenetic groups (phenons) from the similarity matrix are collectively referred to as cluster analyses. An example using the hypothetical data in Fig. 2 is as follows:

(1) The similarity matrix is retabulated, with the strain-pairs listed against the similarity values in steps of, say, 10 % similarity. In this example the pairs exhibiting 90 % similarity are A–B, A–E, A–I, B–E, B–I, E–I and D–H. The pairs with 80 % similarity are C–F, C–G, and F–G and so on.

(2) The new table is searched in descending steps of similarity. Any strain pairs are listed.

(3) New strains are added on to the pairs to form groups. The groups link

at lower similarity levels, until all strains unite into one group. This is shown below:

% Similarity	Groups		
100	No groups		
90	A–B–E–I		D–H
80	A–B–E–I	C–F–G	D–H
70	A–B–E–I	C–F–G–J	D–H
60	A–B–E–I–C–F–G–J		D–H
50	A–B–E–I–C–F–G–J–D–H		

The similarity table rearranged in this new order of strains is shown in Fig. 3.

The clusters are usually shown in a hierarchic taxonomic tree (dendrogram), which summarizes the salient points of the cluster analysis and

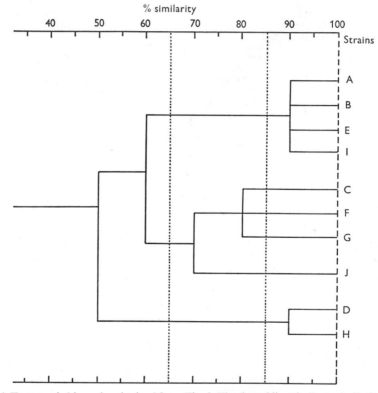

Fig. 4. Taxonomic hierarchy obtained from Fig. 3. The dotted lines indicate similarity levels which have been considered appropriate to different (but unspecified) ranks.

which can be related to taxonomic rank. In Fig. 4 is shown the dendrogram derived from Figs. 2 and 3 by the cluster analysis given above. It must be emphasized that taxonomic relations are multidimensional, and that some distortion is inevitable in reducing them to the few dimensions which can be expressed in dendrograms. The main theoretical difficulty in devising cluster analysis methods is to decide what distortion is most permissible, and it may be that the orthodox hierarchy is not the best device for this purpose. Nevertheless, for practical purposes the relations must be simplified.

In the above example sorting is a simple matter. The affinity of a new member is the same with all members of a group, e.g. for strain J entering group C–F–G the similarities J–C, J–F and J–G are all 70 %. In practice some values will be higher than others. One must therefore decide on the criterion for admission to a group. The simplest is to allow a new entrant to join the group at the highest similarity value between the entrant and any of the existing members of the group. This was used by Sneath (1957 b) as it is easy to programme for a computer. Other criteria can be used: the lowest value was chosen by Sørensen (1948) in ecology (a method with some interesting properties) and the mean value can also be employed.

A better method, using mean values, has been used for the example in the next section on *Bacillus*. This was based on the unweighted variable group method of Sokal & Michener (1958). The nucleus of a group is given by the pair of strains with the highest similarity, and strains are then added to this nucleus. First is added that strain which has the highest mean similarity to the existing members of this nucleus, and it is added on at this mean S level. The other strains are added in the same way in descending order of mean S values between the new entrant and the existing group-members. Two groups fuse at the S level which is equal to the mean of the intergroup S values. In this method each strain of the group has equal weight in determining if a new member is to be admitted. Sokal & Michener (1958) have discussed the advantages and disadvantages of this method compared to a second procedure. In the latter, within any group each of its constituent subgroups has equal weight for this purpose, however many strains it contains. Since they conclude that either method will usually give much the same result (which was borne out also in this example on *Bacillus*), I have used the slightly simpler unweighted method. There are, however, some points about the second (weighted) method which merit further investigation.

Another method of cluster analysis which offers theoretical advantages is that of Rogers & Tanimoto (1960). This has been used by Silvestri and his colleagues who give the procedure in detail (see p. 349), but briefly it is as follows. The OTUs are treated as points in a multi-dimensional space with the affinities treated as distances. In order to detect the centre of a cluster the distances between a given OTU and all others are added. This is done for each OTU in turn. The sum is smallest for that OTU which is the most central in a geometric sense. OTUs within a certain chosen distance of the central one are regarded as a cluster after testing the cluster for homogeneity; the cluster is removed and the process repeated on the remainder. The method is somewhat laborious, so that computing machines are a necessity. Other methods for cluster analysis are described by Sokal (1958) and Rohlfe & Sokal (1961).

Phenons. The phenons, the phenetic groups obtained by cluster analysis, may be prefixed by a number indicating the percentage similarity at which they are formed. Thus an 80-phenon indicates a group whose members are affiliated at 80% similarity or higher. The term phenon is used for any form of phenetic cluster obtained by any method; they may be thought of as groups which are closely equivalent to natural taxa. Taxon is retained for its proper function of meaning any taxonomic group.

Rank. Phenons may be equated with taxonomic ranks, but since rank is mainly arbitrary, no absolute criteria can be given for similarity levels appropriate to genus, family, etc. The important point is that any criterion should be applied uniformly to the whole of a study: a line can be drawn across at a given similarity level, but it must not wander up and down at the whim of the investigator. Scales of similarity will not coincide in two studies if they are based on different sets of features, but the scales can be roughly calibrated against each other if some OTUs are common to both studies (see Fig. 5).

Models. Though not properly a method of cluster analysis, models can be used to obtain a vivid representation of the main relations between taxa (Lysenko & Sneath, 1959; Lysenko, 1961). The relations cannot be expressed in three dimensions without distortion, but for teaching purposes and to assist visualization of the taxonomy such models may be useful. By employing a principal component analysis as a cluster analysis one can obtain the least distorted representation, although trial and error will often yield a sufficiently accurate result.

Keys

The preparation of diagnostic keys is a task which is often neglected. Yet as far as the non-specialist is concerned a good key is often of more value than a systematic hierarchy, even if supplemented with good descriptions. Practical hints on how to draw up a key will be found in the papers of Metcalfe (1954) and Stearn (1956), and the merits of single-feature and multiple-feature keys have been discussed by Sneath (1957a).

The features to employ are (in general) those which are easiest to perform and least susceptible to experimental error. Having chosen these, the ones most useful in making a diagnostic key are those which are

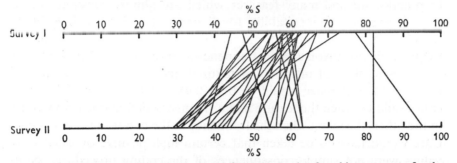

(a) Method of calibration. A line is drawn from the S value found in one survey for the comparison of a particular pair of strains to the S value found in the other survey for the comparison of the same pair of strains. All the comparisons which were made in both surveys are similarly entered.

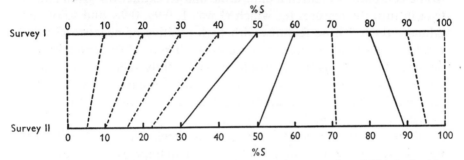

(b) The approximate mean correspondence between the two scales of S is obtained by drawing lines from one scale to the other based on the mean slopes of the lines in figure 5(a). The S values of 0 and 100 % are the same on both scales. Endashed lines are only presumptive, as they are not based on information in figure 5(a).

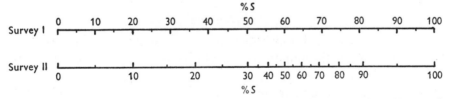

(c) From figure 5(b) the two scales are calibrated against each other by distorting one of them.

Fig. 5. Calibration of one S value scale with another, from Sneath & Cowan (1958), showing calibration of the scale used there (I) with that of the survey of Sneath (1957b) (II).

found only in one taxon, and are found in all its members. For this purpose it does not matter if the feature is positive or negative. However, it may be that few features have these properties. One can be certain that a feature will be present in all members and absent in all non-members only in the case of an 'artificial' classification based on this feature: in this case it will be true because the taxon has this property by definition. In practice we find many features which are almost constant, and a way of measuring their suitability for diagnostic keys is needed. A simple statistic, probably adequate for most work, is the difference between the frequency in one taxon and the frequency in another (G). Thus, if feature A occurs in 50 % of members of taxon 1 and in 96 % of members of taxon 2, the difference would be 0·50–0·96 and $G = -0·46$. The best case would be when the feature had a frequency of 0 in one taxon and 1 in the other, the worst when the frequency in the two taxa was the same. Care would have to be taken that certain high positive or negative G values were not simple consequences of the coding procedure. Non-additive scoring introduces certain difficulties in calculating G.

It would be quite possible and advantageous to programme an electronic computor to search a data table and to extract for given pairs of taxa in turn the features for which G was 1, 0·99, 0·98, and so on, and tabulate them. Those features with high positive or negative G values would be most valuable for making keys. If several features with $G = 0·9$ or $-0·9$ were used this would be sufficiently reliable for ordinary purposes, since this would imply, provided the analysis was based on a reasonably representative sample of strains, that strains aberrant in all of these features would be very rare.

The use of diagnostic tables (Cowan & Steel, 1960, 1961) will prove most useful for identification, and has the advantage over keys that some idea of the *nearest* match to an aberrant strain can be readily seen, while with a key one is led perhaps into a very distant genus by an aberrant feature.

Techniques

Numerical taxonomy is only practicable on a large scale using electronic computers, notwithstanding heroic efforts by workers such as Pohja (1960) and Brisbane & Rovira (1961) in doing this by hand. The cost is far less by machine, and programmes now exist for several machines (see p. 326). Photographic methods, punched cards and similar methods can be used as laborious alternatives (e.g. Sneath, 1957*b*; Pohja, 1960; Brisbane & Rovira, 1961; Lysenko, 1961).

Punched-card machines may be of increasing value in taxonomy, both for identification (e.g. Ainsworth, 1941; Heather, 1958) and sorting, for which they are well fitted. Skerman (1961) has suggested that data on large numbers of strains tested by standardized methods should be recorded on punched cards at one or more centres of microbial systematics, in order to aid identification, coordination and repeated analysis as our knowledge increases.

In microbiology much labour is needed to obtain a small amount of information, due very largely (as Pirie, 1955, points out) to the paucity of morphological features. It is therefore important to devise quick, simple tests. Multipoint inoculators (Beech, Carr & Codner, 1955) or replica plating (Lederberg & Lederberg, 1952; Shifrine, Phaff & Demaine, 1954) would be very useful with plastic Petri dishes divided by internal ribs into sixteen or twenty-five compartments (this would restrict the zones of reaction and check swarming).

EXAMPLES OF ADANSONIAN CLASSIFICATIONS

A review of examples in bacteriology

Adansonian methods have in the last few years been applied to a wide range of bacteria, including genera such as *Streptomyces*, *Mycobacterium*, *Pseudomonas*, *Lactobacillus* and *Micrococcus*, and in general the results have been very satisfactory, as can be seen from the following discussion. They are now being tried with other micro-organisms such as fungi and viruses. In botany and zoology they have been applied to insects (Michener & Sokal, 1957) and plants (Rogers & Tanimoto, 1960; Morishima & Oka, 1960).

The first example in bacteria was a pilot study on the genus *Chromobacterium* (Sneath, 1957 *b*). This confirmed that the strains fell into two main groups, as had been suggested by earlier work (Sneath, 1956; Leifson, 1956). These two main groups are the mesophilic *C. violaceum* and the psychrophilic *C. lividum*. The oxidative strains and the pathogenic strains did not form distinct subgroups of mesophils. Serological investigations confirmed these findings (Sneath & Buckland, 1959; Sneath, 1960). The two species had much the same relation to one another as they had to the genera *Serratia* and *Pseudomonas*, but this need not mean that they should be raised to generic rank, since it may be better to reduce some of the present genera to the rank of species, as Cowan (1956) has suggested.

An attempt was made by Sneath & Cowan (1958) to classify a wide range of bacteria on their overall similarity. Existing records were used, although it was recognized that these were not ideal data for this purpose. A diagram of the resulting taxonomic tree is shown in Fig. 6. The bulk of the Gram-positive bacteria (but not *Bacillus* and a few others) formed a phenon of high rank, group 1. This comprised the streptococci, micrococci, staphylococci and also *Erysipelothrix* and *Listeria*. It was somewhat indistinctly divided into subgroups. *Corynebacterium pyogenes*, which has been noted by Cummins & Harris (1956) to be very similar to the streptococci, fell into group 1 and not with *C. diphtheriae*

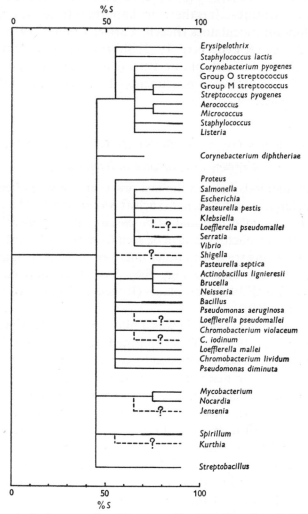

Fig. 6. Taxonomic dendrogram of a wide range of bacteria (from Sneath & Cowan, 1958).

(which formed the small group 3). A chromogenic diphtheroid bacillus was close to *Micrococcus*, which is perhaps not surprising in view of the heterogeneity of the diphtheroid bacilli.

Group 2 was formed mainly of Gram-negative rods. Group 2*a* contained most of the enterobacteria but not *Proteus*, which Stocker (1955) has pointed out on other grounds is not closely related to the typical enterobacteria. The study of Lysenko & Sneath (1959) gives no help here, since this was a methodological study employing a biased sample of features. Besides *Salmonella*, *Klebsiella*, *Escherichia* and *Serratia* this group also contained *Pasteurella pestis* and *Vibrio choleraeasiaticae*. Evidence is now growing for including *P. pestis* in the family Enterobacteriaceae; it shows cross-reactions with coli-dysentery bacteriophages and is similar in many ways to *Shigella* (Flu, 1929; Lazarus & Gunnison, 1947; Stocker, 1955). *Vibrio* is a heterogeneous genus and its affinities are still obscure (see Colwell & Liston, 1961*b*). A subgroup, 2*b*, comprised strains of *Brucella*, *Neisseria*, *Actinobacillus lignieresii* and *Pasteurella septica*, possibly linking with the enterobacteria through *Shigella*. These findings are not surprising, since evidence is accumulating that *Neisseria*, *Actinobacillus*, *Moraxella* and the *Achromobacter-Alcaligenes* group are fairly closely allied (e.g. Henricksen, 1952; Klinge, 1958). Subgroup 2*c* contained *Pseudomonas aeruginosa*; subgroup 2*d* contained strains of *Bacillus*, and subgroup 2*e* contained strains of *Chromobacterium violaceum* and an organism commonly called *Pseudomonas iodinum* (though this latter organism may be grouped here in error). Whitmore's bacillus (*Loefflerella pseudomallei*) gave some trouble: one strain was close to *Pseudomonas* while another was close to *Klebsiella*. Most strains of Whitmore's bacillus seem to belong to the pseudomonads (Brindle & Cowan, 1951; Brygoo, 1957; Bokman, Levine & Lusby, 1957) but the species may be more heterogeneous than is thought. The strain of glanders bacillus was also of somewhat uncertain position in this group. The bacteriophages which lyse Whitmore's bacillus sometimes lyse strains of glanders bacilli, but apparently not typical strains of *Pseudomonas* (Leclerk & Sureau, 1956; Smith & Cherry, 1957). The acid-fast organisms *Nocardia* and *Mycobacterium* formed group 4 together with *Jensenia* (the latter is considered by Gordon & Mihm, 1961, to be a strain of *Mycobacterium rhodochrous*) and represent the actinomycetales. The relations of *Spirillum* (group 5), *Corynebacterium diphtheriae* (group 3) and *Streptobacillus* and *Kurthia* were uncertain as they were not closely similar to any other bacteria studied. The three main groups, the cocci, Gram-negative bacilli and actinomycetales seem to be reasonably natural ones.

Beers *et al.* (1962) compared several scoring methods in several genera. A particularly instructive study has been made by Brisbane & Rovira (1961) on a wide range of soil bacteria (including *Agrobacterium*, *Arthrobacter*, *Nocardia*, *Pseudomonas* and *Rhizobium*). They compared three techniques of classification: division on associated characters, identification with already described forms using Skerman's key (in *Bergey's Manual of Determinative Bacteriology*, 1957, pp. 991–1032), and classification based on overall similarity. They found that Skerman's key was satisfactory for identification in many cases, but in others it resulted in placing together organisms which were clearly very different but which happened to be identical in the small number of features used in the key. This is particularly common, as one would expect, when the genera are poorly known. The attempt to associate characters in the 316 strains was not very satisfactory, possibly because of the very heterogeneous collection of strains they employed, which would tend to swamp significant correlations by poor correlations occurring in different taxa. Brisbane & Rovira used Yule's coefficient of association, Q, which is $ad - bc/ad + bc$ (the letters refer to the symbolism used on p. 305). About a quarter of the associations were significant at the 1 % level, but the values were mostly low. The higher values could be used to divide the strains into groups, some of which were clearly heterogeneous. When a large number of characters was used some improvement resulted, and a few new points emerged, e.g. strains of *Arthrobacter* were usually sensitive to erythromycin and oleandromycin and did not digest casein.

In their trial of the method of overall similarity Brisbane & Rovira included negative matches in their index ('affinity index'), and compared 64 strains for 39 characters. The rhizosphere bacteria formed a spectrum rather than sharp groups. This may be in part due to the rather small number of tests employed. However, some indistinct groups were seen, corresponding to the pseudomonads, to the *Xanthomonas–Agrobacterium–Rhizobium* complex, and to the genus *Arthrobacter*.

Adansonian methods have been applied to actinomycetes by Silvestri and his colleagues (see this Symposium and Gilardi *et al.* 1960; Hill *et al.* 1961). Their results show that the genus *Streptomyces* also forms a spectrum or diffuse 'cloud', in which are some clusters of closely similar strains. Some of these, e.g. the *S. griseus* strains, may perhaps be equated with the rank of species. The position is not unlike that in many genera of fungi, with a large range of variation and somewhat ill-defined 'series' or 'species-groups'. It is not surprising that a few strains labelled *Nocardia* were found in the clusters. This work will give impetus to the current trend to reduce drastically the number of named species of *Streptomyces*, a much needed step in their taxonomy.

Studies on *Mycobacterium* (Bojalil & Cerbón, 1961; Cerbón & Bojalil, 1961) although based on rather few characters, have been in good agreement with recent revisions of the genus, e.g. by Gordon & Smith (1953, 1955) and Gordon & Mihm (1959) and with the serological studies of Parlett & Youmans (1958) and Lind (1960). In addition some new taxonomic groups have been recognized by these studies. Strains of *Mycobacterium fortuitum, M. smegmatis* and *M. phlei* were arranged in three groups as expected, the last two being more closely related to each other than either was to *M. fortuitum.*

The micrococci have been studied by Hill (1959) and by Pohja (1960). Their findings have been in good agreement, and have fitted well with most of the scheme of Shaw, Stitt & Cowan (1951). Hill interpreted his results as follows: among the five species named by Shaw *et al., Staphylococcus aureus, S. saprophyticus* (the group commonly referred to as *S. epidermidis* or the coagulase-negative *S. albus* group) and *S. roseus* (the common pink micrococci) were natural taxonomic groups, while the groups named *S. lactis* and *S. afermentans* were not, since individual strains of the latter two groups varied a good deal. Gregory & Mabbitt (1957) also found *S. lactis* to be heterogeneous. Hill noted that these two groups were largely defined on negative criteria. He found that *S. aureus* and *S. saprophyticus* together formed a group which might be conveniently regarded as the genus *Staphylococcus*, while the other three species could be regarded as the genus *Micrococcus*. Pohja confirmed most of Hill's findings, and in addition he was able to subdivide the *S. lactis* group into several subgroups, the main ones being a halotolerant subgroup and a non-halotolerant subgroup; several other subdivisions were made, but they were based on arbitrary criteria in the main.

Blondeau (1961) has recently studied the group D streptococci using data of Morélis & Colobert (1958). He analysed 173 strains scored for 38 features. A number of authors have suggested that the name *Streptococcus faecalis* should be restricted to strains which are resistant to 1/2500 potassium tellurite, ferment sorbitol, and vigorously reduce tetrazolium (Barnes, 1956), while the others should be named *S. faecium.* Blondeau found that the strains of *S. faecalis sensu strictu* formed a homogeneous group, group A, containing all the typical strains, and showing a subgroup, A2, which corresponded with the variety *liquefaciens*. The haemolytic variety *zymogenes* was not a valid one since haemolytic strains were scattered throughout the collection. *S. faecium* (group B), on the other hand, was much more heterogeneous. The more typical strains formed subgroup B1. Subgroup B2 corresponded to *S. durans*. Many forms intermediate between *S. faecium* and *S. faecalis* were also in group B. A small unnamed subgroup, B3, was noted.

These techniques have been applied by Cheeseman & Berridge (1959) to *Lactobacillus*, but they restricted the characters to the amino acids and peptides extracted from the cells by dilute acetic acid. In this instance the results were not so satisfactory, since a collection of heterofermentative lactobacilli showed little differentiation into clear-cut groups. A few tight clusters were seen, but the general picture was of a 'cloud' of cultures. This is at variance with the recent revision of the systematics of lactobacilli by Rogosa & Sharpe (1959), although these authors comment that the heterofermentative species are not very clear-cut, and the serology shows some puzzling overlapping with homofermentative strains (Sharpe, 1955; Sharpe & Wheater, 1957).

A study of strains of *Pasteurella septica* showed that they formed a reasonably homogeneous group (Talbot & Sneath, 1960). As expected there was a considerable difference between *P. septica* and *P. pestis* (see above). *P. pestis* and *P. pseudotuberculosis* were very similar, as recent work has shown (e.g. Crumpton & Davies, 1957; Meyer, 1959; Lawton, Fukui & Surgalla, 1960). The relation of *P. pestis* to *Escherichia* and *Shigella* was not as close as that found by Sneath & Cowan (1958); so far this is unexplained. Strains of *P. septica* isolated from cats were particularly homogeneous, while strains from dogs were more variable. Human infections (other than those due to bites) were usually due to strains which had probably originated in cats.

The pseudomonads have now been studied by several authors. Colwell & Liston (1961 *a*, *c*) examined strains of *Pseudomonas* and *Xanthomonas* and found that these formed separate groups. A third group was formed by strains of *P. solanacearum*, which was related to the fluorescent pseudomonads, as was one subgroup of *Xanthomonas*. Other studies (Liston, 1960; Liston & Colwell, 1960; Colwell & Liston, 1961 *b*) showed satisfactory separation of strains of a number of genera, including *Pseudomonas*, *Bacillus*, *Micrococcus* and *Escherichia*. The pseudomonads were studied in more detail and four groups were found, a marine psychrophilic group not acidifying glucose, an intermediate group (including *P. fragi* and *Vibrio percolans*), a fluorescent pigmented group (including *P. aeruginosa* and *P. fluorescens*, and divisible into three subgroups) and a non-pigmented mesophilic group including *P. denitrificans*. The vibrios were clearly very heterogeneous. *Aeromonas* was close to the fermentative vibrios and, more distantly, was related to the enterobacteria. Shewan, Hobbs & Hodgkiss (1960) report a study of *Pseudomonas* by Floodgate in which three main groups were found, apparently substantially the same as the first three of Colwell & Liston (1961 *b*), though the numbering of the groups is different. Thornley (1960) has compared *Pseudomonas* with *Achromobacter* and found several groups within the latter genus.

Rhodes (1961) has examined an extensive series of fluorescent pseudomonads using 45 characters, and has confirmed her earlier findings (Rhodes, 1959) that no sharp groups can be seen within the series. Good discrimination of *Pseudomonas* and *Aeromonas* strains was found. Lysenko (1961) has also used overall similarity in studying the pseudomonads, and has employed species descriptions for this: his findings are again in general agreement with those of the authors mentioned above as far as the relations of the main groups go.

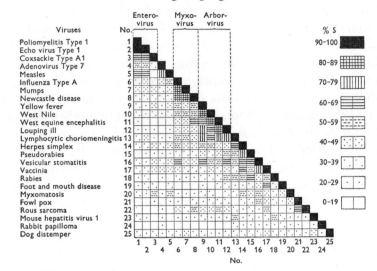

Fig. 7. Shaded similarity matrix of twenty-five animal viruses.

Application to viruses

Classification by overall similarity has also been applied to animal viruses by Andrewes & Sneath (1958). The detailed results were not published there, but a shaded similarity table of their results is shown in Fig. 7. This is based on an inadequate number of characters, some of them of dubious reliability for taxonomic work, so one cannot therefore place very much reliance on the results. The coefficient used was S_J. The figure does however show that three groups which have been intuitively recognized as phenetic are present, the enteroviruses, the myxoviruses and the arboviruses, and this suggests that the method has promise in such a difficult field as virus taxonomy. The work also brought home a second point: that we have very poor comparative data on viruses, for the original table had a large number of gaps where the properties of the viruses were unknown. The relations of measles, lymphocytic choriomeningitis, distemper and foot-and-mouth disease are particularly uncertain, and the pox viruses seem to be badly grouped.

Application to published data: the genus Bacillus

It should be possible to employ existing taxonomic data in studies of this kind. With higher organisms this is usually unobjectionable, for good drawings and exact descriptions are often available. With micro-organisms, however, the pronounced influence of cultural conditions on the expression of characters makes it essential to standardize the tests with care and preferably one should make a deliberate comparative study of all the strains. Nevertheless it should be possible to use published data from standardized tests, and in the following paragraphs a study of this kind is reported, based on the outstanding monograph by Smith, Gordon & Clark (1952) on the genus *Bacillus*. Their data have been supplemented with data on additional species and on nutrition, spore morphology, etc., from the work of Knight & Proom (1950), Proom & Knight (1955), Burdon (1956), Bradley & Franklin (1958), Steel (1961) and Smith & Gordon in *Bergey's Manual* (1957, pp. 613–34). Some species and varieties of doubtful standing were included as if they were full species for comparative purposes. The coded features (character states) totalled 105 after deleting those which were positive or negative throughout. Each species was represented by what seemed to be the most typical reactions if these varied within the species. The similarity index used was S_J, and the S matrix is shown in Fig. 8 after the cluster analysis, which was adapted from the unweighted variable group method of Sokal & Michener (1958), and which employs mean inter-group S values as the criterion for fusion of groups. It has been described in detail in the section on *Cluster analysis*. The resulting hierarchic dendrogram is shown in Fig. 9. It can be seen that there are two main groups.

The first group comprises the better known species of *Bacillus* which belong to the morphological groups 1 and 2 of Smith *et al.* It is divided at the 60 % S level into four subgroups, the *B. cereus* cluster, the *B. subtilis* cluster, the *B. polymyxa* cluster and the *B. alvei* cluster and two single species, *B. stearothermophilus* and *B. pulvefaciens*.

The second main group, containing mainly species of morphological group 3, comprises the *B. sphaericus* cluster, the *B. firmus–B. lentus* cluster and the *B. larvae–B. pasteurii* cluster together with *B. panto-thenticus* and possibly *B. badius* (though the available data on this is scanty, and its affinities are uncertain).

These relations are in reasonable agreement with the taxonomic scheme and figures of Smith *et al.* They differ considerably from the phylogenetic relations postulated by Johnson (1960), and this empha-

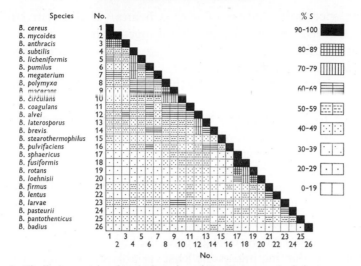

Fig. 8. Similarity matrix of typical strains of *Bacillus* spp., shaded to represent the degree of overall similarity.

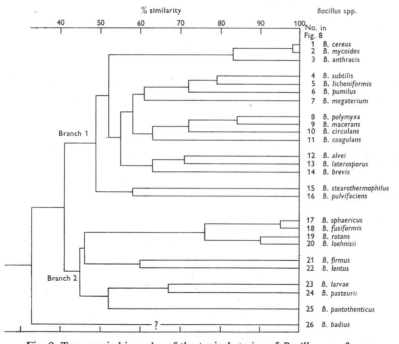

Fig. 9. Taxonomic hierarchy of the typical strains of *Bacillus* spp. from the data in Fig. 8.

sizes the speculative nature of such schemes. If different strains of *Bacillus subtilis*, for example, are placed together in one species on their phenetic affinities, as they undoubtedly are, why are not different species also arranged on the same principle?

One species may be misplaced by the cluster analysis. This is *B. larvae*, which had closest affinity to *B. pasteurii*, *B. macerans* and *B. circulans*, but owing to its low affinity to *B. polymyxa* it is rejected from the *B. polymyxa*–*B. macerans*–*B. circulans* cluster, and is grouped with *B. pasteurii*, though it may be somewhat nearer the first group judging by its other affinities.

In addition to the 'typical' exemplars of the species some exemplars were added which were given the most aberrant scores recorded for that species. Strains as aberrant as this would probably never be found in nature, but they served as some guide to the known variation. The results were not very illuminating, as the least variable species were usually the least well known, as might be expected. *B. cereus*, *B. megaterium*, *B. circulans*, *B. brevis* and *B. subtilis* were most variable, with S values of 50–60 % for the comparison between their 'typical' and 'atypical' strains.

The differential characters obtained from the study by finding high G values as described in an earlier section are shown in Table 3. It is seen that unlike most arbitrary classifications it is difficult to find any feature which unequivocally separates branch 1 species from branch 2 species, although the overall similarity between the branches is much smaller than that of species within the branches. This illustrates a limitation of Adansonian methods. However, if we wish to employ natural taxa for constructing taxonomies we must be prepared to accept the attendant disadvantages. One of these is the difficulty of finding distinctive characters of the taxa, with the consequent difficulty of making diagnostic keys.

DISCUSSION

The pattern emerging from numerical taxonomic studies in bacteria is fairly uniform, and very similar to that in many fungi, where there are many slightly different forms grouped into rather ill-defined 'series' or 'species-groups'. This pattern is common in groups which are largely asexual (e.g. dandelions and blackberries), and may be likened to an ill-made brush, in which the clones are represented by the bristles, and the bristles are clustered erratically into various tufts. The pattern in sexual species is more like a bundle of ropes, where each rope represents a single and well defined sexual species within which the fibres represent the

Table 3. Differential characters for groups of species of Bacillus

The table shows the percentage of species in each group that are typically positive for the characters given. Values in parentheses indicate that it is common to find strains aberrant in the character or that information is scanty, so that less reliance can be placed on it as a differential character. A blank space indicates insufficient data. The groups are specified by the name of the first species and the reference numbers of species in Fig. 9. B. badius is marked + or −. Characters with an asterisk are those most useful for distinguishing branch 1 from branch 2, having G values of ±0·50 or more on comparing the species of the two branches.

Characters	Branch 1					Branch 2			Irregular branch
	B. cereus group 1, 2, 3	B. subtilis group 4, 5, 6, 7	B. polymyxa group 8, 9, 10, 11	B. alvei group 12, 13, 14	B. stearothermophilus group 15, 16	B. sphaericus group 17, 18, 19, 20	B. firmus group 21, 22	B. larvae group 23, 24, 25	B. badius 26
Strongly Gram-positive	100	100	(25)	0	50	(0)	100	33	+
Abundant intracellular 'fat'	(100)	25	0	(67)	0	0	0	0	−
Cells over 3·5 μ in mean length	100	(0)	(50)	0	0	0	0	0	−
Cells over 1·0 μ in mean breadth	100	(25)	0	67	50	0	0	33	−
Spores over 1·5 μ in length*	100	25	(75)	67	(0)	0	0	(33)	+
Spores over 1·0 μ in breadth*	0	25	(75)	67	(50)	0	0	67	+
Spores terminal*	0	0	75	(0)	(50)	100	(0)	(100)	+
Spores ribbed (electron microscopy)*	(75)	(75)	(100)	100	50	0	(50)	(0)	−
Colonies fimbriate	(100)	25	50	(33)	(0)	0	0	(0)	+
Colonies opaque	100	(75)	(75)	(0)	0	(100)	100	0	−
Colonies spreading	0	0	25	(100)	0	(100)	(0)	0	
Colonies rotating	0	0	100	33	100	100	0	33	
Visible growth on nutrient agar	100	100	100	33	(0)	50	100	33	
Heavy growth on nutrient agar	100	100	(25)	0	100	50	0	(33)	
Growth at pH 6·0*	100	100	100	100	100	0	0	0	
Growth on potato*	100	100	(75)	100	100	0	0	7	
Growth anaerobically	100	25	100	67	100	0	0	(67)	
Growth at 45°	(0)	(75)	75	(33)	(50)	0	(100)	(67)	
Acid from glucose	100	100	100	100	50	0	0	(33)	
Acid from L-arabinose	0	100	(100)	(0)	(0)	0	0	(33)	
Acid from D-xylose	0	100	(100)	(0)	50	0	0	(33)	
Hydrolysis of starch	100	75	100	33	(0)	0	100	0	
Utilization of citrate	(100)	(100)	(0)	(33)	(0)	0	0	(0)	
Voges-Proskauer	100	75	50	33	(50)	0	0	(33)	
Hydrolysis of casein	100	100	(25)	100	(50)	(50)	50	0	
Oxidase (Kovacs)	(0)	(0)	0	(67)	(0)	(100)	(50)	(33)	−
Require amino acids for growth	100	0	(50)	100	(50)	(100)	(50)	100	−
Require aneurin for growth	33	0	(75)	(67)	(0)	(100)	(100)	100	−
Require biotin for growth	0	0	100	(33)	(50)	(100)	100	57	+

interwoven lineages. The two patterns must depend on the different genetic patterns: clonal reproduction will produce many minor variants, most of which die out, but a few persist and undergo rare sexual recombination with other clones, leading to new bursts of variation. Within any 'tuft' the organisms will form a diffuse spectrum and adjacent tufts will be often connected by intermediates. The smallest practicable unit of taxonomic nomenclature will be the tuft, or perhaps the whole brush, although for certain special purposes it may be useful to label the bristles (such as serotypes or phage types in *Salmonella*). This suggests that the taxonomy of micro-organisms will undergo considerable simplification in the future.

Correlation of numerical taxonomy and other criteria of taxonomic relationship

Numerical taxonomies are in good agreement with modern systematic arrangements, as is seen from the last section. We know less about their agreement with genetic and serological features. The conceptual basis of numerical taxonomy may have its representation in the genome in the form of deoxyribonucleic acid (though cytogenes may be a partial exception) and it is easy to see how we could in theory compare the nucleotide code in two organisms, and relate this to their phenotypes. We expect that there would be in general good correspondence between genotype and phenotype if many genes were studied. Numerical taxonomy may indeed be superseded by more direct estimates of genetic similarity, though it will be indispensable in explaining that similarity. The work of Doty, Marmur, Eigner & Schildkraut (1960) points the way to this. They have estimated the degree to which single-strand DNA from two organisms will form hybrid double-strand DNA, which depends on the degree to which the two forms of DNA are homologous (itself dependent on the base composition, see Lee, Wahl & Barbu, 1956).

Hybridization by transformation, transduction or recombination must also be dependent on high similarity between the parental genomes, and is increasingly difficult with increasing taxonomic dissimilarity of the parents (Schaeffer, 1958). Recent work reviewed by Jacob, Schaeffer & Wollman (1960) suggests that there is no formal distinction between bacterial genes and bacteriophage genes, and it has been suggested (Sneath, 1962) that bacteriophages (like sex- and colicinogenic-factors) are a primitive form of sexual mechanism. Growth of bacteriophage therefore may amount to another criteria of genetic homology. Unfortunately negative results in these genetic tests have no clear significance, since they can be caused by lack of suitable surface receptors, etc., and they can scarcely form absolute criteria for ranks such as genus and species. However, these tests, and also serological tests, are presumably in effect estimating the overall similarity of the fine structure of parts of the genome, and if these parts are sufficiently numerous and varied the results should correspond closely to those obtained by numerical taxonomy. Serological tests are particularly prone to interference by cell surface factors and a single antigen commonly dominates the reactions. Gel precipitin techniques (reviewed by Ouchterlony, 1958) may be an improvement on the older methods. Serological factors can be included as characters in numerical taxonomies, but we have at present no way of knowing what weight to place on quantitative measures of serological similarity.

Advantages of numerical taxonomy

Numerical taxonomy has the advantages of yielding stable, precise taxonomies based on objective criteria. Such taxonomies are unlikely to need radical revision, since, being polythetic, they are not liable to the catastrophic effects of finding that a character of presumed crucial importance is after all useless. We expect also, on the matches asymptote hypothesis, that additional data will agree well with the previous data. The introduction of quantitative methods will, as in every science, advance taxonomy, and the wide availability of electronic computers makes numerical taxonomy perfectly feasible. There is at present no alternative: we cannot classify or identify micro-organisms at a glance as we can often do with higher organisms where complex morphological features can be assessed intuitively (which is impossible with long tables of biochemical data). If we rely on a few arbitrarily chosen features, we cannot obtain 'natural' taxonomies.

Where there is a fossil record, numerical taxonomy can measure evolution rates. The rates in micro-organisms may be fast enough to measure experimentally by comparing old material (freeze-dried, perhaps) with modern material, or using artificial selection. Numerical taxonomy may also assist in groups like yeasts or fungi imperfecti, where it is difficult to relate an asexual form to the perfect sexual form. The two forms should show very high overall similarity.

Adansonian taxonomy is proving of interest in the field of medical diagnosis for classifying disease syndromes (Doll, Hayhoe & Whitfield, personal communication), and similar methods are already used in fields such as ecology (Williams & Lambert, 1959) and philology (Ross, 1950).

Numerical taxonomy is both feasible and necessary. It is feasible because we may look forward to a time when data is abundant and methods of analysis will be fully automated to yield the desired taxonomic end-result. It is necessary because only in this way will we obtain the natural taxonomies that we desire.

ACKNOWLEDGEMENTS

The assistance of my colleague, Dr R. R. Sokal, is gratefully acknowledged. I am also greatly indebted for facilities in programming and computing and details of programmes to: Mr R. G. Mills (Elliott Bros., Boreham Wood, 402 computor), Mr H. Whitfield (London University 'Mercury' Computor), Mr J. Gower (401 computor, Rothamsted Experimental Station, Harpenden), Dr T. T. Tanimoto (International Business Machine Corp., New York, 704 Taxonomy Application), Dr J. Liston (College of Fisheries, University of Washington, Seattle, U.S.A., IBM 650 computor), Dr W. R. Lockhart (Iowa State University, Ames, Iowa, U.S.A., 'Cyclone' computor).

REFERENCES

ADANSON, M. (1757). *Histoire naturelle du Sénégal. Coquillages. Avec la relation abregée d'un voyage fait en ce pays, pendant les années* 1749, 50, 51, 52 *et* 53. Coquillages, Préface pp. xi, xx, xxix–lxxxviii. Paris: Bauche.

ADANSON, M. (1763). *Familles des Plantes*, Vol. I, Préface, pp. cliv *et seq.*, clxiii, clxiv. Paris: Vincent. 2 vols.

AINSWORTH, G. C. (1941). A method for characterizing smut fungi exemplified by some British species. *Trans. Brit. mycol. Soc.* 25, 141.

ANDREWES, C. H. & SNEATH, P. H. A. (1958). The species concept among viruses. *Nature, Lond.* 182, 12.

BARNES, E. M. (1956). Tetrazolium reduction as a means of differentiating *Streptococcus faecalis* from *Streptococcus faecium. J. gen. Microbiol.* 14, 57.

BATHER, F. A. (1927). Biological classification: past and future. *Quart. J. geol. Soc. Lond.* 83, Proc. lxii.

BECKNER, M. (1959). *The Biological Way of Thought.* New York: Columbia University Press.

BEECH, F. W., CARR, J. G. & CODNER, R. C. (1955). A multipoint inoculator for plating bacteria or yeasts. *J. gen. Microbiol.* 13, 408.

BEERS, R. J. & LOCKHART, W. R. (1962). Experimental methods in computor taxonomy. *J. gen. Microbiol.* (in the Press).

BEERS, R. J., FISHER, J., MEGRAW, S. & LOCKHART, W. R. (1962). A comparison of methods for computor taxonomy. *J. gen. Microbiol.* (in the Press).

Bergey's Manual of Determinative Bacteriology (1923), 1st edition. Baltimore: Williams and Wilkins. (1948), 6th edition. (1957), 7th edition. London: Baillière, Tindall and Cox.

BERGONZINI, C. (1879). I bacteri. *Annuario della Società dei Naturalisti in Modena,* ser. 2, Anno 13, 19.

BISSET, K. A. (1950). Evolution in bacteria and the significance of the bacterial spore. *Nature, Lond.* 166, 431.

BISSET, K. A. (1952). *Bacteria.* Edinburgh: Livingstone.

BISSET, K. A. (1957). Multicellularity in bacteria. *Ergebn. Mikrobiol. (Ergebn. Hyg. Bakt.),* 30, 1.

BLONDEAU, H. (1961). *Utilisation des ordinateurs électroniques pour l'étude de l'homogénéité de l'espèce* Streptococcus faecalis. *Application à la détermination de l'origine de la contamination des semi-conserves de viande.* Lyon: Maurice Fabre.

BOJALIL, L. F. & CERBÓN, J. (1961). Taxonomic analysis of non-pigmented, rapidly growing mycobacteria. *J. Bact.* **81**, 338.

BOKMAN, A. H., LEVINE, H. B. & LUSBY, M. (1957). Glucose catabolism in *Malleomyces pseudomallei. J. Bact.* **73**, 649.

BRADLEY, D. E. & FRANKLIN, J. G. (1958). Electron microscope survey of the surface configuration of spores of the genus *Bacillus. J. Bact.* **76**, 618.

BRINDLE, C. S. & COWAN, S. T. (1951). Flagellation and taxonomy of Whitmore's bacillus. *J. Path. Bact.* **63**, 571.

BRISBANE, P. G. & ROVIRA, A. D. (1961). A comparison of methods for classifying rhizosphere bacteria. *J. gen. Microbiol.* **26**, 379.

BRYGOO, E. R. (1957). Étude sur le position du bacille de Whitmore dans la systematique. *Ann. Inst. Pasteur,* **92**, 689.

BULLOCH, W. (1938). *The History of Bacteriology.* London: Oxford University Press.

BURDON, K. L. (1956). Useful criteria for the identification of *Bacillus anthracis* and related species. *J. Bact.* **71**, 25.

CAIN, A. J. (1958). Logic and memory in Linnaeus's system of taxonomy. *Proc. Linn. Soc. Lond.* **169**, 114.

CAIN, A. J. (1959a). Deductive and inductive methods in post-Linnaean taxonomy. *Proc. Linn. Soc. Lond.* **170**, 185.

CAIN, A. J. (1959b). Taxonomic concepts. *Ibis,* **101**, 302.

CAIN, A. J. & HARRISON, G. A. (1958). An analysis of the taxonomist's judgment of affinity. *Proc. Zool. Soc. Lond.* **131**, 85.

CAIN, A. J. & HARRISON, G. A. (1960). Phyletic weighting. *Proc. zool. Soc. Lond.* **135**, 1.

CAMP, W. H. & GILLY, C. L. (1943). The structure and origin of species. *Brittonia, N.Y.* **4**, 323.

CERBÓN, J. & BOJALIL, L. F. (1961). Physiological relationships of rapidly growing mycobacteria. Adansonian classification. *J. gen. Microbiol.* **25**, 7.

CHEESEMAN, G. C. & BERRIDGE, N. J. (1959). The differentiation of bacterial species by paper chromatography. VII. The use of electronic computation for the objective assessment of chromatographic results. *J. appl. Bact.* **22**, 307.

CIFERRI, R. (1959). Systematic vs. classificatory taxonomy and speciology of the Actinomycetales. *Int. Bull. bact. Nomen. Tax.* **9**, 89.

COHN, H. J. (1872). Untersuchungen über Bacterien. I. *Beitr. Biol. Pfl.* **1** (Heft 2), 127.

COLWELL, R. R. & LISTON, J. (1961a). An electronic computer analysis of some *Xanthomonas* and *Pseudomonas* species. *Bact. Proc.* p. 72.

COLWELL, R. R. & LISTON, J. (1961b). Taxonomic relationships among the pseudomonads. *J. Bact.* **82**, 1.

COLWELL, R. R. & LISTON, J. (1961c). Taxonomy of *Xanthomonas* and *Pseudomonas. Nature, Lond.* **191**, 617.

COWAN, S. T. (1955). Introduction: the philosophy of classification. *J. gen. Microbiol.* **12**, 314.

COWAN, S. T. (1956). 'Ordnung in das Chaos' Migula. *Canad. J. Microbiol.* **2**, 212.

COWAN, S. T. (1959). Bacterial classification—problems and developments, in *Microbiology, Yesterday and Today,* edited by V. Bryson, pp. 54–79. New Brunswick, N.J.: Institute of Microbiology, Rutgers University.

COWAN, S. T. & STEEL, K. J. (1960). A device for the identification of microorganisms. *Lancet,* i, 1172.

COWAN, S. T. & STEEL, K. J. (1961). Diagnostic tables for the common medical bacteria. *J. Hyg., Camb.* **59**, 357.

COWAN, S. T., STEEL, K. J., SHAW, C. & DUGUID, J. P. (1960). A classification of the Klebsiella group. *J. gen. Microbiol.* **23**, 601.

CRUMPTON, M. J. & DAVIES, D. A. L. (1957). A protein antigen associated with smooth colony forms of some species of *Pasteurella*. *Nature, Lond.* **180**, 863.

CUMMINS, C. S. & HARRIS, H. (1956). The chemical composition of the cell-wall in some Gram-positive bacteria and its possible value as a taxonomic character. *J. gen. Microbiol.* **14**, 583.

CUMMINS, C. S. & HARRIS, H. (1958). Studies on the cell-wall composition and taxonomy of Actinomycetales and related groups. *J. gen. Microbiol.* **18**, 173.

DACRE, J. C. & SHARPE, M. E. (1956). Catalase production by lactobacilli. *Nature, Lond.* **178**, 700.

DIBLE, H. J. (1921). The enterococcus and the faecal streptococci: their properties and relations. *J. Path. Bact.* **24**, 3.

DOTY, P., MARMUR, J., EIGNER, J. & SCHILDKRAUT, C. (1960). Strand separation and specific recombination in deoxyribonucleic acids: physical chemical studies. *Proc. nat. Acad. Sci., Wash.* **46**, 461.

FLOODGATE, G. D. (1962). Some remarks on the theoretical aspects of bacterial taxonomy. *Bact. Rev.*

FLU, P. C. (1929). Die Natur des Bakteriophagen. *Zbl. Bakt.* (1 *Abt. Orig.*), **113**, 284.

GILARDI, E., HILL, L. R., TURRI, M. & SILVESTRI, L. G. (1960). Quantitative methods in the systematics of actinomycetales. I. *G. Microbiol.* **8**, 203.

GILMOUR, J. S. L. (1937). A taxonomic problem. *Nature, Lond.* **139**, 1040.

GILMOUR, J. S. L. (1940). Taxonomy and philosophy. In *The New Systematics*, edited by J. Huxley, pp. 461–74. Oxford: Clarendon Press.

GILMOUR, J. S. L. (1951). The development of taxonomic theory since 1851. *Nature, Lond.* **168**, 400.

GORDON, R. E. & MIHM, J. M. (1959). A comparison of four species of mycobacteria. *J. gen. Microbiol.* **21**, 736.

GORDON, R. E. & MIHM, J. M. (1961). The specific identity of *Jensenia canicruria*. *Canad. J. Microbiol.* **7**, 108.

GORDON, R. E. & SMITH, M. M. (1953). Rapidly growing, acid fact bacteria. I. Species' descriptions of *Mycobacterium phlei* Lehmann and Neumann and *Mycobacterium smegmatis* (Trevisan) Lehmann and Neumann. *J. Bact.* **66**, 41.

GORDON, R. E. & SMITH, M. M. (1955). Rapidly growing, acid fast bacteria. II. Species' description of *Mycobacterium fortuitum* Cruz. *J. Bact.* **69**, 502.

GREGORY, M. & MABBITT, L. A. (1957). The differentiation of bacterial species by paper chromatography. V. Preliminary examination of the micrococci. *J. appl. Bact.* **20**, 226.

HALTENORTH, T. (1937). Die verwandtschaftliche Stellung der Grosskatzen zueinander VII. *Z. Säugetierk.* **12**, 97.

HARRISON, A. P. & HANSEN, P. A. (1950). A motile lactobacillus from the caecal feces of turkeys. *J. Bact.* **59**, 444.

HEATHER, C. D. (1958). The use of a card-sorting system in the identification of bacteria. *Texas Rep. Biol. Med.* **16**, 424.

HENRICKSEN, S. D. (1952). *Moraxella*: classification and taxonomy. *J. gen. Microbiol.* **6**, 318.

HILL, L. R. (1959). The Adansonian classification of staphylococci. *J. gen. Microbiol.* **20**, 277.

HILL, L. R., TURRI, M., GILARDI, E. & SILVESTRI, L. G. (1961). Quantitative methods in the systematics of actinomycetales. II. *G. Microbiol.* **9**, 56.

JACOB, F., SCHAEFFER, P. & WOLLMAN, E. L. (1960). Episomic elements in bacteria. *Symp. Soc. gen. Microbiol.* **10**, 67.

JACQUARD, P. (1908). Nouvelles recherches sur la distribution florale. *Bull. Soc. vaud. Sci. nat.* **44**, 223.

JOHNSON, R. M. (1960). Proposed phylogeny in the family Bacillaceae. *Int. Bull. bact. Nomen. Tax.* **10**, 205.

KTINGER, K. (1958). Zur Systematik grammegativer, pleomorphe, Kohlehydrate nicht spaltender und Oxydase-negativer Diplobakterien. *Arch. Hyg., Berl.* **142**, 171.

KLUYVER, A. J. & VAN NIEL, C. B. (1936). Prospects for a natural system of classification of bacteria. *Zbl. Bakt.* (2 *Abt.*), **94**, 369.

KNIGHT, B. C. J. G. & PROOM, H. (1950). A comparative survey of the nutrition and physiology of mesophilic species in the genus *Bacillus*. *J. gen. Microbiol.* **4**, 508.

LAWTON, W. D., FUKUI, G. M. & SURGALLA, M. J. (1960). Studies on the antigens of *Pasteurella pestis* and *Pasteurella pseudotuberculosis*. *J. Immunol.* **84**, 475.

LAZARUS, A. S. & GUNNISON, J. B. (1947). The action of *Pasteurella pestis* bacteriophage on strains of *Pasteurella*, *Salmonella* and *Shigella*. *J. Bact.* **53**, 705.

LECLERC, H. & SUREAU, P. (1956). Recherche des bactériophages anti-bacille de Whitmore dans les eaux stagnantes a Hanoï. *Bull. Soc. Pat. exot.* **49**, 874.

LEDERBERG, J. & LEDERBERG, E. M. (1952). Replica plating and indirect selection of bacterial mutants. *J. Bact.* **63**, 399.

LEE, K. Y., WAHL, R. & BARBU, E. (1956). Contenu en bases puriques et pyrimidiques des acides désoxyribonucléiques des bactéries. *Ann. Inst. Pasteur*, **91**, 212.

LEIFSON, E. (1956). Morphological and physiological characteristics of the genus *Chromobacterium*. *J. Bact.* **71**, 393.

LEVINE, M. (1918). A statistical classification of the colon-cloacae group. *J. Bact.* **3**, 253.

LIND, A. (1960). Serological studies of mycobacteria by means of diffusion-in-gel techniques. IV. The precipitinogenic relationships between different species of mycobacteria with special reference to *M. tuberculosis*, *M. phlei*, *M. smegmatis* and *M. avium*. *Int. Arch. Allergy, Basel*, **17**, 300.

LISTON, J. (1960). Some results of a computer analysis of strains of *Pseudomonas* and *Achromobacter*, and other organisms. *J. appl. Bact.* **23**, 391.

LISTON, J. & COLWELL, R. R. (1960). Taxonomic relationships among the pseudomonads. *Bact. Proc.*, p. 78.

LYSENKO, O. (1961). *Pseudomonas*—an attempt at a general classification. *J. gen. Microbiol.* **25**, 379.

LYSENKO, O. & SNEATH, P. H. A. (1959). The use of models in bacterial classification. *J. gen. Microbiol.* **20**, 284.

MACCACARO, G. A. (1958). La misura delle informazione contenuta nei criteri di classificazione. *Ann. Microbiol. Enzimol.* **8**, 231.

MATTICK, A. T. R., CHEESEMAN, G. C., BERRIDGE, N. J. & BOTTAZZI, V. (1956). The differentiation of species of lactobacilli and streptococci by means of paper partition chromatography. *J. appl. Bact.* **19**, 310.

METCALFE, Z. P. (1954). The construction of keys. *System. Zool.* **3**, 38.

MEYER, K. F. (1959). In *Bacterial and Mycotic Infections of Man*, 3rd edition, p. 400. Edited by R. J. Dubos. Philadelphia: Lippincott.

MICHENER, C. D. & SOKAL, R. R. (1957). A quantitative approach to a problem in classification. *Evolution*, **11**, 130.

MORÉLIS, P. & COLOBERT, L. (1958). Un milieu sélectif permettant l'identification et le dénombrement rapides de *Streptococcus faecalis*. *Ann. Inst. Pasteur*, **95**, 568, 667.

MORISHIMA, H. & OKA, H.-I. (1960). The pattern of interspecific variation in the genus *Oryza*: its quantitative representation by statistical methods. *Evolution*, **14**, 153.

NIEL, C. B. VAN (1946). The classification and natural relationship of bacteria. *Cold Spr. Harb. Symp. quant. Biol.* **11**, 285.

NIEL, C. B. VAN (1955). Classification and taxonomy of the bacteria and blue green algae. In *A Century of Progress in Natural Science—1853–1953*. San Francisco: California Academy of Sciences.

NORRIS, K. P. (1959). Infra-red spectroscopy and its application to microbiology. *J. Hyg., Camb.* **57**, 326.

ORLA-JENSEN, S. (1909). Die Hauptlinien des natürlichen Bakteriensystems. *Zbl. Bakt.* (2. Abt.), **22**, 305.

OUCHTERLONY, Ö. (1958). Diffusion-in-gel methods for immunological analysis. In *Progress in allergy*, vol. **5**, pp. 1–78. Edited by P. Kallós. Basle and New York: Karger.

PARLETT, R. C. & YOUMANS, G. P. (1958). Antigenic relationships between ninety eight strains of mycobacteria using gel-diffusion precipitation techniques. *Amer. Rev. Tuberc.* **77**, 450.

PIA, J. (1928). Die vorzeitlichen Spaltpilze und ihre Lebensspuren. *Palaeobiologica*, **1**, 457.

PIRIE, N. W. (1955). Summing-up. *J. gen. Microbiol.* **12**, 382.

POHJA, M. S. (1960). Micrococci in fermented meat products. Classification and description of 171 different strains. *Suom. Maataloust. Seur. Julk.* no. 96, pp. 1–80.

PRÉVOT, A. R. (1933). Études de systematiques bacteriennes. I. Lois générales. II. Cocci anaerobies. *Ann. Sci. nat.* (10 ser, Bot.), **15**, 23.

PROOM, H. & KNIGHT, B. C. J. G. (1955). The minimal nutritional requirements of some species in the genus *Bacillus*. *J. gen. Microbiol.* **13**, 474.

PROOM, H. & WOIWOD, A. J. (1949). The examination by partition paper chromatography of the nitrogen metabolism of bacteria. *J. gen. Microbiol.* **3**, 319.

RHODES, M. E. (1959). The characterization of *Pseudomonas fluorescens*. *J. gen. Microbiol.* **21**, 221.

RHODES, M. E. (1961). The characterization of *Pseudomonas fluorescens* with the aid of an electronic computer. *J. gen. Microbiol.* **25**, 331.

ROGERS, D. J. & TANIMOTO, T. T. (1960). A computer programme for classifying plants. *Science*, **132**, 1115.

ROGERS, L. A., CLARK, W. M. & DAVIS, B. J. (1914). The colon group of bacteria. *J. infect. Dis.* **14**, 411.

ROGOSA, M. & SHARPE, M. E. (1959). An approach to the classification of the lactobacilli. *J. appl. Bact.* **22**, 329.

ROHLFE, F. J. & SOKAL, R. R. (1961). The description of taxonomic relationships by factor analysis. *System. Zool.* (in the Press).

ROSS, A. S. C. (1950). Philological probability problems. *J. R. statist. Soc.* B, **12**, 19.

SCHAEFFER, P. (1958). Interspecific reactions in bacterial transformation. *Symp. Soc. exp. Biol.* **12**, 60.

SCHOPF, J. M. (1960). Emphasis on holotype? *Science*, **131**, 1043.

SHARPE, M. E. (1955). A serological classification of lactobacilli. *J. gen. Microbiol.* **12**, 107.

SHARPE, M. E. & WHEATER, D. M. (1957). *Lactobacillus helveticus*. *J. gen. Microbiol.* **16**, 676.

SHAW, C., STITT, J. M. & COWAN, S. T. (1951). Staphylococci and their classification. *J. gen. Microbiol.* **5**, 1010.

SHEWAN, J. M., HOBBS, G. & HODGKISS, W. (1960). A determinative scheme for the identification of certain genera of Gram-negative bacteria, with special reference to the Pseudomonadaceae. *J. appl. Bact.* **23**, 379.

SHIFRINE, M., PHAFF, H. J. & DEMAINE, A. L. (1954). Determination of carbon assimilation patterns of yeasts by replica plating. *J. Bact.* **68**, 28.

SKERMAN, V. B. D. (1961). Species concept in bacteria. In *The Evolution of Living Organisms*, vol. **1**, pp. 213–21. Melbourne. Melbourne University Press.

SMITH, P. B. & CHERRY, W. B. (1957). Identification of *Malleomyces* by specific bacteriophages. *J. Bact.* **74**, 668.

SMITH, N. R., GORDON, R. E. & CLARK, F. E. (1952). Aerobic sporeforming bacteria. *Agric. Monogr. U.S. Dept. Agric.*, no. 16.

SNEATH, P. H. A. (1956). Cultural and biochemical characteristics of the genus *Chromobacterium*. *J. gen. Microbiol.* **15**, 70.

SNEATH, P. H. A. (1957a). Some thoughts on bacterial classification. *J. gen. Microbiol.* **17**, 184.

SNEATH, P. H. A. (1957b). The application of computers to taxonomy. *J. gen. Microbiol.* **17**, 201.

SNEATH, P. H. A. (1958). Some aspects of Adansonian classification and of the taxonomic theory of correlated features. *Ann. Microbiol. Enzimol.* **8**, 261.

SNEATH, P. H. A. (1960). A study of the bacterial genus *Chromobacterium*. *Iowa St. Coll. J. Sci.* **34**, 243.

SNEATH, P. H. A. (1961). Recent developments in theoretical and quantitative taxonomy. *System. Zool.* **10**, 118.

SNEATH, P. H. A. (1962). Sex factors as episomes. *Brit. med. Bull.* **18**, 41.

SNEATH, P. H. A. & BUCKLAND, F. E. (1959). The serology and pathogenicity of the genus *Chromobacterium*. *J. gen. Microbiol.* **20**, 414.

SNEATH, P. H. A. & COWAN, S. T. (1958). An electro-taxonomic survey of bacteria. *J. gen. Microbiol.* **19**, 551.

SNEATH, P. H. A. & SOKAL, R. R. (1962). Phylogenetic systematics and numerical taxonomy. (In the Press.)

SOKAL, R. R. (1958). Quantification of systematic relationships and of phylogenetic trends. *Proc. Xth int. Congr. Ent.* **1**, 409.

SOKAL, R. R. (1961). Distance as a measure of taxonomic similarity. *System. Zool.* **10**, 70.

SOKAL, R. R. & MICHENER, C. D. (1958). A statistical method for evaluating systematic relationships. *Kans. Univ. Sci. Bull.* **38**, 1409.

SOKAL, R. R. & SNEATH, P. H. A. *The Principles of Numerical Taxonomy.* (In preparation.)

SØRENSEN, T. (1948). A method of establishing groups of equal amplitude in plant sociology based on similarity of species content and its application to analyses of the vegetation on Danish commons. *Biol. Skr.* **5**, no. 4, 1.

STANIER, R. Y. & VAN NIEL, C. B. (1941). The main outlines of bacterial classification. *J. Bact.* **42**, 437.

STEARN, W. T. (1956). Keys, botanical, and how to use them. In *Dictionary of Gardening.* Supplement, edited by P. M. Synge, pp. 251–3. Oxford: Clarendon Press.

STEEL, K. J. (1961). The oxidase reaction as a taxonomic tool. *J. gen. Microbiol.* **25**, 297.

STOCKER, B. A. D. (1955). Bacteriophage and bacterial classification. *J. gen. Microbiol.* **12**, 375.

TALBOT, J. M. & SNEATH, P. H. A. (1960). A taxonomic study of *Pasteurella septica*, especially of strains isolated from human sources. *J. gen. Microbiol.* **22**, 303.

THORNLEY, M. J. (1960). Computation of similarities between strains of *Pseudomonas* and *Achromobacter* isolated from chicken meat. *J. appl. Bact.* **23**, 395.

TOPLEY, W. W. C. & WILSON, G. S. (1929). *The Principles of Bacteriology and Immunity*, 1st edition. London: Arnold.

VAŇKOVÁ, J. (1957). Motile catalase-producing strains of *Lactobacillus delbrückii*. *Nature, Lond.* **179**, 204.

WATSON, J. D. & CRICK, F. H. C. (1953). Genetical implications of the structure of deoxyribonucleic acid. *Nature, Lond.* **171**, 964.

WHITE, P. B. (1937). Remarks on bacterial taxonomy. *Zbl. Bakt.* (2. *Abt.*), **96**, 145.

WILLIAMS, W. T. & LAMBERT, J. M. (1959). Multivariate methods in plant ecology. I. Association-analysis in plant communities. *J. Ecol.* **47**, 83.

WINSLOW, C.-E. A. & ROGERS, A. F. (1906). A statistical study of generic characters in the Coccaceae. *J. infect. Dis.* **3**, 485.

A QUANTITATIVE APPROACH TO THE SYSTEMATICS OF ACTINOMYCETES BASED ON OVERALL SIMILARITY

L. SILVESTRI, M. TURRI, L. R. HILL AND E. GILARDI

Progetto Sistematica Actinomiceti, Istituto di Microbiologia,
University of Milan, Italy

Essentially the formation of taxa on the basis of overall similarity simply means considering simultaneously a large number of characters instead of only a few as in traditional classifications. For example, by considering one character at a time in traditional classifications of bacteria a single individual could be consigned to one or other of the two large morphological groups, rods and cocci, according to the single character, *shape of the cell*, without considering any of the other characters. The usual practice has been, however, to seek characters which are correlated (positively or negatively) with others, in order to define taxa. In this example the shape of the cell has been chosen to define the group of cocci, for it has been realized that this character is usually correlated with others such as Gram-positivity, the absence of spores and flagella, etc. Another aspect of traditional classifications is that characters are considered one at a time, in a hierarchical order. The criteria on which such a hierarchy of characters should be founded have not, so far, been precisely defined. By examining the manner in which traditional classifications have developed the conclusion is easily reached that the characters have been empirically ranked according to the number of kinds of organisms in which they are present. In essence such classifications have been constructed by considering the least possible number of characters, chosen according to their associations and ranked according to their frequency, the characters which are most frequent defining the highest ranks.

This traditional procedure has been justified on two grounds: (1) the practical difficulty of handling large quantities of data—a difficulty which, until the advent of electronic computers, was almost insurmountable, and (2) the wish of taxonomists to obtain simultaneously a taxonomy and a simple diagnostic key, which, of course, should be constructed as economically as possible. It may well be that the importance attached to diagnostic keys is still one of the main motives why many workers are reluctant to adopt classification methods based on overall similarity. The time has come, however, to recognize that the problem of identification is distinct from that of pure classification (that is, the grouping together of like individuals) and that dealing with the two problems separately avoids the possibility that one could prejudice the other. Here we shall limit ourselves to the problem of classification; problems of identification are discussed by Steel (p. 405).

A consequence of confusing the problem of classification with that of identification is that monotypic taxa are defined as groups of individuals all possessing one discriminating character. But since, especially with micro-organisms, there are no characters which do not mutate, there is the continual necessity of creating new species (always monotypic) each time new individuals are isolated and studied which have mutated in the character that defines the taxon. It is not by chance that the greatest proliferation of new species occurs in those sections of microbiology which are the most intensively studied; e.g. until a few years ago, the Enterobacteriaceae, and for the last ten years, the streptomycetes. This process of multiplication of new species will not be halted (notwithstanding the good intentions of empirical 'lumpers') so long as taxa are based on only a few characters.

As taxa formed on the basis of overall similarity are polytypic, no single character by itself is indispensable for the attribution of an individual to a given taxon. The problem of identification, on the other hand, then becomes rather more complicated, but this is not an insurmountable difficulty. Furthermore, the advantages of the greater stability of such polytypic taxa are such as to render worthwhile the search for more advanced diagnostic methods. One such method, based on the theory of information, has already been proposed by Maccacaro (1958).

OVERALL SIMILARITY AND NATURAL CLASSIFICATION

As Sneath (1957a) remarked 'the underlying assumption of scientific classification is that there is a natural order, a system of similarities, which can be discovered by investigation'. By 'natural order' is usually meant a system of relationships which reflects phylogeny and which is, therefore, in agreement with the evolution and the genetics of the organisms being studied. The reasons why biologists consider a classification most satisfactory when it is nearest to this natural order are fairly obvious. It is pertinent, however, to discuss to what extent a classification based on overall similarity contributes to revealing natural order.

First, it is important to remember that in micro-organisms the absence of palaeontological data, and the scarcity of information on ecology and the exchange in nature of genetic material means that the fundamental requirements for the construction of a natural system are lacking. Attempts made so far in this direction, e.g. by Bisset (1952), although very stimulating, are speculative and are debatable from many points of view. Many microbiologists, on the other hand, believe that it is impossible to make a natural system of classification for micro-organisms, and further that it is impossible to define natural microbial species.

According to Mayr (1942) natural species 'are constituted by groups of interbreeding populations which are isolated reproductively from similar groups'. According to Pontecorvo (1955) 'the criterion for classifying an individual in a species is that of its potential contribution to the genetical pool of the species'. Today, micro-organisms can no longer be considered asexual, for there is no lack of evidence that they have preserved or developed (according to different points of view) several methods of exchanging genetic factors. The existence of a parasexual cycle in the Actinomycetales (Sermonti & Spada-Sermonti, 1955) cannot be ignored, nor can the likelihood of transduction by means of actinophages (Alikhanian & Iljina, 1958). None the less, our knowledge is too limited to be of any real value for the delimitation of the gene-pool of species.

If the restriction of genetic exchange is the characteristic which defines and delimits the natural species (this being a method of ensuring the constancy of a particular set of genes, which it is advantageous to the organism to preserve because they correspond to an adaptive peak, see Wright, 1940), then when the existence of different species is demonstrated not only are the interruptions of the mating continuum revealed but also breaks in the adaptive continuum. This indeed reveals the existence of highly adapted sets of genes which correspond to the summits of the adaptive peaks; such peaks are surrounded by progressively less well-adapted forms, and are separated from each other by more-or-less empty valleys.

The interruptions of the mating continuum serve to render the valleys more marked, thus giving a better resolution of the peaks. But they are not the only conditions determining the existence of adaptive peaks and valleys. The principal determining factors are the pressure of selection and the division of the habitable continuum into discrete ecological niches. We think therefore that whenever sufficiently separated peaks can be demonstrated it is possible to talk of natural species even in the absence of criteria based on the existence of interruptions in the mating continuum.

This opinion has already been expressed some years ago by Mayr (1957):

The most satisfactory solution in taxonomic practice has been a frankly dualistic one. It consists in defining the term species biologically in sexual organisms and morphologically in asexual ones. There is more justification in this procedure than a mere pragmatic one.

The growing elucidation of the relations between genotype and phenotype also justify this approach. Reproductive isolation is affected by physiological properties which have a genetic basis. Morphological characters are the product of the same gene complex. Once this is clearly understood, a new role can be assigned to morphological difference associated with reproductive isolation, namely that of indicators of specific distinctness. This permits the assumption that the amount of genetic difference which, in a given taxonomic group, results in reproductive isolation will be correlated with a certain amount of morphological difference. If this is true, it is permissible to conclude from the degree of morphological difference the probable degree of reproductive isolation. To base this inference on genetic reasoning is new; the method itself, however, of determining empirically with the help of morphological criteria whether or not a population has reached species status goes back to classical taxonomy. This inference method is by no means a return to a morphological species concept, since reproductive isolation always remains the primary criterion and degree of morphological difference only a secondary indicator, which will be set aside whenever it comes in conflict with the biological evidence. It is possible to use the same kind of inference to classify asexual organisms into species.... If a group were a complete morphological *continuum*, any attempt to break it up into species would be doomed to failure. Curiously enough there seem to be a number of discontinuities which make taxonomic subdivision possible. The most reasonable explanation of this phenomenon is that the existing types are the survivors among a great number of produced forms, that the surviving types are clustered around a limited number of adaptive peaks, and that ecological factors have given the former *continuum* a taxonomic structure. Each adaptive peak is occupied by a different kind of organism, and it is legitimate to call each of these clusters of biotypes a species.

Mayr's expression 'degree of morphological differences' should be interpreted with a broad meaning, corresponding in practice to what we define as overall similarity. When this correspondence is made clear it is quite easy to understand why overall similarity is the best way to reveal the existence of a natural order in apomictic populations. There is no certainty, however, that such a classification has a phylogenetic significance. Without fossil evidence no phylogenetic conclusions can be deduced from simple estimates of similarity. Similar structures can arise from parallel evolution. We can take an example from the mammals (the evolution of which is much more solidly based on palaeontology than that of most groups) to show how easily one can be lead astray by this pitfall: how much more easily could such mistakes be made in micro-biology! We refer to Wood's (1949) account of the fossil evidence show-ing that the extinct woolly rhinoceros and the living white African rhino-ceros, which were thought to be very closely related, have in fact quite a different ancestry. That they have the morphological similarity which warrants considering them very closely related cannot be denied, yet the fossil evidence shows without doubt that such similarity is derived from parallel evolution in two different stocks.

THE CHOICE OF CHARACTERS

The existence of interruptions in the phenotypic continuum and the division of the phenotypes into clusters which are centred on the adap-tive peaks is only a hypothesis, but a hypothesis one cannot avoid if one wishes to construct a classification which is not otherwise wholly arti-ficial. The interruptions of the continuum, when they exist, are a con-sequence of the elimination by natural selection of a part of all the pos-sible combinations of characters. Of course not all the interruptions are equally wide or definite. In nature, sometimes breaks in the continuum of considerable width are observed. These important breaks attract little attention from systematists, though they constitute a grave problem for the evolutionist. These wider interruptions not connected by clear inter-mediate forms indeed represent weak points in the Neo-Darwinian theory of evolution. Some workers, in order to explain them, have been forced to introduce such concepts as that of macroevolution (Goldschmidt, 1940). However, it is manifestly true that the separation between adap-tive peaks is not always very sharp. Among bacteria, and in particular actinomycetes, it may well be that there is poor resolution of the peaks.

It is evident that for a species which occupies a very specialized eco-logical niche, or which possesses notable morphological or functional complexity, any deviation from the standard type would bring about a reduction of its fitness. Thus it is comprehensible that it is species of this sort which systematists will define as a 'good' species, i.e. one which is homogeneous and well defined. Micro-organisms, however, present characteristics which make one think that in them such restriction of the variability giving a very homogeneous type is of poor selective value.

The large size of microbial populations, the brief life of the single cell and the lack of geographical variation all tend to the conclusion that fit-ness has been sacrificed for greater flexibility—which in taxonomic terms would mean the absence of well separated species (Silvestri, 1960). On the other hand, a result analogous to that of natural selection (i.e. the creation of interruptions in the phenotypic continuum) could be created artificially by the systematist if he considers only a few isolated examples of the group under study or only a few characters. In both cases the result is the apparent absence of some phenotypes and the illusory appearance of a discontinuity. The possibilities of error are of two kinds: to create artificially a discontinuity where it does not exist, and to be unable to demonstrate a discontinuity where it does exist.

Errors of the first kind can be due to employing too few characters. It is never easy to say what is the minimum number of characters necessary to avoid this type of error, for it is dependent on the degree of separation of the adaptive peaks. The better the peaks are separated the less is the number of characters needed. The number can be established experimentally by adding extra characters until the additions cease to cause the fusion of previously separated groups. The battery of tests is sufficient when the acquisition of new knowledge and its incorporation into the system alters the results very little.

Errors of the second kind can be due to an unbalanced and non-representative choice of characters. When the characters used all belong to one cluster of highly correlated characters they may not give sufficient resolution between the peaks. Furthermore, a battery of characters may be both unbalanced and insufficient in number, thus giving both types of error at the same time. For a classification to be based on overall similarity, a fairly large number of characters should be used. These characters should be varied ones, taking into consideration as many different aspects of the organisms as possible.

Tests employed in this study

In our study of the actinomycetes the tests used included (a) macro-morphology and coloration of the colonies, (b) micromorphology of the sporophores, (c) production of pigments, (d) reaction to physical agents, (e) capacity to attack certain substrates, (f) sensitivity to a number of antibiotics, (g) utilization of various carbon sources, (h) utilization of various nitrogen sources, (i) sensitivity to actinophages, and (j) possession of some polysaccharide antigens.

A full list of the tests used will be found in Table 1. For each test or type of test the number of code-marks employed is shown. For example, sensitivity to eight antibiotics was tested, and for each antibiotic three possible responses were recorded: resistant, fairly sensitive, and very sensitive. In the coding procedure these three possibilities are represented by two code marks, and the alternatives were $- -$, $+ -$ and $+ +$. Hence, a total of 16 code marks was obtained from the antibiotic sensitivity tests.

Table 1. *List of differential characters*

Character	No. of code marks	Character	No. of code marks
Cultural behaviour on glycerol-asparagine agar		Physiology and biochemistry	
Growth in 10 days	1	Melanoid pigment on peptone-iron agar	1
Colour of the reverse aspect of the growth	3	Growth in tryptone-yeast extract broth	3
Sporulation	1	Growth in tryptone-yeast extract broth at pH 5·5, 8·5 and 10·0	3
Colour of the aerial mycelium	6		
Texture of the aerial mycelium	3	Nitrate reduction	1
Electron microscopy of the spores	2	Growth on 6% and 9% NaCl tryptone-yeast extract agar	2
Diffusible pigments present	1	Growth on tryptone yeast extract agar at 45°	1
Shrinking of the agar near the colony	1	Production of cellulase	2
Hardness of the growth	1	Production of haemolysins	3
Cultural behaviour on starch agar		Proteolysis of gelatin	3
Growth in 10 days	1	Proteolysis of albumin	2
Sporulation	1	Utilization of various N sources	8
Micromorphology of the sporophores	3	Utilization of various C sources	22
Hydrolysis of the starch	2	Antibiotic sensitivity tests	16
		Sensitivity to various actino-phages	6
		'Indirect' haemagglutination tests	6

Both Sneath (1957 *a*, *b*) and Michener & Sokal (1957) have emphasized that it is important that the battery of tests used should be ample. It should also be quite diversified, including as wide a range as possible of existing knowledge, in order to obtain a classification which has biological significance. The use of electronic computors and other purely mechanical means does not itself constitute a guarantee that the results will have a biological significance, or even any significance at all. The criticisms advanced by Mayr (1959) and Inger (1958) against the use of methods of multi-variate analysis in systematics are to be interpreted as a warning that one should not forget the naturalistic aspects of the problems under study, for computers can only analyse the data fed to them.

THE CHOICE OF STRAINS

An apparent and artificial break in the phenotypic continuum can be due to the systematist taking into consideration only a few strains. In theory this error is avoided by taking a randomized sample of the population intended for study. However, this solution is not an easy one, for a simple sampling of the strains isolated in nature can give a false impression in so far as single populations (corresponding to single adaptive peaks) may differ in size. In a truly randomized sample, strains corresponding to small populations may not be represented, and thus their absence will give rise to artificial breaks in the continuum. The objective to aim for is not that of indiscriminate sampling, but rather a sample in which all the phenotypes are represented in such numbers as to be reasonably proportional to the variability of the population. Ideally, each peak ought to be represented by a number of individuals proportional to the width of its base.

We have been guided in our choice of strains by opinions fairly widespread among students of actinomycetes. We think it likely that in systematic studies to date there has been far too much splitting and that the number of species having a biological (or adaptive) significance is less than the number of species described in the literature.

To test this hypothesis, we decided to introduce into our study a large number of cultures labelled with different names, in the hope that many of these would be grouped together in an analysis based on overall similarity. Our hypothesis is a typical 'lumping' hypothesis and it should (and will) be rejected whenever grouping is not observed.

On the other hand, to avoid the error of accepting this hypothesis simply because our battery of tests was too collective, we have also attempted to represent some species by several examples. A number of strains isolated by independent workers, but labelled by them with the same name, was therefore introduced into our sample.

In order to relate our work (at least approximately) with those already carried out, or in course of elaboration, in other bacterial groups, a certain number of strains other than members of the actinomycetales (as defined in *Bergey's Manual*, 1957) was also included in our sample.

Our sample consisted of 190 strains (see Table 2), received under 134 different names; 159 strains were labelled as members of 122 species of *Streptomyces*; 24 strains were labelled as members of 12 species of *Nocardia*. *Streptosporangium*, *Micromonospora*, *Mycobacterium*, *Corynebacterium*, *Escherichia*, *Staphylococcus* and *Pasteurella* were each represented by a single strain of a single species. For the bacteria outside the actinomycetales, typical strains were chosen, and were those used by Sneath & Cowan (1958) in their study. These were obtained from the National Collection of Type Cultures, London.

Table 2. *List of strains employed in the study, arranged in the groups and spheres given by the computer analysis*

The strains are listed under the name they bore when they were received, preceded by the number used in the text, which is the number in the collection of the Progetto Sistematica Actinomiceti, and followed by their strain number, if any, in other culture collections (for abbreviations see footnote).

GROUP A

Sphere II

99 *Streptomyces kentuckensis*, ATCC 12691 (centrotype of sphere II)
133 *S. rubrireticuli*, NRRL B 1707
120 *S. ruber*, CBS
85 *S. cinnamoneus*, NRRL B 1285
114 *S. thioluteus*
113 *S. hiroshimensis*
86 *S. albireticuli*, NRRL B 1670
80 *S. netropsis*, NRRL 2268
118 *S. roseoverticillatus*

132 *S. griseocarneus*, NRRL B 1068
188 *S. longispororuber*, Gause 11668/54
24 *S. madurae*, IPV 212 x
111 *S. aburaviensis*, S 66
116 *S. albireticuli*
74 *S. rimosus*, Lepetit TR/1
89 *S. alboniger*, NRRL B 1832
150 *S. platensis*, NRRL 2364
185 *S. roseoflavus*, Gause 3489

To the main stem of sphere II are attached the strains

46 *S. lavendulae*, ATCC 8664

112 *S. toyocaensis*, 278

Sphere XXII

151 *S. alboniger*, ATCC 12461
14 *S. oidiosporeus*, IPV 63 x

73 *S. rimosus*, Waksman 3560

Sphere XIX

154 *Streptomyces* sp., Merck MA 418
149 *S. hygroscopicus*, NRRL B 1503

40 *S. aureofaciens*, ATCC 10762
93 *S. aureofaciens*, ETH 13387

To the main stem of sphere XIX are attached the strains

72 *Streptomyces* sp., Lepetit Cl 3141/1

82 *S. phaeochromogenes*, NRRL B 1517

Sphere VIII

138 *S. virginiae*, NRRL B 1447
115 *S. acidomyceticus*

75 *S. virginiae*, NRRL B 1446
117 *S. olivoverticillatus*

To the main stem of Group A is attached strain

171 *S.violaceus*, Gause 3959/54

GROUP D

Sphere XIV

5 *S. aureus*, IPV (centrotype of sphere XIV)
4 received from IPV as *S. aureofaciens*, but it may have been mislabelled
146 *S. parvulus*, NRRL 1628

107 *S. parvulus*, ATCC 12434
179 *S. longisporoflavus*, Gause 81/53
87 *S. coelicolor*, NRRL B 1257
83 *S. rochei*, NRRL B 1559
136 *S. antibioticus*, ATCC 10382

To the stem of sphere XIV is attached strain

42 *S. coelicolor*, ATCC 10147

Sphere XXVI

6 *S. flavus*, IPV 106 x

7 *S. halstedii*, IPV 370 x

Sphere XXIV

8 *S. scabies*, IPV 96 x

19 *S. violaceus*, IPV 550 x

Table 2 (*cont.*)

Sphere XX

9 *S. roseoflavus*, IPV 190x
20 *S. chartreusis*, IPV 554x

21 *S. viridans*, IPV 555x

Sphere XXVIII

48 *S. viridochromogenes*, ATCC 3356
    (possibly mislabelled)
176 *S. globisporus*, Gause 13024

127 *S. setonii*, CBS
134 *S. violaceoniger*, NRRL B 1476

Sphere XXI (remains isolated in the formation of higher-order groups)

178 *S. umbrinus*, Gause 1703/53
147 *S. phaeochromogenes*, NRRL
    B 1266

177 *S. glaucescens*, Gause 8731

To the main stem of sphere XXI is attached strain

98 *S. hawaiensis*, ATCC 12236

GROUP C

Sphere VII

17 *S. griseus*, IPV 423x (centrotype of
    sphere VII)
62 *S. griseus*, Kutzner H 81
45 *S. griseus*, ATCC 10137
59 *S. griseus*, NCTC 6962
66 *S. griseus*, Kutzner H 122
67 *S. griseus*, Kutzner K 932
140 *S. griseus*, Merck MA 8 A 8 b

64 *S. lavendulae*, Kutzner H 93
    (according to Kutzner it is not a
    strain of *S. lavendulae*)
70 *S. griseus*, Welsch S 17
173 *S. longisporus*, Gause 7740/58
172 *S. rubiginosohelvolus*, Gause 10/53
189 *S. badius*, Gause 1203/53
122 *S. microflavus*, CBS, ETH 10206
94 *S. praecox*, ATCC 3374
124 *S. flavogriseus*, CBS

Sphere IV

145 *S. parvus*, NRRL B 1445 (centro-
    type of sphere IV)
65 *S. griseus*, Kutzner H 95 (accord-
    ing to Kutzner this is different
    from *S. griseus*)

128 *S. fimicarius*, CBS
104 *S. odorifer*, ATCC 6246
143 *S. cellulosae*, NRRL B-1222

Sphere XII

137 *S. olivaceus*, NRRL B 1125
    (centrotype of sphere XII)
101 *S. griseolus*, ATCC 3325

102 *S. argenteolus*, ATCC 11009
3 *S. flavovirens*, IPV 169x
141 *S. vinaceus*, NRRL 2285

Sphere V

190 *Streptomyces* sp., PRL 1772

135 *S. venezuelae*, NRRL B 902

To the main stem of sphere V is attached strain

15 *S. coeruleus*, IPV 930

Sphere X

50 *S. scabies*, Robinson P 29
90 *S. echinatus*, ETC 8331
108 *S. flaveolus*, ATCC 3319
84 *S. phaeofaciens*, NRRL B 1516

39 *S. verne*, ATCC 3353
181 *S. coeruleorubidus*, Gause 12531/54
23 *S. antibioticus*, IPV

To the main stem of group C are attached two other strains

76 *S. griseus*, NRRL B 150

77 *S. hygroscopicus*, NRRL B 1865

Table 2 (cont.)

GROUP B

Sphere III

11 *S. diastaticus*, IPV 46 (centrotype of sphere III)
12 *D. rubrocyanodiastaticus*, IPV 307
187 *S. coeruleofuscus,* Gause 5051/56
169 *S. atroolivaceus*, Gause 1580/53
142 *S. viridochromogenes*, NRRL B 1227

63 *S. violaceoruber*, Kutzner H 83
25 *S. violaceoruber*, IPV 858
148 *S. diastaticus*, NRRL B 1270
13 *S. viridochromogenes*, IPV 877
153 *S. graminofaciens*, Merck MA 317
180 *S. acrimycini*, Gause 7699

Sphere I

152 *S. calvus*, ATCC 13382 (centrotype of sphere I)
170 *S. daghestanicus*, Gause 13897/54

91 *S. macrosporus*, ETH 7534
10 *S. roseus*, IPV 229 x

Sphere VI

126 *S. carnosus*, CBS (centrotype of sphere VI)
22 *S. bobiliae*, ATCC 3310
184 *S. flavidovirens*, Gause 12287
144 *S. olivochromogenes*, NRRL B 1341

103 *S. canus*, ATCC 12237
100 *S. griseoroseus*, ATCC 12125
139 *S. albogriseolus*, NRRL B 1305
123 *S. galtieri*, CBS

Sphere XXV

92 *S. tendae*, ETH 11313
168 *S. coerulescens*, Gause 4562

88 *S. violaceoruber*, NRRL B 1260

Sphere IX

18 *S. violaceus*, IPV 286 x (centrotype of sphere IX)
156 *S. fradiae*, ATCC 10745

41 *S. bikiniensis*, ATCC 11062
182 *S. cyanofuscatus*, Gause 99/54
97 *S. californicus*, ATCC 3317

Sphere XVII

96 *S. intermedius*, ATCC 3329
105 *S. annulatus*, ATCC 3307
106 *S. rutgersensis*, ATCC 3350

43 *S. erythraeus*, ATCC 11912
16 *S. sulphureus*, IPV 510
58 *S. coelicolor*, Kutzner H 16

To the main stem of group B are attached three strains

69 *S. violaceoruber*, Bradley
36 *Nocardia polychromogenes*, CBS

78 *S. purpurascens*, NRRL B 2269

Sphere XVIII (remains isolated in the formation of higher-order groups)

27 *Nocardia leishmanii*, CBS
28 *N. minima*, CBS
31 *N. caprae*, CBS

166 *N. asteroides*, Gordon 443 (1)
34 *N. madurae,* CBS
38 *Streptosporangium roseum*, CBS

GROUP E

Sphere XV

2 *Streptomyces albidoflavus*, IPV 875 (centrotype of sphere XV)
1 *S. albus*, IPV 82 x

60 *S. albus*, ATCC 618
47 *S. rimosus,* NRRL 2234
175 *S. kurssanovi*, Gause 7069 a/53

To the main stem of sphere XV is attached strain

57 *S. albus*, Kutzner H 8

Table 2 (*cont.*)

Sphere XI

165 *Nocardia asteroides*, Gordon 727	163 *N. cuniculi*, ATCC 6864
160 *N. sylvodorifera*, ATCC 7372	164 *N. asteroides*, Gordon 3045 B
167 *N. asteroides*, Gordon 443 (2)	52 *Mycobacterium phlei*, NCTC 8151
162 *N. farcinica*, Gordon 3318	159 *N. asteroides*, Gordon 3045 A
26 *N. lutea*, CBS	68 *N. erythropolis*, CBS
161 *N. phenotolerans*, Gordon 652	32 *N. caviae*, CBS
158 *N. asteroides*, ATCC 9504	30 *N. brasiliensis*, CBS
35 *N. blackwelli*, CBS	29 *N. corallina*

Sphere XXVII

33 *N. asteroides*, CBS	55 *Escherichia coli*, NCTC 9001
37 *Micromonospora fusca*, CBS	56 *Staphylococcus aureus*, NCTC 8532

GROUP F

Sphere XIII

157 *Streptomyces* sp., Gordon 3554	183 *S. candidus*, Gause 5855/54
(centrotype of sphere XIII)	51 *S. gedanensis*, ATCC 4880
81 *Streptomyces fradiae*, NRRL 1195	95 *S. gelaticus*, ATCC 3323
174 *S. roseolilacinus*, Gause 14250	131 *S. hygroscopicus*, Lilly M 5–13184
110 *S. cacaoi*, ATCC 3082	119 *S. craterifer*
61 *S. fradiae*, Kutzner H 80	129 *S. fradiae*, NRRL 2703

To the main stem of sphere XIII are attached four strains

155 *Nocardia formica*, Merck MA 143	121 *S. novaecaesareae*, CBS
(it is not a nocardia)	125 *S. clavifer*, CBS
44 *Streptomyces fradiae*, ATCC 10745	

Sphere XXIII

130 *S. orientalis*, Lilly M 43–05865	49 *S. rimosus*, IPV GP 887
186 *S. cremeus*, Gause 815/54	

The addresses of workers and of institutes (indicated above by abbreviations) that provided strains are as follows:

ATCC = American Type Culture Collection, 2112 M Street, N.W., Washington 7, D.C., U.S.A.

CBS = Centraal Bureau vor Schimmelcultures, Baarn, Netherlands.

NRRL = North Regional Research Laboratory, Peoria, Ill., U.S.A.

IPV = Istituto di Patologia Vegetale, Milan, Italy.

NCTC = National Collection of Type Cultures, Colindale, London, N.W. 9, England.

PRL = Prairie Regional Laboratory, National Research Council, Saskatoon, Sask., Canada.

ETH = Eidgenossische Technische Hochschule, Institut für Spezielle Botanik, Zürich 6, Switzerland.

Professor S. G. Bradley, University of Minnesota, Minneapolis 14, Minn., U.S.A.

Professor E. Küster, Department of Industrial Microbiology, University College, Dublin, Ireland.

Professor J. B. Robinson, Department of Microbiology, Ontario Agricultural College, Guelph, Canada.

Professor G. F. Gause, Institute of Antibiotics, Academy of Medical Sciences, Bolshaia Pirogovskaia 11, Moscow, U.S.S.R.

Dr R. Gordon, Rutgers University, New Brunswick, N.J., U.S.A.

Professor M. Welsch, Laboratoire de Microbiologie Générale, Université de Liège, Liège, Belgium.

Table 2 (*cont.*)

Merck, Sharp and Dohme, Research Laboratories, Rahway, N.J., U.S.A.
Lederle Laboratories, Microbiology Department, Pearl River, New York, N.Y., U.S.A.
Lilly Research Laboratories, Indianapolis 6, Ind., U.S.A.
Lepetit S.p.A., Milan, Italy.
Dr H. J. Kutzner, Institut für Biochemie des Bodens, Brunswick, Germany
Professor S. A. Waksman, Rutgers University, New Brunswick, N.J., U.S.A.

THE MEASUREMENT OF OVERALL SIMILARITY

Three types of indices for measuring overall similarity have been proposed by different authors. Sturtevant (1942) used the number of discordances ('mis-matches') evaluated on a constant battery of 33 characters. To be able to use the actual number of discordances (or concordances, which amounts to the same thing) it is necessary for the battery of characters to be the same for all the individuals. In our case this was not possible as some subordinate characters are not taken into consideration in all comparisons. For example, on comparing a *Streptomyces* with a *Nocardia* the character 'presence of aerial mycelium' would be calculated as a discordance, but one must not calculate as a further discordance a character relative to the form of the sporophores, or the surface of the spores, since these are absent in *Nocardia*. The battery of tests in which two *Streptomyces* are compared is therefore somewhat greater than that used to compare a *Streptomyces* with a *Nocardia*. As it was not therefore possible to keep the number of tests constant, it was impossible to use the index proposed by Sturtevant.

Sneath (1957a, b) proposed an index of similarity which consisted of a ratio between the number of concordances between characters having a positive score and the number of comparisons made. The index of Sneath avoids the difficulty of that of Sturtevant, in so much that being formulated as a ratio it is applicable also in those cases where the number of comparisons varies. Yet even this index of similarity presents a great inconvenience in our opinion—that of not taking account of the concordance between characters which both have negative scores. In a preceding paper (Hill, Turri, Gilardi & Silvestri, 1961) a detailed discussion of this problem is given. Considerations of a theoretical nature on one hand and the more satisfactory results obtained on the other, have convinced us that the same amount of information is contained in a positive score as in a negative score.

Sokal & Michener (1958) have described an index called by them the 'matching-coefficient' which takes into account characters scored both as positive and as negative. However, they did not use matching coefficients because: (1) such coefficients had an unknown sampling distribution, (2) they were not suitable in their case, in which many characters with multiple alternatives (see below) were used, because matching coefficients distort the resemblances based on characters with multiple alternatives, and (3) the calculation of these coefficients would have been more difficult with the IBM equipment they had available.

As in our case characters with multiple alternatives were few, the only real inconvenience in using matching coefficients was that of not knowing their sampling distribution. We are aware that this unknown distribution gives rise to some limitations, yet equally we have not thought it necessary to adopt the product-moment correlation coefficients proposed by Sokal & Michener (1958) especially as in our first pilot studies (made before the work of Sokal & Michener was known to us) the similarity index of Sneath was used and a radical change would have involved a considerable amount of re-programming for the computer.

The similarity index, $\% \, M$, used in the present study was:

$$\% \, M = \frac{n_c}{n_c + n_d} \times 100,$$

where n_c = number of concordances between positive responses and also between negative responses; n_d = number of discordances; $n_c + n_d = n_{ff}$ = number of comparisons made.

The use of $\% \, M$ maintains, none the less, the 'Adansonian' character of the classification, since the three fundamental principles of this type of classification are retained, namely, that it is based on overall similarity, that equal weight is give to all characters and that grouping of the individuals is based on correlated characters.

CODING OF DATA

In our terminology, a character is any feature to which at least two different attributes can be attached. In principle, because of the way computers function, it would be preferable if the attributes were never more than two and that they were mutually exclusive. This occurs in some more simple cases, e.g. the character 'aerial mycelium' gives rise to a simple alternative of only two attributes, 'present' or 'absent'. A feature which in all the individuals in the trial possesses less than two attributes is not a character. If aerial mycelia were present in all the individuals this feature could not be considered a character. As, from our point of view, the information contained in both attributes is equally important, we consider it unimportant which of the two attributes is marked as positive, though we retain the usage of scoring the attributes as + and −.

The scoring of characters

Usually it is not difficult to define the characters in such a manner that only two mutually exclusive attributes can be attached to them. In some cases, however, it is not possible to accommodate all the characters in this simple scheme. The principal exceptions are of three types: (1) quantitative data, (2) characters with multiple alternatives, and (3) characters which are subordinate to other characters.

(1) *Quantitative data.* Quantitative characters are those in which the degree of expression of the character can be measured. For example, the character 'proteolytic action on gelatin' can be estimated by measuring in millimetres the zones of clearing in the vicinity of the streaks, e.g. recognizing four degrees of proteolytic action: (0) absent, (1) present but less than 2 mm., (2) present but less than 4 mm., (3) present and more than 4 mm. To represent these four degrees of proteolytic action three code marks A, B and C are employed:

	A	B	C
(0)	−	−	−
(1)	+	−	−
(2)	+	+	−
(3)	+	+	+

In this way, in the calculation of M, the denominator (the number of comparisons) is constant for all the comparisons between the strains. The numerators can vary from 0 (the comparison between (0) and (3)) up to a value equal to that of the denominator (the comparison between (0) and (0), (1) and (1), etc.). Intermediate values are obtained in comparisons between intermediate classes.

The inconvenience of this type of coding is that the effective weight of a character increases with an increase in the number of subclasses. This is a deviation from the rigorous application of the Adansonian principle. A justification of this procedure can be given, however, since the likelihood that a character which presents different degrees of expression may reasonably be considered to have more weight. None the less, we have avoided using more than three code marks per character, that is, we have avoided scoring of more than four possible degrees of reaction.

(2) *Characters with multiple alternatives.* These present some analogy with quantitative ones, but the difference lies in the mutual exclusion of certain of the alternatives. For example, the sporophores can be: (*a*) straight, (*b*) flexuous, (*c*) looped, (*d*) spiral, but for each strain only one of these alternatives is possible. A character with four alternative

responses in our coding is scored for four code marks, A, B, C and D as follows:

	A	B	C	D
(a)	+	−	−	−
(b)	−	+	−	−
(c)	−	−	+	−
(d)	−	−	−	+

In this way, a comparison between two identical strains would give $M = 4/4$, whilst between different strains $M = 2/4$.

In general, it can be said that if n is the number of the alternatives of the character (and therefore of the code marks used), the values of M for comparisons between identical strains is n/n, whilst between different strains $M = n-2/n$. It has the inconvenience that with an increase in the number of alternatives the discriminating value of the character decreases. If in a battery of characters there are many of this type, all the similarity indices would tend to become equal, the strains thus resulting being uniformly related to each other. A possible solution could be to introduce a subprogramme which would instruct the computor to consider the different code marks of a character with multiple alternatives as a single comparison, thus giving a single concordance or discordance. As in our battery such characters were relatively rare we thought it unnecessary to complicate the computor programme further.

(3) *Characters which are subordinate to other characters.* These present some analogy with quantitative characters, in the sense that whenever the principal character (i.e. the code-mark to the left) is negative all the marks on its right can never be positive and any score for the individual aspects of the principal character is absurd. For example, the principal character 'spores' has two attributes, 'present' or 'absent'; it is then obvious that in the case of spores being absent the scoring of the character 'surface of the spores' is absurd. However, for those individuals having spores a subordinate character with two attributes, 'spores smooth' or 'spores spiny', is possible.

Subordinate characters for strains in which the principal character is negative are indicated in the coding by the mark NC (not counted). In the computer programme an instruction was included not to count comparisons such as $+/NC$, or $-/NC$, or NC/NC for the calculation of $\% M$. For this reason, in our trial the n_{ff} value (i.e. the total number of comparisons made for a given pair of strains) is smaller than the total number of code-marks by which the whole battery of characters is represented, since almost all strains had one or more characters scored as NC.

Thus, the above example becomes codified in this way:

		A	B
(a)	Smooth spores	+	+
(b)	Spiny spores	+	−
(c)	Spores absent		NC

The comparison (a) to (b) gives $M = \frac{1}{2}$, the comparison (a) to (c) or (b) to (c) gives $M = 0/1$.

CALCULATIONS

The calculations were carried out with an IBM 650 computer, at the Centro di Calcolo Numerico of the University of Genoa.

The first operation carried out by the computer is to calculate the matching coefficients between each strain and every other strain. In our case this amounted to almost 18,000 values of $\% M$ (see below).

The $\% M$ between two strains can be interpreted as the probability that an attribute selected at random from all the attributes that they possess will have the same score in the two strains (Rogers & Tanimoto, 1960). A ratio of almost 1 (100 %) would indicate that the two strains are almost identical. A ratio of 0·50 would indicate a random distribution of the attributes between the two strains, and this value is obtained if there is no correlation between the tests in the two strains considered (Hill et al. 1961). A ratio significantly less than 0·50 is evidence of a negative correlation between the attributes of the strains under examination.

Cluster analysis

It is now necessary to analyse the M values so as to form clusters of strains which we hope will approximate to satisfactory taxonomic groups. A 'distance' d_{ij} between the strains i and j has been proposed by Rogers & Tanimoto (1960). It can be defined as

$$d_{ij} = -\log_2 M_{ij},$$

where M_{ij} is the matching coefficient between the strains i and j.

The strains i and j can be imagined as two geometrical points in a suitable multidimensional space, i.e. a semimetric space, separated by the distance d_{ij} (Rogers & Tanimoto, 1960). If i and j are almost identical, the value of d_{ij} is close to zero. If i and j have in common 50 % of the attributes, which corresponds to the situation of indifference, the value of d_{ij} becomes 1. If i and j differ in more than 50 % of the attributes the value of d_{ij} is greater than 1.

The convention of regarding the strains $i, j, \ldots, n$ as geometric points in a multidimensional space poses the problem of determining if they are arranged homogeneously in this space or not. How this is done will become evident from the following description of the computer programme, which is given in some detail below.

The programme of the computer consists of the following fundamental operations:

(1) Calculation of the coefficient M for every possible pair of strains. If n is the total number of strains under examination, the number of comparisons possible (ignoring comparisons between a strain and itself and also reciprocal comparisons) is $\frac{1}{2}[n(n-1)]$. In our case n was 190 and hence the number of coefficients of M was 17,955.

(2) A value of R ('ranking order') and H ('hierarchical order') is calculated for each strain. R is the number of strains with which the strain under consideration has a value of $M > 0.65$, whilst H is the product of these R coefficients. R therefore represents the number of relationships higher than a fixed value, whilst H is a measure of the closeness of the clustering of the R strains around the strain under consideration. The limit $M > 0.65$ for the calculation of R and of H was chosen by us arbitrarily on the basis of our previous experience (Gilardi, Hill, Turri & Silvestri, 1960; Hill *et al.* 1961).

(3) The strains are re-ordered in decreasing values of R, and when for two or more strains R is equal, they are ordered in decreasing values of H. The whole collection of strains becomes ordered in such a way that the strain occupying the first position in the re-ordered sequence is that strain which is at the centre of a zone of maximum clustering of strains, whilst the succeeding strains are at the centres of zones in which the strains are progressively less clustered. The strains at the centres of zones of maximum clustering are called 'nodes', while these zones are called 'spheres'. The next operation is to choose a distance from the first node which represents the radius of the sphere within which those strains having their closest relationship with the first node are found. The most common method used is that of establishing a value M_p equal to the antilog of the distance which separates the first node from that strain which is at the centre of a second, independent sphere, such a strain being called a second node. The second node could be considered independent from the first one, whenever the sphere isolated employing the value M_p can be further reduced (see below). The choice of the second node, and hence the value M_p, is left to the discretion of the worker, and may not be easy. It is obvious that it should be chosen from among those strains which immediately follow the first node in the re-ordered sequence, i.e. from among those strains having R and H values not very different from those of the first node. Furthermore, the inconveniences arising from choosing too small a radius or too great a radius are evident; the most peripheral strains might be excluded in the first case, and too many strains would be included in the second, thus making the following step (the rendering of the spheres homogeneous) very lengthy. Of the two possible errors, the choice of too small a radius is the more serious, for the error of choosing too great a radius can be corrected by subsequent operations. Generally, we have chosen as second node that strain nearest the

first node in its values of R or H, or both, having an M value with the first node greater than 0·69 and less than 0·75, as we have previously ascertained (Gilardi *et al.* 1960; Hill *et al.* 1961) that fairly homogeneous groups tend to form around such values.

(4) Those strains which fall within the sphere of the radius $- \log_2 M_p$ centred around the first node are now selected, i.e. those strains having a value of $M \geqslant M_p$ with the first node. Strains thus selected are removed from the collection for closer study.

(5) As Rogers & Tanimoto (1960) have already shown, the group of strains removed because they all had values of M with the first node of $\geqslant M_p$, may not constitute a homogeneous group. By a homogeneous group is meant a group in which the distances between all the strains within the group are more-or-less equal. Rogers & Tanimoto proposed that the homogeneity of the sphere should be determined by the calculation of an index u_n, based on estimating the entropy of the system. We have not used this estimation of homogeneity for two reasons, one being that the work would have been too onerous for a computer which uses punched cards (such as the IBM 650 which was at our disposal), the other being that our lack of knowledge of the distribution of the M coefficients does not permit us to apply a significance test, as has also been noticed by Brambilla & Moeller (personal communication). To isolate the homogeneous zone from the group of strains comprised within the sphere of radius $- \log_2 M_p$, and starting with the consideration that strains comprised within a homogeneous zone should have similar R and H values, we have proceeded as follows:

(i) The isolated strains are re-ordered in decreasing values of R and H.

(ii) Strains having an R value very inferior to the possible maximum R (if N = number of strains in the sphere, $R_{\max} = N - 1$) are rejected; these rejected strains pass into the residual collection, i.e. the collection of strains remaining after those of the sphere have been removed (compare step 4). It should be added that a strain having a low value of R would not be rejected if an examination of all its M values with the residual strains revealed that it had no other significant relationships, for this would mean that its closest affinities, though low, were with the sphere under study.

(iii) Conversely, those strains in the residual collection having values of M with the first node which were but little inferior to M_p, are added and then checked to see if their inclusion has caused the group to become inhomogeneous (that is the range of R values is greatly widened). If they did cause inhomogeneity, they were returned to the residual collection, unless they had no other significant relationships. In this manner, the spheres have been considered as 'open' spheres and we have sought the most homogeneous groups possible. When these conditions were satisfied the strains comprised within the homogeneous zone were removed from the collection.

(6) All the operations from (2) onwards were repeated with the residual collection in order to isolate another first node, another second node (hence another M_p) and another sphere (which after being rendered homogeneous would be removed) and the process repeated again on the residual collection. These operations were repeated until only those strains which did not belong to any sphere remained. These remaining strains were studied individually and

attached to the taxonomic trees (see below) at what seems the most appropriate place in virtue of the highest values of M which they possessed.

In this way some 166 strains were classified into 28 'spheres' ('clusters' in the terminology of Rogers & Tanimoto).

TAXONOMIC TREES

The next problem was to determine the inter-relationships of these 'spheres' and to construct a taxonomic tree.

As a first step, for each sphere the intra-group mean M value was calculated, that is the mean of the M values between the strains within the sphere. All the inter-group mean M values should then have been calculated (each sphere compared with every other sphere), but this was not possible, however, as about 15,500 of the punched cards would have had to be selected and re-ordered by hand (due to limitations of the available equipment). Instead an $i \times i$ table (Sneath, 1957b) was drawn up listing only the *centrotypes* of each of the spheres. A centrotype is defined as a strain which is the node of a homogeneous and definitive sphere. Not all nodes are centrotypes since some spheres may be neither homogeneous nor definitive. Centrotypes may be regarded as being approximations to the most typical strains of the clusters. New R and H values were calculated from this table (it was found convenient to lower the M limit for the calculation of R and H from $M > 0.65$ to $M > 0.60$ for this purpose and hence these R and H values were called R_{60} and H_{60} respectively). In the way described above homogeneous 'higher order' groups of centrotypes were isolated. Six such groups were identified, whilst two spheres remained isolated (spheres have been given Roman numerals whilst higher order groups have been given letters). Inter-group mean M values were calculated between those spheres comprised within the same higher order group. In this way the number of inter-group mean M values to calculate was reduced from about 275 to about 50. Six taxonomic trees were drawn up from these mean values. Each represented one higher order group and showed the inter-relationships of the spheres one to another within the framework of a single higher order group; they are shown in Figs. 1 to 6. To relate the higher order groups one to another it would have been ideal to calculate inter-group mean M values based on the M values for all the strains comprised within each higher order group but in practice the manual re-arrangement of the cards was impossible. Instead, mean values were calculated between the higher order groups by considering each one to be composed only of the centrotypes of the spheres. The general taxonomic tree (Fig. 7) drawn up on the basis

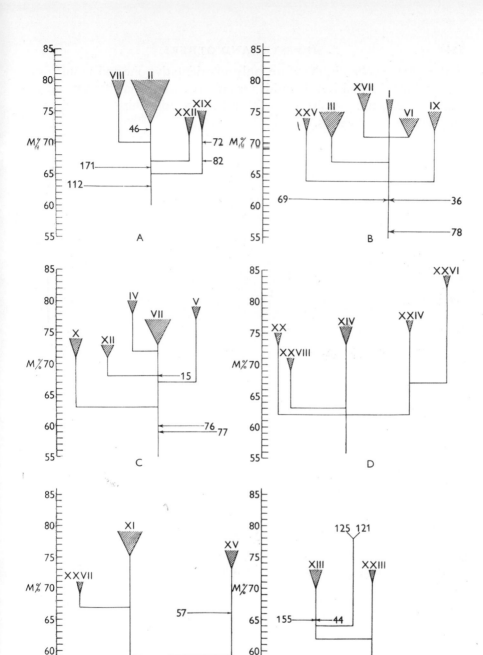

Figs. 1–6. Taxonomic trees of single higher-order groups A–F. On the left side of each figure is a scale representing the % M values. Spheres (roman numerals) are represented by triangular shaded areas, the width at their bases being approximately proportional to the number of strains comprised within the sphere, and the ordinates of their apices corresponding to intra-sphere mean % M values. The points of fusion of the stems of the single spheres with either the stems of other spheres or the main stem of the group correspond to the intersphere mean % M values. Arabic numbers represent strains attached to the stems according to their mean % M values with the spheres.

of these mean values is, therefore, only an orientative one and should not be considered definitive. For this reason no attempt has been made to draw up a comprehensive tree with all the relationships referred to a single scale of M values.

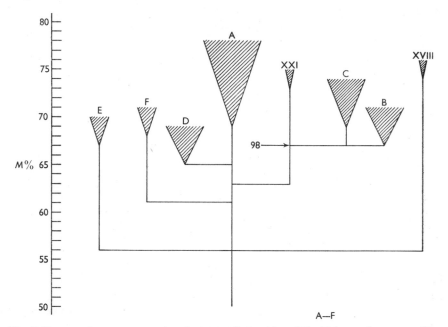

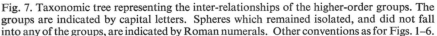

Fig. 7. Taxonomic tree representing the inter-relationships of the higher-order groups. The groups are indicated by capital letters. Spheres which remained isolated, and did not fall into any of the groups, are indicated by Roman numerals. Other conventions as for Figs. 1–6.

RESULTS AND DISCUSSION

In our study we have for the present been content with forming a certain number of spheres, twenty-eight in number. We believe that it is premature to propose revisions of the nomenclature, or to suggest a new systematics of the Actinomycetales. It will be necessary first to solve some other problems if a system is to be constructed which is stable and not subject to continual revision.

First of all, we consider that the method used by us to segregate the spheres can be improved. When a more rapid and more suitable computer is available it will be possible not only to evaluate the R index of the spheres centred around single strains but also to estimate the similarity of spheres and to study the zones which they have in common.

Secondly (again requiring a more suitable computer), it will be necessary to carry out the process of grouping the spheres together into higher order groups by considering not only the distances between the respective centrotypes, but the means of all the distances between all the strains comprised within the spheres. In the course of this procedure some spheres may become fused and then subsequently subdivided during the succeeding operations.

Thirdly, it is necessary to see in which cases it is possible to make an internal repartition of some of the spheres. For this work, a computer which can receive special subprogrammes for single groups will be necessary. Subdivisions within a group should be done by recalculating the M values between the strains comprised within the sphere after having eliminated from the original battery of characters those having the same attribute for all the strains within the sphere (Hill *et al.* 1961). Through this process the principle of a hierarchy of characters would be reintroduced, but it would no longer be a hierarchy based on *a priori* opinions of the importance of the characters but would be based *a posteriori* on their observed distribution in different taxa.

Fourthly, before proposing any revision of the systematics it will be necessary to prove that the limits of the spheres which have been found have a 'biological significance', i.e. that they correspond to true adaptive peaks. The evidence for this can be obtained, as we have already mentioned, only *a posteriori*, by introducing new strains into the trial and determining whether their admission alters the pattern already obtained, or whether they tend to fall within the spheres and not in the intervening spaces.

Only when these steps have been completed will it be possible to maintain that a reasonably stable classification will have been reached and that reasonable proposals for re-ordering the systematics can be made.

Just to underline the provisional nature of the results obtained we have maintained the groupings of strains into spheres, numbered in the same order that the computer gave them. We could, for example, have replaced the terms 'sphere' and 'higher order groups' with expressions having a biological significance and recognized by the Code of Nomenclature, such as 'species', 'series', etc. We could also have named the spheres after the name of the centrotype. It seems to us however that a reserved attitude is best at present. It is also premature to ask what taxonomic rank should be given to the spheres and groups. Certainly some spheres show a remarkable homogeneity so that one might plausibly consider them to be of the rank of species.

Discussion of some of the salient points of the taxonomic trees

As mentioned above, some of the spheres are very homogeneous. The sphere VII of group C, for example, includes 15 strains. Eight were received labelled *Streptomyces griseus*. One was labelled *S. lavendulae*, but Kutzner (1956) when he examined this strain (H93) placed it in his group I which also contains strains of *S. griseus*. Two other strains *S. rubiginosohelvolus* and *S. badius* should belong according to Gause (1958) to the series *helvolus*, which is the name given by the Soviet workers to what in the West is called the series *griseus*. Two further strains, *S. microflavus* and *S. praecox* have already been studied by Ettlinger, Corbaz & Hütter (1958) and according to them should be included in the species *Streptomyces griseus*. Finally in this sphere, there is *S. longisporus* which was placed by Gause (1958) in the series *albus* despite the fact that its aerial mycelium had a yellowish colour, and there is also *S. flavogriseus* of which we have been unable to find in the literature an opinion on its systematic position.

The whole of group C is rather homogeneous. Spheres IV and XII contain many strains belonging to the series *griseus* in the opinion of those authors who tend to be 'lumpers'. Sphere V comprises three strains; 135 (*S. venezuelae*), 190 which is a strain isolated by Taber (1960) and is alkali dependent, and 15, which is the holotype *S. coeruleus* and was isolated by Baldacci (1944).

In our trial a certain number of strains were included which were labelled with either the same name or with synonymous names. Two strains labelled *Streptomyces albireticuli* (86 and 116) fell in the same sphere II of group A. Two strains labelled *S. alboniger* (89 and 151) fell in the same group A but in two neighbouring spheres (II and XXII). Two strains of *S. aureofaciens* fell in the same sphere XIX of group A. Four strains were received with the label *S. rimosus*. Strains 73 and 74 fell in two spheres (XXII and II) of group A. Both produce oxytetracycline: 73 is the strain number 3560 of Waksman's collection, and 74 is an isolate of the Lepetit Laboratories. Strain 47 is the holotype strain of *Streptomyces rimosus*, NRRL B2234, and fell in sphere XV of group E. It is the only strain falling outside group A for which production of tetracycline has been confirmed. Strain 49 was obtained from Lepetit Laboratories, who in turn received it from IPV eight years ago. It falls in sphere XXIII of group F. It is not known if it was an original isolate of Baldacci or if it came from another laboratory, nor is it known if it produces oxytetracycline. Group E is the most heterogeneous of our groups: it is possible that in a further analysis it will be split and that sphere XV will appear nearer to group A than it seems now. Two other strains producing a tetracycline were included in our collection. One was *S. platensis*, which fell in sphere II of group A, and the other was a strain received as *Streptomyces* sp., strain CL 3141/1, producing tetracycline, which was attached to the main stem of sphere XIX of group A.

Two strains labelled as *S. virginiae* (75 and 138) both fell in the sphere VIII of group A, while *S. lavendulae* (46) which is known to be related, but different from *S. virginiae*, was attached to the stem of sphere II of group A. Two strains of *S. diastaticus* (11 and 148) both fell in sphere III of group B. Two strains of *S. parvulus* (107 and 146) both fell in sphere XIV of group D.

Two strains of *Streptomyces scabies* and two strains of *S. antibioticus* gave results which require further investigation, because two of them (*S. antibioticus* 23 and *S. scabies* 50) both fell in sphere X of group C while the other two strains fell in two different spheres of group D. Three strains of *S. albus* (1, 57 and 60) fell in sphere XV of group E or were attached to the stem of sphere XV. Three strains of *S. hygroscopicus* (77, 131 and 149) fell in three different groups: C, A and F. It is possible that in this case different organisms are called by the same name by different workers.

Very interesting is the classification of a group of strains which were received as *Streptomyces coelicolor, S. violaceoruber, S. fradiae, S. violaceus* and *S. novaecaesareae*. The results seem to be in disagreement with the opinion of Kutzner & Waksman (1959) that there are two distinct species, *S. violaceoruber* and *S. coelicolor*. The latter belongs according to them to the *S. griseus* group, but none of these strains fell in group C which is the group corresponding to *S. griseus*. Seven strains fell in group B. Strains 25 and 63 fell into sphere III of that group. It is possible that they are the same strain, as we received strain 25 from Baldacci and strain 63 from Kutzner, both having received the strain originally from Tonolo. Strains 18 and 156 both fell in sphere IX. Strain 18 was received from IPV as *S. violaceus*, and strain 156 was from Gordon who sent it as the original 3535 strain of *S. fradiae* of Waksman's collection: as such it has the same origin as strains 44 and 61 of *S. fradiae* (received respectively from Lepetit and from Küster) but these two strains fell in group F together with two other strains also received as *S. fradiae*.

Strains 58 and 88 of *Streptomyces coelicolor* and *S. violaceoruber* are respectively the CBS Beijerink strain and the NRRL B 1260 strain, which arrived in our hands through the courtesy of Küster and Giolitti respectively. According to Kutzner & Waksman (1959) both these strains should be considered as belonging to the species *S. coelicolor* of the

S. griseus group, but in our study they fell respectively in spheres XVII and XXV of group B. Strain 69 was received from Bradley as *S. violaceoruber* and in our study it was attached to the main stem of group B. Strains 19 (*S. violaceus*), 42 (*S. coelicolor*) and 87 (*S. coelicolor*) fell in group D (in sphere XXIV the stem of sphere XIV and within sphere XIV respectively). Strain 87 is NRRL B 1257, and according to Kutzner & Waksman it is *S. coelicolor* of the *S. griseus* group, whilst strain 42 is ATCC 10147, which according to Kutzner & Waksman belongs to *S. violaceoruber*.

Strains 61, 81 and 129 (all labelled as *S. fradiae*) fell in sphere XIII of group F, while strain 44, also labelled *S. fradiae*, and strain 121 (*S. novaecaesareae*) were attached to the main stem of this group.

Our results demonstrate that it is impossible to draw a sharp line of separation between strains of *Streptomyces coelicolor* and *S. violaceoruber* when the classification is based on overall similarity. The strains in group B are considered to be *S. violaceoruber*, but in group D both kinds are found. Furthermore, neither of the two kinds was found in group C, which comprises the streptomycetes of the *S. griseus* group. The fact that the strains of *Streptomyces* producing red or blue pigments are found in several groups and that out of three strains which were derived from the same 3535 isolate of Waksman two fell in group F and one in group B, give the impression that these organisms are endowed with great ability to vary. At the same time these facts are quite in agreement with the opinion of such 'lumpers' as Ettlinger *et al.* (1958) who considered that the strains referred to as *S. violaceoruber* and *S. fradiae* were in some way related.

Six strains were received as belonging to the *S. viridis* group: two strains, 13 and 142 (NRRL B 1227), fell in sphere III of group B. Two other strains received from IPV were labelled as *S. chartreusis* (strain 20) and *S. viridans* (strain 21) and both fell in sphere XX of group D. Strain 48 was received from Lepetit, and should be the same as NRRL B 1227. Actually its cultural properties do not correspond to *S. viridochromogenes*, the aerial mycelium being pale yellow, melanoid pigment being absent, and the surface of the spores being smooth. It falls in sphere XXVIII of group D. The last strain, 79 (NRRL B 1511), did not belong to any sphere. It may well be a single representative of an independent sphere. A further four strains (53 *Corynebacterium*, 54 *Pasteurella*, 71 *S. mediterranei* and 109 *S. coeruleus*) also showed no significant relationship to any sphere. They were not included in either the taxonomic trees or Table 2.

Conclusion

In conclusion, although we believe that to base a classification on overall similarity undoubtedly represents an advance, none the less we consider the methods so far used for this end are far from being wholly satisfactory. Further work directed along the lines suggested above will therefore be necessary.

ACKNOWLEDGEMENT

The work reported in this paper has been supported by a grant from Lepetit Antibiotici.

REFERENCES

ALIKHANIAN, S. I. & ILJINA, T. S. (1958). Mutagenic action of actinophages. *Nature, Lond.* **181**, 1476.

BALDACCI, E. (1944). Contributo alla sistematica degli attinomiceti. XV. *Actinomyces coeruleus*, n.sp. *Atti. Ist. bot. Univ. Lab. Crittog. Pavia*, **3**, 180.

Bergey's Manual of Determinative Bacteriology (1957). 7th edition. Baltimore: Williams and Wilkins Co.

BISSET, K. A. (1952). *Bacteria.* Edinburgh: Livingstone.

ETTLINGER, L., CORBAZ, R. & HÜTTER, R. (1958). *Zur Systematik der Actinomyceten.* 4. Eine Arteneinteilung der Gattung *Streptomyces* Waksman et Henrici. *Arch. Mikrobiol.* **31**, 326.

GAUSE, G. F. (1958). *Zur Klassifizierung der Actinomyceten.* Jena: Fischer.

GILARDI, E., HILL, L. R., TURRI, M. & SILVESTRI, L. (1960). Quantitative methods in the systematics of *Actinomycetales.* I. *G. Microbiol.* **8**, 203.

GOLDSCHMIDT, R. (1940). *The Material Basis of Evolution.* New Haven: Yale University Press.

HILL, L. R., TURRI, M., GILARDI, E. & SILVESTRI, L. (1961). Quantitative methods in the systematics of Actinomycetales. II. *G. Microbiol.* **9**, 56.

INGER, R. F. (1958). Comments on the definition of genera. *Evolution*, **12**, 370.

KUTZNER, H. J. (1956). Beitrag zur Systematik und Ökologie der Gattung *Streptomyces* Waksman et Henrici. (*Dissertation*). Inst. für Biochemie des Bodens, Braunschweig-Völkenrode.

KUTZNER, H. J. & WAKSMAN, S. A. (1959). *Streptomyces coelicolor* Müller and *Streptomyces violaceoruber* Waksman et Curtis, two distinctly different organisms. *J. Bact.* **78**, 528.

MACCACARO, G. A. (1958). La misura dell'informazione contenuta nei criteri di classificazione. *Ann. Microbiol. Enzimol.* **8**, 231.

MAYR, E. (1942). *Systematics and the origin of species.* New York: Columbia University Press.

MAYR, E. (1957). Difficulties and importance of the biological species. In *The Species Problem*, edited by E. Mayr. Washington: American Association for the Advancement of Science.

MAYR, E. (1959). Trends in avian systematics. *Ibis*, **101**, 293.

MICHENER, C. D. & SOKAL, R. R. (1957). A quantitative approach to a problem in classification. *Evolution*, **11**, 130.

PONTECORVO, G. (1955). The impact of genetics. *J. gen. Microbiol.* **12**, 330.

ROGERS, D. J. & TANIMOTO, T. T. (1960). A computer program for classifying plants. *Science*, **132**, 1115.

SERMONTI, G. & SPADA-SERMONTI, I. (1955). Genetic recombination in *Streptomyces*. *Nature, Lond.* **176**, 121.

SILVESTRI, L. (1960). Vantaggi e problemi di una sistematica adansoniana dei microorganismi. *Nuovi Ann. Ig. Microbiol.* **11**, 1.

SNEATH, P. H. A. (1957a). Some thoughts on bacterial classification. *J. gen. Microbiol.* **17**, 184.

SNEATH, P. H. A. (1957b). The application of computers to taxonomy. *J. gen. Microbiol.* **17**, 201.

SNEATH, P. H. A. & COWAN, S. T. (1958). An electro-taxonomic survey of bacteria. *J. gen. Microbiol.* **19**, 551.

SOKAL, R. R. & MICHENER, C. D. (1958). A statistical method for evaluating systematic relationships. *Kans. Univ. Sci. Bull.* **38**, 1409.

STURTEVANT, A. H. (1942). The classification of the genus *Drosophila* with description of nine new species. *Univ. Tex. Publ.*, no. 4213, 1.

TABER, W. A. (1960). Evidence for the existence of acid-sensitive actinomycetes in soil. *Canad. J. Microbiol.* **6**, 503.

WOOD, H. E. (1949). Evolutionary dates and trends in rhinoceroses. In *Genetics, Palaeontology and Evolution*, edited by G. L. Jepsen *et al.* Princeton (N.J.): Princeton University Press.

WRIGHT, S. (1940). The statistical consequence of Mendelian heredity in relation to speciation. In *New Systematics*, edited by J. Huxley. Oxford: Clarendon Press.

THE PHYLOGENETIC CONCEPT IN BACTERIAL TAXONOMY

K. A. BISSET

Department of Bacteriology, University of Birmingham

NATURAL RELATIONSHIP IMPLICIT IN CLASSIFICATION

Although it is a fact of which most people interested in the problem are well aware, it is nevertheless necessary, before embarking upon a discussion of the influence (actual or potential) of the phylogenetic concept in the taxonomy of bacteria, to emphasize that the situation of systematic bacteriology in this respect, as in most others, is entirely different from that of other fields of systematic biology. In most groups of plants or animals a certain amount of information bearing upon the problem of evolutionary relationships has been generally available and generally accepted for so long that it is simply taken for granted in any discussion of taxonomic problems. No zoologist would find it possible to take seriously a system of classification which cut across the concept that a nereid worm, a crayfish, a cockroach and a bluebottle represent something very like stages in an evolutionary series, whereas the comparable stages represented by a lungfish, an amphibian, a reptile and a bird could be described, and indeed explained, by any educated person.

This being so, it should be understood that where a systematist, dealing with biological material of this sort, may upon occasion decry an excessive reverence for the phylogenetic principle in classification, and suggest the advantages of what he may regard as a more strictly rational approach, he is almost certainly not to be taken as implying that these fundamental notions should be disregarded. They are, in fact, as I have already suggested, taken for granted. A botanist who describes phylogenetic tree-diagrams as 'the most noxious of all weeds' (Ingold, 1959) does not thereby reject the principle; he merely suggests a less dogmatic type of device to illustrate it, and the effect is not entirely dissimilar.

In the case of bacteria, however, this background information is so scanty as to render its interpretation very speculative, and so little known as to have had practically no effect upon general taxonomic work in the group. We simply have not reached the stage at which any logical device that may assist in the solution of our problem can safely be disregarded. When we have achieved the point from which other biological disciplines depart, in their development of cognate arguments, we shall possibly find ourselves in the position of being able to choose a novel route. Until that time, it could only be regarded as presumptuous for bacterial systematists, dealing with a tiny (if important) fraction of the living world, to depart from the principles whereby the great majority are classified. Nor, in my opinion, would any practical advantage accrue from an attempt to do so. All systems of classification of living things are implicitly phylogenetic, being based upon the idea of degrees of relationship. The use of such expressions as genus, family or tribe is not accidental. If it be pleaded that the Linnean school took no thought for evolution, it can only be answered that phylogeny was most decidedly implicit in their works, as their terminology alone reveals, and that the evolutionary principle was the first-born child of modern systematics; it came into being so soon as able minds had access to the information. In my opinion, any intelligent scholar or philosopher, howsoever rigorously segregated from contamination with evolutionary notions, would, if given full access to the information embodied in systematic biology and palaeontology, inevitably propound the thesis afresh for himself, sooner or later. The principle is not even confined to living creatures, but may be applied with success to other matters, for example, language (Hall, 1961).

I trust that I may have adequately established my point: that some minor derogation of too great a reliance upon the phylogenetic principle in taxonomy, on the part of authorities in the zoological or botanical spheres, should not be taken as bearing in any way upon the contemporary situation in bacteriology, where, so far from having a surplus of this commodity, we have very little of it, and certainly none to spare. Nor is there any shame in attempting to amass a little more of it, for use in the construction of those hypotheses which are a necessary stage in the progress of any scientific advance.

THE CONTRIBUTION OF PALAEONTOLOGY

A further contention, which is often proposed, quite mistakenly, in the comparison of bacterial systematics with those of animals and plants, is that the absence of a fossil record precludes any real attempt at the solution of the evolutionary problem in respect of bacteria (for example, Murray, 1960). This belief is based upon the supposition that palaeontology has been one of the major sources of information in the study of evolution in the larger forms of living creatures, whereas the truth is almost the reverse of this. Not only did modern concepts of evolution arise, as I have already pointed out, from the classification of contemporary forms, but for long palaeontology served mainly to test the hypotheses derived from these sources; indeed, the information it provided would have been difficult indeed to interpret, in the absence of such hypotheses. It is, of course, true that the development of certain interesting creatures, such as the horses and elephants, can be followed in astonishing detail in the fossil record, but the all-important changes in the mechanisms of reproduction, which mark the evolution of a mammal from its reptilian ancestors, can be studied only by inference in material from which all soft tissues have vanished without trace. The foundation of the theory lies in comparative anatomy of existing forms, without which the significance of the fossils would have been lost. Palaeontology is thus capable of adding some highly interesting glosses to the margin of the record, and can make suggestions about the dating of the process, but, by itself, it would have told us little or nothing of the probable evolution of, for example, the mammals, whereas much of the story can readily be deduced from a study of living material.

Indeed, there is equally little truth in the suggestion that phylogenetic speculation is not indulged in by zoologists and botanists, in the absence of any fossil record. Two contemporary problems of very great interest fall into precisely this category. Of the origin of the angiosperms there is practically no fossil evidence whatsoever, and of that of man himself there was, until recently, equally little; but both have been the subjects of extensive theoretical speculation, which continues to the present date (Whitehouse, 1960; Le Gros Clark, 1959), and is unlikely to be extinguished in the foreseeable future.

PRACTICAL ADVANTAGES OF THE PHYLOGENETIC APPROACH

If, then, it is accepted that some form of phylogenetic basis for classification must be regarded as normal, in cases comparable with that of the bacteria, it is also true that, where such evidence can be adduced, it provides the best basis for classification, not merely for idealogical reasons, but because it is most convenient in actual use. It is, of course, possible to construct arbitrary groupings by the use of almost any character or characters whatever, but all these are of equal value, only if they are all (other considerations apart) equally stable. In a natural grouping, based upon the interpretation of phylogenetic relationships, and informed by an evolutionary hypothesis which bears examination in the light of the known facts, the wider groups are found to be defined by the more stable, the narrower groups by the more variable characters. This fact is implicit in the very nature of a natural grouping, and is of the utmost value in practical classification. It might be considered superfluous to emphasize the importance of stability in the characters upon which taxonomic distinctions are based, but it is none the less true that, in bacteriology, very many definitions of groups, large or small, have proved to be valueless because of the undue weight accorded to variable or unstable characters.

Yet another important principle of sound taxonomy, with which the phylogenetic systems are usually in good accordance, whereas *ad hoc* classifications frequently are not, is that groups of similar status should be defined always by comparable criteria (Bisset, 1958). This principle has also been violated, with philosophically disastrous results, by bacterial systematists. I have already pointed out, in a previous Symposium in this series, that the confusion caused by the arbitrary inclusion, under the heading of autotrophic bacteria, of chemosynthetic algae, and other protista, has been one factor in the slowness of development of an acceptable systematology for bacteria in general (Bisset & Grace, 1954). Such errors could hardly have survived the necessity for the systematist to justify, even to himself, such a grouping within even a very skeletal phylogenetic framework.

However much it may be pleaded that the function of classification is the practical one of identifying the subject of an observation, it is difficult to deny the existence of the secondary purpose of attempting to show each species in its relationship to the whole system (cf. Hillaby, 1961). It is my contention that the first purpose is best served where both are served as well as possible.

THE PHYLOGENETIC CONCEPT IN BACTERIOLOGY

Although information bearing upon the phylogenetic relationships of bacterial groups is scanty and little known, it is just as true of bacteriological systematists as of zoologists and botanists, that they feel the need for some such basis to their studies. There is little evidence in the pages of Bergey's *Manual* to suggest that it is supposed to be constructed upon phylogenetic lines, but this is nevertheless true, at least in theory (Breed, 1956), and even the most strictly practical handbooks of medical bacteriology permit a slight acknowledgement of the existence of phylogenetic considerations, by the use of the expression 'higher bacteria', to describe the Actinomycetes, as well as by the normal use of phylogenetic terms for groupings. Nevertheless, I am aware of only three examples of general evolutionary theories applicable to the classification of bacteria, and of these, one is entirely morphological and one equally entirely physiological: the third, for which I am myself responsible, attempts to take both viewpoints into consideration, and since, not unnaturally, I regard it as the most logically satisfactory attempt, so far, at the solution of a difficult problem, I propose to examine some aspects both of my original theory, and of certain elaborations and modifications of it which I have subsequently suggested, in the light of improved information.

To explain shortly the two, first-mentioned theories: these are the morphological scheme of Kluyver & van Niel (1936), and the physiological hypothesis of Lwoff (1944) and Knight (1945). The former commences from the premise that the simplest, and therefore most primitive morphology is that of a coccus, and it derives the apparently more complex bacteria independently from this source: one line of descent culminates in the spirilla, one in *Streptomyces*, and a third in the sporing bacilli. The defects of this scheme are unfortunately numerous, but a few examples will suffice, First, a coccus is not usually of genuinely simple morphology at all, but may possess a complex multicellular structure (Bisset, 1954), suggesting a relationship with the sporing bacilli. The possibility that the cocci may, in fact, be derived from ancestors resembling sporing bacilli is discussed below, in another context. Secondly, the theory of Kluyver and van Niel requires multiple, independent origins for such fundamental structures as spores and flagella, and this is highly unlikely. Lastly, the theory takes no account of physiological evolution, and suggests that non-exacting, saprophytic, and even autotrophic forms may be derived from specialized, often parasitic, and nutritionally exacting ancestors. This is quite contrary to all accepted belief upon this problem.

By contrast, the theory of Lwoff and of Knight suggests that the descent of bacteria may be traced by an examination of their stage of evolution in a process of progressive loss of synthetic power. This is unquestionably true, so far as the main or background picture is concerned, and so long as the effect of biological convergence is properly taken into account. In general, the nutritionally less exacting organisms may be regarded as more primitive, and the more exacting, as more highly evolved for a specialized mode of life; but it is important not to lose sight of the possibility that two, quite unrelated species may become adapted to a similar environment, and thus evolve a similar type of physiology. Information from this source is of the greatest value as an adjunct to morphology, in the classification of bacteria, but the example of the autotrophic bacteria is a warning to those who would promote physiology, as a taxonomic panacea, to the disregard of morphology.

It is, indeed, often urged that just this should be done, in certain selected cases, but it is usually found that morphology (like evolution, in the cases already discussed) is taken for granted in the larger groupings. Those who cast aspersions upon attempts to distinguish species of *Bacillus* or *Streptomyces* by morphological criteria, are seldom found to advance constructive suggestions as to how otherwise the corresponding families might be defined.

In parenthesis, at this stage, I would interject that, although nobody who has read thus far can reasonably suspect me of claiming morphology to be an infallible guide, it may be safer to emphasize that many of the same reservations as should be borne in mind in the use of physiology in taxonomy must be applied also to morphology. Such examples as the indiscriminate lumping together of all bacteria possessing a stalk, howsoever different the origins of these stalks may be, give evidence of at least occasional failure to do so, with results no less unfortunate than in the case of the comparable misuse of physiological evidence.

OVERALL EVOLUTIONARY TRENDS IN BACTERIA

My own first attempts at the establishment of an evolutionary system of classification (Bisset, 1950, 1952) were concerned with the overall problem of the entire group. The appearance exists of a general trend of development in bacteria, analogous with that which is found in almost every other natural group, from an aquatic to a terrestrial mode of life; and this seems to have progressed in parallel with the process of evolution by physiological loss, suggested by Lwoff and Knight. The more primitive bacteria, on this reckoning, are aquatic, spiral, polar flagellate and nutritionally unexacting. They may be photosynthetic or chemosynthetic to a varying degree. The more advanced forms are straight rods, cocci or branched filaments; their flagella are numerous and peritrichous, enabling them to swarm on moist, solid surfaces, or have disappeared (cf. also Leifson, 1960); they frequently possess spores capable of aerial distribution. Many of these advanced bacteria are nutritionally exacting, none is autotrophic. The most successful terrestrial bacteria are probably *Bacillus* and *Streptomyces*, and the morphology of the latter converges with that of certain fungi, although there is little doubt, both from its nuclear cytology and (probably more convincing to those who have not studied the foregoing) from the chemical structure of its cell walls (Cummins & Harris, 1958) that it is truly bacterial in its relationships. The morphology of *Bacillus* also converges with that of certain yeasts, although the relatively primitive character of flagellation is retained by many species; this point is of some significance in consideration of the question of the origin and further evolution of superficially simpler types of bacteria, by degeneration from these highly organized terrestrial genera. The latter possibility was neglected in my original theory, where the assumption was made that all the less structurally complex Gram-positive bacteria are less highly evolved than the complex ones. In fact, it is distinctly possible that certain of the former may be descended from the latter. This state of affairs is, of course, known to exist in plants and animals, where the processes of neoteny and degeneration, often associated with specialization of habitat or mode of life, have produced an apparent simplification in the structure of highly evolved species, by comparison with their own progenitors. It cannot, however, properly be argued that the Gram-positive bacteria have a separate origin from the Gram-negatives, being derived from some fungus-like ancestors, beyond and above *Streptomyces*. Apart from the evidence of their nuclear cytology and cell-wall composition, the possession by many bacilli of that typically bacterial organelle, the unifibrillar flagellum in peritrichous arrangement, renders their descent from a non-flagellate ancestor highly improbable, and some degree of relationship with the other flagellate bacteria correspondingly probable. The cytological and chemical resemblances between *Bacillus* and *Streptomyces* are so close that widely diverse origins cannot well be attributed to them, even although *Streptomyces* has no trace of flagellation.

It is not difficult to conceive the development of *Bacillus*-like rods from those spirilla which possess resting cells with some of the characters of endospores, by the same sort of process whereby a typical bacterium might be derived from those whose resting cells resemble microcysts. Although the evolution of *Streptomyces* demands a lengthier process, in which a sporing bacillus might well be an intermediate phase, some spirilla possess the potentialities for producing branched forms, as well as cocci, peritrichously flagellate rods and stalked cells (Bisset, 1961). The suggestion that *Bacillus* is a relatively primitive form of Gram-positive bacterium (although a successful colonizer of the terrestrial environment) is borne out, to some extent, by electrically computed analysis of taxa (Sneath & Cowan, 1958), wherein this genus is shown to be more closely related to the Gram-negative group than are the, presumably, more highly evolved Gram-positives, including not only actinomycetes but also those superficially less complex forms, to which I have already referred, whose origin is probably complex and multiple, but including a degenerative process in many cases: the drooping side-branches of the evolutionary tree.

RETROGRESSIVE EVOLUTION IN BACTERIA

The possibility of retrogressive developments in the phylogeny of bacteria, whereby, for example, *Micromonospora* might have evolved, by adaptation to a specialized environment, from the universally distributed *Streptomyces*, or *Clostridium* from *Bacillus*, was suggested in connexion with the earlier evolutionary scheme (Bisset, 1952), but the existence of a general principle, operating in a remarkably similar manner, in parallel, in several different groups, became apparent in the course of an attempt to correlate the results of a fairly extensive systematic study of the oral flora (Bisset & Davis, 1960; *q.v.* also for much of the relevant literature). The conclusion drawn from this study, so far as phylogenetics of bacteria are concerned, is that many of the most important oral parasites show signs of being members of degenerative series, in respect both of their morphology and physiology; and a comparison of these oral forms with parasitic bacteria in general showed that there exists a very widespread tendency for such series to occur among Gram-positive genera. This argument is developed at length elsewhere (Bisset, 1959a), but, for present purposes, it suffices to indicate the main tendencies that are exhibited. These are remarkably similar in every case, and consist of the progressive reduction in size and morphological complexity, loss of Gram-positivity, and loss of enzyme systems, including catalase; so that the more advanced (or degenerate) parasites become anaerobic, as well as superficially Gram-negative and nutritionally exacting. Such degeneracy, as an accompaniment to the adoption of a parasitic existence, is a commonplace of zoology or botany, but its association with such weighty taxonomic characters as Gram staining and anaerobiosis is of some importance in the classification of bacteria.

Usually, it is possible to refer the putative origins of these series to highly developed and successful saprophytic genera. The rather obvious, and indeed well known if not fully recognized, case of the weakly Gram-positive, anaerobic *Clostridium*, apparently the gut-parasitic representative of *Bacillus*, although still capable in some degree of a free, saprophytic existence, has already been referred to; but several much more complete series can be conceived. That which leads from free-living *Sarcina*, often motile, sometimes sporogenous, through *Staphylococcus* and *Neisseria* to the tiny, anaerobic, almost Gram-negative *Veillonella*, limited in mode of life to the parasitic metabolism of a single type of compound, is one of the more spectacular. A similar series in Actinomycetes, nearly all the parasitic genera of which do, in fact, have an oral habitat, is less striking only because its members are less well known to most bacteriologists. The saprophytic ancestor is presumably *Streptomyces*, whence a range of progressively degenerate *Leptotrichia* leads to *Fusiformis*, the counterpart of *Veillonella* in the former example. The true *Actinomyces*, parasitic and microaerophilic, would appear to be separately derived through some intermediate with the morphology of *Micromonospora* (Bisset, 1957), and this is confirmed by the cell-wall analyses of Cummins & Harris (1958), Davis & Baird-Parker (1959), and Davis & Freer (1960), which show *Actinomyces* to be distinct in this respect from the other parasitic actinomycetes.

It is tempting to attribute the origins of all the morphologically less complex Gram-positive bacteria to similar processes, associated either with parasitism or a specialized habitat of some other kind, but there is not enough evidence to do more than hazard a guess in most cases, and often less than that, although the cell-wall analyses referred to in the last paragraph give interesting hints at what may be the truth. It is logically possible to derive the true cocci from *Bacillus*, through the motile, sporogenous sarcinae, and the streptococci (once more parasitic and catalase-deficient) similarly, through the lactobacilli, but the latter process may well have originated from some vanished or unrecognized forerunner of *Bacillus*. The simpler branched forms provide a correspondingly less simple problem, and no rules appear to be generally applicable. The true corynebacteria have a very limited habitat upon mucous membranes of mammals, and in this respect, as in several others, converge with *Streptococcus*. *Nocardia* is possessed of a versatility only rivalled by that of *Pseudomonas*, but resembles *Corynebacterium* in its cell-wall composition, bearing some resemblance also to *Bacillus* and rather more to the saprophytic actinomycetes. Those readers who have borne with me so far will not find it difficult to suggest alternative explanations for these observations (cf. Bisset, 1959*b*).

SOME GENERAL CONCLUSIONS

It has been said that if a systematist were presented with the task of classifying not a natural group, but an assemblage of different types of vehicle, he would be at a loss how to begin (Lam, 1959), because of the difficulty of deciding which of their many characters should be regarded as important. This might well be the situation if the classification were to be confined to new, mass-produced cars; here the systematist is in precisely the situation of the actual microbial systematist (if the latter chooses to work, as it were, *in vacuo*), but all that is actually lacking is information. Given a selection of vehicles, ranging in style from ox-waggons through broughams to veteran, vintage, second-hand and eventually brand-new motor cars, of as many different makes as possible, our systematist, unless he were violently prejudiced or exceedingly dense, would have very little trouble in establishing an evolutionary system and phylogenetic classification. He might well find it possible to work out that a modern Daimler has closer relationships with a Mercedes than with a Jaguar, even though it now shares a machine-shop with the latter. If what might be called the palaeontology of the system were subjected to scrutiny, I have little doubt that our investigator, having observed such features, in extinct lines, as the disk-brakes on an early Lanchester, the steering-column gear-change of a Darracq, or the roller-bearings in the wheel-hub of a prehistoric Celtic cart, would be tempted to describe these as advanced characters in otherwise primitive forms. And if he went so far as to compare the wheels of the same cart, with delicate spokes, and iron tyres, in addition to the efficient hub-bearings already noted, with those of its lineal descendent in medieval Provence, tyreless, solid wood on a solid hub, he might draw the further conclusion that the latter, although ostensibly primitive, was actually degenerate.

Arbitrary, and supposedly practical classifications of similar material do most certainly exist, as for example in the road-tax regulations of Britain, where are to be found such definitions as *tricycle not equipped with means for reversing*, whereunder might be included a mini-car, a motor-rickshaw, or a velocipede with an auxiliary engine. In my opinion, precisely such anomalies of classification occur in systematic bacteriology, where the assistance of the phylogenetic principle, as a guide, is not sought.

In previous Symposia of this Society, I have remarked upon the gratification that I am able to obtain when wiser men than myself succeed in proving by the solution of equations, that what I have long believed is actually true. So, in this case, it is cheering to find, here and there, among the by-products of paper-chromatography and the electric computer, some little facts to bear out my own ideas, especially in the field of phylogenetic speculation where facts are so hard to find. The value of cell-wall analyses is too obvious to require emphasis, especially in the case of intermediate groupings. Among the finer branches of the tree, the present problem is to judge which types of compound are the more significant. A similar question arises in the mathematical studies of Sneath & Cowan (1958), since it is difficult, in the present context, to agree that all criteria are of equal value, but some of their more tentative conclusions are of great interest: apart from the problem of *Bacillus*, which will be further discussed below, there is their suggestion that the typical Gram-negative rods (which, phylogenetically speaking, may be considered as ranging from *Vibrio* to *Proteus* in an ascending series, according to their degree of adaptation to a terrestrial environment) are closely related, by comparison with the much more divergent Gram-positives, and have little claim, in many cases, to their abhorrent generic names. The exception is *Proteus* itself, which appears, on phylogenetic reasoning, to be a highly evolved form, and which bears its generic claims honourably in the hands of the computer. There is much to be said for the idea that these Gram-negative bacteria should be disrated into species of the serviceable genus *Bacterium,* whereas there is room for several genera in the family Bacillaceae, even without taking into consideration the vexed relationships of the nitrogen-fixing genera. If bacteria have a single origin, then the electrically computed relationships of *Bacillus* with the Gram-negatives are presumably indicative of its primitive stage in the Gram-positive line, and, apart from the evidence already discussed, which points rather to this conclusion, there is a further point, not normally taken into consideration in arguments of this nature, which connects *Bacillus* closely with the spirilla, as the probable general ancestor. This is the production of small, motile gonidia, as a means of reproduction. It is commonly found in *Bacillus* and *Spirillum* (and also in the nitrogen-fixers), but is unusual elsewhere among bacteria. As it is quite a normal process in the flagellate protista, from which all flagellate life, including bacteria, must eventually be derived (Bisset, 1959 *b*), it can be regarded as a primitive character, comparable with the flagellum itself.

Consideration of Gram-positive and Gram-negative lines of evolution emphasizes the necessity for distinguishing between what might be called primary and secondary Gram-negatives. The latter are Gram-positives that have lost their ability to retain the Gram stain, although in fact this loss is seldom complete. It is apparently associated with the adoption of a more specialized mode of life, often parasitism, as in the cases described in the last section, and is correspondingly prominent among the bacteria studied by the large proportion of investigators with some degree of interest in medical problems. True Gram-negative bacteria never show any trace of a tendency to retain the Gram stain, and are distinct in many other respects from the foregoing. They also seem to be a very small group and, apart from pseudomonads, not especially numerous or successful, by comparison with the Gram-positives. The pseudomonads, including most species that are usually classified as vibrios (Davis & Park, 1962), are, by contrast, so numerous, successful and versatile that they may reasonably be regarded as the counterpart of *Bacillus,* although much less fully adapted to a terrestrial existence. To derive a pseudo-monad from a spirillum requires little exercise of imagination, whereas any member of the Gram-negative group could readily be derived from a pseudomonad.

My revised views upon the phylogenetic classification of bacteria, in the most general terms, are that the same fixed points, in outline, seem to hold good; *Spirillum* remains the best choice for the aquatic ancestor, and a variety of successful adaptations to a terrestrial environment have been made. The suggestion that now requires to be added is that many specialized forms seem to have been derived from a rather small range of successful genera, notably *Bacillus* and *Streptomyces* (of which the latter is more advanced, and may stem from the former), and possibly the pseudomonads in the Gram-negative group. Even on the assumption that there is some validity in the more speculative portions of this argu-ment, there remain certain enigmas, of which one of the most obscure is the role of *Nocardia* and its allies. These are sometimes specialized and often versatile, and have apparent affinities both with advanced and with primitive groups. Here, however, we can solace ourselves once more by being in good company. If such charming and interesting creatures as penguins and tortoises show a similar reluctance to oblige the systemat-ists by fitting neatly into any really satisfactory schemes, we may be permitted our *Nocardia*.

REFERENCES

Bisset, K. A. (1950). Evolution in bacteria and the significance of the bacterial spore. *Nature, Lond.* **166**, 431.

Bisset, K. A. (1952). *Bacteria.* Edinburgh: Livingstone.

Bisset, K. A. (1954). The cytology of *Micrococcus cryophilus. J. Bact.* **67**, 41.

Bisset, K. A. (1957). Some observations on the mode of sporulation and relation-ships of monosporous Actinomycetes. *J. gen. Microbiol.* **17**, 562.

Bisset, K. A. (1958). Letter. *Int. Bull. Bact. Nom. Taxon.* **8**, 133.

Bisset, K. A. (1959a). Characters associated with parasitism in Gram-positive bacteria. *Nature, Lond.* **183**, B.A. 29.

Bisset, K. A. (1959b). Bacteria. *Vistas in Botany,* **1**, 313. London: Pergamon Press.

Bisset, K. A. (1961). Morphological variation in *Spirillum* spp., with observations on the origin of Hyphomicrobia. *J. gen. Microbiol.* **24**, 427.

Bisset, K. A. & Davis, G. H. G. (1960). *The Microbial Flora of the Mouth.* London: Heywood.

Bisset, K. A. & Grace, J. B. (1954). The nature and relationships of autotrophic bacteria. *Autotrophic Micro-organisms. Symp. Soc. gen. Microbiol.* **4**, 28.

Breed, R. S. (1956). The relationship of bacteria and viruses to other living things. *Canad. J. Microbiol.* **2**, 201.

Cummins, C. S. & Harris, H. (1958). Studies on the cell-wall composition and taxo-nomy of Actinomycetales and related groups. *J. gen. Microbiol.* **18**, 173.

DAVIS, G. H. G. & BAIRD-PARKER, A. C. (1959). The classification of certain filamentous bacteria with respect to their chemical composition. *J. gen. Microbiol.* **21**, 612.

DAVIS, G. H. G. & FREER, J. H. (1960). Studies on an oral aerobic actinomycete. *J. gen. Microbiol.* **23**, 163.

DAVIS, G. H. G. & PARK, R. W. A. (1962). A taxonomic study of certain bacteria currently classified as *Vibrio* species. *J. gen. Microbiol.* **27**, 101.

HALL, R. A. (1961). How pidgin English has evolved. *New Scientist,* **9**, 413.

HILLABY, J. (1961). Taxonomy: a neglected science. *New Scientist,* **9**, 262.

INGOLD, C. T. (1959). Fungi. *Vistas in Botany,* **1**, 348. London: Pergamon Press.

KLUYVER, A. J. & VAN NIEL, C. B. (1936). Prospects for a natural system of classification of bacteria. *Zbl. Bakt.* (2. *Abt.*), **94**, 369.

KNIGHT, B. C. J. G. (1945). Growth factors in microbiology. Some wider aspects of nutritional studies with micro-organisms. *Vitamins & Hormones,* **3**, 105.

LAM, H. J. (1959). Taxonomy and general principles and angiosperms. *Vistas in Botany,* **1**, 3. London: Pergamon Press.

LE GROS CLARK, W. E. (1959). *The Antecedents of Man.* Edinburgh: University Press.

LEIFSON, E. (1960). *Atlas of Bacterial Flagellation.* New York and London: Academic Press.

LWOFF, A. (1944). *L'Évolution Physiologique. Études des Pertes de Fonctions chez les Microorganismes.* Paris: Hermann.

MURRAY, R. G. E. (1960). The evolution of bacteria. *Evolution: its Science and Doctrine. Symp. Roy. Soc. Canada,* p. 123.

SNEATH, P. H. A. & COWAN, S. T. (1958). An electro-taxonomic survey of bacteria. *J. gen. Microbiol.* **19**, 551.

WHITEHOUSE, H. L. K. (1960). Origin of angiosperms. *Nature, Lond.* **188**, 957.

PREREQUISITES FOR VIRUS CLASSIFICATION

N. W. PIRIE

Rothamsted Experimental Station

The agents causing infectious disease were vigorously and, within the technical limitations of the time, intelligently discussed in the period from Fracastoro (1546) to Bradley (1721); then came the doldrums that preceded Pasteur. Linnaeus and his pupils, e.g. Nyander (1757), put several of these agents among the Acarids, although they must have realized that their knowledge was inadequate for attempting any classification at all. But the urge to do something with every known entity is strong; the agents of disease were therefore shoved in at a point where they would be least objectionable. This casual treatment is odd because Linnaeus was a professor of medicine and wrote extensively on medical themes.

Since the time of Pasteur, so much knowledge has been won about the larger micro-organisms that systems of classification are justified; but the Linnean urge still operates and many people try to include viruses in their systems. Partial justification for the tendency to carry reverence for Linnaeus so far as to copy his bad habits, comes from the use of the word taxonomy which carries the connotation of getting men into line in an army—it matters little how unlike they are so long as the result is tidy, If the science had been called diatithetics, from διατίθημι, which can carry the connotation of arranging goods as in a shop, we would be constrained to be more careful. The point would be brought out that the primary object of classification is use; it should help us to find the entities classified and should not merely be a means of getting them out of the way.

We can easily be misled by the obvious and salient features of the group being classified. Thus animals could be divided into those living in water or on land, those usually naked or hairy, those with horns and without, the retromingent and promingent, and so on. The possibilities of idiosyncratic classification are endless and each would have a specialist band of devotees such as, to take in order the examples cited, war-time food-controllers, parasitologists, taxidermists and catheter manufacturers. We classify on the basis of a point of view and with an end in view and, so long as the classification meets these needs, it is valid. The search for Order, or Design, in Nature supplies the stimulus to look for something better than this—for the attempt to construct *the* classification of a group and not just *a* classification. When that is done the things classified must be studied in more detail; so many of their attributes must be considered before the lines of classification are drawn that there is little prospect of new knowledge compelling a rearrangement. But it is observation and not logic that ultimately shows which of the systems are idiosyncratic. In this article several examples will be mentioned where confusion has been, or could be, caused by using only one quality, even when that quality is dramatic, as a complete criterion for designing a scientifically, rather than a practically, useful grouping. The implication is that the same troubles would arise were similar attempts made in virus classification.

Etymologically, the word species means 'what can be seen' and all early classification depended on differences between organisms that were apparent to the unaided eye without even looking inside the organism. It is amazing to read Buffon on the American opossums; he fusses away about the distribution of claws on their hind toes as a feature distinguishing opossums from all other animals (this was before Australian fauna had reached laboratories) and attaches little importance to the peculiarities of their urino-genital structure, although he was aware of some of them. Linnaeus attached more importance, in animals at any rate, to internal structure. He used, for example, similarities in skull structure to define relationships; but embryology and biochemistry had not then developed far enough to be woven into the system. Gilbert White probably introduced the first non-structural quality into accepted classification when he distinguished the chiff-chaff from the willow warbler because of its different song. This is important for our theme, for it gave an activity as much importance in classification as a structure.

The significance of evolution

Classification, as most speakers in this Symposium will probably point out, is not the same thing as labelling species, but it depends on the species having been labelled. It also depends on there being an agreed or tacit definition of the group being classified. Linnaeus was entitled to assume that people knew what plants and animals were; all he had to do was arrange them. But virus research is not a subject like Botany or Zoology, instead, it is like Agriculture in that it gets its unity from our directed interest and not necessarily from an intrinsic uniformity in the subject material. Attempts to group all the viruses together may therefore be as ill-conceived as would be an agriculturist's attempt to relate potatoes and eggs because of their comparable size, shape, edibility, and role in the perpetuation of the species. In justification for this point of view, three possible ways in which viruses appeared or are still appearing may be mentioned:

(1) They can be the extreme form of degeneration of micro-organisms so that, from merely being able to multiply in a host, they have become totally parasitic and dependent on the host's synthetic systems.

(2) They can arise in a cell when, as a result of an aberration in metabolism, it produces a structure robust enough to withstand normal scavenging processes, and able to act as a model for further synthesis.

(3) They can be structures with qualities similar to those needed in possibility (2) but coming into the cell from outside—from another species for example.

Of these three, possibilities (1) and (3) are probably the most generally accepted. The possibility that anything similar to the viruses we now study was a stage in the evolution of more elaborate organisms, though often touted, need not be taken seriously. Present-day viruses demand so much from an environment before they can multiply in it that they are improbable components of the pre-biotic world.

The group we are attempting to classify is therefore uncertain and so is the concept of a species in it. Mayr's dictum (1953) that 'the most objective property of species is perhaps the gap between different species. It is the place where gene exchange is interrupted' is admirable in the context in which he used it. But it does not apply here because a virus can exchange genetic material with its host and this, in principle, permits a degree of hybridization unknown in the metabionta. By hind-sight this compatibility is not altogether surprising for the simpler a structure becomes, the more likely becomes an accidental congruity.

A brief summary of the last two paragraphs is that there is no reason to think that viruses are related, as plants and animals are generally held to be, by an evolutionary sequence. Many taxonomists maintain that evolution is not a fundamental part of their science and point out that much of Linnaeus's scheme is still looked on as valid, although he preceded Darwin; they also point out that the fossil record is so incomplete, especially for plants, that phylogeny is somewhat arbitrary and may, in places, be being deduced from present-day classification rather than vice versa. They also accept the possibility of polyphyletic origins for certain groups, which implies that a valid taxonomy can stand on its own legs without regard to the origins of the objects classified. Nevertheless, most of us think that, unless a classification is intended for practical use only, it should make phylogenetic sense, and that if the members of groups such as the angiosperms or teleosts have come to resemble each other by convergent evolution, the grouping is unsatisfactory and the group will be sorted out when knowledge increases. The unique position of Linnean classification depends on this; though the family tree may not be known, we assume that a metabiontal species evolved in only one way. But we cannot make this assumption about viruses; the appeal to phylogeny is not, therefore, helpful now nor likely to become so in the foreseeable future. There is little hope of bringing all the viruses into one comprehensive system that has scientific validity. All that will probably be achieved is the establishment of some groups of viruses within which relationships can be defined, but the groups may remain unrelated to one another.

QUALITIES USEFUL IN CLASSIFICATION

The number of qualities needed for classification depends on the size of a group. When qualities are simply present or absent n are needed for the unequivocal labelling of 2^n species; for classification 2 or $3n$ qualities would probably be needed but the precise number depends on the degree of subdivision that is proposed. About 10 independent pieces of information would therefore be needed concerning each of the 200–500 viruses before they could even be unequivocally labelled and 20 or more for their classification. This illustrates clearly one reason why classification is easier when organisms are visible and complex rather than invisible and simple; more can be found out about them. As much information is gained by a glance at a flower as by a year's work with a virus. Successful classification depends on the use of much more than the theoretical, minimum, amount of information. All the properties of viruses should therefore be used in their classification, for success probably depends as much on the number of different directions from which evidence is coming as on anything else.

Morphological classification

This is the theme of another paper at this Symposium (see p. 145) so it need only be treated briefly. It is obvious that chaos would be introduced into plant and animal classification if size and external shape were regarded as very important; these properties have assumed importance in virus classification because the particles have often been referred to as molecules and that disguises their commonly pleomorphic character. This loose phraseology raises few difficulties with the smaller, more-or-less spherical viruses. X-ray evidence shows that those viruses that can be crystallized have constant diameters; electron-micrography or ultra-centrifugation allows viruses to be arranged at present into perhaps ten size categories with the probability of greater refinement in future. The crystal form complements electronmicrographic evidence about particle shape but so far has shown little rationality; thus many unrelated viruses crystallize, as spheres might reasonably be expected to do, in rhombic dodecahedra, whereas preparations of serologically related members of the tobacco necrosis group of viruses crystallize in surprisingly diverse manners (Bawden & Pirie, 1942).

Tobacco mosaic virus (TMV), and other elongated viruses, have not so far been crystallized, but X-ray evidence on dried orientated prepara-tions suggest that they have constant cross-sections. The particle lengths, in spite of reiterated claims for constancy (Boedtker & Simmons, 1958; Hall, 1958), are variable (Pirie, 1957a), and Johnson (1951) claimed that the mode, with TMV, depends on the host plant. This point needs fuller study by modern and more refined technique. It may be that this varia-tion is caused by destruction or aggregation in the host or during pre-paration for electron micrography, but, until it has been controlled, proposals (Brandes & Wetter, 1959) that viruses should be classified by length measurements, should be treated sceptically, in spite of their attractive simplicity.

The fundamental reason why size and external shape will probably not play a large part in a scheme for classifying the smaller viruses is that they do not permit sufficiently fine resolution by present-day methods. One sphere or rod is very like another. Morphology assumes more importance with large viruses such as vaccinia and some bacterial viruses but it will become really useful only when it is extended to the inside of the particle.

Chemical classification

As a prelude to any attempt to use chemical methods of classification, the success of these methods in the domain of pure chemistry deserves attention. As always, the initial problem was labelling and it was to this that such writers as John Locke (1700) directed attention. With the development of a satisfactory conception of the nature of an element, various pieces of classification could start, e.g. Dobereiner's Triads which grouped the then known halogens and the alkaline earth metals. New-lands 'Law of Octaves' was a major success but it was not quite com-plete enough to win general acceptance. That had to wait for the genius of Mendeleef with the Periodic Table which gives a unique and unequivocal classification that was, in the end, strengthened by the apparent anomalies (e.g. the inversions of A and K; Co and Ni; Te and I). Nearly a hundred years earlier Bergman (1784) had tried to classify salts along Linnean lines; it is easy now to see why he failed and Mendeleef succeeded. First, Mendeleef tackled the simpler problems of the elements and he had much more information to help to expose bad bits of classification. Secondly, Mendeleef relied on atomic mass and this, as we now know, has a close connexion with the actual architecture of the atom. But the third reason is the most relevant. We now classify salts interchangeably by grouping under the metals or under the acids and see that it is purely convenience that makes us use the former arrangement predominantly. Bergmann, and some would-be virus classifiers, did not realize that the sequence of words in a Linnean classi-fication is not arbitrary but vital (cf. Pirie, 1952, 1955) and that the Linnean appearance of such names as sodium chloride or ferrous sulfate is spurious.

The elements, therefore, can be classified unequivocally and the salts arbitrarily. As molecular complexity increases, the problem of chemical classification becomes completely chaotic. Some groups of organic molecules, the saturated fatty acids, for example, are straightforward; they are arranged in order of size, but sometimes split into two series according to whether they have an odd or even number of carbon atoms. With increasing diversity of substituents, problems arise because the same structure can be considered from different points of view. This is well illustrated by the early controversy over the stereochemical nam-ing of threonine. It was called threonine because of its relationship with threonic acid and naturally occurring threonine has the orientation of the threonic acid that, because of its derivation through the sugar series from D glyceraldehyde, is called D. But this orientation is that of the amino acids found in proteins and it is there called L. There is no satis-factory solution; the molecule can equally logically be regarded as hav-ing two separate derivations, but it is arbitrarily called L because it is more often handled by those interested in proteins and amino acids than by those interested in sugars. The sugars illustrate another aspect of the problem. The first volume of that monument to chemical logic, *Beil-steins Handbuch der Organischen Chemie*, treated glucose and similar sugars as straight chain polyhydroxy compounds. Fifteen years later (1933) volume **17** appeared and it was then known that in most circum-stances they were six-membered heterocycles containing one oxygen atom and so should be dealt with in that volume. At the right place there was a note to this effect promising treatment in the *Ergänzungs-*

werk. But when this appeared, logic admitted defeat, and a special volume on carbohydrates, considered as an arbitrary group in their own right, was announced and it was published in 1938. Chemical classification is clearly not in such a happy state that it can be accepted as axiomatic that increasing knowledge of the chemistry of viruses will lead automatically to their classification. It is, however, probable that this increasing knowledge will help, as it has in the classification of other groups. We may go on to consider the extent of this probable help.

Aristotle, knowing neither *Chironomus* and the root nodules of legumes, nor those antarctic fish with no red corpuscles, used the presence of haemoglobin as the criterion for membership of a group that is more or less the same as our vertebrates. It would have seemed logical, ninety years ago, to say that, if an organism contained cellulose it was not an animal. Then cellulose was found in tunicates; but they have so many other biochemical peculiarities that they are recognized as universal exceptions and cellulose remained a useful criterion for a plant. Now it is well known as a component of ageing tissue even in man (Hall, Lloyd & Saxl, 1958) and so loses all value. Similarly, the use of hydroxyapatite in bone-like structures is not limited to the vertebrates but appears in *Polytoma* and *Polytomella* (Pautard, 1958). The systematic study of the occurrence of essential oils, alkaloids, raphide crystals and other substances of generally unknown function, which is often called biochemical taxonomy but would be better called analytical taxonomy, has not so far proved helpful (Gibbs, 1958). Even at the species level, elementary analysis can be misleading. Thus Carlisle (1958) finds that some individuals of *Molgula manhattenensis* contain niobium instead of the normal vanadium.

Simple analyses are therefore not likely to be useful. The smaller viruses, such as TMV, are not known to contain anything besides protein, ribonucleic acid (RNA), iron (Loring & Waritz, 1957; Loring, Al-Rawi & Fujimoto, 1958), and possibly calcium (Pirie, 1956) and 1:7 diamino-4-azaheptane (Johnson & Markham, 1962). The large viruses generally contain lipids, and ribonucleic acid is replaced by deoxyribonucleic acid (DNA). These chemical criteria have been used (Cooper, 1961) as the basis for a classification but obviously they do not allow even enough permutations for labelling. At one time, persistent efforts were made to correlate the presence of RNA or DNA with the ability of a virus to infect plants, animals, or bacteria. This correlation seemed groundless *a priori* and it has gradually been demolished as more analyses have been published on carefully made virus preparations; its last remnant disappeared with the discovery of a small bacterial virus containing RNA (Loeb & Zinder, 1961).

Although the simple presence or absence of such components as RNA, DNA and lipids is not sufficient for a classification, any classification must recognize the role that these components appear to play in synthetic processes; one would question any arrangement that grouped an RNA and a DNA virus together. In this connexion it is pleasant to see the increasing interest now being taken in lipids for they too have considerable capacities for showing specificity; only ten years ago it was generally believed that nucleic acids were not sufficiently complex to be the vehicles of specificity. The detailed structure of a macromolecule is likely to have great relevance for classification. In this size-range, chemical structure plays the role of morphology in metabionts. Before the study of chemical structure can be usefully undertaken, it is essential to explore the range of variation within what is being regarded as one species, for we cannot assume that the environment, that is to say the synthetic preconceptions of the host, is unimportant. This is well understood by taxonomists working with other material. Many hundreds of specimens from as diverse a set of environments as possible are compared to see which features are plastic and which invariable, and ideally a new species is not accepted until it can be shown that all the examples of it have properties falling outside the range of normal variation of any other species. Nothing of this sort has been attempted on a comprehensive scale for any virus and the evidence that the same chemical entity results, regardless of the conditions of multiplication, is ludicrously inadequate. Indeed, those detailed studies that have been made show that what is apparently the same virus can have significantly different properties when coming from different environments. Thus Johnson (1951) found shorter particles in exudates from pepper than from other plants infected with TMV, Bawden (1958) described a strain of TMV that had a different amino acid composition and physical and serological properties according to the host on which it was grown and it is claimed (Lindner, Kirkpatrick & Weeks, 1961) that preparations from different hosts have different infectivities. Clearly the virus may have only a limited capacity to impose its own pattern on the host; it may be built up from what is readily available, somewhat as a caddis worm makes its case out of whatever it finds on the bottom of a stream. The reasons for expecting this *a priori* have already been discussed (Pirie, 1950, 1957*b*) and an outline has been given of the analytical steps, that would be needed before amino acid differences, already claimed between strains of TMV, should be taken seriously.

Amino acid, or nucleotide analysis, is a precise method for determining the number of pieces in a structure; serological comparison is a rough method for showing up differences in their disposition. A rational classification, based on chemical information, must however depend on detailed knowledge of molecular structure and this will not be quickly gained; sperm whale myoglobin is at the moment the only protein for which a plausible morphology has been proposed. We know the amino acid sequences, or parts of them, for other proteins but this is only half of the problem. As Haldane (1956) has wisely pointed out, the word macromolecule has been extended to cover what ought to be called megamolecules for $\mu\alpha\chi\rho\delta s$ means long and $\mu\epsilon\gamma\alpha\sigma$ big. The relevant molecules may well be long chains with a certain amount of cross linking but, as with cats-cradles or any other structure made from the convolutions of thread, specificity depends on the precise morphology—called in this case topology. The prerequisite for a chemically based classification of viruses would be three-dimensional models of the arrangement of the amino acids, nucleotides, and other components in preparations of different viruses from different environments, and enough experience to know which differences are significant.

The attempt to classify in terms of macromolecular morphology will act as a powerful stimulus to attempts at the structural classification of molecules that have hitherto been classified functionally. A beginning has already been made and certain similarities appear among the haemoglobins and between enzymes that share a name though coming from different sources. The recognition that enzymes, and other proteins, from the same source may be heterogeneous (Colvin, Smith & Cook, 1954; Perrone, Disitzer & Iachan, 1959) is a further important step towards differentiating the essential from the variable parts of a structure. The biological advantages that may follow from this heterogeneity have been discussed in general (Markert & Moller, 1959) and in the specific case of the lactic dehydrogenases (Kaplan, Ciotti, Hamolsky & Bieber, 1960). A particularly interesting example is the variation among the p-aminobenzoate-metabolizing enzymes in different *Pneumococcus* mutants (Hotchkiss & Evans, 1960) because they were studied by measuring differences in the response to different analogues to the substrate. These presumably reflect differences in the surface configuration of the enzyme. Until the nature of this tolerated variation has been fully analysed we will not, to use an animal analogy, be able to distinguish the essential parameters of a species from mere variations in colour or hair length.

Discussion of issues such as these is sometimes condemned as being

philosophical. It is none the worse for that. We all have a philosophy—
it is the code of expectation that leads us to look on a new phenomenon
as either natural or surprising—the important thing is to find out what
our philosophy is as a first step to deciding whether we intend to go on
adhering to it. An essentially metaphysical approach to viruses is apparently more widespread than a chemical approach; it underlies the suggestion, made from time to time in medical journals, that TMV is the cause
of the increased incidence of lung cancer among smokers. This presupposes (Pirie, 1960) that viruses are in some way special, and share
what Duns Scotus called a *hiccity* and Kant a *noumena* and we would
now call a characteristic functional group, so that there is a general virus
quality that could be abstracted or considered separately from the other
aspects of the particle. It is because there is no hint of evidence for this
that such an attitude may be condemned as metaphysical; if it depends
on anything it depends on the alchemical doctrine of signatures '*similia
similibus curantur*' modified to read 'like effects will be produced by like
causes'. This is repeatedly contradicted by the facts of biochemistry.
Different organisms often use entirely different substances to bring about
the same physiological effect, e.g. the tapetum can be made of riboflavin,
guanine, zinc cysteine, cholesterol derivatives or parallel fibres (A. Pirie,
1961) and nitrogen is fixed in different ways by plants in the many genera
where this faculty is found (Bond, 1959). It is unlikely, therefore, that
virus classification will depend either on any feature that is not part of
normal biochemistry, or on any one type of feature. This is not a laby-
rinth from which we will escape by following a single clue.

Biochemical classification

The essential difference between biochemistry and chemistry is that the
former is concerned with the manner in which substances act *in vivo*
rather than with their composition and structure. Biochemistry is therefore getting nearer to the essence of our problem for, by definition,
viruses cause changes in the host. The presence of the same substance or
mechanism in two organisms is only valid evidence of a relationship
when alternative substances or mechanisms are available. To take an
analogy from human affairs: a certain pattern painted on pots, or a
certain written symbol for a letter, if used by two groups of people, suggests strongly that they have had contact because these things are
arbitrary. But the use of the wheel or the basic processes of weaving is
not evidence for contact because there is only one way of solving certain
problems. The uniformity of biochemistry constantly poses this problem:

do two different organisms use the same mechanism or substance because they are related or because there is only one efficient way of doing the job and this arises independently from time to time in different phyla? There has been considerable illogicality about biological thinking on these matters. Uniformity is often used as evidence for common descent by people who, in discussing the origins of life, assume that this is intimately bound up with the origins of proteins and nucleic acids. To them, life without proteins is unthinkable; this means that they are assuming that there is only one way of doing certain things. If this is so, if enzymes have to be made of protein, biochemical uniformity becomes an uncertain guide either to evolution or classification.

The biochemical classification of viruses would depend essentially on grouping them according to the processes used in the synthesis of their components and the assembly of the components into finished virus particles. It is conceivable, though no doubt improbable, that the components exist normally in the uninfected host and all that the incoming infective particle has to do is act as a 'crystal focus' to promote an anomalous aggregation so that the host suffers because of the sequestration of essential metabolites (Pirie, 1937). If we discount this possibility and postpone discussion of the evidence that can be got from a study of host enzymes and reactions to a later section, all that remains to be considered here is the evidence for enzyme-like participation by the virus in its own multiplication.

As we move from the autotrophic micro-organisms through the saprophytes we can arrange a sequence of increasing biochemical inadequacy so that the further along the sequence we move the more components a culture must have. Early in the succession we reach a region where the nature of the components is unknown and crude extracts have to be used. Further along, extracts fail and we get obligate parasites such as the rust fungi and *Plasmodium*. The general assumption is that this type of obligate parasitism is a consequence of our ignorance; the organism needs something that is rather unstable and so is not present in extracts made as hitherto. Or it may need coenzymes at the high concentration in which they exist in certain regions of the host cell and cannot make use of them when diluted as in extracts. The host is not just a bag of substrates; it has its own internal geography. With increasing knowledge, and care in making extracts, the missing components should be found and the group of obligate parasites will shrink. These obligate parasites, though in some ways inadequate, contain many enzymes. Several of the larger viruses, e.g. influenza and bacteriophage T2, carry enzymes that appear to help them to penetrate the host cell-wall; it is therefore reasonable to accept them as genuine virus components. The small plant viruses that have been thoroughly studied cannot infect an undamaged plant, their enzyme activity is feeble, and, with TMV at any rate, it is reasonable to assume (Pirie, 1956) that it is a consequence of secondary absorption from the environment.

These issues were discussed at length in the 1952 Symposium of this Society. Bawden & Pirie (1953) argued that viruses did not use the host as a specialized environment supplying inert pieces for the virus to organize and that there was no reason to assume that they had any other capacity than the ability to misdirect the synthetic mechanisms of the host. This point of view, rephrased in modern jargon in the form 'the virus carries information into the cell', is now widely accepted. The apparent absence of enzymes from these viruses may mean only that the correct substrates for the virus's synthetic actions have not been tested' but, if the absence is real, attempts to grow viruses on media containing only substrates and coenzymes are bound to fail. Some part of the integrated synthetic system, for example microsomes and mitochondria or their fragments, would be needed. According to this outlook, the biochemical distinction between viruses and other micro-organisms is that the viruses need the organized machinery of the cell whereas the others need only its products, and it is essentially an accident that this distinction is so closely correlated with size. When examined carefully the distinction is not quite so clear cut as at first appears. It is easy enough to distinguish between an enzyme and its substrate: an enzyme does a job and is then ready to do it again whereas the substrate is changed. But a coenzyme is also, at the end of the cycle, ready to do the job again. The distinction between an enzyme and a coenzyme seems to depend on size and our attempted new definition of a virus is not much more logically based than the old. When two substances are working together in a cycle the larger is the enzyme and the smaller the coenzyme, but each acts on the other and neither can be looked on as the more dynamic.

The study of enzyme reactions is therefore still a problematic or even improbable approach to the classification of viruses. This is not unexpected when we consider the small part it plays in the classification of other groups. When bacteria are 'put through the sugars' an enzyme survey is being made; it would be better if the results were expressed more precisely and stated what acid or gas was being produced and at what rate (Pirie, 1955). The appearance of new enzymes by adaptation is a source of trouble as is the loss of enzymes by certain strains. Occasionally, however, the claim is made for the invariable association of an enzyme with a distinct part of a classificatory scheme, thus ornithine transaminase (Scher & Vogel, 1957) appears to be present in all organisms except blue-green algae and Gram-negative bacteria.

Work on either the chemical or biochemical properties of viruses is generally limited to a study of the minimum structure needed for infectivity; it is assumed that anything that can be stripped away without loss of infectivity is simply a contaminant in the chemical sense of the term. There is no reason to accept this assumption and many examples have been given (Pirie, 1946, 1949, 1953, 1957 b) of separable components that normally accompany viruses in the initial extracts, and of changes brought about during purification. In those articles this Procrustean attitude towards the process of 'purification' was likened to such processes as the cutting off of the ears and tail from a rabbit on the grounds that they were not necessary for its survival. What we are trying to classify may therefore be the *écorché* rather than the organism. In the present context a better simile would be that the attempt to classify viruses from a study of the minimum and most highly refined phase of its existence is like trying to classify animals by a study of sperm and ova. Chemical and morphological studies would only serve at present for a patchy and uncertain system but it is generally agreed that the specifications for the complete organism are contained in the structure of these rudimentary stages in the developmental cycle. A hyperbiochemistry should be able to read in the structure of gametes the form of completed organisms. Ignorance is not the only factor that keeps this from being done, or even from being an immediate probability. Superficially the same form can be attained in unrelated complete organisms by convergent evolution, and similar characters can appear in unrelated species by the action of different genes (Harland, 1933). Nevertheless, it is reasonable to assume that there is some stability in the controlling chemical structures. This expectation depends on the same principles that underlie much conventional morphological classification. A useful structure depends on the integrated action of many different parts so that, to get another structure that will act in the same way, rather than a monstrosity, several simultaneous and radical changes would have to occur. This is unlikely. We therefore find the basic plan of an organ such as a foot persisting from the amphibia on through 100–200 million years and appearing in perhaps a million species. When morphological stability of this degree is possible, it is reasonable to think that there will be corresponding, though unknown, stability in the basic plan of the specifications. The complexity of the genetic structure of plants and animals makes this hyperbiochemistry remote and, though interesting, it would not be particularly useful at present. The viruses are simpler and classification along these lines is likely to come earlier with them than with the gametes.

Classification by the capacities and reactions of the host

Having considered the intrinsic properties of viruses—composition, morphology, structure, and activities *in vitro*—that could be used in classification, we come to the property by which the category 'virus' is defined; its relationship to a host. A few aspects of this relationship can be dismissed quickly. Unrelated viruses in unrelated hosts share certain common attributes, as Bradley (1721) recognized when he compared the transmission of striping in plants grafted with a bud from a striped plant with the transmission of an animal disease. By a lucky accident he chose smallpox as the example and so compared two viruses with one another. If we accept the general principles of plant and animal classification as valid, host range is of little use to us. Virus infections, like bacterial infections, follow no obvious phyletic rules; the same virus can cause disease in monocotyledons and dicotyledons, or plants and insects (Jensen, 1959; Watson & Sinha, 1959). Unlike bacteria, the same virus is not known to infect vertebrates and plants but it would be possible to erect only a limited classification on that exclusion. Furthermore, susceptibility to infection is not a completely clear-cut property of a host. It is bedevilled by latency or symptomless carriage by mild and short-lived infections; by infections that can only be demonstrated in bizarre circumstances, for example the insect virus (L'Héritier, 1948) that only manifests itself in high concentrations of CO_2; by viruses that multiply only in the presence of another virus (Kassanis & Nixon, 1961); and by effects of the physiological state of the host on its susceptibility. Variations in temperature or light intensity before or after attempted infection can alter by a factor of ten or even a hundred the apparent susceptibility of a host plant. Such extreme dependence on physiology has been less often demonstrated in animal or bacterial hosts, partly because it has been less often looked for and partly because these hosts are themselves less tolerant of physiological change. But in animal tissue cultures, where temperature and pH can be controlled, equally dramatic effects are found (Lwoff & Lwoff, 1960).

More intimate aspects of the host may however, in time, play a part in classification; we may be concerned less with what the virus multiplies *in* and more with what it multiplies *on*. Viruses, by definition, are obligate parasites and the reason for this, by general consent, is that they use the organized enzyme systems of the host. These systems are now being studied *in vitro* actively and progress is being made on the separation of intracellular particles bearing specific activities so that differences in the activity of preparations consisting predominantly of microsomes, mitochondria, chloroplasts, etc., are well known (e.g. Pierpoint, 1960*a*, *b*). As this knowledge increases it should become possible to determine the type of particle associated with the multiplication of each virus and the existing categories of intracellular particle will no doubt undergo further subdivision. This knowledge will be the basis of a rational biochemical classification. Its validity obviously depends on a pure assumption: that particles concerned with the same type of action will prove to be recognizably similar throughout an extensive group of hosts. This assumption may well be challenged but it is an extension into an intermediate size range of the well established homology of organs on the one hand, and, on the other hand, the use of the same basic biochemical mechanisms by almost all the organisms that have been studied. A crude analogy for such a system would be the differentiation of the categories *coin*, *key* and *corkscrew* because they get a characteristic reaction from slot machines, locks, and bottles respectively although all are of comparable size and made of metal. The rationale behind this type of biochemical classification is that the multiplication of viruses is limited to certain hosts, not only by the difficulty of getting into the host cell, but also by the absence from some cells of systems whose normal metabolism can be so modified, by the invading virus, as to lead to the production of more virus.

This aspect of the biochemistry of viruses can be studied in many ways. Ultimately it should be possible to isolate parts of the metabolic hierarchy of the host cell that can synthesize their appropriate viruses *in vitro*. As a first step, however, it should be possible to inhibit the multiplication of some viruses by relatively specific inhibitors. This will not necessarily be a step towards the chemotherapy of virus infection, for the inhibited system would presumably have been useful in the normal cell so that its inhibition would be as lethal as the infection, but inhibition of multiplication by the same substance will be as good a unifying feature between viruses as any now in use. A more indirect approach would be to follow the early manifestations of virus infection. There is already a suggestive lead in the 10 % increase in the respiration of tobacco leaves that occurs within an hour of infection (Owen, 1955), although this was not found with *Nicotiana glutinosa* (Owen, 1958). This phenomenon needs confirmation and detailed study, with isotopically labelled substrates, of the type of respiration that is being stimulated. The preferential use of one substrate would show which enzyme systems were used in the first stage of virus multiplication.

If the conclusions in the last paragraph are valid and the metabolic systems used for virus synthesis have been diverted from some other activity, light may be thrown on the nature of this normal activity by a study of the morphology of the virus particle. This mutual relationship between studies on normal and perverted hosts has proved fruitful in many other aspects of research; somewhat on the principle that Herodotus attributes to the Persians of making up their minds on all important issues when drunk and then reviewing, when sober again, the conclusion come to. There are two extreme cases. The subunits of the particle may come together without the active intervention of the host by a process analogous to crystallization, so that the final form may give more information about the surface properties of the subunits than about the system that made them. This appears to be the state of affairs with TMV and it may also happen with the very regular particles such as tomato bushy stunt and poliomyelitis viruses. At the other extreme come large bacterial viruses, such as T2, with an elaborate morphology. The obvious interpretation of the structure is that it is an aberration of some structure in the normal host. The question is: what? The choice is wide and need not be restricted to structures of a similar size; a change in size may be one feature of the aberration. There are many examples, insect salivary gland chromosomes for example, of ill-defined environmental influences leading to great enlargement or diminution of a structure. This is a pure speculation and the only justification for it is that it may supply a motive for more persistent effort to extend the host range of the bacterial viruses. A difference in the form of the same virus when grown on different hosts should help in identifying the structure of which the virus is a caricature.

CONCLUSION

The first essential step in classification is aesthetic—a synoptic survey of the domain to be classified to see which are the essential and useful features in it. The second is logical—using the criterion chosen, to see if it leads anywhere to obvious nonsense. The third is the scientific step—to see, if the criterion seems to work, why it works. And *why*, a generally misleading word, is legitimate here because it is a comment on a process going on in a human head. When these steps are followed with one of the outstandingly successful pieces of classification, Linnean classification of plants and animals, it appears that evolution and the stages of phylogeny are the factors responsible for success. These factors may well not operate generally with viruses and this will introduce an arbitrary element into virus classification. But even an arbitrary arrangement depends on the existence of enough information to put detail into a synoptic view. The prerequisite for virus classification is more information about viruses.

A survey of the traditional types of information—external morphology, chemical composition, host reaction etc.—shows that, if used alone, they would lead to curious pieces of classification among the larger organisms and bacteria; it can be assumed that they would apply even less well among viruses. We need, as a supplement, the infant science of macro- or mega-molecular morphology. Some principles of classification will have to be introduced for large molecules in any event, and their development will be speeded up if an insistent demand comes from those interested in viruses. Other biologists might join in too, for a rational classification of large molecules would be as useful a guide in all other branches of biology as morphology is today, and successful classification depends on the presence of many different lines of evidence.

If we had enough independent pieces of information, confidence could be put in mechanized classification (Rogers & Tanimoto, 1960; Sneath, 1957 a, b) in which every fact that is admitted as relevant has equal weight; but the amount of information needed in such a system is enormous, for this approach to the problem depends, to use communication-engineering terminology, on great 'redundancy'. When information is scanty, either because of the undeveloped state of the subject or because of the intrinsic simplicity of the things being classified, it is inevitable that alternative arrangements of equal apparent validity will be possible. This will cause trouble because biologists are so accustomed to thinking that classification is at fault when the same organism is claimed as a member of two different families that they tend to overlook the fact that chemistry can operate successfully without laying down emphatic rules to settle, for example, whether glucuronic acid is to be thought of among the sugars or the acids.

When there is enough information, useful and agreed classification can precede the recognition of the principles that make it valid. Thus mammals had been grouped together, before their presumed evolutionary relationship validated the grouping, regardless of shape and size and whether they walked, swam, or flew, and this was done at a time when any resemblances between them were thought of as a whim on the part of a creator. The grouping depends on the morphological arrangements that about half the members of each species make for coping with milk secretion. The unifying feature is not milk secretion itself, pigeons and some sharks can manage that and make use of similar biochemical mechanisms for it, but the integration of capacity and structure in a manner not found outside the group.

From our knowledge of viruses no unifying principle emerges with a comparable impact on our experience or imagination; this can mean two things: that we do not know enough about them and there is a genuine unifying principle somewhere: that there is no unifying principle and we have slipped into the error of trying to group together entities united only by their ability to misdirect synthetic systems in the host. The first I have stigmatized as a metaphysical approach at the moment though it is conceivably correct; the second, if correct, is the explanation of the difficulties taxonomists have got into hitherto when handling viruses. These are not the fault of the taxonomists but of the viruses; but the taxonomists are at fault for not recognizing this.

REFERENCES

BAWDEN, F. C. (1958). Reversible changes in strains of tobacco mosaic virus from leguminous plants. *J. gen. Microbiol.* **18**, 715.

BAWDEN, F. C. & PIRIE, N. W. (1942). A preliminary description of preparations of some of the viruses causing tobacco necrosis. *Brit. J. exp. Path.* **23**, 314.

BAWDEN, F. C. & PIRIE, N. W. (1953). Virus multiplication considered as a form of protein synthesis. In *The Nature of Virus Multiplication. Symp. Soc. gen. Microbiol.* **2**, 21.

BERGMAN, T. O. (1784). Meditationes de Systemate Fossilium Naturali. *Nova Acta Soc. Sci. Upsal.* **4**, 63.

BOEDTKER, H. & SIMMONS, N. S. (1958). The preparation and characterisation of essentially uniform tobacco mosaic virus particles. *J. Amer. chem. Soc.* **80**, 2550.

BOND, G. (1959). Fixation of nitrogen in non-legume root-nodule plants. In *Utilization of Nitrogen and its Compounds by Plants. Symp. Soc. exp. Biol.* **13**, 59.

BRADLEY, R. (1721). *A General Treatise of Husbandry and Gardening.* London.

BRANDES, J. & WETTER, C. (1959). Classification of elongated plant viruses on the basis of particle morphology. *Virology*, **8**, 99.

CARLISLE, D. B. (1958). Niobium in Ascidans. *Nature, Lond.* **181**, 933.

COLVIN, J. R., SMITH, D. B. & COOK, W. H. (1954). The micro-heterogeneity of proteins. *Chem. Rev.* **54**, 687.

COOPER, P. D. (1961). A chemical basis for the classification of animal viruses. *Nature, Lond.* **190**, 302.

FRACASTORO, H. (1546). *De Contagione et Contagiosis Morbis et Curatione.* Venice.

GIBBS, R. D. (1958). Chemical evolution in plants. *J. Linn. Soc. Lond., Bot.* **56**, 49.

HALDANE, J. B. S. (1956). Die Bedeutung der Makromoleküle für Evolution und Differenzierung. In *Vergleichend biochemische Fragen. 6 Colloquim der Ges. f. physiol. Chem.* Berlin: Springer.

HALL C. E. (1958). Lengths of tobacco mosaic virus from electron microscopy. *J. Amer. chem. Soc.* **80**, 2556.

HALL, D. A., LLOYD, P. F. & SAXL, H. (1958). Mammalian cellulose. *Nature, Lond.* **181**, 470.

HARLAND, S. C. (1933). Homologous structures in related species of cotton controlled by quite different genes. *Proc. 7th Int. Gen. Congress*, p. 138.

L'HÉRITIER, PH. (1948). Sensitivity to CO_2 in *Drosophila*. *Heredity*, **2**, 325.

HOTCHKISS, R. D. & EVANS, A. H. (1960). Fine structure of a genetically modified enzyme as revealed by relative affinities for modified substrate. *Fed. Proc.* **19**, 912.

JENSEN, D. D. (1959). A plant virus lethal to its insect vector. *Virology*, **8**, 164.

JOHNSON, J. (1951). Virus particles in various plant species and tissues. *Phytopathology*, **41**, 78.

JOHNSON, M. W. & MARKHAM, R. (1962). (In the Press.)

KAPLAN, N. O., CIOTTI, M. M., HAMOLSKY, M. & BIEBER, R. E. (1960). Molecular heterogeneity and evolution of enzymes. *Science*, **131**, 392.

KASSANIS, B. & NIXON, H. L. (1961). Activation of one tobacco necrosis virus by another. *J. gen. Microbiol.* **25**, 459.

LINDNER, R. C., KIRKPATRICK, H. C. & WEEKS, T. W. (1961). Effect of source host on infectivity of tobacco mosaic virus isolates. *Phytopathology*, **51**, 15.

LOCKE, J. (1700). *An Essay Concerning Human Understanding*. Book 4, chap. 6, paragraph 35, 4th edition. London.

LOEB, T. & ZINDER, N. D. (1961). A bacteriophage containing RNA. *Proc. nat. Acad. Sci. Wash.* **47**, 282.

LORING, H. S. & WARITZ, R. S. (1957). Occurrence of iron, copper, calcium and magnesium in tobacco mosaic virus. *Science*, **125**, 646.

LORING, H. S., AL-RAWI, S. & FUJIMOTO, Y. (1958). Iron content of TMV and properties of its infectious nucleic acid. *J. biol. Chem.* **233**, 1415.

LWOFF, A. & LWOFF, M. (1960). Sur les facteurs de développment viral et leur rôle dans l'évolution de l'infection. *Ann. Inst. Pasteur*, **98**, 173.

MARKERT, C. L. & MOLLER, F. (1959). Multiple forms of enzymes: tissue, ontogenetic and species specific patterns. *Proc. nat. Acad. Sci. Wash.* **45**, 753.

MAYR, E. (1953). Concepts of classification and nomenclature in higher organisms and microorganisms. *Ann. N.Y. Acad. Sci.* **56**, 391

NYANDER, J. (1757). *Exanthemata viva*. Uppsala.

OWEN, P. C. (1955). The respiration of tobacco leaves in the 20-hour period following inoculation with tobacco mosaic virus. *Ann. appl. Biol.* **43**, 114.

OWEN, P. C. (1958). Photosynthesis and respiration rates of leaves of *Nicotiana glutinosa* infected with tobacco mosaic virus and of *N. tabacum* infected with potato virus X. *Ann. appl. Biol.* **46**, 198.

PAUTARD, F. G. E. (1958). Bone salts in unicellular organisms. *Biochim. biophys. Acta*, **28**, 514.

PERRONE, J. C., DISITZER, L. V. & IACHAN, A. (1959). Electrophoretic heterogeneity of trypsin. *Nature, Lond.* **184**, 1225.

PIERPOINT, W. S. (1960*a*). Mitochondrial preparations from the leaves of tobacco (*Nicotiana tabacum*). 2. Oxidative phosphorylation. *Biochem. J.* **75**, 504.

PIERPOINT, W. S. (1960*b*). Mitochondrial preparations from the leaves of tobacco (*Nicotiana tabacum*). 3. Glycollic oxidase and fumarase activity. *Biochem. J.* **75**, 511.

PIRIE, A. (1961). Cholesterol in the tapetum lucidum of the eye of the opossum, *Didelphis virginiana*. *Nature, Lond.* **191**, 708.

PIRIE, N. W. (1937). The meaninglessness of the terms life and living. In *Perspectives in Biochemistry*, 11. Cambridge.

PIRIE, N. W. (1946). The state of viruses in the infected cell. *Cold Spr. Harb. Symp. quant. Biol.* **11**, 184.

PIRIE, N. W. (1949). The association of viruses with other materials in the cell and in extracts. *Exp. Cell Res.* (Suppl.), **1**, 183.

PIRIE, N. W. (1950). A biochemical approach to viruses. *Nature, Lond.* **166**, 495.

PIRIE, N. W. (1952). Concepts out of context. *Brit. J. Philos. Sci.* **2**, 269.

PIRIE, N. W. (1953). Some host components that effect viruses during isolation. In *Symp. Interaction of virus and cells*, **11**. Rome.

PIRIE, N. W. (1955). Summing-up: to Discussion on Principles Microbial of Classification. *J. gen. Microbiol.* **12**, 382.

PIRIE, N. W. (1956). Some components of tobacco mosaic virus made in different ways. *Biochem. J.* **63**, 316.

PIRIE, N. W. (1957a). The anatomy of tobacco mosaic virus. *Advanc. Virus Res.* **4**, 159.

PIRIE, N. W. (1957b). Material in virus preparations not necessary for the manifestation of characteristic virus properties. In *The Nature of Viruses. Ciba Foundation Symp.*

PIRIE, N. W. (1960). Lung cancer and tobacco mosaic virus. *Lancet*, i, 707, 978.

ROGERS, D. J. & TANIMOTO, T. T. (1960). A computer program for classifying plants. *Science*, **132**, 1115.

SCHER, W. I. & VOGEL, H. J. (1957). Occurrence of ornithine δ-transaminase: a dichotomy. *Proc. nat. Acad. Sci. Wash.* **43**, 796.

SNEATH, P. H. A. (1957a). Some thoughts on bacterial classification. *J. gen. Microbiol.* **17**, 184.

SNEATH, P. H. A. (1957b). The application of computers to taxonomy. *J. gen. Microbiol.* **17**, 201.

WATSON, M. & SINHA, R. C. (1959). Studies on the transmission of European wheat striate mosaic virus by *Delphacodes pellucida* Fabricius. *Virology*, **8**, 139.

NOMENCLATURE AND TAXONOMY

R. ROSS

British Museum (Natural History), London, S.W. 7

The general theme of this Symposium is the question of what are the proper bases of a taxonomic classification of micro-organisms. This contribution, however, is concerned merely with the attaching of names to the categories* that make up that classification. Experience has shown that this, like the formulation of the classification, presents many difficulties. Partly because the reasons for these difficulties are imperfectly understood, nomenclature engenders much irritation, and it is hoped that this paper, by contributing to an understanding of the difficulties, will help to reduce the irritation, even if it contains little in the way of suggestions for overcoming them.

CONCEPTS AND NAMES

The relationship between concepts and the terms used to denote them has been exercising philosophers very considerably in recent years. In spite of this, and of the consequent general interest in the subject, consideration of it has entered little into discussions by scientists on the methodology of their subject. The principal reason for this is that scientists use terms in accordance with what are termed stipulative definitions (Robinson, 1950). When a physicist uses such words as 'energy', 'work', 'force', they have a precise and invariable meaning because physicists are agreed that they shall be used in accordance with a particular explicit definition. When the same words are used in general communication, they have a wide range of meaning determined not by any definition or series of definitions but by usage, and the particular meaning on any occasion is determined by context. The definitions in dictionaries (lexical definitions) are not stipulative definitions like those of scientific terms; they do not state the senses in which words are to be used but merely record the tacit and imprecise conventions of their users about the significance to be attached to them. Difficulty in associating word and concept

---

* I have here used the term 'category' rather than 'class' for the groups of all ranks in which individuals are brought together in a classification because 'class' is used for a category of a particular rank in taxonomic terminology. The terms 'taxonomic category' and 'taxon' are, of course, synonymous. Under the Bacteriological Code category is synonymous with rank.

arises in any case where the word used has a wide range of meaning and the particular meaning intended is not made precise by the context.

It would seem at first sight that there should be no more difficulty in dealing with the names of taxonomic categories (taxa) than with the terms used for physical concepts, or those for morphological categories, such as 'cell', 'nucleus', vacuole', etc. All the codes of nomenclature require that the characters of the taxon to which any name applies must be indicated by means of a description, a figure, or both. It might therefore appear that all names of taxa had stipulative definitions. This, however, is not so, and it follows from the nature of taxa and the present state of taxonomy that it cannot be so.

There are many possible ways of classifying living organisms, each classification differing according to the purpose for which it is made. That purpose determines the criteria to be used, and when the purpose is precise not only are the criteria precisely determined but also, in general, they can be applied with precision. Taxonomic classification, however, to which the scientific names of organisms are attached, has a very ill-defined purpose; there is in fact much argument amongst taxonomists as to what that purpose is. The statement that the purpose of a taxonomic classification is to express general biological affinity would probably command most widespread assent. All attempts to formulate a classification with this purpose must be based on observation of organisms; the criteria to be used cannot be deduced *a priori* from the purpose of the classification. They are therefore subject to change as more organisms are examined and as further and more detailed information is acquired about those already known. In consequence, the system of taxonomic classification is never static. The range of entities (the individuals and populations studied by taxonomists) to be included in it increases steadily, and opinions alter with time as to the criteria by which the categories that comprise it are to be distinguished. At any one time, also, there may be differences of opinion among taxonomists about these criteria (cf. the treatment of the Chroococcaceae by Drouet & Daily (1956) and Desikachary (1959)).

The fact that taxonomic classification aims at the expression of general biological affinity results not only in changes with time in the criteria to be employed and differences of opinion about them; it also affects the nature of the criteria adopted. Taxa are normally found to be distinguished from one another not so much by single clear-cut differences as by differences in the extent to which they exhibit a series of characteristics. Furthermore, characters which are important as indicators of affinity in one group of organisms may have little or no significance in another.

The criteria of a taxonomic classification are therefore often complex and imprecise, and vary in the different parts of the system.

The other major source of difficulty is the immense number of concepts with which taxonomy deals. A recent estimate (Spector, 1956) is that there are about 938,000 known species of animals and 343,000 of plants. When it is realized that any change in the criteria used to distinguish a taxon is equivalent to the introduction of a new concept, the immense number of concepts with which taxonomy deals becomes even more apparent. The vocabulary of a learned man with broad general interests has been variously estimated at up to about 50,000 words (Ogden, 1930). A large proportion of these represent different concepts in different contexts, but this figure may nevertheless give some indication of the order of the maximum number of concepts that a human mind can memorize and use. The difference between the figures for vocabulary and for number of taxa is one of the reasons why it is impossible to hold more than a small fraction of the taxonomic system in the mind. The criteria used to distinguish taxa are complex and of a subtle nature, and most workers (especially those studying micro-organisms, whose permanent preservation is so difficult) normally encounter representatives of only a small proportion of the taxa in a particular fragment of the system. The result is that familiarity with even a small part of the taxonomic classification is a rather rare achievement. Therefore, for most biologists, the name of a taxon does not usually convey a concept whose characteristics are known unless an authoritative work on the group is consulted.

CONVENTIONS AND CODES OF NOMENCLATURE

We can now proceed to consider how in practice a system of nomenclature has been applied to a system of categories as numerous and as unstable in their circumscription as taxa. As a preliminary, however, it will be useful to remind ourselves of the fact that the names of taxa, although written with an initial capital and often printed in italics, are not proper names in the sense of being names of individual entities (e.g.: Carolus Linnaeus, the Newlands Oak, London) but are terms denoting categories, just as are 'man', 'tree', 'city'.

Another necessary preliminary is to point out that taxonomic classification is a hierarchical system in which every category except the highest (which comprises all organisms) and the lowest (whose components are individuals) is subclass to a single higher class and super-class to one or more lower classes. This was originally so because such an arrangement conformed to the logical theory of classification, but evolution gives a basis in biological theory for assuming that a system based on general biological affinity will be of an hierarchical form.

In the early days of systematics names changed (at least at the level of species) as the system of classification changed. Before the middle of the eighteenth century the name of a species was descriptive and indicated what distinguished that species from other species of the genus. Therefore, as more species became known, names had to be altered to take account of additional distinguishing characters. This system was superseded early in the second half of the eighteenth century by the binomial system we use today, in which names at all levels are no more than labels. The speed with which Linnaeus's innovation was accepted and his names ousted all others was in great part due to the fact that the previous system was too cumbersome and too unstable to be conveniently used. In the works in which binomial nomenclature was introduced, Linnaeus described about 5900 species of plants (*Species Plantarum*, ed. 1, 1753) and 4400 species of animals (*Systema Naturae*, ed. 10, 1758).

In contrast to the system which it superseded, the binomial system retains the same names despite changes in the system; alterations are only made in consequence of changes in the rank of a taxon, or its position (i.e. if it is moved to a different higher taxon). Names are only eliminated when it is found that more than one refers to the same taxon. New names (as distinct from new combinations of previously published epithets with generic names, necessitated by changes in position and rank) are, in general, only introduced when additional taxa are recognized. Thus the same name may be used by different authors for taxa with very different circumscriptions, and, except in monographs, floras, and similar works, there will usually be no indication of the circumscription from the context. Furthermore, a taxon of a rank below that of genus can have different names without any alteration of circumscription if different taxonomists consider it to have different positions or ranks; also, if the rank of a taxon above the level of genus is changed, the termination of its name is altered, and no change in circumscription need accompany this change of rank. Both of these characteristics of the modern binomial system are disadvantages.

We have seen already that the pre-Linnaean system, in which names changed as criteria and circumscriptions changed, became too cumbersome when the number of species recognized was a hundred times less than it is today and when the rate of change of taxonomic systems was proportionately even less. It is possible that an alternative system could be devised, in which names changed with changes of circumscription and which could be applied to current taxonomic classification, but none has been devised so far. The retention of names despite changes in circumscription, moreover, is in accordance with the opinion of most biologists that taxonomic categories are not mere man-made abstractions but have a reality in nature. For example, Fries in 1821 and Corner in 1950 apply the name *Clavaria* to the same taxonomic category, in spite of differences in circumscription, but Corner describes and circumscribes it more accurately. This view stems from the opinion that the purpose of taxonomy is to formulate a classification that expresses a grouping of organisms that exists naturally and is not arbitrarily imposed by the taxonomist.* The existence of such a natural grouping has been contested, but most taxonomists, over most of the field with which they deal, find that the assumption that there is such a grouping accords with their own observations.

The disadvantages of change of name with change of position and rank need to be set against two advantages; first, position and rank are indicated by the name and secondly, there is less strain on the memory than if all names at all levels were quite independent. These, in my view, heavily outweigh the disadvantages, for changes of name associated with changes of rank and position cause little confusion, at least to those familiar with the way in which the present nomenclatural system works. This judgement may, however, be the result of such familiarity, combined perhaps with conservatism.

There are, however, many changes of name that are not associated with changes of position or rank, and these are the principal sources of confusion and irritation. Two factors have operated throughout the history of the binomial system. The same taxon has been independently given more than one name for various reasons: failure to be aware of previously published names, or to recognize that they applied to the taxon in question, or the use of criteria for separating taxa which later authors have not accepted as sufficient for the purpose. Conversely, the same name has been applied to different taxa, sometimes through failure to appreciate that more than one was involved, sometimes through differences of opinion about which it should apply to. There are also cases where, through ignorance of the fact that a name had been previously used, it was used again independently for a quite different taxon. It was the consequent need of regulating the choice of names for taxa and the way in which names were to be applied that led to the formulation of

* This statement of the purpose of a taxonomic classification differs from that given on p. 395 above, but the two are not inconsistent.

nomenclatural codes. It was found necessary also to include provisions about (1), the form that names for taxa of each rank should take, (2), what sort of characters of the taxon was to be recorded if the names were to be taken into account, (3), how they were to be changed when position or rank was changed, and various minor matters.

Although the Codes differ in detail, they are founded on two main principles, priority and the type method. Priority has always been generally accepted as a principle of the binomial system of nomenclature. It determines which one of the various names that have been applied to a taxon shall be used for it—'Each taxonomic group with a particular circumscription, position, and rank can bear only one correct name, the earliest that is in accordance with the rules' (Principle IV of the *International Code of Botanical Nomenclature*, cf. *Bacteriological Code*, Principle 9). The original justification for the adoption of this principle was that it alone provided a fixed nomenclature and avoided arbitrary and invidious choices of name that might vary from author to author (De Candolle, 1813). A further justification for its retention is that the earliest name is likely to have been the most used and therefore to be the most widely familiar of those applied to the taxon. Unhappily, however, this is far from always the case. Names in obscure publications that have been consistently overlooked for long periods are often found to ante-date well known and widely used ones.

NOMENCLATURAL TYPES

The type method, which determines the application of names, has only found general acceptance in this century. A name is permanently attached to the material studied when the original account of the taxon named was being prepared and this material is the *nomenclatural type* of the name. When this material consists of more than one specimen or other element (some accounts are based on previously published illustrations), the author may designate one as type, and the name is then permanently attached to this; if he does not, one of them may be chosen as type later, and this must be that on which the original account was primarily based, if one can be preferred to another on this count. Where the original material has been preserved and is accessible, this system works moderately well, although, as more and more types are examined, unpleasant shocks are continually received. Techniques for the adequate preservation of micro-organisms of many groups have not been worked out, however, and even where such techniques were available original material was often not preserved. In such cases an attempt has to be

made by anyone revising the classification of a group to decide the taxon
to which a name refers. Theoretically, if the revisor is unable to do this, he
must reject the name. In practice, however, names are rarely rejected for
this reason but are applied on the basis either of guesses or of the
opinions of previous authorities. Where the name applied to a taxon is
changed because examination of a type shows that a name has been misapplied, one can hope that no further change for the same reason will be
made. However, where no types exist, or existing types have not been
examined, changes due to differences of opinion about the application of
names can, and do, still occur. An attempt is made to reduce these by
the designation, in cases where no type survives, of a specimen to serve
instead of it (a neotype), but the only authority for connecting this with
the name is the opinion of the designator, and anyone who disagrees
with that opinion rejects the choice of neotype. The Bacteriological Code,
however, has provision for official neotypes.

It must be stressed that a nomenclatural type is not necessarily typical,
nor even intended to be typical, of the taxon to the name of which it is
attached. According to the Botanical Code (Art. 7) 'A nomenclatural
type (*typus*) is that constituent element of a taxon to which the name of
the taxon is permanently attached, whether as an accepted name or as a
synonym'. Many cultures in 'collections of type cultures' may be
typical of the taxa they represent; very few indeed are nomenclatural
types.

EXCEPTIONS

All the codes of nomenclature provide for exceptions to be authorized
where the consequences of name changes due to the strict application of
the rule of priority or of the principle of types would result in serious
confusion and inconvenience. Exceptions to the Botanical Code cannot
be made below the level of genus. Those to the Bacteriological and Zoological Codes can be made for names of taxa of any rank, but the
machinery by which they are authorized is ponderous and can only deal
with a very limited flow of cases. The capacity of the much simpler
botanical procedure is not large. Proposals to extend the scope of the
provisions for exceptions in the Botanical Code to include names of
species have been discussed of recent years but rejected. This is in part
due to an expectation that the machinery for considering proposals for
exceptions would be unable to deal with the number that would come
forward. Much of the opposition, however, has been due to the quite
illogical belief that, since priority and the type method are the principles
underlying the code of nomenclature, to make exceptions to them for the

avoiding of confusion is to sacrifice principle to expediency, and hence is unprincipled in the pejorative sense. This line of reasoning, or perhaps one should say this prejudice, fails to take account of the fact that taxonomic nomenclature is but a special case of the relation between terms and concepts and a basic principle of that relationship is expediency. The purpose of words is to serve as a vehicle of communication and they fulfil this purpose most efficiently when they immediately and unequivocally convey to the recipient the concept intended by its originator. Judged by this standard, and no other is appropriate, the system of taxonomic nomenclature founded on the principles of priority and the type method is not a very efficient one. This is largely due to the nature and number of the concepts with which it deals and the fact that for a long period its development was scarcely regulated; detailed codes of nomenclature commanding widespread acceptance are a twentieth-century development. When it is decided to make exceptions to these codes (and over-rule the principles of priority and the type method in the interests of mitigating confusion and increasing clarity of reference) a higher principle is over-riding conflicting ones of lesser importance. Sheer weight of numbers unfortunately makes it impossible for an authoritative body to deal with every deserving case of change of name. Most cases must be handled in accordance with a set of rules of general application and exceptions can only be made for the most glaring.

WHAT MUST BE DONE?

What are we who have inherited this inefficient system to do? The alternatives are either to devise a completely new one or to try to make the present one more efficient. A new one, if it is to command universal acceptance, must be simpler than the old and as easy to memorize, and I find it difficult to conceive that such a system will be found readily. The principal reasons for unnecessary inefficiency in the present system are that names have been overlooked, that names have been misapplied, or that other names have been preferred to those that should have been adopted under the appropriate code. This last is of course of frequent occurrence in works written before the current codes (which are of necessity retrospective) were drawn up, but some recent authors also, either wilfully or inadvertently, ignore the codes. If these factors could be eliminated, the present system would, in my judgement, be as efficient a system of nomenclature for taxonomic categories as the nature of these permits.

The indications are that the bringing to light of over-looked names in

old literature is approaching completion. There is great difficulty, however, in keeping abreast of current literature. If assistance in doing this,
such as is provided by the *Zoological Record*, were available over the
whole range of micro-organisms, both taxonomic work and nomenclature would be much facilitated. The time still seems very distant when
there will be general agreement for all names on whether they can be
applied and what is their type, but a conscientious effort by all engaged
in taxonomic revision to try to ascertain the original intended application of all the names with which they deal would bring a rapid improvement. Whilst it might at this stage result in many changes of name, it
would contribute greatly to stability in the future.

There are some authors of taxonomic works who do not follow the
regulations of the appropriate code but assign names to taxa on the basis
of personal choice. As far as the Plant Kingdom, at least, is concerned,
those dealing with micro-organisms seem to have been particularly
prone to act in this way. Such action, however, is bound to lead to
instability of nomenclature. Those who exercise personal choice will
differ among themselves, and others will observe the appropriate code
and differ again. Amongst workers on higher plants this sort of ir-
responsibility has been almost eliminated by the pressure of public
opinion. The same result, with much consequent benefit, could be
achieved in microbial nomenclature if those writing on the taxonomy of
micro-organisms would follow the appropriate code (which does not
preclude the making, in appropriate cases, of modifications or exceptions through the established procedure) and make it plain that they
considered this the only reasonable course to take, and if others referring to micro-organisms would adopt the names used by authors who
follow the codes in preference to those used by authors who do not.

THE INDEPENDENCE OF TAXONOMY AND
NOMENCLATURE

This contribution has so far dealt with the relationship between nomenclature and taxonomy from the standpoint of the efficiency with which
names act as means of communication. There is another important
aspect of their relationship, which is that taxonomy must be independent
of nomenclature. There is in any field of thought always the danger that
the development of concepts may be limited by the language available
for expressing them. This limitation is imposed not so much by the
absence of appropriate terms as by the structure of the language. The fact
that the system of taxonomic nomenclature is wedded to a hierarchical

classification makes it particularly dangerous in this way. Some experimental taxonomists have attempted to express their cytological, genetical, and ecological results in terms of the system of taxonomic nomenclature although the inter-relationship between their results and general biological affinity is often obscure. In consequence their results are inadequately systematized and the names introduced are not readily usable. It is impossible satisfactorily to combine into one system classifications made for different purposes. Accordingly, unless the relationship which the distribution of particular characteristics bears to the purpose of taxonomic classification can be seen, classifications based on those characteristics must be kept separate from the system of taxonomic classification and its accompanying nomenclature.

These considerations have particular relevance to micro-organisms that are studied almost entirely in culture. To a very large extent these are known only from a limited number of clones, and information on the variation of populations in nature is often completely lacking. Without such information it is very difficult to distinguish individual idiosyncrasies from characters of significance for delimiting taxa. It is thus very difficult to fit classifications of organisms based on characters observed when studying cultures into the framework of a general taxonomic classification and its accompanying system of nomenclature. Where a classification is what Ciferri (1959) has called 'classificatory taxonomy'* (to call it taxonomy of any sort is in my view a misnomer) its units should not be treated nomenclaturally as taxa, but should have an independent nomenclature, such as that of the groups and serotypes of Enterobacteriaceae, or, in a different field, that of horticultural varieties. Only classifications of the kind that Ciferri calls 'systematic'† should be treated as falling within the scope of taxonomic nomenclature, and even with these there should be no hesitation about departing from the standard hierarchical framework if the facts do not readily fit into it.

REFERENCES

CIFERRI, R. (1959). Systematic vs. classificatory taxonomy and speciology of the Actinomycetales. *Int. Bull. bact. Nomen. Tax.* **9**, 89.
CORNER, E. J. H. (1950). *A Monograph of Clavaria and Allied Genera. Annals of Botany Memoirs*, no. 1. London: Oxford University Press.

* '*Classificatory taxonomy* (or classification) distributes the micro-organisms of a certain rank on the basis of a reduced (small) number of easily recognizable characteristics showing divergences or similarities, without consideration of relationship or descent....This is, of course, an artificial taxonomy, simplified and more or less subjective.'

† '*Systematic taxonomy* (or systematics) distributes the micro-organisms of a certain rank with due consideration of all the affinities, immediate or remote, and the probable descent.'

DE CANDOLLE, A. P. (1813). *Théorie élémentaire de la botanique.* Paris: Déterville.

DESIKACHARY, T. V. (1959). *Cyanophyta.* New Delhi: Indian Council Agric. Res.

DROUET, F. & DAILY, W. A. (1956). Revision of the coccoid Myxophyceae. *Butler Univ. bot. Stud.* **12**, 1.

FRIES, E. M. (1821). *Systema Mycologicum, sistens Fungorum ordines, genera et species huc usque cognitas,* **1**. Lundae: Berling.

OGDEN, C. K. (1930). *The Basic Vocabulary.* London: Kegan Paul.

ROBINSON, R. (1950). *Definition.* Oxford: Clarendon Press.

SPECTOR, W. S. (ed.) (1956). *Handbook of Biological Data.* Philadelphia and London: W. B. Saunders and Co.

THE PRACTICE OF BACTERIAL IDENTIFICATION

K. J. STEEL

National Collection of Type Cultures, Central Public Health Laboratory, Colindale, London, N.W. 9

We are constantly reminded that identification and classification are not synonymous: the problems of identifying a given micro-organism differ from those of putting it in its correct (phylogenetic) place in the order of things. How and why do these problems differ?

Taxonomy can be defined as the art of classifying, for it undoubtedly is an art, and classifying is the arrangement, distribution or sorting of the objects under consideration. Thus taxonomy implies that we have several objects to classify. The practice of diagnosis, on the other hand, is the characterization and identification of a particular object. It implies the ability to describe an object in terms which convey the investigator's findings and, unlike taxonomy, is a science. Having described our object we are then in a position to classify it; whereas description is absolute and objective, taxonomy is subjective.

The word diagnosis (or diagnostic) is used in two senses: (1) almost synonymous with identification (or identity), as in medicine, and (2) a listing of the differential characters of a taxon (as diagnoses of plants, fungi and animals are published as laid down in the botanical and zoological codes). I have tried to distinguish between these usages where there might be confusion. To refer to a micro-organism in the second way would be cumbersome and inconvenient, and it is usual to attach a name to the description. Such names often have taxonomic meanings but the diagnostician is using them merely as identifying tags or labels and is not unduly perturbed by their meanings for taxonomists. It may be argued that we are being inconsistent, for as description precedes classification, so classification precedes nomenclature, but nomenclature should be our servant, not our master (Ainsworth, 1955).

What is the aim in diagnosis? I consider that it is the identification of the micro-organism as accurately as possible in the shortest practical time. Often we are interested in an organism on account of its malevolence—it may be causing disease of animals or plants, corroding metal pipes or damaging textiles—but it might be a benevolent organism, such as Fleming's *Penicillium* contaminant which led to the discovery of penicillin.

In identification, speed is imperative and second only in importance to accuracy. The diagnostician is constantly subjected to pressures exerted from various directions, whereas the taxonomist can usually work systematically and methodically through his range of tests before reaching his conclusions. Consequently identification has often to be made on the results of a few expeditious tests. However, ease and speed must not be substituted for accuracy. Rightly or wrongly, more emphasis in identification is placed on some characters than others and the Adansonian principle of giving equal weight or importance to each character is not followed. Identification may also be biased or coloured by what experience has taught us and we must be constantly on our guard against this.

The question arises whether the full identification of a micro-organism is always necessary. In clinical bacteriology it is more useful to report rapidly that 'a Gram-negative rod sensitive to chloramphenicol and the tetracyclines but resistant to penicillin and streptomycin was isolated', than after some delay to provide an exact identification of an organism which the clinician may never have heard of! Epidemiologically it may be of value to be able to state the phage type of a particular strain of *Salmonella typhi*, but it is of no practical concern in determining the treatment of the patient from whom it was isolated. In notifiable infectious diseases (which in this country include about twenty-five human conditions) a definite identification must be made, but in other illnesses the diagnosis can often safely be left at the presumptive stage.

DIAGNOSTIC METHODS

Under this heading I shall review briefly the methods and techniques that provide information from which we can make a description or identification of a micro-organism. The methods are very varied and an attempt to survey them all has not been made here.

Characters detectable by the senses

Micro-organisms can be recognized by the senses of sight, touch and smell. Touch is not used directly but with a loop or wire, for example to distinguish friable from butyrous colonies. *Haemophilus influenzae* and *Pasteurella septica* each has a characteristic odour when grown on blood agar (presumably due to indole production) but this is insufficient for an identification. Hearing plays no part in our examination and it would be a foolish worker who used his sense of taste.

Sight is the most valuable sense in diagnostic work, and both macroscopic and microscopic methods of examination of material may be used. Other contributors to this Symposium have focused attention on the morphological aspects of micro-organisms. Here it may be noted that the morphology of bacteria in smears from natural materials and from pure cultures is not necessarily the same. For example, the grape-like clusters of staphylococci typical of pus-smears are often not seen in films taken from plate cultures. Similarly, 'Bacterium anitratum' in smears may resemble the gonococcus but in culture it often becomes bacillary. In this connexion we may remember the story of the young pathologist who diagnosed *Pasteurella pestis* from a Gram stain—he had over-decolorized sporing bacilli! Morphology may also vary as a result of chemotherapy.

Although cell and colonial morphology can be helpful they are in themselves seldom diagnostic. Thus the presumptive identification as a haemolytic streptococcus of a colony from a throat swab culture on a blood agar plate may be shown by simple staining to be incorrect; the organism may be Gram-negative and prove on further examination to be *Haemophilus haemolyticus*. The formation of a slime-wall by colonies of the typical paratyphoid B bacillus has long been used to distinguish it from the 'java' variety. Anderson (1961) found the phosphate concentration of the medium to influence slime-wall formation and further showed that, under suitable conditions, slime-wall production is widely distributed in the Enterobacteriaceae.

Cell appendages such as flagella and fimbriae are of little diagnostic value. Motility can be easily demonstrated, but the type of flagellation and the presence or absence of fimbriae can only be satisfactorily shown with an electron microscope. Thus the importance of these characters moves from the realm of diagnosis to that of taxonomy. This was recognized by Cowan, Steel, Shaw & Duguid (1960) in their classification of the *Klebsiella* group; although it made use of fimbriation, this character was not essential for the identification of the species and subspecies defined.

Colour

Marine biologists will be familiar with the luminescent bacteria (*Photobacterium* spp.) associated with fish, but other workers must be content with pigmented organisms. Colony colour may be of help in identifying an unknown organism; it has, for example, a minor place in the classification of staphylococci proposed by Shaw, Stitt & Cowan (1951). The plant-pathogenic xanthomonads generally have yellow coloured colonies but most bacterial human pathogens are unfortunately devoid of pigment. Strains of *Staphylococcus aureus* (as defined by Shaw *et al.* 1951) may have golden, yellow or white colonies (despite their name) and achromogenic *Pseudomonas* strains are commonly isolated from burns. On the other hand, the mycologist has a much more colourful array of organisms to deal with, where even a difference in colour between the surface and undersurface may be of diagnostic value. Provided allowance is made for the possible effect of environment (e.g. medium, pH and temperature) on the quality and quantity of pigment production, the presence of pigment can be diagnostic but its absence is of little value. Old cultures of *P. aeruginosa* on solid media often show an iridescence which is helpful but not characteristic or specific.

Fluorescence

Comparatively little use has been made of natural fluorescence in microbiology. An important use is in the examination of suspected cases of ringworm of the scalp. In this disease, hairs infected with *Microsporum audouinii* or *M. canis* fluoresce intensely under Wood's light. *Trichophyton schoenleinii* shows a duller fluorescence and can be distinguished microscopically by the endothrix infection of the hair. Both *Microsporum* species give rise to small spore ectothrix infections which can only be distinguished by cultural methods. Other dermatophytes causing ringworm of the scalp do not cause the hair to fluoresce. Thus fluorescence has only limited value in this disease as a delay of 4–21 days may elapse before the fungus can be culturally identified with certainty and a decision made whether to institute radiological epilation or rely on topical therapy.

It has been suggested (Sonea & de Repentigny, 1960) that primary or auto-fluorescence might be an aid in the identification of micro-organisms. Cells of all strains examined showed a blue fluorescence which could be obviated by the use of a yellow filter. Fluorescence then divided the organisms into two groups, the largest having exclusive yellow-green fluorescence and the remainder (2 yeasts and 4 bacterial species) showing a reddish fluorescence. Environmental conditions could affect the colour but a reddish fluorescence was not seen among members of the first group. Dowdle & Hansen (1961) noted a bluish green to yellowish green primary fluorescence of spores of *Bacillus* spp. which tended to interfere with their fluorescent antibody staining methods.

Fluorescence microscopy has long been applied to the examination of sputum for tubercle bacilli; auramine is used as the fluorochrome and the method is at least as sensitive as the conventional Ziehl-Neelsen staining technique. The use of acridine orange as a fluorescent stain for pathogenic fungi and yeasts in smears, tissue sections and fresh preparations has been reported (Chick, 1961).

Fluorescent antibody techniques

The most notable advance in diagnostic procedures has undoubtedly been the advent of fluorescent antibody techniques. Coons & Kaplan (1950) showed that when bacteria were allowed to react with homologous immune globulin which had been labelled with a fluorescein compound they fluoresced on examination with ultra-violet light. This reaction has now been widely applied to the identification of bacteria, fungi, protozoa, viruses and yeasts in pure culture, tissue and clinical specimens. The technique has been the subject of reviews by Coons (1959), who deals particularly with its diagnostic applications, and by Umiker & Gadebusch (1960), Antona & Mannucci (1961) and Beutner (1961), to whom reference can be made.

Theoretically any fluorochrome may be used for labelling the antibodies but only fluorescein and rhodamine have been widely used. The advantages claimed for this technique are speed, sensitivity and specificity. Identification can be made even when only a few organisms are present in the specimen and it is immaterial whether they are viable or not. Cultural and fluorescent antibody techniques are in good agreement, although exceptions do occur. The technique cannot replace conventional bacteriological methods as yet, but should be used in conjunction with them. Though a positive fluorescent antibody reaction does not constitute a confirmed diagnosis, it is strong evidence; in clinical microbiology it is sufficiently good evidence to institute therapy pending confirmation by conventional techniques.

Before the new technique can be universally adopted many problems have to be solved. In theory, diagnosis could be made on the observation of a single fluorescing cell, yet how much reliance should be placed on this? Are slides to be examined as painstakingly as if one were searching a film for stained tubercle bacilli? As with other serological techniques, non-specific reactions occur and it is important to know the microbial flora likely to be met in various specimens. Some of the limitations of the technique have been discussed by Carski (1961), Cherry (1961) and White (1961).

Since the reviews cited above, papers have been published dealing with the application of the method to the following micro-organisms, among others: meningococci (Metzger & Smith, 1960), streptococci (Wolfe, Cameron & West, 1960; Warfield, Page, Zuelzer & Stulberg, 1961), *Bordetella pertussis* (Levina & Neimark, 1960; Donaldson & Whitaker, 1960; Kendrick, Eldering & Eveland, 1961), *Haemophilus influenzae* type B (Page, Caldroney & Stulberg, 1961), *Listeria monocytogenes* (Smith, Marshall & Eveland, 1960), and the virus of Colorado tick fever (Burgdorfer & Lackman, 1960).

The fluorescence of normal human sera obtained as controls by Smith *et al.* (1960) was a limitation of the technique in the diagnosis of infectious mononucleosis. Divergent results between fluorescent antibody and conventional cultural diagnosis were obtained by Kendrick *et al.* (1961) and Page *et al.* (1961), but usually the presence of fluorescent organisms which could not be cultivated was correlated with clinical evidence of infection and effective antibiotic therapy. Similar results were obtained by Warfield *et al.* (1961), who investigated the incidence of group A streptococci in throat smears. Cross-reactions with heterologous groups of streptococci and other bacteria in the smears were effectively eliminated by absorption of the serum with Group C streptococci.

The fluorescent treponemal antibody technique was claimed to give results similar to those of the treponema immobilization test in the detection of syphilis antibodies (Mannucci & Spagnoli, 1961), and Wilkinson (1961) found it had a high level of sensitivity and specificity when compared with the Wassermann reaction, Price's precipitation reaction, the Reiter protein complement-fixation test and the treponemal immobilization test.

The application of the technique for the early identification of slow-growing organisms has been described by Chadwick & Slade (1960). Impressions of the micro-colonies on plates were taken on coverslips which were dried, fixed and stained with the fluorescein-labelled globulins of the appropriate antiserum. Micro-colonies treated with their homologous labelled antisera fluoresced brightly under ultra-violet light. The result was easily distinguished from that obtained with heterologous labelled antisera or labelled normal sera. By this method it was possible to identify *Brucella suis*, *Pasteurella pestis* and *P. tularensis* within 20 hr. of inoculating a plate with material suspected of containing one of these organisms. At this time, the cultures show insufficient growth to permit the satisfactory use of conventional serological methods.

In order to improve the specificity of the method for *Bacillus anthracis*, Dowdle & Hansen (1961) used an indirect phage-fluorescent antiphage staining system based upon the assumption of specific adsorption of phage by sensitive cells and of specific reaction of the phage with fluorescein-labelled antiphage serum. Only 9 of 91 strains of various saprophytic *Bacillus* spp. reacted with this staining procedure, whereas 42 stained with fluorescent antibodies to the spore antigens of *B. anthracis* and 43 with antibodies to the somatic antigens.

Serology

The conventional serological tests comprise agglutination, complement-fixation and precipitation techniques. To these three has now been added the fluorescent antibody technique (see above). Antigenic analysis is a field in which considerable progress has been made. This is most obvious in the Enterobacteriaceae where the ever-increasing number of *Salmonella* serotypes recognized, although a tribute to its delicacy, complicates diagnostic work.

A major difficulty is the possession by various members of a family of common antigens which masquerade under different designations, e.g. Salmonella antigen O 35 = Arizona antigen O 20 = Escherichia antigen O 111. Kampelmacher (1959) has listed some of the common antigenic relations between members of these genera but many more need to be defined. This tends to make diagnosis by serology alone rather precarious, although its value as a confirmatory technique or for identification at sub-specific levels is not doubted.

However, the occurrence of common antigens in unrelated organisms can be advantageous. For example, the presence of similar antigens in certain strains of *Proteus* and some rickettsias forms the basis of the Weil-Felix reaction for the diagnosis of typhus and scrub-typhus. The significance of the antigenic relation between *Candida albicans* and *Salmonella* (Aksoycan, LeMinor & LeMinor, 1960) is of more doubtful practical value.

Serological studies of the aerobic spore-forming bacilli have not been very fruitful (Brown, Treece & Smith, 1958) and it is fortunate that there is only one pathogenic member, *Bacillus anthracis*, and this can be identified by other criteria (see Burdon & Wende, 1960; Dowdle & Hansen, 1961).

Biochemical methods

These time-honoured tests are some of the basic tools of the diagnostician. Unfortunately many of them leave much to be desired and have lagged behind the considerable advances made in microbiological biochemistry.

In the field of carbohydrate utilization, the most notable advance has been the introduction of the test of Hugh & Leifson (1953) for determining the method by which bacteria attack carbohydrates, whether by fermentation or oxidation. This division generally splits organisms at the generic level (e.g. *Pseudomonas* is oxidative and *Aeromonas* is fermentative), although in some genera individual species react differently, e.g. in the genus *Neisseria* (Berger, 1960). Cowan (1953*a*) has found that many organisms whose carbohydrate katabolism is oxidative show greater action on 'sugars' when an ammonium-salt medium (Smith, Gordon & Clark, 1952) is used in place of the normal peptone or serum water base.

Organisms which are considered to be without action on carbohydrates can under certain conditions be shown to produce acid from them; Pickett & Nelson (1955) demonstrated the formation of acid from several carbohydrates by species of *Brucella* when heavy suspensions of the organisms were incubated with the carbohydrates in a peptone-free buffered medium. Taxonomically this is upsetting but diagnostically it may or may not be significant, depending on what criteria are used to identify the genus.

The microtests of Clarke & Cowan (1952) in which heavy bacterial suspensions and chemically defined solutions were used have been applied to fermentations, reduction of methylene blue and of nitrate, production of acetoin, catalase, hydrogen sulphide and indole, and the hydrolysis of gelatin, starch and urea. When compared with conventional techniques, they have the advantage that only one enzymic system is under investigation in a particular test and the absence of culture medium ensures that side reactions do not oppose or interfere with the main reaction. Further advantages are the speed with which results are obtained and the economy of materials. Sources of error do exist in such methods (Cowan, 1953*b*) and the results of microtests may not always agree with those obtained with growing cultures (Cowan, 1953*a*). A limitation of this type of test is that we are dealing with preformed (or constitutive) enzymes; in order to assess the potential enzymic activities of micro-organisms it may be necessary to vary the test conditions or the medium upon which the organism is first grown (Clarke & Cowan, 1952).

The need for rapid identification of pathogenic bacteria has led to a surfeit of what I call 'blunderbuss' tests, that is the inoculation of one or two tubes of composite medium to provide results of several often unrelated biochemical features. Examples of these are Gillies's modification of Kohn's medium for the preliminary identification of *Salmonella* and *Shigella* (Gillies, 1956) and the dulcitol-sucrose-salicin-iron-urea agar of Papadakis (1960), also for *Salmonella*. These two media permit the detection of up to seven and five biochemical properties respectively, with motility as well in Gillies's medium.

It is remarkable how much interest has been shown in the family Enterobacteriaceae, and in the information now available as a result of concerted and co-operative work. It is to be regretted that all families have not yet been studied as thoroughly. I would make a plea for greater application of biochemical tests to micro-organisms other than those for which the tests were devised. In this respect, the tests for amino-acid decarboxylase activity (Møller, 1955), for differentiation of certain members of the Enterobacteriaceae, have been found to be of value in the genus *Pasteurella* (Steel, unpublished observations).

Skinner & Fletcher (1960) regarded the methods used for carbohydrate fermentation by yeasts as primitive, and called for research on better tests. They were convinced that improvements in methods for demonstrating fermentation by yeasts were overdue and stated 'if the alcoholic fermentation is used as a taxonomic criterion, efforts should be made to find methods that can be depended upon to demonstrate this type of metabolic activity—or the lack of it'. They were of the opinion that whereas the difference between none and some fermentative power was fundamental, qualitative differences between degrees of fermentation were likely to be of only trivial importance and to represent strain differences.

In standardizing our test procedures do we want the whole truth or merely a partial truth which is of greater diagnostic value? Hydrogen sulphide production is a character often used in diagnostic procedures, especially among the enteric group of organisms. The addition of cysteine (Clarke, 1953) to the broth used for the test results in many more positive reactions, and hydrogen sulphide is detected more readily with lead acetate papers than with ferric chloride or lead acetate agar. Thus increased test sensitivity provides more information on the enzymic activity of an organism but is of less value in diagnosis since more organisms give positive results.

By varying the sensitivity of a test we can often alter the result; for example, the sensitivity of the original Voges-Proskauer test has been greatly increased by the use of creatine (O'Meara, 1931), α-naphthol (Barritt, 1936) or a mixture of each with ferric chloride (Batty-Smith, 1941). By the use of such modifications more positive results are obtainable but the main advantage is one of reaction speed. The high sensitivity of Barritt's (1936) modification may tend to obscure differences between members of the 'coliform group' that are clearly recognizable when a less sensitive test is used, but all interpretation is arbitrary and the diagnostician can select the sensitivity of his test so as to be of most use to him.

Inhibition tests

Many culture media contain agents to inhibit or suppress the growth of particular micro-organisms. Generally, however, such media are not sufficiently specific to permit an immediate diagnosis. The use of inhibitory agents for particular micro-organisms has found wider value and commonly used ones include ethylhydrocupreine hydrochloride ('optochin') to which pneumococci are sensitive whereas other α-haemolytic streptococci are usually not (Bowers & Jeffries, 1955), and bacitracin for the diagnosis of group A streptococci; Maxted (1953) found all except 1·7 % of 2386 bacitracin-sensitive β-haemolytic strepto-cocci to be group A and only 2·5 % of 851 bacitracin-resistant strains were group A. A vibriostatic agent (2:4-diamino-6:7-di-*iso*propyl-pteridine), designated O 129 (Shewan, Hodgkiss & Liston, 1954) has been used to distinguish vibrios from pseudomonads. *Aeromonas* strains have been found to be resistant to this pteridine compound (Eddy, 1960), which thus shows promise of both taxonomic and diagnostic value. Inhibition by dyes has long been used for species determination in the genus *Brucella* (see Castañeda, 1961), and appears to be of value in other genera, e.g. *Azotobacter* (Callao & Montoya, 1960).

The problem of drug sensitivity must be considered carefully. The wide use of antibiotics has given rise to certain bacteria whose resistance far exceeds that of their forebears of several years ago, e.g. staphylococci. Increased resistance could throw a diagnostic scheme, which depended on drug sensitivity, into confusion and, while it may now be true to say that strains of *Pasteurella* are penicillin-sensitive, this may not hold in the future. Perhaps if the use of inhibitory agents in diagnostic procedures is restricted to those substances not in common use outside a laboratory we may obviate this possibility and maintain a fixity of sensitivity.

Bacteriophage sensitivity

Phage-typing of bacteria occupies a large number of workers. The high incidence of staphylococcal infections has stimulated interest in the epidemiological study of such outbreaks and in these cases phage-typing is invaluable. The typing of typhoid and paratyphoid B bacilli and *Staphylococcus aureus* was extensively reviewed by Anderson & Williams

(1956) and a satisfactory scheme for typing *Salmonella typhimurium* was devised by Callow (1959, see Anderson & Wilson, 1961). Epidemiological studies of *Pseudomonas aeruginosa* infections based on phage-typing (Gould & McLeod, 1960) are now possible, but preliminary study with the bacteriophages of *Clostridium perfringens* has been disappointing, because over half the strains examined were not susceptible to any of the phages (Smith, 1959). In soil microbiology attention has been directed to *Azotobacter* phages (Duff & Wyss, 1961); those isolated were not species-specific, however, in terms of the present concept of the taxonomy of this genus.

The isolation of phages from strains of *Bordetella bronchiseptica* has been reported (Rauch & Pickett, 1961). They were not, however, specific in their host range, only 73 % of the strains being lysed by the phages which also lysed *B. parapertussis*. Strains of *B. pertussis*, *Brucella* spp. and (surprisingly) *Alcaligenes faecalis* were insensitive to these phages. The authors felt that a search for lysogeny among other strains of *B. bronchiseptica* might provide a battery of phages with which a complete typing scheme could be established.

Phage-typing is with few exceptions applicable only at the sub-species level and is of little value to the routine worker. Chadwick (1959) however has reported that identification of *Bacillus anthracis* can be aided by the use of a specific α-phage which does not affect the other members of the genus, and Burdon & Wende (1960) have obtained similar results with γ-phage. Other phages with a reasonable degree of specificity at the species level are staphylococcal phage RG which never lyses *Staphylococcus aureus* (coagulase-positive staphylococci of Shaw *et al.* 1951), and a brucella phage specific for *Brucella abortus* (van Drimmelen, 1959).

Virus diagnosis

Viruses, at least of animal origin, can usually be diagnosed in one or more of three ways:

(i) Microscopically by examining smears or sections for the presence of, or for cytopathic effects of, the virus.

(ii) By cultivation in tissue culture, fertile eggs or experimental animals.

(iii) Serologically: virus infection produces an antibody response which can be demonstrated by testing the acute and convalescent phase sera in neutralization, haemagglutination-inhibition or complement-fixation tests. Although the results of such tests are retrospective they may be useful for epidemiological surveys.

The advent of fluorescent antibody techniques is expected to contribute much to viral diagnosis. An account of modern aids to the diagnosis of virus diseases has been given by Dudgeon (1961) and of the use of tissue culture in virus diagnosis by Schmidt & Lennette (1961).

Chromatography

Because of their technical complexity and time-consumption chromatographic methods are unlikely to be of value in diagnosis. A further disadvantage is the necessity of having pure cultures. For taxonomic purposes, however, it is a very useful technique. Most workers have studied cell-wall composition (e.g. Cummins & Harris, 1956; Davis & Baird-Parker, 1959; Roberts & Stewart, 1961) analysing the hydrolysates for amino acid and 'sugar' content. The work of Cummins & Harris (1956), which suggested that *Corynebacterium pyogenes* might be more correctly classified as a streptococcus, is an indication of the taxonomic value of chromatography, but the diagnosis of this organism as either a corynebacterium or a streptococcus corresponds with current usage. In the diagnostic tables of Cowan & Steel (1961) this organism appears with both groups.

Other workers have studied the free amino acid pool occurring within the cells. Cheeseman (1959) contends that this could be of use to the bacteriologist in routine work on the genus *Lactobacillus*. These methods have been extended to the genus *Bacillus* (Jayne-Williams & Cheeseman, 1960) with promising results for the taxonomy of this genus. Steenson & Robertson (1961) regard the technique as more successful in distinguishing strains having wide biochemical differences than those which are biochemically similar. They investigated group D streptococci, isolated from cheese, by chromatographic and conventional bacteriological methods; only *Streptococcus durans* was well defined by paper chromatography.

French workers (see Asselineau, 1961) have made preliminary studies, using gas chromatography, on the nature of the fatty acids extractable from bacteria. Although only four species were used it was suggested that the technique be applied to the identification of genera.

Spectroscopy

Ultra-violet spectroscopy is not likely to be of value in microbiological work because of the high purine and pyrimidine content of micro-organisms. Riddle *et al.* (1956) and Norris (1959) have reviewed the applications of infra-red spectroscopy in microbiology. The technique is applicable to bacteria, viruses and cellular extracts using infra-red radiation in the $1–16\mu$ wavelength range. Norris (1959) regarded differentiation between closely related strains of organisms as being possible, but considered that the technique was not suitable for the identification of whole cells, a major difficulty being the occurrence of common absorption bands in many micro-organisms. On the other hand, Riddle *et al.* (1956) were more optimistic although they recognized that certain bacteria could not be distinguished by infra-red spectroscopy. It is doubtful, however, whether any of the instrumental physico-chemical techniques will find much use in diagnostic work, although they may possibly prove very valuable in taxonomic studies.

ANALYSIS OF THE RESULTS

Having determined the characters and reactions of an unknown micro-organism we are in a position to undertake an analysis of the accumulated results with the hope of arriving at a satisfactory identification. Unless they are carried in the head, some means of recording the results is necessary. The methods available are legion and are matters of personal preference; I am only going to mention two—the descriptive chart and the punched card.

Descriptive charts

These are not in themselves of diagnostic value. They do mean, however, that when the information has been recorded the worker has most of the information necessary to make a diagnosis.

Two descriptive charts for use in characterizing bacteria were issued by the Society of American Bacteriologists. They are the standard Descriptive Chart issued in 1934 and, a simpler one, the Descriptive Chart for Instruction in 1939; both charts are $8\frac{1}{2} \times 11$ in. in size. A similar chart used at the National Collection of Type Cultures (Cowan, 1951) measures 13×6 in.

Punched cards

These are not meant to replace descriptive charts but can be used in association with them. The amount of descriptive material on the charts is such as to make its recording on a punched card difficult. Hugh (personal communication), who has used punched cards over the past eight years, has two series of cards for the Gram-negative rods, one for glucose fermenters and the other for non-fermenters. The cards accommodate 48 and 46 reactions respectively and an unknown organism can be identified as one of 21 or 13 genera or species respectively.

The use of a punched card system in diagnosis means that a set of standard cards with which to compare the unknown is needed. If, for example, the identification is based on 9 independent characters, all of which can be either positive or negative, then the number of possible combinations is $2^9 = 512$. If two of these characters can be recorded as positive, delayed positive or negative then the number of combinations will be 1152. Does this mean that the 1152 punched cards with which to compare the results of the unknown organism are needed? Nine is not a large number of characters on which to base an identification, but if the number be increased then the number of possible combinations soon becomes astronomical. Fortunately all the theoretical combinations of characters are not likely to be encountered in practice, although allowance must be made for them. If the particular combination of characters of the unknown does not tally with that of recognized micro-organisms should the unknown be regarded as an aberrant strain, a new species or remain unidentified?

The taxonomist however may be dealing with 75–100 characters and electronic sorting is a valuable asset; the diagnostician cannot rely on the availability of a computer and must be more practical in his outlook. The magnitude of the problem was shown by Riddle *et al.* (1956) who obtained 1395 infra-red spectra from a study of 650 strains of 201 bacterial species; 637 of the spectra were regarded as standards and the nucleus of a catalogue of spectra was formed by coding and punching this information into cards.

When the necessary information has been accumulated and recorded, how do we proceed to make an identification? Obviously we must have standards with which to compare the unknown isolate, but where do we find such standards? Because of the paucity of information in the past it was usual to attempt a 'katabolic' diagnosis, that is to take a taxonomic system and work backwards from higher taxa to lower until a description was found which corresponded to that of the unknown micro-organism.

Bergey's Manual of Determinative Bacteriology (1957) is without doubt the most elaborate of current systems of classification. Unfortunately, there are some who consider the contents of the Manual sacrosanct, whereas Cowan (1959), on the other hand, has stated ' . . . with each edition of the Bergey Manual, the older it is, the less its effect on the mind of man; those who come after us will look upon the current edition as we look upon the first edition: interesting but useless'. Between these two extreme views come those of many workers who find *Bergey's Manual* unsatisfactory in one way or another. Generally this is due to lack of information and to indefinite descriptions of organisms in fields other than their own. This is not to detract from the overall value of the work but rather to point out that some sections are inadequate because they are often based on incomplete literature reports and on cultures which are no longer extant.

Those who attempt to use the *Manual* to identify micro-organisms in a 'katabolic' way find it full of pitfalls, the main one being that criteria used to classify the material are often not those that have been used for identification. van Niel (1946) demonstrated how *Aerobacter aerogenes* could be fitted into the family Rhizobiaceae in the fifth edition of the *Manual*.

The katabolic approach to identification is gradually being superseded by the 'anabolic' where a diagnosis is built up from the available data. This is the basis of various diagnostic keys, schemes and tables upon which I want to enlarge. Such anabolic methods often have no resemblance to classificatory systems and in this lies their merit.

Diagnostic keys, schemes and tables

Dichotomous keys in floras are familiar to botanists. Generally there is more than one approach available, so that if a character is omitted it is still possible to make a correct identification. In bacteriology this type of key is gaining in popularity owing mainly to the efforts of Skerman (1949, 1957, 1959). His first mechanical key (1949) was presented in order that it could be tested and criticized with a view to rectifying its omissions and mistakes. Skerman noted that the fault in *Bergey's Manual* lay in the attempt to combine a system of classification with one of identification. In his view, keys for identification should not be classificatory keys used in reverse, but should be specially prepared. His first key was strongly criticized but these criticisms paved the way for a much better key (1957) which, although not strictly dichotomous, was designed to enable the user to determine whether any isolated organism bore a resemblance to an organism described in *Bergey's Manual*. No attempt was made to fit the key to any system of classification and it was designed solely for the purpose of identification of described genera.

Skerman's third key (1959) is more comprehensive than his previous ones. An unknown organism can be traced to its relevant genus and the generic diagnosis confirmed by reference to descriptions of 220 genera which are given in the second section of the guide. This section may also suggest additional tests which need to be made. After reaching the generic diagnosis, however, recourse must be made to *Bergey's Manual* (1957) if a specific diagnosis is required. However, the key is still open to some criticism: an example is the dichotomy which depends on the production or non-production of acid from lactose within 40 days; this occurs in a part of the key dealing with rapidly growing Gram-negative rods and one can hardly wait this length of time for a negative result.

Simple diagnostic schemes for particular genera are quite common and are found in many textbooks. At the other end of the scale is the Kauffmann-White Schema which shows the antigenic formula of every recognized serotype of the *Salmonella* group. The serotypes are allotted to one of 9 alphabetically designated groups (A–I) or several further undesignated groups, in accordance with the O-determining antigen or antigen-complex. Sometimes, sub-groups (e.g. of groups C and E) are designated because of common determining factors. The fact that two different serotypes are shown as possessing an antigenic component with the same designation does not necessarily mean that the two components are identical. The schema has never pretended to offer the complete antigenic constitution of the designated serotypes.

What is especially required are schemes covering a wider variety of species such as whole families or so-called 'orders'. An interesting diagnostic scheme was devised by Fey (1959) for the aerobic, Gram-negative rods. The unknown strain is evaluated on the basis of eight reactions, each of which carries a number of points; the reactions and points are: acid from mannitol (5), gas from glucose (10), acid from lactose (20), indole production (40), urease activity (80), motility (160) and growth in the presence of KCN (320). The points are summed for each positive reaction and the species or genus corresponding to this number is looked up in a table. When the same sum corresponds to more than one organism, a further differentiation may be made by additional biochemical or serological tests. As an example, a strain which produced acid from mannitol and was negative in the other reactions would have five points; this total corresponds to certain serotypes of *Shigella boydii* and *S. flexneri* or *Salmonella gallinarum* which can be distinguished serologically. A motile urease-producing strain negative in the other reactions has 240 points which corresponds in Fey's table to *Bordetella bronchiseptica;* in my hands, however, all strains of this organism grow in the presence of KCN and would therefore have a total of 560 which corresponds to *Proteus mirabilis*!

van Niel (1946) preferred the use of a small number of properties which must be independent and consistently applied so as to avoid overlapping. He suggested the composition of separate keys, distinguishing the various bacteria primarily by their morphology, physiology, biochemical reactions, and pathogenic or serological properties. As examples he cited keys for the red-coloured bacteria and for the cellulose-decomposing organisms. The fact that *Cytophaga rubra* occurred in both groups was logically inherent in the method of approach and was not a disadvantage. He believed that such a system would accomplish three major objectives: (i) all known bacteria would find a place in one or more of the keys and would consequently be determinable, (ii) unsatisfactory taxa could be abolished without the organisms composing them becoming indeterminable, and (iii) the system of cross-indexing the organisms by means of a multiplicity of characters would bring out common properties; this would tend to direct attention to the possible identity of organisms frequently found together in the keys.

Table 1. *Stage* 1 *diagnostic table for Gram-positive bacteria*

(From Cowan & Steel, 1961.)

	a_1	a_2	a_3	b_1	b_2	c_1	c_2	c_3	d	e	f	g_1	g_2
Shape	S	S	S	S	S	R	R	R	R	R	R	R	R
Acid-fastness	−	−	−	−	−	−	−	−	−	−	−	+	−
Spores	−	−	−	−	−	−	−	−	−	+	+	−	−
Motility	−	−	−	−	+	+	−	+	−	d	d	−	−
Catalase	+	+	+	−	−	+	+	+	−	+	−	d	+
Oxidase	−	−	−	−	−	−	−	−	−	d	−	−	+
Glucose (acid)	+	+	−	+	+	+	d	−	+	d	d	+	+
Glucose F or O	F	O	−	F	F	F	F	−	F	F or O	F	O	O

Organisms (diagonal diagnostic staircase, reading across the columns above):

Staphylococcus (a_1, a_2 ?, a_3 ?)

Micrococcus

Aerococcus

Leuconostoc

Streptococcus

Listeria

Corynebacterium

Kurthia

Erysipelothrix

Lactobacillus

Actinomyces

Bacillus

Clostridium

Mycobacterium

Nocardia

+ = 100–80% strains positive, d = 79–21% strains positive, − = 20–0% strains positive, S = sphere, R = rod, F = fermentation, O = oxidation.

The Determinator (Cowan & Steel, 1960) is a mechanical device to simplify comparison of a list of pre-determined characters of an unknown organism with similar lists of characters of known organisms. Diagnostic tables for use with the Determinator have been prepared (Cowan & Steel, 1961) which it is hoped will be of value in the identification of bacteria of medical and veterinary interest (e.g. Tables 1 and 2). The tables are in three stages corresponding roughly to family or genus, species and subspecies. As the authors point out, the tables are not meant to identify without doubt a particular organism but may serve to focus attention on possibilities. The tables do not necessarily correspond with recognized taxa and some organisms occur in more than one table. Tables of this nature approach van Niel's (1946) criteria.

Table 2. *Stage 2 table for the Gram-positive catalase-positive cocci*

(From Cowan & Steel, 1961. After determining the row and column in Table 1 to which an unknown organism belongs the worker consults one of the second stage tables. This table is an extension of the first part of Table 1.)

	Staph. aureus	*Staph. saprophyticus*	*Staph. lactis*	*Staph. roseus*	*Staph. afermentans*	*A. viridans*
Catalase	+	+	+	+	+	±
Coagulase	+	−	−	−	−	−
Nitrate reduction	+	d	+	d	d	−
Gelatin liquefaction	+	d	d	−	d	−
Urease	+	d	d	d	d	−
VP	+	+	−	−	−	−
Glucose (acid)	+	+	+	+	−	+
Glucose F or O	F	F	V		−	F
Red pigment	−	−	−	+	−	−

V = some strains F, others O.

An intriguing device—the Logoscope—has been devised by Nash (1954, 1960, and personal communication). It resembles a slide rule and is designed to simplify the task of correlating particular combinations of signs and symptoms with the diseases which may give rise to them. Text-books will tell the physician the possible causes of symptoms but the logoscope refers him to the causes of combinations of symptoms. The most elaborate logoscope developed makes provision for 700 million different combinations. Nash (1960) points out that the device 'helps diagnostic thinking to become more methodical, systematic, comprehensive and demonstrative', but he emphasizes that it is not a substitute for knowledge and experience. Logoscopy is an aid to classificatory diagnosis and is not confined to medicine. I believe it to have many possibilities in microbiology, although the most difficult task would be programming the logoscope to answer the question 'in which microorganisms have these characters been described?'

Diagnosis by negatives ('rule out')

By this I mean that attitude of mind and process of thought by which a micro-organism can be excluded from a particular genus or species. For example, streptococci are catalase-negative and non-motile, therefore if an unknown organism produces catalase it cannot be a streptococcus. However, Langston, Gutierrez & Bouma (1960a) isolated two strains from silage fermentations which produced catalase and appeared to be closely related to *Streptococcus faecalis* var. *liquefaciens*. The same workers (1960b) also isolated motile streptococci (*S. faecium* var. *mobilis*) from grass silage and such motile strains are not uncommon among the group D streptococci (Hugh, 1959; Cowan & Steel, 1961).

Such trends of thought can be of value if we make the assumption that a positive result is of more value than a negative one; that is, the performance of a reaction or the presence of a character is more important than non-performance or absence. An example of this is motility, the presence of which rules out the genera *Klebsiella* and *Shigella*, whereas lack of motility does not necessarily exclude *Escherichia* or *Salmonella*. Similarly, the presence of sulphur globules in cells of purple bacteria is indicative of the family Thiorhodaceae; their absence does not automatically exclude this family and place the organisms in the Athiorhodaceae, as it is possible that absence of sulphur is due to lack of hydrogen sulphide to act as a hydrogen donor.

We have a saying 'the exception proves the rule' which is abbreviated from what was originally a legal maxim 'exception proves the rule in the cases not excepted'. The literature abounds with reports of micro-organisms which behave in an irresponsible manner and put the taxonomists to confusion! Recent examples include a lactose-fermenting strain of *Salmonella typhi* (Hofmann, Kiesewalter & Müller, 1960), a sucrose-fermenting strain of *S. poona* (Dixon & Curtis, 1960), and salicin-fermenting strains of *Shigella sonnei* (Serény, 1959). All members of the genus *Neisseria* are regarded as failing to reduce nitrates to nitrites but this did not deter Lindqvist (1960) from proposing a new species (*N. ovis*) which does reduce nitrate.

DISCUSSION

I have already stated that diagnosis and taxonomy are not synonymous and that the diagnostician and taxonomist are not necessarily working towards the same goal. This is well shown in the genus *Staphylococcus*. A classification of this genus was proposed by Shaw *et al.* (1951) by which five species (*S. afermentans, S. aureus, S. lactis, S. roseus* and *S. saprophyticus*) were recognized. Their criteria were coagulase production, acid and acetoin production from glucose, and pink pigmentation. Hill (1959) applied the Adansonian method of classification to staphylococci and concluded that *S. aureus, S. saprophyticus* and *S. roseus* were 'natural' groups, whereas *S. afermentans* and *S. lactis* were not; individual strains of these two species were as different from each other as from the other three species. Pohja (1960) agreed that *S. lactis* was a heterogeneous group, although 136 of his 171 strains of micrococcus isolated from meat could be placed in 10 subgroups all representing *S. lactis*, as defined by Shaw et al. (1951).

For diagnostic purposes, however, need a scheme be taxonomically correct? Diagnostic keys are generally simpler than taxonomic ones and this is meritorious. The classification of Shaw et al. (1951) cannot fail to accommodate any aerobic, catalase-producing, Gram-positive coccus, because it is based upon few characters and if a strain is positive in one of them it is automatically assigned to a species. Admittedly this is not good taxonomy but it makes for easy identification. Incorrect identification is possible, however, when a test gives misleading results; for example, on one occasion five strains of staphylococci isolated from dogs were found, using human plasma, to be coagulase-negative but to produce acetoin, and thus corresponded to *S. saprophyticus* according to Shaw et al. (1951). However, as I had reason to doubt this, the coagulase test was repeated using horse, rabbit and sheep plasma; evidence of coagulase production was obtained with rabbit plasma and the strains were identified as *S. aureus*.

The microbiologist can learn much from the chemist. If we consider qualitative chemical analysis as analogous to conventional bacteriological diagnosis, then the microtests of Clarke & Cowan (1952) are akin to micro- or semimicro-analysis. The chemical spot test (in which organic reagents form characteristic colours, compounds or crystals with acid radicles and metallic ions on a spotting-tile or absorbent paper) has a microbiological equivalent in the oxidase test of Kovacs (1956); this is more sensitive and economical than the older methods where the reagent was poured over the culture on solid medium (Steel, 1961). Erlich (1960) used a test in which mycobacterial cultures were rubbed into disks saturated with an alcoholic solution of auramine; tubercle and some of the 'anonymous' acid-fast bacilli gave a bright yellow colour when sodium hydroxide solution was dropped on to the discs. The reaction was believed to be due to the presence of mycolic acid in the bacilli. A spot test has also been used for the diagnosis of tubercle bacilli based on their abundant production of niacin (nicotinic acid); it is a colour reaction relying on the interaction of niacin with cyanogen bromide in the presence of aniline, benzidine or *o*-tolidine (Gutiérrez-Vásquez, 1960; Tarshis, 1961). The catalase test is often carried out in the form of a spot test on a glass slide, but with these few exceptions, and if slide-agglutination techniques are excluded, spot tests have so far found little use in microbiology. Spot tests appear to be a very useful weapon in the microbiologist's armamentarium but first we must overcome a good deal of prejudice and wean workers from carrying out their biochemical tests in tubes.

Attempts to decrease the time elapsing before results are obtainable have utilized oxidation-reduction potential indicators, such as the tetrazolium salts. These have the advantage that their colour change often precedes visible growth of the micro-organism, and use has been made of this phenomenon in antibiotic sensitivity determinations and phage typing (see Dooley, 1961). Further application of the principle may well be of value in a diagnostic laboratory.

The unexpected

The possibility that the specimen examined contains the unexpected must be borne in mind. The isolation of *Haemophilus influenzae* from unusual sites was recorded by Rogers, Zinnemann & Foster (1960); these included the urinary tract, perianal abscess, the lumen of the appendix, paronychia, etc. The authors did not regard their findings as exceptional, but thought they would be a common experience if routine investigations permitted the isolation of this organism.

In this connexion the possibility of diagnosing infections due to the pleuro-pneumonia (PPLO) group must not be overlooked. Many authors, including Klieneberger-Nobel (1959), have reported the presence of these organisms in cases of non-gonococcal urethritis, and they have also been associated with chronic respiratory disease of chickens (Yamamoto & Adler, 1958). This is not the place to enter into the controversy on the relations of PPLO, bacteria and L-forms but the possible significance of these agents must be borne in mind. An account of the cultivation and identification of PPLO by microscopy and staining techniques was given by Madoff (1959).

The fungi, too, must not be overlooked. The increased incidence of *Candida albicans* is believed by many to be due to excessive use of antibiotics. Mackenzie (1961) obtained 246 yeast isolates from 1004 clinical specimens; of the 23 species represented, *C. albicans* made up 56 % of the total, but *Torulopsis glabrata* and *Rhodotorula mucilaginosa* were common.

It is unfortunate that some degree of specialization in microbiology is necessary. But for this we would be more mindful of looking for the unusual when we failed to diagnose the usual. Failing to find *Xanthomonas pelargonii* in a sickly geranium plant, we might look for the pelargonium leaf-curl virus.

Attention is also being paid to disease caused by micro-organisms ordinarily considered to be non-pathogenic. The so-called 'Bacterium anitratum' is an example of such an organism; it has been isolated from various diseases and its pathogenicity has been briefly reviewed by Green (1960). Opsahl (1961), in common with other workers, has reported these Gram-negative diplococci which, in smears, are difficult to distinguish from gonococci.

Mis-diagnosis

What factors predispose to mis-diagnosis? I suggest the following: (i) non-uniformity of diagnostic criteria; (ii) experimental variation; (iii) lack of relevant information regarding the specimen; (iv) inconsistency of diagnosis by different microbiologists; (v) personal factors associated with training and experience.

In any particular field a standard set of diagnostic tests should be adhered to, but this does not mean that the rules must be inflexible and unchanging. New tests may be found to be valuable but should be well substantiated before being accepted for diagnostic use. Different workers have their own ideas of which tests are considered important and necessary for diagnosis (as distinct from taxonomy). An example of this occurred with strains isolated from water and received as indole-producing *Klebsiella aerogenes*. In the oxidase test (Kovacs, 1956) these strains were oxidase-positive, and further investigation led to their identification as *Aeromonas* spp. Eddy (1960) has also demonstrated that members of this genus may be mis-identified as *Citrobacter freundii*, *Escherichia coli* or other 'paracolons'. He recommends that Kovacs' oxidase test be added to the tests recommended in Report (1956) for the coli-aerogenes group.

Mis-diagnosis may sometimes be traced to failure to supply all the relevant information so that the microbiologist does not know the extent of the normal flora of the specimen to be expected, or whether it may have been altered as a result of chemotherapy. Again, death or overgrowth by other organisms may have occurred in the interval between sampling and laboratory examination. Regarding a possible variation between the results of different workers, there is scope for a survey of the results of identification of the same 'unknown' sample by microbiologists in different laboratories in a manner analogous to that by which proposed International Standards for biological materials are assayed.

Microbiologists are not infallible as was pointed out by Wilson (1959) in the fourth Marjory Stephenson Memorial Lecture to this Society. They differ as much as other people in intelligence and judgement. The trend towards early specialization means that many present-day micro-biologists have little or no practical experience in clinical medicine, agriculture, dairy husbandry, horticulture or whatever particular field to which their microbiology is applied. Consequently they may not realize or understand the possible implications of a particular set of circumstances before passing their opinions. Habits of thought are acquired from one's character and temperament as well as from circumstances related to education, experience and specialized training. Personal interest or inclination may lead the microbiologist to focus his attention in certain directions and the 'riding of hobby-horses' is not unknown!

The value of experience gained by intensive personal observation in a variety of different fields, along with a close study of the literature in others, cannot be stressed too strongly. Experience can teach one the relative value to be placed on different criteria, but no amount of experience can justify the 'identification' of a micro-organism by looking simply at its colonies upon a plate. We must endeavour to approach our diagnostic work objectively without bias or pre-judgement, although I realize that this is far easier said than done. Murray (1954) has stated 'there is so much that depends absolutely on the exact identification of a micro-organism that there is no justification for relying on opinion and prejudice'.

REFERENCES

AINSWORTH, G. C. (1955). The principles of microbial classification. Nomenclature, the handmaid of classification. *J. gen. Microbiol.* **12**, 322.

AKSOYCAN, N., LeMINOR, L. & LeMINOR, S. (1960). Antigènes communs entre les *Candida* et les Salmonella-Arizona. *Ann. Inst. Pasteur*, **99**, 723.

ANDERSON, E. S. (1961). Slime-wall formation in the salmonellae. *Nature, Lond.* **190**, 284.

ANDERSON, E. S. & WILLIAMS, R. E. O. (1956). Bacteriophage typing of enteric pathogens and staphylococci and its use in epidemiology. *J. clin. Path.* **9**, 94.

ANDERSON, E. S. & WILSON, E. M. J. (1961). Die Bedeutung der Salmonella typhi-murium-phagen-typisierung in der Human- und Veterinärmedizin. *Zbl. Bakt.* (1. *Abt. Orig.*), **181**, 368.

ANTONA, D. D' & MANNUCCI, E. (1961). Gli anticorpi fluorescenti nella diagnostica di laboratorio (fondamenta delle metodiche). *Ann. Sclavo*, **3**, 37.

ASSELINEAU, J. (1961). Sur quelques applications de la chromatographie en phase gazeuse a l'étude d'acides gras bactériens. *Ann. Inst. Pasteur*, **100**, 109.

BARRITT, M. M. (1936). The intensification of the Voges-Proskauer reaction by the addition of α-naphthol. *J. Path. Bact.* **42**, 441.

BATTY-SMITH, C. G. (1941). The detection of acetyl-methyl-carbinol in bacterial cultures. A comparative study of the methods of O'Meara and of Barritt. *J. Hyg., Camb.* **41**, 521.

BERGER, U. (1960). Über den Kohlenhydrat-Stoffwechsel von Neisseria und Gemella. *Zbl. Bakt.* (1. *Abt. Orig.*), **180**, 147.

Bergey's Manual of Determinative Bacteriology (1957), edition 7. Edited by Breed, R. S., Murray, E. G. D. & Smith, N. R. London: Baillière, Tindall and Cox.

BEUTNER, E. H. (1961). Immunofluorescent staining: the fluorescent antibody method. *Bact. Rev.* **25**, 49.

BOWERS, E. F. & JEFFRIES, L. R. (1955). Optochin in the identification of *Str. pneumoniae. J. clin. Path.* **8**, 58.

BROWN, E. R., TREECE, E. L. & SMITH, C. W. (1958). Immunologic studies on the antigenic inter-relationships between *Bacillus cereus, B. anthracis, B. mycoides* and the nonrhizoid variant of *B. mycoides. Bact. Proc.* 49.

BURDON, K. L. & WENDE, R. D. (1960). On the differentiation of anthrax bacilli from *Bacillus cereus. J. infect. Dis.* **107**, 224.

BURGDORFER, W. & LACKMAN, D. (1960). Identification of the virus of Colorado tick fever in mouse tissues by means of fluorescent antibodies. *J. Bact.* **80**, 131.

CALLAO, V. & MONTOYA, E. (1960). The use of dyes to distinguish between species of the genus *Azotobacter. J. gen. Microbiol.* **22**, 657.

CALLOW, B. R. (1959). A new phage-typing scheme for *Salmonella typhi-murium. J. Hyg., Camb.* **57**, 346.

CARSKI, T. R. (1961). The use and limitations of the fluorescent antibody technic in the identification and localization of viruses. *Amer. J. clin. Path.* **35**, 260.

CASTAÑEDA, M. R. (1961). Laboratory diagnosis of brucellosis in man. *Bull. World Hlth Org.* **24**, 73.

CHADWICK, P. (1959). Rapid identification of *Bacillus anthracis* by microscopical observation of bacteriophage lysis. *J. gen. Microbiol.* **21**, 631.

CHADWICK, P. & SLADE, J. H. R. (1960). Identification of bacteria by specific antibody conjugated with fluorescein isothiocyanate. *J. Hyg., Camb.* **58**, 147.

CHEESEMAN, G. C. (1959). The application of chromatographic techniques for the identification of species and strains of lactobacilli. *J. appl. Bact.* **22**, 341.

CHERRY, W. B. (1961). The use and limitations of the fluorescent antibody technic in the identification of bacteria in body fluids and exudates, and from cultures. *Amer. J. clin. Path.* **35**, 256.

CHICK, E. W. (1961). Acridine orange fluorescent stain for fungi. *Arch. Derm., Chicago*, **83**, 305.

CLARKE, P. H. (1953). Hydrogen sulphide production by bacteria. *J. gen. Microbiol.* **8**, 397.

CLARKE, P. H. & COWAN, S. T. (1952). Biochemical methods for bacteriology. *J. gen. Microbiol.* **6**, 187.

COONS, A. H. (1959). The diagnostic application of fluorescent antibodies. *Schweiz. Z. allg. Path.* **22**, 700.

COONS, A. H. & KAPLAN, M. H. (1950). Localization of antigen in tissue cells. II. Improvements in a method of the detection of antigen by means of a fluorescent antibody. *J. exp. Med.* **91**, 1.

COWAN, S. T. (1951). National Collection of Type Cultures. *Brit. med. Bull.* **7**, 189.

COWAN, S. T. (1953a). Microchemical methods for the characterization of bacteria. *Chem. & Ind.* p. 883.

COWAN, S. T. (1953 b). Fermentations: biochemical micromethods for bacteriology. *J. gen. Microbiol.* **8**, 391.

COWAN, S. T. (1959). Bacterial classification—problems and developments. In *Microbiology Yesterday and Today*, p. 54. Edited by V. Bryson. New Brunswick, N.J.: Institute of Microbiology, Rutgers, The State University.

COWAN, S. T. & STEEL, K. J. (1960). A device for the identification of microorganisms. *Lancet*, i, 1172.

COWAN, S. T. & STEEL, K. J. (1961). Diagnostic tables for the common medical bacteria. *J. Hyg., Camb.* **59**, 377.

COWAN, S. T., STEEL, K. J., SHAW, C. & DUGUID, J. P. (1960). A classification of the Klebsiella group. *J. gen. Microbiol.* **23**, 601.

CUMMINS, C. S. & HARRIS, H. (1956). The chemical composition of the cell wall in some Gram-positive bacteria and its possible value as a taxonomic character. *J. gen. Microbiol.* **14**, 583.

DAVIS, G. H. G. & BAIRD-PARKER, A. C. (1959). The classification of certain filamentous bacteria with respect to their chemical composition. *J. gen. Microbiol.* **21**, 612.

DIXON, J. M. S. & CURTIS, B. A. (1960). A sucrose-fermenting strain of *Salmonella poona*. *Mon. Bull. Minist. Hlth Lab. Serv.* **19**, 193.

DONALDSON, P. & WHITAKER, J. (1960). Diagnosis of pertussis by fluorescent antibody staining of nasopharyngeal smears. *Amer. J. Dis. Child.* **99**, 423.

DOOLEY, E. S. (1961). Bacteriophage impregnated disks with a redox indicator for rapid typing of resistant strains of *Staphylococcus aureus*. *J. Lab. clin. Med.* **57**, 807.

DOWDLE, W. R. & HANSEN, P. A. (1961). A phage-fluorescent antiphage staining system for *Bacillus anthracis*. *J. infect. Dis.* **108**, 125.

DRIMMELEN, G. C. VAN (1959). Bacteriophage typing applied to strains of *Brucella* organisms. *Nature, Lond.* **184**, 1079.

DUDGEON, J. A. (1961). Modern aids to diagnosis of virus diseases. *Brit. med. J.* i, 1269.

DUFF, J. T. & WYSS, O. (1961). Isolation and classification of a new series of *Azotobacter* bacteriophages. *J. gen. Microbiol.* **24**, 273.

EDDY, B. P. (1960). Cephalotrichous, fermentative gram-negative bacteria: the genus *Aeromonas*. *J. appl. Bact.* **23**, 216.

ERLICH, H. (1960). Rapid identification of mycobacterial colonies. I. The auramine test. *Amer. Rev. resp. Dis.* **81**, 218.

FEY, H. (1959). Differenzierungsschema für gramnegative aerobe Stäbchen. *Schweiz. Z. allg. Path.* **22**, 641.

GILLIES, R. R. (1956). An evaluation of two composite media for preliminary identification of Shigella and Salmonella. *J. clin. Path.* **9**, 368.

GOULD, J. C. & McLEOD, J. W. (1960). A study of the use of agglutinating sera and phage lysis in the classification of *Pseudomonas aeruginosa*. *J. Path. Bact.* **79**, 295.

GREEN, J. D. (1960). Bacterium anitratum meningitis. *Arch. intern. Med.* **106**, 870.

GUTIÉRREZ-VÁZQUEZ, J. M. (1960). Further studies on the spot test for the differentiation of tubercle bacilli of human origin from other mycobacteria. *Amer. Rev. resp. Dis.* **81**, 412.

HILL, L. R. (1959). The Adansonian classification of the staphylococci. *J. gen. Microbiol.* **20**, 277.

HOFMANN, S., KIESEWALTER, J. & MÜLLER, W. (1960). Ein lactose-positiver Typhus-Stamm. *Zbl. Bakt.* (1. *Abt. Orig.*), **179**, 528.

HUGH, R. (1959). Motile streptococci isolated from the oropharyngeal region. *Canad. J. Microbiol.* **5**, 351.

HUGH, R. & LEIFSON, E. (1953). The taxonomic significance of fermentative versus oxidative metabolism of carbohydrates by various Gram negative bacteria. *J. Bact.* **66**, 24.

JAYNE-WILLIAMS, D. J. & CHEESEMAN, G. C. (1960). The differentiation of bacterial species by paper chromatography. IX. The genus *Bacillus*: a preliminary investigation. *J. appl. Bact.* **23**, 250.

KAMPELMACHER, E. H. (1959). On antigenic O-relationships between the groups *Salmonella, Arizona, Escherichia* and *Shigella. Leeuwenhoek ned. Tijdschr.* **25**, 289.

KENDRICK, P. L., ELDERING, G. & EVELAND, W. C. (1961). Fluorescent antibody techniques. Methods for identification of Bordetella pertussis. *Amer. J. Dis. Child.* **101**, 149.

KLIENEBERGER-NOBEL, E. (1959). Pleuropneumonia-like organisms in genital infections. *Brit. med. J.* i, 19.

KOVACS, N. (1956). Identification of *Pseudomonas pyocyanea* by the oxidase reaction. *Nature, Lond.* **178**, 703.

LANGSTON, C. W., GUTIERREZ, J. & BOUMA, C. (1960a). Catalase-producing strains of streptococci. *J. Bact.* **80**, 693.

LANGSTON, C. W., GUTIERREZ, J. & BOUMA, C. (1960b). Motile enterococci (*Streptococcus faecium* var. *mobilis* var.n.) isolated from grass silage. *J. Bact.* **80**, 714.

LEVINA, E. N. & NEIMARK, F. M. (1960). Detection of *Haemophilus pertussis* by the fluorescent antibody technique. *J. Microbiol., Moscow (English edition)*, **31**, 779.

LINDQVIST, K. (1960). A *Neisseria* species associated with infectious keratoconjunctivitis of sheep—*Neisseria ovis* nov.spec. *J. infect. Dis.* **106**, 162.

MACKENZIE, D. W. R. (1961). Yeasts from human sources. *Sabouraudia*, **1**, 8.

MADOFF, S. (1959). Isolation and identification of PPLO. *Ann. N.Y. Acad. Sci.* **79**, 383.

MANNUCCI, E. & SPAGNOLI, U. (1961). La reazione di immunofluorescenza per la ricerca degli anticorpi della lue (precisazioni di tecnica). *Ann. Sclavo*, **3**, 49.

MAXTED, W. R. (1953). The use of bacitracin for identifying group A haemolytic streptococci. *J. clin. Path.* **6**, 224.

METZGER, J. F. & SMITH, C. W. (1960). Rapid identification of *Neisseria meningitidis* by fluorescent antibody technic. *U.S. Forces med. J.* **11**, 1185.

MØLLER, V. (1955). Simplified tests for some amino acid decarboxylases and for the arginine dihydrolase system. *Acta path. microbiol. scand.* **36**, 158.

MURRAY, E. G. D. (1954). A surmise on some trends in bacteriology. *Lancet*, i, 221.

NASH, F. A. (1954). Differential diagnosis. An apparatus to assist the logical faculties. *Lancet*, i, 874.

NASH, F. A. (1960). Diagnostic reasoning and the logoscope. *Lancet*, ii, 1442.

NIEL, C. B. VAN (1946). The classification and natural relationships of bacteria. *Cold Spr. Harb. Symp. quant. Biol.* **11**, 285.

NORRIS, K. P. (1959). Infra-red spectroscopy and its application to microbiology. *J. Hyg., Camb.* **57**, 326.

O'MEARA, R. A. Q. (1931). A simple delicate and rapid method of detecting the formation of acetylmethylcarbinol by bacteria fermenting carbohydrate. *J. Path. Bact.* **34**, 401.

OPSAHL, R. (1961). Bacterium anitratum (*Acinetobacter anitratum*) isolated from a case with cerebral abscess and purulent meningitis. *Acta path. microbiol. scand.* **51**, 72.

PAGE, R. H., CALDRONEY, G. L. & STULBERG, C. S. (1961). Immunofluorescence in diagnostic bacteriology. I. Direct identification of *Hemophilus influenzae* in smears of cerebrospinal fluid sediments. *Amer. J. Dis. Child.* **101**, 155.

PAPADAKIS, J. A. (1960). Dulcitol-sucrose-salicin-iron-urea agar (DSSIU)—a new medium for differential diagnosis of Salmonellae. *J. Hyg., Camb.* **58**, 331.

PICKETT, M. J. & NELSON, E. L. (1955). Speciation within the genus *Brucella*. IV. Fermentation of carbohydrates. *J. Bact.* **69**, 333.

POHJA, M. S. (1960). Micrococci in fermented meat products. Classification and description of 171 different strains. *Suom. Maataloust. Seur. Julk.*, no. 96, 1.

RAUCH, H. C. & PICKETT, M. J. (1961). *Bordetella bronchiseptica* bacteriophage. *Canad. J. Microbiol.* **7**, 125.

REPORT (1956). The nomenclature of coli-aerogenes bacteria. Report of the coli-aerogenes Subcommittee of the Society for Applied Bacteriology. *J. appl. Bact.* **19**, 108.

RIDDLE, J. W., KABLER, P. W., KENNER, B. A., BORDNER, R. H., ROCKWOOD, S. W. & STEVENSON, H. J. R. (1956). Bacterial identification by infrared spectrophotometry. *J. Bact.* **72**, 593.

ROBERTS, W. S. L. & STEWART, F. S. (1961). The sugar composition of streptococcal cell walls and its relation to haemagglutination pattern. *J. gen. Microbiol.* **24**, 253.

ROGERS, K. B., ZINNEMANN, K. & FOSTER, W. P. (1960). The isolation and identification of *Haemophilus* spp. from unusual lesions in children. *J. clin. Path.* **13**, 519.

SCHMIDT, N. J. & LENNETTE, E. H. (1961). Virology on the bookshelf. Application of tissue culture technics to diagnostic virology in the public health laboratory. *Amer. J. publ. Hlth*, **51**, 511.

SERÉNY, B. (1959). *Sh. sonnei* cultures fermenting salicin. *Acta microbiol. Acad. Sci. hung.* **6**, 217.

SHAW, C., STITT, J. M. & COWAN, S. T. (1951). Staphylococci and their classification. *J. gen. Microbiol.* **5**, 1010.

SHEWAN, J. M., HODGKISS, W. & LISTON, J. (1954). A method for the rapid differentiation of certain non-pathogenic, asporogenous bacilli. *Nature, Lond.* **173**, 208.

SKERMAN, V. B. D. (1949). A mechanical key for the generic identification of bacteria. *Bact. Rev.* **13**, 175.

SKERMAN, V. B. D. (1957). A key for the determination of the generic position of organisms listed in the manual. In *Bergey's Manual of Determinative Bacteriology*, 7th ed. 1957. London: Baillière, Tindall and Cox.

SKERMAN, V. B. D. (1959). *A Guide to the Identification of the Genera of Bacteria, with Methods and Digests of Generic Characteristics*. Baltimore: Williams and Wilkins Co.

SKINNER, C. E. & FLETCHER, D. W. (1960). A review of the genus *Candida*. *Bact. Rev.* **24**, 397.

SMITH, C. W., MARSHALL, J. D., Jr. & EVELAND, W. C. (1960). Identification of *Listeria monocytogenes* by the fluorescent antibody technic. *Proc. Soc. exp. Biol., N.Y.* **103**, 842.

SMITH, H. W. (1959). The bacteriophages of *Clostridium perfringens*. *J. gen. Microbiol.* **21**, 622.

SMITH, N. R., GORDON, R. E. & CLARK, F. E. (1952). Aerobic sporeforming bacteria. *Agric. Monogr. (U.S. Dep. Agric.)*, no. 16.

SONEA, S. & DE REPENTIGNY, J. (1960). Observations sur les couleurs de la fluorescence primaire des microorganismes. *Canad. J. Microbiol.* **6**, 519.

STEEL, K. J. (1961). The oxidase reaction as a taxonomic tool. *J. gen. Microbiol.* **25**, 297.

STEENSON, T. I. & ROBERTSON, P. S. (1961). A comparison of biochemical and paper chromatographic methods for the identification of group D streptococci from Cheddar cheese. *J. Dairy Res.* **28**, 57.

TARSHIS, M. S. (1961). Further investigations on the usefulness of the niacin test for differentiating human tubercle bacilli from other mycobacteria. II. A comparative study of three direct qualitative micro-methods using stored cultures of varying ages. *Tubercle, Lond.* **42**, 101.

UMIKER, W. O. & GADEBUSCH, H. H. (1960). Fluorescence microscopy: a review. *Univ. Mich. med. Bull.* **26**, 199.

WARFIELD, M. A., PAGE, R. H., ZUELZER, W. W. & STULBERG, C. S. (1961). Immunofluorescence in diagnostic bacteriology: II. Identification of group A streptococci in throat smears. *Amer. J. Dis. Child.* **101**, 160.

WHITE, J. D. (1961). The use and limitations of the fluorescent antibody technic in the identification and localization of bacteria in specimens of tissue. *Amer. J. clin. Path.* **35**, 257.

WILKINSON, A. E. (1961). Fluorescent treponemal antibody test. A preliminary report. *Brit. J. vener. Dis.* **37**, 59.

WILSON, G. S. (1959). Faults and fallacies in microbiology. The fourth Marjory Stephenson Memorial Lecture. *J. gen. Microbiol.* **21**, 1.

WOLFE, M. D., CAMERON, G. M. & WEST, M. E. (1960). Further observations on the fluorescent antibody technique as a procedure for detecting group A streptococci in throat cultures. *Publ. Hlth Lab.* **18**, 120.

YAMAMOTO, R. & ADLER, H. E. (1958). Characterization of pleuropneumonia-like organisms of avian origin. *J. infect. Dis.* **102**, 143.

THE MICROBIAL SPECIES—
A MACROMYTH?

S. T. COWAN

*National Collection of Type Cultures, Central Public Health
Laboratory, Colindale Avenue, London, N.W. 9*

Je m'en vais chercher un grand peut-être—
Last words attributed to François Rabelais, 1553
(Cohen & Cohen, 1960)

If this Symposium had been on Chemical Classification, it would have been relatively simple to define the different units such as element, salt, organic compound and so on, but in biology our units are much less precise, and the species, which is probably referred to most of all, is an enigma. Mine is the twentieth and last contribution to the Symposium; each of the other nineteen papers will have contained the word species, and—writing without seeing any of them—I am sure the word has been used to cover at least nineteen concepts. The word 'species' may have been used in nineteen different ways, but it will have been readily understood by the readers of this book, although to each reader, just as to each contributor, the concept behind it will be different. Among biologists there are those who are confident that they know what a species is, and these are people living in the twentieth century, not in the pre-Darwinian era as you might imagine. Let me quote from a hand-book on evolution, of anonymous (1959) authorship but published with the authority and prestige of the Trustees of the British Museum: 'the reproach that such species are subjective concepts and have no existence outside the mind of the scientist who "made" them...cannot be levelled at the biological criterion of the species, which is that of a group of organisms reproductively isolated from all other organisms'. But the anonymity of the hand-book clearly conceals the plurality of its authorship, for a less dogmatic assertion appears only two paragraphs later: 'species are not necessarily the end-products of finite changes, but stages in a continual process of potentially infinite change' so that in two paragraphs the hand-book skips a hundred years. The size of the problem is indicated by Hillaby's (1960) statement that there are about three-quarters of a million known species of insects, and that 20 million specimens of insects have been lodged in the Natural History Museum.

With species a source of confusion to the less categorical botanists and zoologists, how much more difficult it must be for the microbiologist, dealing with populations that normally do not increase by sexual reproduction and are seldom isolated (reproductively or otherwise) from other microbial populations. To review the subject of microbial species it seems logical to study the use of the word 'species', both historically and biologically, and to consider the kind of biological unit to which it may be applied; this will demand consideration of the problems of classification in an evolving population, and it is certain that I shall go over ground that has already been covered more adequately by the other contributors to the Symposium.

USE OF THE WORD 'SPECIES'

Species is an old word and has been used with various (but perhaps related) meanings. Genus and species are two of the Five Predicables of Porphyry's Isagoge or Introduction to the Categories, genus being a group of things that is divisible into subgroups of species, and species the groups into which a genus may be divided. The biological use of 'species' derives from that of the logician, and John Locke (1689), in *An Essay Concerning Human Understanding*, gave definitions which, although not intended to be applied to the then undiscovered microbe, have hardly been bettered. Here is an example: '*genera* and *species*... depend on such collections of ideas as men have made, and not on the real nature of things'. This definition goes to the heart of the problem. Except for certain pathogens, where cause and effect can easily be proved and the species characterized by its specific pathogenicity, microbial species are populations of small cells, each of which is made up of a cell-wall (with its own characteristics) and the contents of the cell (with another set of characteristics). In the past both the cell-wall and the cell constituents have been analysed serologically, but in more recent years attention has been directed to their chemical nature. Biochemists may look upon microbes as bags of enzymes and to this concept another of Locke's definitions seems applicable: 'our distinct species are nothing but distinct complex ideas, with distinct names annexed to them'.

Biologists have not improved on Locke's definitions. In a book entitled *The Origin of Species* we might expect a definition of the subject but Darwin did not attempt one. In the following quotations the page numbers refer to a modern reprint of the last (6th) edition of *The Origin of Species* (Thompson, 1958):

Nor shall I here discuss the various definitions which have been given of the term species. No one definition has satisfied all naturalists; yet every naturalist knows vaguely what he means when he speaks of a species. Generally the term includes the unknown element of a distinct act of creation (p. 50).

Hence, in determining whether a form should be ranked as a species or a variety, the opinion of naturalists having sound judgment and wide experience seems the only guide to follow (p. 54).

The term species thus comes to be a mere useless abstraction, implying and assuming a separate act of creation (p. 56).

From these remarks it will be seen that I look at the term species as one arbitrarily given, for the sake of convenience, to a set of individuals closely resembling each other, and it does not essentially differ from the term variety which is given to less distinct and more fluctuating forms (p. 59).

Undoubtedly there is one most important point of difference between varieties and species; namely, that the amount of difference between varieties, when compared with each other or with their parent-species, is much less than that between the species of the same genus (p. 64).

Often 'species' is defined in terms of 'genus', so that the definitions of genus and species are interdependent. This concept of dividing a large group into subgroups which are themselves divisible into sub-subgroups was used in the third century by Porphyry in constructing his Tree, and the same principle is used by the biologist to draw up trees of the usual biological classification. Unfortunately, at this stage the microbiologist, even more than the biologist, is deceived by his own works. Remembering his history books he thinks of these trees in terms of kinship or relationship, and he goes on to draw the unwarranted assumption that the tree he has drawn reveals the phylogenetic relations of the organisms. As used in microbiology the trees are generally made as an aid to diagnosis or identification, and are based on easily ascertainable characters; if they were to show true relationships much more fundamental characters (probably obscured by the ones we use for diagnosis) would need to be found and used in the tree.

BACTERIAL EVOLUTION

It is not my purpose to suggest here that different bacteria have all evolved from a single primordial kind, each adapting to its own surroundings so that after millions of years they have acquired individual characteristics. We now recognize that micro-organisms are not static units; they show a continuous adaptation to their environment, and it is pertinent to ask why, when they are transferred to new surroundings, they do not immediately become unrecognizable. If they made this change suddenly and completely they would achieve something equivalent to a transformation of species. We must suppose that on transfer to unfavourable surroundings most of the organisms die and only a small proportion of the inoculum survives. The survivors may be able to cannibalize the bodies of their less fortunate fellows and so utilize compounds synthesized by their kind. Meanwhile, adaptation is taking place, slowly at first, but with gradually increasing tempo. In this evolving microcosmos we are indeed looking for trouble when we try to arrange the individuals in an orderly manner, and before we start on such a project we should find out what considerations are involved.

We should consider whether our arrangement is intended to show a progression of adaptations from source-form to end-form, or whether it is to show (or to try to show) a series of relationships each of different degree as in the genealogical trees. Is our arrangement intended to be didactic, erudite or strictly practical? Since we do not normally ask ourselves these questions, they remain unanswered.

Enumeration or cataloguing hardly comes into classification, as each specimen may be a separate subdivision or unit within the catalogue. We should also distinguish between classification and identification. Identification demands the characterization of a single specimen so that it can be compared with previously identified specimens; a characterization for diagnosis is based on certain selected characters (differentiae) which are known to have special value; unlike classification, where large numbers of characters of equal weight are compared, as few as eight characters are sufficient to make a diagnosis (to the level of genus) of the common bacterial pathogens (Cowan & Steel, 1961). When specimens have been identified by using the differentiae, several specimens may be sorted into groups of similar and dissimilar units and form the basis of a classification. This is where microbiologists forsake principle for expediency; the limited number of differentiae are often regarded as adequate for characterization, and characters believed to be unimportant are either not investigated or not recorded. The truth of this statement can be seen not only in the seven editions of *Bergey's Manual of Determinative Bacteriology* (1923–57), but in the papers describing bacteria, the papers on which the *Manual* is based.

To make a classification we must create units into which the specimens can be sorted; a decision must be made whether these units are to be of equal value or whether they are to be graded in the form of steps or ranks. The decision will be based on convenience and, to some extent, on the purpose of the classification. The names of the units will also be determined by convenience; they can be as simple as a numerical sequence, as in first-, second- and third-class railway travel, or they can be as complicated (and definitive) as the deme terminology of Gilmour & Heslop-Harrison (1954) for plants. When a classification deals with living things it is usual, but not essential, to cast the units in terms of a hierarchical system and use a terminology based on a genealogical tree, with names such as family, genus and species. Other names have been suggested instead of species, but whatever we call our working unit, we define it to suit our purpose.

'The boundaries of the species, whereby men sort them, are made by men' (Locke, 1689) is as true in microbiology today as it was in a philosophical sense three hundred years ago. Since it is a conception that exists only in the mind of the beholder, the biological species is a unit without parallel in any other science. Just as no two observers see the same rainbow, so no two biologists conceive exactly the same species. Yet to most biologists the species, although indefinable, is something real; this sense of reality may be a relic of an upbringing which involved a literal interpretation of what was clearly a poetic description of the origin of the world. We know that it cannot be a divine creation because, like all living things, the species as it exists today consists of survivors of an earlier population, survivors that have adapted themselves to their surroundings, often adverse. A microbial species is a population, not a particular specimen; it follows that, like any other population, it is made up of many different individuals each of which shares certain features with its fellows. Camp (1951) prefers to call the unit a 'binom' until such time as its genetic relations to other units have been defined; this is a compromise between the older static species of special creation and the post-Darwinian dynamic unit which shows an evolutionary pattern and has indefinable limits. It can be combined with the 'type' concept of classical taxonomy, the type acting as the centre of the unit (which we call species or binom according to our whim), the less typical individuals being grouped about the type, their distance from the centre being inversely proportional to their community with the type (Fig. 1).

The main unit of a biological classification is the species which is intended to be an assemblage of specimens so similar that experienced workers would say they were alike. This is much the same as defining a species as what a competent worker says is a species. The futility of this type of definition was well illustrated by Camp (1951) in quoting three 'competent' systematists (two of whom were past presidents of the American Society of Plant Taxonomists and were thus entitled to be described as competent specialists) who classified the same material, the blackberries and raspberries (*Rubus*) native in North America, and divided them into 494, 205 and 24 species! Between the extremes of these three experts there is a 20-fold difference in the number of species recognized, which means that, in a population that one would call homogeneous, another found twenty different kinds. It is interesting to note that *Rubus* did not present any taxonomic difficulties to Linnaeus (Ramsbottom, 1938).

Julian Huxley (1940) says that species are natural units which: (*a*) have a geographical distribution area; (*b*) are self-perpetuating as groups; (*c*) are morphologically (rarely only physiologically) distinguishable from other related groups; and (*d*) normally do not interbreed with related groups.

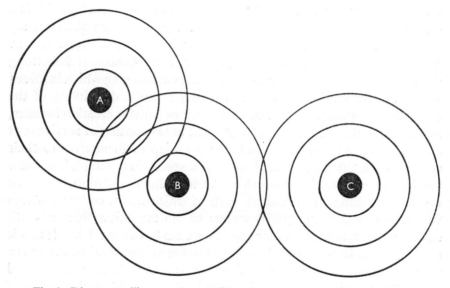

Fig. 1. Diagram to illustrate the use of the type concept, by which an unknown organism B is shown to have a closer affinity to type A than to type C.

To quote Huxley (1938) again, the chief effect of geographical isolation is the insertion of 'biological discontinuities of different degrees of completeness into populations showing continuously-varying adaptive differentiations, thus accentuating the closeness of adaptation' and also, by adding some degree of non-adaptive differentiation, increasing the diversity. A species distinction created by geographical isolation is shown by two gulls (*Larus argentatus* and *L. fuscus*) native in the British Isles where they do not interbreed (Fisher & Lockley, 1954). Both are probably derived from a form found in the Behring Straits; from there it is assumed the gulls migrated both eastward and westward encircling the North Pole as a 'ring species' with ten intermediates differing mainly by colour of legs and mantles. Because the ends of the chain do not interbreed we have two apparently different species in the British Isles, but the dividing line between the species has to be made arbitrarily between two interfertile intermediates. In this connexion it is interesting to note that Breed, Conn & Baker (1918) wrote that 'the living species (of bacteria) represent only the ends of evolutionary lines, and that one modern form must not be considered the ancestor of another'.

Most biologists will today accept the theory that geographically separated groups may evolve into different species (Smith, 1958), but the effect of the environment is more debatable. That acquired characters can be transmitted to the progeny is a view that is not generally accepted, though Cannon (1958, 1959) thinks that Lamarck's ideas have been distorted and grossly misrepresented. It is possible that microbiology may provide the evidence that Lamarck's followers have been seeking, for a microbial population (a strain) that acquires a property in a new environment may retain it for some time when transferred back to the old (Penfold, 1911; Klieneberger, 1927) though a re-adaptation may sometimes occur within five generations (Spiegelman, 1951). Examples of complete and permanent adaptation (or mutation) are seen in strains of *Brucella abortus* which, when first isolated, need CO_2 for growth but quickly lose this character on subculture; and some strains of *Haemophilus* species become less fastidious after prolonged subculture and no longer require X and/or V factor(s). Such strains have become completely adapted to a non-parasitic existence and may well provide good reasons why Lamarckism should not be summarily dismissed. If the change affected many characters the adaptation to the new environment might make the strain appear to change from one species to another, but in such cases it would be debatable whether the original strain had been 'pure' or composed of two populations each of which became dominant in turn in the different environments. Shimwell (1959) goes so far as to say that 'the majority of *Acetobacter* cultures are, or soon become, mixtures of two or more "species"'. Extending their observations beyond the genus *Acetobacter*, Shimwell & Carr (1960) found such variation in colony form on different media that they concluded that 'existing classifications, based on the study of cultures under different chemical and physical conditions, may be nothing more than the classification of mixed and composite cultures, which may vary in cell composition according to the tests applied'.

THE TYPE CONCEPT

Buchanan (1955), the authority on bacterial nomenclature, is a firm believer in the type concept and says that: 'A bacterial species may then be defined as the type culture together with such other cultures or strains of bacteria as are accepted by bacteriologists as sufficiently closely related. The designation of type cultures of the type species of the various bacterial genera is a matter of major importance.... The delimitation of the boundaries of the species is not attempted, the circumscription of the species is the task of the systematist; it is not nomenclature.' The last sentence shows that Buchanan has in mind the species name; but the species itself must be delimited before the nomenclaturist has a right to give it a name. Omission of the essential characterization is the cause of so many synonyms for one organism.

This definition acknowledges the fact that the type strain of a species need not be the most characteristic strain of that species just as a type species need not be the best known of a genus. The rules for the selection of bacterial types are laid down in the Bacteriological Code (1958) and the annotations to Rule 9d indicate that in order of preference the type strain is (1) one designated by the original author of a name (holotype); (2) if he failed to designate a holotype then one of his strains may be chosen by a later worker (lectotype); (3) a strain selected by subsequent workers when none of the original author's strains is available; most type strains are of this kind and are called neotypes. The type concept can also be criticized on the grounds that a single strain cannot indicate the variation admissible in a species; according to Braun (1953) a 'typical' representative of a species is the particular mutant predominating under laboratory conditions of growth.

The type concept is not entirely theoretical but it is more complex than a series of circles drawn around the type centres as shown in Fig. 1. In reality it is multidimensional and can best be shown, though still only incompletely, in the form of models such as those constructed by Lysenko & Sneath (1959) to show the complex relations of the intestinal and other bacteria we call the Enterobacteriaceae.

The subdivision of bacteria has not followed any particular plan; each group has been considered in isolation and not in relation to its fellows. To some extent the degree of subdivision can be correlated with the importance of the organism in some field; for example, the finer subdivisions (serotypes and phage types) of the Salmonella group are of importance in epidemiological surveys, but they contribute little to the treatment of the individual patient. They are thus important to the epidemiologist and the Medical Officer of Health, but hardly at all to the family doctor. Because bacteria often form a series of intergrading forms arbitrary decisions must be made about the allocation of a single isolate to one or other of the subdivisions, a good example being the arbitrary placing of certain bacteria in the Salmonella or Arizona groups (Seligmann & Saphra, 1951); other examples are given in Cowan (1959a).

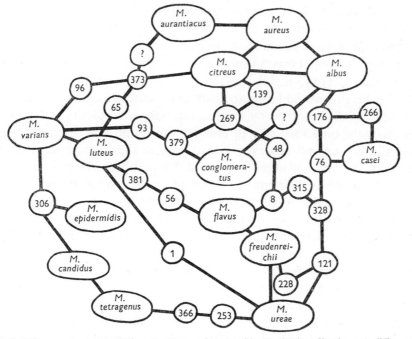

Fig. 2. Diagram to show relations between micrococci in Hucker's collection. A difference of one character separates each circle. Numbers are those of strains in Hucker's collection, and the species names are those used by Hucker. (From Rahn (1929) by permission of Gustav Fischer Verlag.)

Since micro-organisms share many features in common, they resemble a spectrum of gradually changing form; if there are breaks in the spectrum divisions can be made at these breaks, but if the change is continuous it is difficult to know where to draw the lines demarcating the different units. Rahn (1929) thought that species were defined too completely. Taking an example from Hucker's (1924a, b) monographs on micrococci, in which many intermediates were found in spite of the recognition of a large number of species, Rahn arranged the species and intermediates as circles in a complex figure, each circle differing from its neighbour by only one character (Fig. 2). In Hucker's collection Rahn found representatives for each, except two, of the circles in his figure.

The plan for making subdivisions may be likened to the subdivision of a group of people of varying height. Adult men and women show every variation from about 4 ft. 6 in. to 7 ft.; if we plot the number or proportion against height we shall get a typical Gaussian distribution curve, but the absence of useful dips or peaks prevents us from breaking up the series. However, if we combine height with colour of hair, in a particular group we might find that among the tall (T) most were fair (F) and among the short (S) most were dark (D); by combining these features we could arrange our series as say, TF 35, SD 30, TD 20, SF 15, giving us two main groups TF and SD. In each of these main groups we could find the mean height (say 5 ft. 9 in. and 5 ft. 1 in.) and make our central figures (or types) as 5 ft. 9 in. and fair and 5 ft. 1 in. and dark. Individuals of other heights would be grouped about these centres. In this argument I have simplified matters by recognizing only two colours of hair with height as the only variable. In practice we should find some people of doubtful colour and observers would vary in their descriptions of the pigment. So it is in microbiology; different observers will score the same character in different ways. To add to the subjectiveness of the observations (and this can only be eliminated by making all measurements quantitative), we find a subjectiveness in interpretation; for example, one observer might put 5 ft. 3 in. people in the tall group, another would put them in the short group. Thus, even when the observation is exact (as in height) the allocation of that observation depends on the standard, which is subjective. Four subgroups are now recognizable in the population we are sampling, people who form a series of gradually increasing height. If we now add a third character and choose sex we are complicating the picture. Sex is determined not by one character but by a series of anatomical, physiological and psychological factors, so that between the complete male and female there are at least 15 intersex types (Armstrong, 1958). The addition of sex divides our 4 subgroups not into 8 (as the layman might suppose) but into any number from 4 (if they are all of one sex) to $4 \times 17 = 68$. In this example we have used only three main features, height, colour of hair and sex. The more features we use, or the more ways in which the features can be expressed, the more numerous will be the subdivisions unless certain of the features are linked with other features. The more features we use, the more exactly will the ultimate unit be defined.

Shimwell & Carr (1961) distinguish between the type concept (based on an extant culture) and the Linnaean concept (based on a description of an extinct culture), and point out that because characterization was so inadequate the Linnaean concept should not be applied to micro-organisms described before the twentieth century. Linnaeus is regarded as a protagonist of the fixity-of-species school, but Ramsbottom (1938), in reviewing his writings, showed that at least some degree of change and variability became acceptable in the later years of his life. Few now question evolution and because micro-organisms multiply rapidly, evolutionary changes take place more quickly than in forms of life with generation times reckoned in years rather than minutes. Are we, then, attempting the impossible in trying to define a species, and wasting our time in trying to characterize constantly changing features? Braun (1953) thinks that a description of a bacterial species should indicate its potential mutational range.

It is clear that we cannot apply to microbes Huxley's (1940) criteria for species because in laboratory studies sexual reproduction seems to be a rare event in the life of most micro-organisms. van Niel (1955), after quoting Babcock & Stebbins as saying 'The species, in the case of a sexual group, is an actuality as well as a human concept; in an agamic complex it ceases to be an actuality', goes on to say that we cannot hope to apply the modern concepts of biologists to micro-organisms 'so as to render the bacterial and myxophycean species "actualities" rather than merely "human concepts"'.

DEVELOPMENT OF NEW IDEAS ON MICROBIAL SPECIES

In 1946 van Niel advocated the discontinuance of the terms genus and species for bacteria, and the development of multiple diagnostic keys; later he (van Niel, 1955) supported Winogradsky's (1952) 'biotypes' untrammelled by type species, the type concept and other restrictive practices enjoined by the Bacteriological Code.

The Société Française de Microbiologie had a discussion on the species concept, and Lwoff (1958) in opening pointed out that because bacteria are, in general, asexual, it is difficult to find a starting-point. The descendants of a single strain would all be considered to be of the same species in spite of the fact that, by mutation and selection, the descendants might differ in several ways from the parent culture. In his view the species is merely a stage in an evolutionary process, a stage in a precarious equilibrium. Vendrely (1958) expressed a hope that analysis of DNA might show species differences; the relation between the amino acid content of DNA, particularly the ratio between adenine + thymine to guanine + cytosine, was thought to have taxonomic significance and to show species differences. Schaeffer (1958) thought that confusion would be lessened if authors of dichotomous keys used the terms group and subgroup instead of genus and species. In Thibault's (1958) view the subdivision of bacteria is too rigid, and a new nomenclature and a new taxonomy must be developed.

The discussion of the Société Française seemed to mark a turning point at which bacterial taxonomists began to take notice of genetics and to rely less on the older criteria. Also in 1958 at a Rutgers University symposium, after giving a paper on classification (Cowan, 1959 a), I was assured by several biochemists that they were about to settle the whole problem, presumably because DNA is supposed to bear the genetic information transferred in transformation, transduction and conjugation (Ravin, 1960). I have not yet seen the solution of all our problems and there still seems to be plenty of work for taxonomists to do.

It was also in 1958, at the meeting of the International Committee on Bacteriological Nomenclature, that another discussion took place on what unit should be regarded as a species. This was followed by Kauffmann's (1959 a, b) proposal that among the Enterobacteriaceae the serotype should be the species unit; a proposal that was later extended to the pneumococci (Kauffmann, Lund & Eddy, 1960), and by implication, to all other groups of bacteria that could be subdivided by serological analysis. I pointed out (Cowan, 1959 b) that this was an extreme proposal, and suggested that it would be more logical to go to the other extreme and regard each group (Salmonella, Arizona, Escherichia, etc.) as a species of one genus (the present family Enterobacteriaceae). At that time both suggestions seemed to be extreme and since they would involve too many changes in nomenclature, would be quite unacceptable. Taylor (1959) also protested against the proposed synonymy of species and serotype.

In 1961 Kauffmann modified his definition of a species to read 'A species is a group of related sero-fermentative phage-types'. This definition is difficult for the non-specialist to understand and Kauffmann explains that 'sero-fermentative' refers to the *Salmonella* species that were characterized biochemically and serologically in the first Report (1934) of the Salmonella Subcommittee, and gives as an example the type species, *Salmonella cholerae-suis*. Certain salmonellas, for example *S. typhi* and *S. paratyphi*-B, can be subdivided into phage types, and these he calls 'sero-fermentative phage types'. However, it is not clear whether the species as now defined by Kauffmann is a sub-division of a serotype, or is the smallest unit that can be characterized by present-day techniques.

Genetics now play a greater part in the thought put into defining a microbial species and among the newer definitions Bryson (1959), with his tongue in his cheek, produced: 'A microbial species may be defined as a group of minute organisms possessing certain collective properties and limits of genetic and phenotypic variability, as established by a statistically unique but not necessarily uniform system of hereditary determinants'. At the same symposium I (Cowan, 1959a) said that the argument about the fixity of species might 'end by providing a definition of a bacterial species as the lowest rank that cannot be altered by artificial means' but I did not explain what I meant by 'artificial means' and, looking back, the phrase is now as obscure to me as Robert Browning's poems were to him (Chesterton, 1903).

Ravin (1960) has pointed out that the living universe is not a vast community of genetically interacting organisms but is divided into populations between which 'gene flow' is impossible. The breaks in the gene flow form the barriers which separate the 'biological species' of the 'modern systematist trained in genetics'.

We need not be despondent at our inability to define species; the botanists and zoologists, although they deal more often with interbreeding forms, have equal difficulties. Consider for a moment the species *Paramecium aurelia* which has two mating types (corresponding to sexes). This 'species' is divided into a number of varieties (subspecies) which do not normally interbreed; when mating between different varieties does occur it has fatal consequences for the participants. It appears, therefore, that the varieties have the mating qualities of distinct species and that taxonomists have made a major error in assessing the rank of *Paramecium aurelia* as a species (Sonneborn, 1947).

HIERARCHICAL SYSTEMS IN MICROBIOLOGY

So far our attempts to define a microbial species have proved fruitless, and we may be able to shorten the argument by asking ourselves the simple question: do we need or want species? Various substitutes have been proposed for the species, the deme terminology (Gilmour & Heslop-Harrison, 1954), the binom (Camp, 1951), the biotype (Winogradsky, 1952) and the 'biological species' (Ravin, 1960) are examples, and none of them assumes that living things can be arranged in a hierarchical system.

Trees of Porphyry are not confined to biological problems of classification; they are equally applicable to the subdivision of motor cars (Cowan, 1957, 1959a) or joiners—things that join (Fig. 3).

In a biological classification this type of tree shows subdivisions that are possible with the knowledge available and is thus an alternative

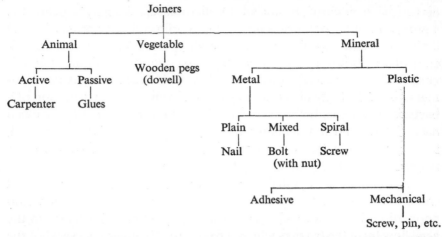

Fig. 3. Tree to show how joiners may be classified; an alternative scheme is shown in Fig. 4.

method of expressing a diagnostic key; it does not indicate the degree of relationship that would be shown by a genealogical tree. With increasing knowledge other relations may be found; for example, when we remember that beaten egg (white and yolk) is used in cooking as a binding agent, we realize that the passive animal adhesives need subdividing. We also see that the tree could be redrawn in many other ways; one of which, using different criteria, is shown in Fig. 4.

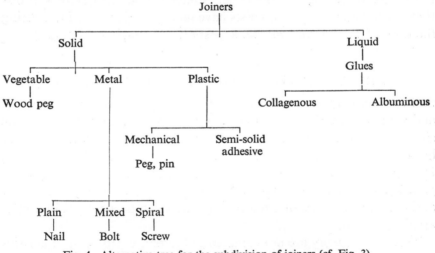

Fig. 4. Alternative tree for the subdivision of joiners (cf. Fig. 3).

The Tree of Porphyry is a device used consciously or unconsciously by all who classify by breaking down the larger unit. In biology we have tried to make it more meaningful by assigning ranks to the different levels and creating a hierarchical system, but by doing so we have added to our difficulties because many have assumed that it has magically developed a phylogenetic significance. Turrill (1952) would have us be more honest and admit that the trees only show resemblances. Rank depends on circumstances rather than on qualities, as was shown in 1960 when a Congolese Sergeant-Major became a General overnight. In orthodox taxonomy the rank of a bacterium cannot be expressed in a simple relation to other organisms, for every individual is treated as belonging to a number of categories of consecutive rank (*Bacteriological Code*, 1958, Principle 7(*a*)) of which, as Pirie (1955) has pointed out, only the individual organism is real. All higher ranks are figments of the imagination and occur only in the minds of taxonomists. The units larger than the individual are populations which we name colonies, strains, species and so on, and many taxonomists believe that the arrangement is natural (i.e. phylogenetic), and like a marriage made in Heaven. In fact, all these arrangements are artificial and are more like marriages of convenience. We should always bear in mind that the individual elements making up these taxonomic units are not necessarily alike but each, as Gilbert (1883) said, through the mouth of Sergeant Willis, 'is either a little Liberal or else a little Conservative', or in the more modern idiom of Orwell (1945), 'all...are equal but some are more equal than others'.

Steel (p. 419) has mentioned the relative merits of anabolic and katabolic analysis in identification, and, since only the individual is real, we might make better classifications by a building up rather than breaking down. This is the approach of the specialist and, working with a restricted range of organisms, he is able to make a satisfactory and workable classification. In practice we cannot characterize a microbial unit smaller than a strain (or isolate) and the range of variability of the individual strains in the next larger unit will depend on the particular worker; thus all these units (taxa) are subjective. To one the next larger unit will be a species, to another a subspecies (or variety), to a third a serotype, and to a fourth a phage type. What the unit is called does not matter in the classification of a restricted range, but when comparisons are made with other specialist ranges (I avoid the word 'group' deliberately because it has often been given a special meaning, sometimes, as in streptococci analogous to species, sometimes, as in the Enterobacteriaceae to genus) it is necessary to align the ranks of the classifications of two or more restricted ranges. Thus Kauffmann's (1959*a, b*) suggestion that *Salmonella* serotypes should be regarded as species might appeal to some, but not all (Taylor, 1959) of those working only with the enteric bacteria, but it appalled the more general taxonomist trying to classify all kinds of bacteria in a uniform scheme (Cowan, 1959 b).

It can be argued, as was done very forcefully and adequately by Dr G. S. Wilson at a meeting of the International Committee on Bacteriological Nomenclature at Stockholm in 1958, that it is convenient to have different qualities for equivalent ranks in different ranges of bacteria, and that we should subordinate general principles to convenience. van Niel (1946) pointed out that bacterial taxonomy has often been founded on convenience in identification, and advocated the development of multiple determinative keys without any major effort to reconcile them. This is a practical but anarchistic solution to a difficult problem, and we should remember that, although the abandonment of principles in wartime may lead to victory, taxonomic theorists are not yet at war. If we assume, and not all microbiologists are willing, that microbes can be arranged in a series of groups within groups, we should pause to consider the minimal differences between units of the same level (rank). Few have attempted to do this: Breed (1928) said that bacterial species 'should show several distinguishing characteristics, not one'. Sneath (1958) did not think it safe to divide a taxon unless at least five correlated features were different, and Bryson (1959) thought that 'one or two mutations, even though leading to conspicuous biochemical or morphological differences do not seem adequate... to establish a "new" species'. Barnett (1957) discussed the number of tests that need to be applied to distinguish between species and expressed his conclusions in a mathematical formula.

Interfertility among bacterial 'species' or 'genera' seems to be proved, and Schaeffer reviewed the evidence up to 1958; it is particularly common among the 'genera' within the family Enterobacteriaceae, where crosses between *Escherichia coli* and *Salmonella* species (or serotypes) are easily made. Zinder (1960) and Baron, Spilman & Carey (1960) provide two recent examples, but in earlier experiments Luria & Burrous (1957) produced progeny with characters found in the Arizona group (or genus) in nature. Not all *Escherichia* × *Salmonella* crosses are fertile but it seems clear that since *Escherichia* × *Salmonella* → Arizona and *Escherichia* × *Shigella* → A–D group that the *Escherichia*, *Salmonella*, Arizona and *Shigella* groups should be regarded as an interfertile unit which in botany or zoology would be called a species. On quite different grounds Ewing & Edwards (1960) subdivided the enterobacteria into four divisions, one of which contained the *Escherichia* and *Shigella* (ES) and another the *Salmonella*–Arizona–*Citrobacter* (SAC) groups. Interfertility has not yet been shown among other members of the Enterobacteriaceae, but should the *Klebsiella–Enterobacter–Hafnia–Serratia* (KEHS) subgroup be found to be interfertile but not able to cross with the ES and SAC subgroups, a great deal of reclassification of the family will be needed, and perhaps the large number of 'genera' will be collected into one genus with three or four subdivisions or species representing ES, SAC, KEHS and PP (*Proteus*–Providence) subgroups. It might be pertinent to ask whether the Enterobacteriaceae are more unstable than other bacteria? The answer can only be found by further work, but the papers of Shimwell (1959), and Shimwell & Carr (1960, 1961) suggest that not only are bacteria continually evolving, but that this happens at such a rate that the concept of a fixed species becomes sheer nonsense. It may well be that we are on the threshold of a new era in taxonomic reality in which the fixity-of-species concept will be finally abandoned, and we shall recognize that to describe a particular unit (species) in precise terms is attempting the impossible.

AND THE FUTURE?

'If it can be said of anyone that he brought order out of chaos it is most applicable to Linnaeus: *Deus creavit, Linnaeus disposuit*' (Ramsbottom, 1938). But the age of chaos is still with us and I shall try to indicate what steps I think are needed to bring some order into our affairs.

Cain (1959a) says that 'more pure nonsense has been talked (and published) about phylogeny in birds than in any other group of animals' and we could make the same remark about microbes, for we have no evidence of their phylogeny. We should forget all we have been told about the evolution of one form from another and assume that the primordial types are all extinct (Breed *et al.* 1918). From this it follows that the hierarchical system is inapplicable and with it the genealogical tree. Other kinds of tree may, however, have their uses in the shape of diagnostic keys.

In place of trying to classify micro-organisms by breaking down into orders, families, tribes, genera, species and strains, we should probably do better by building up from the smallest practical unit, the strain (isolate) or, if it had been derived from a single cell, the clone. Sneath (1957a, b) proposed a method of classification based on the correlation of all known features and not only on those considered to be important. This method used an electronic computor and when data from a wide variety of bacteria were fed to the machine, the sorting produced a classification not unlike that developed over the years by orthodox methods (Sneath & Cowan, 1958). Skerman (1961) thinks that we should make

more use of the memory of computors by storing for future consideration the results of certain specified tests carried out on all cultures. Once
in the machine the data could be reanalysed as occasion required and
would provide a means of finding out the relation of mutants to existing
forms.

What evidence there is suggests that the groups (or 'genera') of the
Enterobacteriaceae may be the equivalent of interfertile subspecies of
other biological sciences; but these would be suspect by those purists
who regard a species as the type strain and other strains like it. It seems
to me that the type concept has only nomenclatural value. It relates a
culture to a name; if the culture can be allotted to a taxonomic unit its
name can be considered (probably with others) as a label for the unit.
But a type strain does not indicate the plasticity of the unit and thus has
but limited use either in classification or diagnosis. I do not intend to
discuss the many difficulties of nomenclature; I have already indicated
(Cowan, 1956) how confusion could be reduced by adopting for bacteria
a suggestion made for fungi by Ainsworth & Ciferri (1955), namely by
setting up a Register of Names. But when we do turn our attention to
the principles of biological nomenclature, we should consider carefully
Cain's (1959b) proposal for a uninominal system.

As realists we recognize that the species concept is untenable in microbiology; as practical workers we must accept plastic units (with reasonably defined limits) to which we can attach names, not as an exercise in
nomenclature but for the purpose of identification. The codes of
nomenclature were drawn up when species and genera were regarded as
static (with an allowance for minor variation) and now may be more of a
hindrance than a help. A numerical system, or a combination of letters
and numbers might be more practical, and, best of all, a system of
punched cards bearing the description of the unit. With such a system we
should need to use standardized methods (Clarke, 1955) so as to avoid a
situation that arose in the seventeenth century in the days of Ray and
Willughby when, Cain (1959a) tells us, it was not only possible for the
descriptions of the same animal written by different authors to be mistaken for different species but also the different sexes of the same animal
were written up as though they were different. A punched card system
would bring together the major groups and quickly show the differences
between individuals. Skerman (1961) made a somewhat similar suggestion, though his plan calls for access to an electronic computor, and he
would try to work his scheme as an international effort.

While these ideas are suitable for the collection and analysis of data,
something else would be needed for day-to-day identification and charac-

terization. For this purpose we might adapt one of the diagnostic schemes that have been proposed. For bacteria the first successful and the only comprehensive scheme was one by Skerman and published in the seventh edition of *Bergey's Manual* (1957); this was a development of an earlier scheme (Skerman, 1949) and has since been revised (Skerman, 1959). If, instead of working out an unknown organism to the name of a genus, we used the sectional letters and numbers of his key of 1959 we could form a coded identification complex (CIC), e.g. 1,2:B6:D1,2,4,7,-15,17,19,23 = *Neisseria*. This CIC has a great many characters and records mainly a series of negatives but it should be possible, especially when dealing with a more limited group of organisms, e.g. medical bacteria, to use simple diagnostic tables of differentiae (Cowan & Steel, 1961) from which a simpler coding could be made.

If it is possible to give an adequate characterization for identification in the form of a CIC, a complete description would need the space available on a fairly elaborately coded punch-card. However, the CIC could be made more precise than a generic or specific name by recording certain characters of the strain under investigation; its use would have to be confined to the laboratory, and, for reporting, it would need translation into the nearest equivalent genus and species names, or after the introduction of a rationalized uninominal system, into the 'uninom'. Neither Skerman's diagnostic keys nor our diagnostic tables are intended to classify bacteria, though both may suggest affinities that have so far been overlooked.

AND SO WHAT?

This modern expression pithily puts the question that all who have read so far are entitled to ask, and it is only fair that I should try to summarize the conclusions reached. Because I am a bacteriologist my conclusions apply especially to bacteria and may not be wholly applicable to other microbes.

First of all I think we can answer the question posed by the title of this paper: the microbial species does not exist; it is impossible to define except in terms of a nomenclatural type, and it is one of the greatest myths of microbiology.

Next we can say with confidence that microbes cannot, on present knowledge, be arranged in a hierarchical system to show their phylogeny. The great unravelling of microbial relations awaits the results of more crossing experiments and it is to the geneticists that we must look for future advances in phylogeny.

On the other hand, better characterization and separation of microbial units will depend on the progress made by biochemists in analysing the different parts of microbes and substituting a biochemical characterization for the old biological one based on simple morphology, staining and sugar reactions, serology, and so on. A start has already been made by the analysis of cell-walls (Cummins & Harris, 1956), extracted whole cells (Mattick, Cheeseman, Berridge & Bottazzi, 1956), surface antigens (Kauffmann, Lüderitz, Stierlin & Westphal, 1960; Westphal, Kauffmann, Lüderitz & Stierlin, 1960), and DNA (Rolfe & Meselson, 1959).

Data will continue to accumulate at such a rate that punched card systems and electronic computors will be called for to help in their analysis, and when these aids are more generally available Adansonian principles can be applied to the sorting process.

We cannot apply names to microbes until we have solved the taxonomic problems, and since we cannot yet define the simplest microbial unit I have not discussed nomenclature except to indicate that the codes of nomenclature do not seem to be applicable. In revising these codes we should think seriously of dropping binomial nomenclature and work towards a uninominal system.

In the Society's 1954 discussion on classification I asked a simple question: 'are we wasting our time in trying to classify microbes?' (Cowan, 1955). After reading this paper there can be no doubt that I am *still* wasting my time.

REFERENCES

AINSWORTH, G. C. & CIFERRI, R. (1955). Mycological taxonomic literature and publication. *Taxon*, **4**, 3.

ANONYMOUS (1959). *A Handbook on Evolution*, 2nd edition. London: Trustees of the British Museum.

ARMSTRONG, C. N. (1958). The clinical diagnosis of sex. *Proc. R. Soc. Med.* **51**, 23.

BACTERIOLOGICAL CODE (1958). *International Code of Nomenclature of Bacteria and Viruses*. Edited by R. E. Buchanan, S. T. Cowan, T. Wikén & W. A. Clark. Ames, Iowa: State College Press. [Reprinted with corrections 1959. Iowa State University Press.]

BARNETT, J. A. (1957). Some unsolved problems of yeast taxonomy. *Leeuwenhoek ned. Tijdschr.* **23**, 1.

BARON, L. S., SPILMAN, W. M. & CAREY, W. F. (1960). Diploid heterozygous hybrids from matings between *Escherichia coli* and *Salmonella typhosa*. *J. exp. Med.* **112**, 361.

Bergey's Manual of Determinative Bacteriology (1923–57). Seven editions: 1st, 1923; 2nd, 1926; 3rd, 1930; 4th, 1934; 5th, 1939; 6th, 1948; 7th, 1957. Baltimore: Williams and Wilkins Co.

BRAUN, W. (1953). *Bacterial Genetics*. Philadelphia: W. B. Saunders Co.

BREED, R. S. (1928). The present status of systematic bacteriology. *J. Bact.* **15**, 143.

BREED, R. S., CONN, H. J. & BAKER, J. C. (1918). Comments on the evolution and classification of bacteria. *J. Bact.* **3**, 445.

BRYSON, V. (1959). Some contributions of genetics to microbiology. In V. Bryson (editor), *Microbiology Yesterday and Today*, p. 80. New Brunswick, N.J.: Institute of Microbiology, Rutgers, The State University.

BUCHANAN, R. E. (1955). Taxonomy. *Ann. Rev. Microbiol.* 9, 1.

CAIN, A. J. (1959a). Taxonomic concepts. *Ibis*, 101, 302.

CAIN, A. J. (1959b). The post-Linnaean development of taxonomy. *Proc. Linn. Soc. Lond.* 170, 234.

CAMP, W. H. (1951). Biosystematy. *Brittonia*, 7, 113.

CANNON, H. G. (1958). *The Evolution of Living Things*. Manchester: University Press.

CANNON, H. G. (1959). *Lamarck and Modern Genetics*. Manchester: University Press.

CHESTERTON, G. K. (1903). *Robert Browning*. London: Macmillan and Co.

CLARKE, P. H. (1955). The principles of microbial classification. Methods for determining the biochemical activities of micro-organisms as applied to classification. *J. gen. Microbiol.* 12, 337.

COHEN, J. M. & COHEN, M. J. (1960). *The Penguin Dictionary of Quotations*, p. 294. Harmondsworth: Penguin Books Ltd.

COWAN, S. T. (1955). The principles of microbial classification. Introduction: the philosophy of classification. *J. gen. Microbiol.* 12, 314.

COWAN, S. T. (1956). 'Ordnung in das Chaos' Migula. *Canad. J. Microbiol.* 2, 212.

COWAN, S. T. (1957). A taxonomist looks at the Enterobacteriaceae. *J. Path. Bact.* 73, 312.

COWAN, S. T. (1959a). Bacterial classification—problems and developments. In V. Bryson (editor), *Microbiology Yesterday and Today*, p. 54. New Brunswick, N.J.: Institute of Microbiology; Rutgers, The State University.

COWAN, S. T. (1959b). Nonconformism in nomenclature. *Int. Bull. bact. Nom. Tax.* 9, 131.

COWAN, S. T. & STEEL, K. J. (1961). Diagnostic tables for the common medical bacteria. *J. Hyg., Camb.* 59, 357.

CUMMINS, C. S. & HARRIS, H. (1956). The chemical composition of the cell wall in some Gram-positive bacteria and its possible value as a taxonomic character. *J. gen. Microbiol.* 14, 583.

EWING, W. H. & EDWARDS, P. R. (1960). The principle divisions and groups of Enterobacteriaceae and their differentiation. *Int. Bull. bact. Nom. Tax.* 10, 1.

FISHER, J. & LOCKLEY, R. M. (1954). *Sea-Birds; an Introduction to the Natural History of Sea-Birds of the North Atlantic*. London: Collins.

GILBERT, W. S. (1883). *Iolanthe*, Act II. London: Chappell and Co.

GILMOUR, J. S. L. & HESLOP-HARRISON, J. (1954). The deme terminology and the units of micro-evolutionary change. *Genetica*, 27, 147.

HILLABY, J. (1960). Taxonomy: a neglected science. *New Scientist*, 9, 262.

HUCKER, G. J. (1924a). Studies on the Coccaceae. II. A study of the general characters of the micrococci. *Tech. Bull. N.Y. St. agric. Exp. Sta.*, no. 100.

HUCKER, G. J. (1924b). Studies on the Coccaceae. IV. The classification of the genus *Micrococcus* Cohn. *Tech. Bull. N.Y. St. agric. Exp. Sta.*, no. 102.

HUXLEY, J. S. (1938). Discussion following the Presidential Address by J. Ramsbottom (1938). *Proc. Linn. Soc. Lond.* 150, 253.

HUXLEY, J. S. (1940). Introductory: towards the new systematics. In Julian Huxley (editor), *The New Systematics*, p. 1. Oxford: Clarendon Press.

KAUFFMANN, F. (1959a). On the principles of classification and nomenclature of Enterobacteriaceae. *Int. Bull. bact. Nom. Tax*, 9, 1.

KAUFFMANN, F. (1959b). Definition of genera and species of Enterobacteriaceae. Request for an Opinion. *Int. Bull. bact. Nom. Tax.* 9, 7.

KAUFFMANN, F. (1961). The species-definition in the family Enterobacteriaceae. *Int. Bull. bact. Nom. Tax.* **11**, 5.

KAUFFMANN, F., LÜDERITZ, O., STIERLIN, H. & WESTPHAL, O. (1960). Zur Immunchemie der O-Antigene von Enterobacteriaceae. I. Analyse der Zuckerbausteine von Salmonella-O-Antigenen. *Zbl. Bakt.* (1. *Abt. Orig.*), **178**, 442.

KAUFFMANN, F., LUND, E. & EDDY, B. E. (1960). Proposal for a change in the nomenclature of *Diplococcus pneumoniae* and a comparison of the Danish and American type designations. *Int. Bull. bact. Nom. Tax.* **10**, 31.

KLIENEBERGER, E. (1927). Künstliche Gewinn- und Verluständerungen im Salizin- (bzw. Arbutin-) Vergärungsvermögen eines Coli-Bakteriums in besonders ausgedehnten Versuchsreihen. *Zbl. Bakt.* (1. *Abt. Orig.*), **101**, 461.

LOCKE, J. (1689). *An Essay Concerning Human Understanding*, book III, chapter VI.

LURIA, S. E. & BURROUS, J. W. (1957). Hybridization between *Escherichia coli* and *Shigella*. *J. Bact.* **74**, 461.

LWOFF, A. (1958). La notion d'espèce bactérienne à la lumière des découvertes récentes. L'espèce bactérienne. *Ann. Inst. Pasteur*, **94**, 137.

LYSENKO, O. & SNEATH, P. H. A. (1959). The use of models in bacterial classification, *J. gen. Microbiol.* **20**, 284.

MATTICK, A. T. R., CHEESEMAN, G. C., BERRIDGE, N. J. & BOTTAZZI, V. (1956). The differentiation of species of lactobacilli and streptococci by means of paper partition chromatography. *J. appl. Bact.* **19**, 310.

VAN NIEL, C. B. (1946). The classification and natural relationships of bacteria. *Cold Spr. Harb. Symp. quant. Biol.* **11**, 285.

VAN NIEL, C. B. (1955). Classification and taxonomy of the bacteria and bluegreen algae. In *A Century of Progress in the Natural Sciences*—1853–1953. San Francisco: California Academy of Sciences.

ORWELL, G. (1945). *Animal Farm*, chapter 10. London: Secker and Warburg.

PENFOLD, W. J. (1911). Studies in bacterial variation with special reference to the chemical functions of the members of the typhoid-coli group. *J. Hyg., Camb.* **11**, 30.

PIRIE, N. W. (1955). The principles of microbial classification. Summing-up. *J. gen. Microbiol.* **12**, 382.

RAHN, O. (1929). Contributions to the classification of bacteria. IV. Intermediate forms. *Zbl. Bakt.* (2. *Abt. Orig.*), **78**, 8.

RAMSBOTTOM, J. (1938). Linnaeus and the species concept. *Proc. Linn. Soc. Lond.* **150**, 192.

RAVIN, A. W. (1960). The origin of bacterial species. Genetic recombination and factors limiting it between bacterial populations. *Bact. Rev.* **24**, 201.

REPORT (1934). The genus *Salmonella* Lignières, 1900. Issued by the Salmonella Subcommittee of the Nomenclature Committee of the International Society for Microbiology. *J. Hyg., Camb.* **34**, 333.

ROLFE, R. & MESELSON, M. (1959). The relative homogeneity of microbial DNA. *Proc. Nat. Acad. Sci., Wash.* **45**, 1039.

SCHAEFFER, P. (1958). La notion d'espèce bactérienne à la lumière des découvertes récentes. La notion d'espèces aprés les recherches récentes de génétique bactérienne. *Ann. Inst. Pasteur*, **94**, 167.

SELIGMANN, E. & SAPHRA, I. (1951). An unusual enteric pathogen. *Publ. Hlth Rep., Wash.* **66**, 1369.

SHIMWELL, J. L. (1959). A re-assessment of the genus *Acetobacter*. *Leeuwenhoek ned. Tijdschr.* **25**, 49.

SHIMWELL, J. L. & CARR, J. G. (1960). Are species of bacteria unclassifiable? *Leeuwenhoek ned. Tijdschr.* **26**, 383.

SHIMWELL, J. L. & CARR, J. G. (1961). The type culture concept in *Acetobacter* and other genera. *Leeuwenhoek ned. Tijdschr.* **27**, 65.

SKERMAN, V. B. D. (1949). A mechanical key for the generic identification of bacteria. *Bact. Rev.* **13**, 175.

SKERMAN, V. B. D. (1959). *A Guide to the Identification of the Genera of Bacteria.* Baltimore: Williams and Wilkins Co.

SKERMAN, V. B. D. (1961). Species concept in bacteria. In *The Evolution of Living Organisms*, **1**, 213. Melbourne: University Press.

SMITH, J. M. (1958). *The Theory of Evolution.* Harmondsworth: Penguin Books Ltd.

SNEATH, P. H. A. (1957a). Some thoughts on bacterial classification. *J. gen. Microbiol.* **17**, 184.

SNEATH, P. H. A. (1957b). The application of computors to taxonomy. *J. gen. Microbiol.* **17**, 201.

SNEATH, P. H. A. (1958). Some aspects of Adansonian classification and of the taxonomic theory of correlated features. *Ann. Microbiol. Enzimol.* **8**, 261.

SNEATH, P. H. A. & COWAN, S. T. (1958). An electro-taxonomic survey of bacteria. *J. gen. Microbiol.* **19**, 551.

SONNEBORN, T. M. (1947). Recent advances in the genetics of *Paramecium* and *Euplotes*. In *Advances in Genetics*, **1**, 263. New York: Academic Press Inc.

SPIEGELMAN, S. (1951). The particulate transmission of enzyme-forming capacity in yeast. *Cold Spr. Harb. Symp. quant. Biol.* **16**, 87.

TAYLOR, J. (1959). Why christen a Salmonella? *Int. Bull. bact. Nom. Tax.* **9**, 159.

THIBAULT, P. (1958). La notion d'espèce bactérienne à la lumière des découvertes récentes. La notion d'espèce dans le groupe Shigella. *Ann. Inst. Pasteur*, **94**, 213.

THOMPSON, W. R. (editor) (1958). Charles Darwin: *The Origin of Species*. Everyman's Library, no. 811. London: J. M. Dent and Sons Ltd.

TURRILL, W. B. (1952). Some taxonomic aims, methods, and principles. Their possible applications to the algae. *Nature, Lond.* **169**, 388.

VENDRELY, R. (1958). La notion d'espèce bactérienne à la lumière des découvertes récentes. La notion d'espèce a travers quelques données biochimiques récentes et le cycle L. *Ann. Inst. Pasteur*, **94**, 142.

WESTPHAL, O., KAUFFMANN, F., LÜDERITZ, O. & STIERLIN, H. (1960). Zur Immunchemie der O-Antigene von Enterobacteriaceae. III. Analyse der Zuckerbausteine Kreuzreagierender Salmonella-Arizona- und Escherichia-O-Antigene. *Zbl. Bakt.* (1. Abt. Orig.), **179**, 336.

WINOGRADSKY, S. (1952). Sur la classification des bactéries. *Ann. Inst. Pasteur*, **82**, 125.

ZINDER, N. D. (1960). Hybrids of *Escherichia* and *Salmonella*. *Science*, **131**, 813.

APPENDIX I

THE PROPOSAL AND SELECTION OF SCIENTIFIC
NAMES FOR MICRO-ORGANISMS

[This Appendix, which is intended to give practical guidance on certain common nomenclatural procedures, should be consulted in conjunction with the contribution to this Symposium by Ross (pp. 394–404) and with the observations by Corliss (pp. 59–62) on the nomenclature of protozoa.]

The scientific names of micro-organism are the international grid references by which one microbiologist is able to relate his observations with those of another. They are also the code to a very efficient information retrieval system. The international regulations for the proposal and selection of such names are designed to standardize the traditional practices of taxonomists and since the practices of zoologists, botanists, and bacteriologists differ, microbiologists are subject, in matters of nomenclature, to three codes, the *International Code of Zoological Nomenclature* (first published in 1901, current version 1961), the *International Code of Botanical Nomenclature* (1906, current version 1961), and the *International Code of Nomenclature of Bacteria and Viruses* (1948, current version 1959), which are issued subject to the sanction of the International Congresses of Zoology, Botany, and Microbiology, respectively.

There is a fourth code, the *International Code of Nomenclature for Cultivated Plants* (1953, current version 1961) which is of peripheral interest to microbiologists. This code is designed to regulate the nomenclature of agricultural, silvicultural, and horticultural varieties (or cultivars) of plants and its provisions could be applied to certain micro-organisms in commercial use. In particular the useful term 'cultivar' should have wider currency wherever man deliberately propagates a form which has no natural distribution (see p. 258).

Although the Zoological, Botanical, and Bacteriological Codes are independent they are firmly based on certain common principles of which the most important are: (1) the designation of species by Latin binomials (binominals (Zoological Code) or binary names) which provide characteristic, international labels; (2) the Law of Priority which ensures the use of the oldest available names as a means of stabilizing nomenclature; (3) the regulation of the application (sense) of names by the Type Method which ensures precision in the application of names; and (4) the provision that a species may have as many correct names as there are opinions as to its taxonomic position which allows for divergences and changes in taxonomic opinion. In addition, the codes lay down the categories into which taxonomic groups (or taxa [sing. taxon]) may be divided or grouped, the requirements for the effective publication of names, and guidance on the coining of names.

The codes and their various supplements are long and complex. The interpretation of the Zoological Code is governed by nearly six hundred 'Opinions' promulgated by the International Commission of Zoological Nomenclature. The Botanical Code has been the most frequently revised. The Bacteriological Code closely follows the Botanical in style but, like the Zoological, there is provision for 'Opinions', by the Judicial Commission on Bacteriological Nomenclature. Differences of opinion on the detailed interpretation of the codes can lead to argument and here, in spite of the dangers attending over-simplification, it is only possible to indicate, with particular reference to species, some requirements for the proposal of new names—either for hither-to undescribed organisms ('new species') or for the reclassification of organisms already described ('name changing')—and the selection of names.

NEW SPECIES

As there is no objective definition of species for most micro-organisms and as the tradition of species varies from one group to another the best advice to a microbiologist with little taxonomic experience who believes he is working with an undescribed organism which he wishes to propose as a new species, is for him to consult a specialist on the taxonomy of the particular group of micro-organisms in question. Sometimes, as for yeasts, it is possible to obtain an opinion on the unknown organism by the payment of a fee, more frequently however it is a question of a favour, but such favours are usually willingly granted, especially if a pure culture, accompanied by a careful and full description of its characters, is offered for examination. To take such expert opinion is one major (although not infallible) safeguard that the organism is in fact undescribed. To submit the description for publication in a journal of good international standing lessens the chance that the name proposed will be illegitimate because its publication does not fulfil the requirements of the particular nomenclatural code. The receipt of specialist advice and the prospect of editorial guidance does not however absolve an author from studying the code for himself. Much of the prevailing nomenclatural confusion could have been avoided if the codes had been more widely and more carefully read.

Apart from requirements to ensure *effective* publication of a new specific name (requirements which are usually covered by publication in any reputable scientific periodical), there are under all three codes four main requirements to fulfil, or to bear in mind, if a new specific name is to be *validly* published, i.e. is to be in line with the codes. These, which if acted upon would eliminate much nomenclatural confusion, are set out briefly below.

In all three Codes the 'Rules' (which are obligatory) are set out as a series of Articles (Botanical and Zoological) or Rules (Bacteriological). These are supplemented by Recommendations which, though not obligatory, detail desirable procedures.

Protozoa and other micro-organisms classified in the Animal Kingdom
(Zoological Code)

(1) The name proposed must be in Latin binomial form (Articles 5; 11b, c), and must not be a junior (or later) homonym (Art. 53), but it may be a tautonym (Art. 18b).

It may duplicate a name of an organism not belonging to the Animal Kingdom, but 'it is preferable not to propose for a genus of animals a name already in use for a genus outside the animal kingdom' (Rec. 2A).

A new name should be followed immediately by an appropriate statement in abbreviated form, e.g. 'sp.n.', and a zoologist should not introduce the same name as new in more than one publication (Appendix E, 7, 22). See *Algae and Fungi* (1) below.

It may be noted that the word which follows the generic name in a specific binomial is called the 'specific name' (or 'trivial name') by zoologists (Art. 5) but the 'specific epithet' by botanists for whom the complete binomial is the 'specific name'.

(2) The required 'statement that purports to give characters differentiating the taxon' (Art. 13a (i)) (the diagnosis) should be given in English, French, German, Italian or Latin (Appendix E, 4), cf. *Algae and Fungi* (2) below.

(3) An illustration is not obligatory, but is desirable (Appendix E, 17).

(4) The designation of the nomenclatural type of a species is not obligatory but a 'zoologist when describing a new species should clearly designate a single specimen as its holotype' (Rec. 73A).

Algae and fungi (*Botanical Code*)

(1) The name proposed must be in Latin binomial form (Art. 23); it must be neither a later (junior) homonym nor a tautonym.

Though not obligatory it is useful to elucidate the etymology of the name (Rec. 73A).

Attention may be drawn to the new name, which it is usual to print in bold face type, by following the name of the authority for the name with the abbreviation 'sp.nov.' [species nova]. This abbreviation should be used only at the place of first publication of the name, never when the name is used subsequently. See also *Protozoa* (1) above.

(2) There must be a Latin diagnosis (Art. 36).

That is, there must be a concise description of the essential and differential characters of the species in Latin to supplement any similar or more detailed description in a modern language.

(3) For algae the Latin diagnosis must be accompanied by an illustration or by a reference to a previously published illustration (Art. 39).

Though only obligatory for algae, an illustration is always desirable (Rec. 32 D).

(4) The nomenclatural type must be designated (Art. 37).

For many algae and fungi the type should be a dried specimen (for which the place of collection (the type locality) and the date should be given); when this is impossible, the type may be a description, usually accompanied by an illustration. When the type is a specimen its permanent location (i.e. the museum, herbarium, or culture collection with, if possible, the reference number of the specimen or culture) should be given. If, as is desirable, the type material is divided and portions are deposited in one or more national herbaria, one specimen must be designated as the type (or *holotype*) the other specimens, being *isotypes*. Living types for algae are not permissible under the Botanical Code; for fungi, according to a decision of the Montreal Congress, 1959, they are not forbidden. See *Bacteria* (4) below.

Bacteria (*including actinomycetes*) (*Bacteriological Code*)

(1) The name proposed must be in Latin binomial form (Principle 4; Rule 6); it must be neither a later (junior) homonym nor a tautonym. The generic name must not duplicate the generic name of a plant or a protozoan (Rule 24d).

(2) A Latin diagnosis is not obligatory but in works written in a language unfamiliar to the majority of workers in bacteriology, it is recommended that the authors publish simultaneously the diagnosis in a more familiar language (Rec. 12a).

(3) An illustration is not obligatory but it is desirable to figure any unusual morphological characters.

(4) The type must be designated and the type of 'a species or subspecies is preferably an authentic culture, but it may be a specimen or preparation, illustration or description' (Rule 9a).

Subcultures of the type culture should be deposited in several national culture collections. One of these subcultures should be designated as the type. See *Algae and fungi* (4) above.

Viruses (*Bacteriological Code*)

The starting date for viruses under the Bacteriological Code has not yet been decided. Virus nomenclature is therefore still unregulated.

It may be noted that under all three Codes the nomenclatural type of a family is a genus and that of a genus a species and the name proposed for a family or a genus is illegitimate unless the type (the type genus or type species, respectively) is unambiguously designated.

NAME CHANGING

The names of micro-organisms may have to be changed merely on nomenclatural grounds, that is to say because the names do not conform to the requirements of the particular current international code of nomenclature. Some aspects of such changes are dealt with below under 'Selection of Names'. All the codes have provisions for allowing exceptions to the rules to be made when certain changes required by the rules would result in confusion by disturbing some long standing usage.

Names more often have to be changed in order to bring them in line with developments in taxonomy or with a particular author's taxonomic views. Such changes, if the taxonomy is accepted, are inevitable.

Of taxonomic changes which have to be reflected by name changes some do and some do not involve a change in rank. An example of the first is a change under the Botanical Code of a subgenus to the status of a genus (or of a variety to the status of a species) and of the second, under all three codes, the transfer of a species from one genus to another.

On formal occasions (and always to avoid ambiguity) a generic name or a specific binomial is followed by the name of the author or authors who first proposed the name. This is for reasons of precision and gives a valuable clue to the source of the original description of the taxon and hence to the type.

Under the Zoological Code (Art. 22) the author's name is usually followed by the date of publication of the name, i.e. *Taenia lata* Linnaeus, 1758; in bacteriology dates are usually omitted, i.e. *Pectobacterium* Waldee. Under both the Zoological (Art. 43, 46) and the Bacteriological (Rules 5, 7) Codes, genus and subgenus, and also species and subspecies (which according to the Bacteriological Code is a synonym of variety), are of equivalent rank so that the taxonomic change of a subgenus to genus does not involve a change of rank as it does under the Botanical Code. Changes in rank of a taxon and transfer of a species from one genus to another under the Botanical and Bacteriological Codes are indicated by 'double citation' that is to say the name of the original author of the name at the lower rank or of the specific epithet is given in parenthesis and is followed by that of the author making the transfer. Under the Zoological Rules the name of the first author is given in parenthesis but that of the second author is usually omitted (Art. 51). For example, under the Botanical Code *Cordyceps* (Fr.) Link indicates that *Cordyceps* was used as a subgenus by Fries; under the Bacteriological Code *Erwinia carotovora* (Jones) Holland that Holland transferred to *Erwinia* a species originally described by Jones with the same epithet but in another genus; under the Zoological Code *Dibothriocephalus latus* (Linnaeus, 1758) that Linnaeus classified this species in another genus or subgenus (see above). It is desirable for the orderly development of taxonomy that name changes should be made consciously and for taxonomic reasons. It is always desirable to draw attention to such changes, e.g. by the use of 'comb.nov.' after the new name.

Under the Botanical Code a new transfer or new combination published after 1 January 1953 is not validly published unless the basionym (the name-bringing or epithet-bringing synonym) is clearly indicated with full reference to its author and original publication (Art. 33), e.g. *Didymosphaeria danica* (Berlese) Wilson & Knoyle comb.nov. (basionym, *Leptosphaeria danica* Berlese, *Icones Fungorum*, **1** (2), p. 87, 1892). During recent years many deliberate transfers have not fulfilled the requirements of this Article. To cite the basionym is a practice which should be generally followed by microbiologists.

SELECTION OF NAMES

The correct name for any taxon of given circumscription is the first (i.e. the oldest) name to have been applied to that taxon which fulfils the requirements of the current version of the particular international code of nomenclature (the provisions of which are retroactive). The Codes, therefore, lay down starting-points for nomenclature, and all three codes acknowledge the outstanding work of Linnaeus in codifying the systematics of living things and introducing binomials for species. The starting-point under the Zoological Code (Art. 3) is Linnaeus, *Systema Naturae*, ed. 10, 1758; that for Bacteriology (Rule 10) Linnaeus, *Species Plantarum*, ed. 1, 1753, which is also the starting-point under the Botanical Code (Art. 13) for myxomycetes, lichens, and most algae (and also for flowering plants, ferns, and liverworts). The nomenclature of fungi starts from two later works: Persoon, *Synopsis methodica fungorum*, 1801 (Uredinales, Ustilaginales, Gasteromycetes), and Fries, *Systema mycologicum*, 1821–28 (other fungi).

A name in use before a starting-point date may be validated by being 'taken up' by a later author; for purposes of priority, however, such a name dates from the first use by the later author. For example the maize smut (Ustilagiales) has been commonly designated *Ustilago zeae*, but although the specific epithet *zeae* was first proposed by Beckman in 1768 it was not validated by post-1801 use until 1822, after the proposal of the specific epithet *maydis* for this smut by De Candolle in 1815; the correct name for the maize smut when classified in the genus *Ustilago* is therefore *Ustilago maydis* (DC.) Corda [DC. = the conventional abbreviation for De Candolle who proposed the epithet which Corda was the first to transfer to *Ustilago*]. Other reasons for rejecting a name are that the name is a homonym, i.e. it exactly duplicates an earlier name based on a different type, or, under the Botanical or Bacteriological Codes, that it is a tautonym, i.e. the specific epithet duplicates the generic name (the Zoological Rules permit tautonyms, e.g. *Passer passer*). Under the Bacteriological Code a name must be rejected if it duplicates a protozoan name, e.g. the generic name *Phytomonas* Bergey *et al.* 1923 cannot be used because of its use by Donovan, 1909, for a genus of protozoa.

Many taxa are or have been of uncertain taxonomic position and many have been described as new on more than one occasion; therefore any name selected usually has a number of synonyms, which for a common ubiquitous organism such as *Candida albicans* may be more than a hundred. Synonyms are of two kinds. For example, *Escherichia coli* (Migula) Castellani & Chalmers, *Bacillus coli* Migula, and *Bacterium coli* (Migula) Lehmann & Neumann are different names for one organism, the bacillus named by Migula. Only one type is involved so the three names are nomenclatural (or 'obligate') synonyms to which everyone must agree. All are legitimate and the choice depends on the classification adopted. Current usage favours the first. In *Bergey's Manual* (ed. 6) *Bacillus schafferi* Freudenreich is listed as a synonym of *E. coli*. A second type is involved so this synonymy is one of taxonomic opinion, the two names are taxonomic (or 'facultative') synonyms and whether these two names are synonymous must always remain a matter of opinion. In citing synonyms it is good practice to cite the taxonomic synonyms in chronological order, each being followed by any nomenclatural synonyms chronologically arranged. It is sometimes desirable to indicate on whose authority a name is cited as a taxonomic synonym by the use of 'fide', i.e. *E. coli* (syn. *Bacillus schafferi* Freudenreich, fide Weldin, 1927).

One further point to remember when compiling synonymies is not to list misdeterminations as synonyms or to attribute a binomial to an author who has used it in a wrong sense. Such usages, if compiled (and the Botanical Code (Rec. 50D) gives guidance on how to do this), should be kept clearly distinct from the synonymy proper.

Usually in experimental work or in ecological studies dealing with many species it is not necessary to cite full synonymies but to follow a standard monograph, such as Raper & Thom's *Manual of the Penicillia* for species of *Penicillium*, and to make clear that this has been done so that, if the identifications are correct, the taxonomic usage can be ascertained by reference to the monograph in question.

BIBLIOGRAPHY

The Codes

International Code of Zoological Nomenclature adopted by the XV International Congress of Zoology, London, July 1958. 1961, 176 pp. London: International Trust for Zoological Nomenclature (19 Belgrave Square, London, S.W. 1).
[International Rules of Zoological Nomenclature as at the opening of the Paris Congress, 1948, see HEMMING, F., *Bull. zool. Nomen.* **14**, i–xxviii, 1958.]
International Code of Botanical Nomenclature adopted by the Ninth International Botanical Congress, Montreal, August 1959. 1961, 369 pp. Utrecht: International Bureau of Plant Taxonomy and Nomenclature. [This replaces the 1956 (Paris) edition.]
International Code of Nomenclature of Bacteria and Viruses (1958), 156 pp. Ames, Iowa: Iowa State College Press. [Reprinted, 1959, with a few corrections.]
International Code of Nomenclature for Cultivated Plants (1961), 30 pp. (*Regnum Vegetabile*, 22.) Utrecht: International Bureau for Plant Taxonomy and Nomenclature.

Journals

The Bulletin of Zoological Nomenclature (1943–). London: International Trust for Zoological Nomenclature.
Taxon (1951–). Utrecht, Netherlands: International Bureau for Plant Taxonomy and Nomenclature.
International Bulletin of Bacteriological Nomenclature and Taxonomy (1951–). Ames, Iowa, U.S.A.: Iowa State University Press.

These three journals include official comments on the respective Codes, details of 'Opinions', proposals for amending the Codes, and other matters of taxonomic and nomenclatural interest.

Commentaries

SCHENK, E. T. & MCMASTERS, J. H. (1956). *Procedure in Taxonomy*, 3rd edition (by A. Myra & S. W. Muller), 119 pp. Stanford, California: Stanford University Press; London: Oxford University Press. Based on the 1913 version of the Zoological Code (which is reprinted, as it is in edition 1, 1936, and edition 2, 1948), but gives much useful general advice.
BISBY, G. R. (1953). *An Introduction to the Taxonomy and Nomenclature of Fungi*, 2nd edition, 143 pp. Kew: Commonwealth Mycological Institute. Based on the 1950 version of the Botanical Code (which is reprinted and annotated for mycologists), but gives much useful general advice.
[The articles by AINSWORTH, G. C. (The rules of nomenclature for micro-organisms, *J. gen. Microbiol.* **2**, 97–102, 1948) and AINSWORTH, G. C. & COWAN, S. T. (Rules of nomenclature for fungi and bacteria, *ibid.* **10**, 465–74, 1954) cover a number of points dealt within this Appendix.]

Lists of generic names

NEAVE, S. A. (editor) (1939–40). *Nomenclator Zoologicus*. A list of names of genera and subgenera in zoology from the tenth edition of Linnaeus 1758 to the end of 1935. Vols. **1–4**. Vol. **5**, 1950, covers 1936–45. London: Zoological Society. A compilation of over 240,000 names. For later names the *Zoological Record* should be consulted.

Zoological Record (1864–). London: Zoological Society. Published in sections (Sect. 2, Protozoa; Sect. 19 all new generic and subgeneric names) as yearly volumes listing the taxonomic literature and generic and specific names.

HEMMING, F. (editor) (1958). *Official List of Generic Names in Zoology. First Instalment: Names 1–1274. Official Index of Rejected and Invalid Generic Names in Zoology. First Instalment: Names 1–1169.* London: International Trust for Zoological Nomenclature. A similar pair of lists (1958) deal with specific names.

Index Kewensis an enumeration of the genera and species of Flowering Plants, 2 vols. (1895) and 12 supplements (1901–59). Oxford: Clarendon Press. A list of generic (and specific) names of flowering plants with places of publication.

Ainsworth and Bisby's Dictionary of the Fungi, 5th edition, 1961. Kew: Commonwealth Mycological Institute. Lists generic names of fungi up to about 1959. For later names the *Index of Fungi*, vol. 3– , should be consulted.

The various editions of *Bergey's Manual* (especially ed. 6) include most generic names of bacteria.

LESSEL, E. F., *Int. Bull. bact. Nomen. Tax.* **10** (Suppl.), 87–192, 1960, has listed the generic names of the actinomycetes.

JEFFERS, E. E. & HOLT, J. G., *Int. Bull. bact. Nomen. Tax.* **11**, 29–61, 1961, list taxa of the Myxobacteriales.

APPENDIX II

CULTURE COLLECTIONS

Culture collections play an indispensable role in the international organization of microbial taxonomy by maintaining a wide range of living organisms available for comparative taxonomic work and for experimental studies. Every microbiologist who proposes a new specific or subspecific taxon is most strongly urged to deposit type cultures, or cultures from type material, with one or more national culture collections. Also, microbiologists who have made experimental studies of unusual organisms, taxonomic comparisons, or ecological surveys are also urged to deposit in established collections representative examples of the cultures on which their published results are based. This greatly facilitates confirmatory studies and ensures the preservation of interesting and rare organisms.

There are many culture collections varying from large national collections with wide interests and supported by public funds to small, specialized, and unsubsidized laboratory collections. The somewhat arbitrary selection noted below includes some representative examples of larger collections and in addition clues are provided for the location of others. Many collections issue catalogues, usually at irregular intervals.

UNITED KINGDOM AND THE BRITISH COMMONWEALTH

Details of the main Commonwealth collections and the micro-organisms maintained in them are given in the series: *British Commonwealth Collections of Micro-organisms*; *Directory of Collections and List of Species maintained in Australia*, 45 pp. [49 collections];...*in Canada*, 48 pp. [52];...*in India*, 36 pp. [81];...*in New Zealand*, 16 pp. [12];...*in United Kingdom, Ghana, and Trinidad*, 70 pp. [98, 2, 1]. London: H.M. Stationery Office, 1960.

U.K. Collections include:

ALGAE AND PROTOZOA
Culture Collection of Algae and Protozoa, Botany School, Downing Street, Cambridge.

FUNGI
Pathogenic to man and animals
Mycological Reference Laboratory, London School of Hygiene and Tropical Medicine, Keppel Street, London, W.C. 1.
Wood-rotting
Forest Products Research Laboratory, Princes Risborough, Aylesbury, Bucks.

Yeasts (non-pathogenic)
National Collection of Yeast Cultures, Brewing Industry Research Foundation, Nutfield, Redhill, Surrey.

Other fungi
Commonwealth Mycological Institute Collection of Fungus Cultures, Ferry Lane, Kew, Surrey.

BACTERIA

Industrial and marine
National Collection of Industrial Bacteria and National Collection of Marine Bacteria, Torry Research Station, Aberdeen, Scotland.

Dairy
National Collection of Dairy Organisms, National Institute for Research in Dairying, Shinfield, Reading, Berks.

Pathogenic to man and animals
National Collection of Type Cultures, Central Public Health Laboratory, Colindale Avenue, London, N.W. 9.

Pathogenic to plants
National Collection of Plant Pathogenic Bacteria, Plant Pathology Laboratory, Hatching Green, Harpenden, Herts.

VIRUSES

A number of *plant viruses* are available from Agricultural Research Council Virus Research Unit, Huntingdon Road, Cambridge.

FRANCE

ALGAE, FUNGI

Museum National d'Histoire Naturelle, Laboratoire de Cryptogamie, 12 rue de Buffon, Paris (5e).

BACTERIA

Institut Pasteur, 25 Rue du Docteur Roux, Paris (15e).

JAPAN

BACTERIA, FUNGI

Japanese Type Culture Collection, Nagao Institute, Kitashinagawa, Tokyo.

Institute for Fermentation, Osaka. [Bacteria and fungi of industrial interest; also protozoa].

NETHERLANDS

FUNGI

Centraalbureau voor Schimmelcultures, Javalaan 20, Baarn, Netherlands. [*General.*] [*Yeasts*, Yeast Division, Centraalbureau voor Schimmelcultures, Delft, Netherlands.]

BACTERIA (of ecological interest)

Laboratory of Microbiology, Julianalaan 67A, Delft, Netherlands.

SOUTH AMERICA
FUNGI

Second General Catalogue of Latin American Mycological Collections, 1955 (Centro de Cooperacion Cientifica para America Latina de la U.N.E.S.C.O., Bulevar Artegas 1320, Casilla de Correos 859, Montevideo, Uruguay).

U.S.A.
BACTERIA, FUNGI

American Type Culture Collection, 2112 M Street, N.W., Washington 7, D.C. (also animal and plant viruses, bacteriophages, algae and protozoa); Northern Regional Research Laboratory, Northern Utilization Research Branch, Peoria, Ill.

GENERAL

The UNESCO-sponsored International Centre for Information on and Distribution of Type-cultures, 19 Avenue Cesar Roux, Lausanne, Switzerland, provides an information service and from its index of collections and species attempts to locate any culture asked for.

HAUDUROY et al. (1953). *Dictionnaire des bactéries* includes a long and useful list of bacteria preserved in culture collections (see p. 474).

APPENDIX III

SOME KEY WORKS ON THE TAXONOMY OF MICRO-ORGANISMS

The literature on the taxonomy of micro-organisms is vast, widely scattered, and frequently difficult of access. The selection which follows includes some particularly useful works bearing on the taxonomy of the different groups covered by the Symposium. Apart from the larger reference works cited, most of the books listed are in print and should be easily accessible, if not personally owned, to every worker interested in the systematics of any particular group or groups. Where there has been a choice, works in English have been given preference.

PROTOZOA

General works

COPELAND, H. F. (1956). *The Classification of Lower Organisms*, 302 pp. Palo Alto, California: Pacific books. A novel treatise with some drastic, thought-provoking departures from the conventional treatment of the systematics of various protozoan groups.

CORLISS, J. O. (1960). Comments on the systematics and phylogeny of the protozoa. *Syst. Zool.* **8** (1959), 169–90. Reviews some of the more difficult problems facing the modern protozoan systematist, with indication of approaches to their solutions; includes a revised 'phylogenetic tree', the first published since 1880.

DOFLEIN, F. & REICHENOW, E. (1949–53). *Lehrbuch der Protozoenkunde*, 6th ed., 1214 pp. Jena: G. Fischer. For long the established leading protozoological text-book.

DOGIEL, V. A. (1951). *General Protistology*, 603 pp. Moscow. In Russian. A second edition of this major work is now in preparation, to appear in Russian and English translations simultaneously.

GRELL, K. G. (1956). *Protozoologie*, 284 pp. Berlin: Springer. Systematic considerations are included, although the book is devoted primarily to discussion of experimental and cytogenetic aspects of modern protozoology.

HALL, R. P. (1953). *Protozoology*, 682 pp. New York: Prentice-Hall. A thorough text-book with detailed considerations of the taxonomy of suprafamilial categories; includes a special chapter on the history of protozoan classification.

HYMAN, L. H. (1940). *The Invertebrates* vol. **1**, *Protozoa through Ctenophora*, 726 pp. New York: McGraw-Hill. A general consideration of the protozoa, including their systematics.

HYMAN, L. H. (1959). *The Invertebrates* vol. **5**, *Smaller Coelomate Groups*, 783 pp. New York: McGraw-Hill. Contains a retrospective chapter bringing information on the protozoa up to date.

JÍROVEC, O., WENIG, K., FOTT, B., BARTOŠ, E., WEISER, J. & ŠRÁMEK-HUŠEK, R. (1953). *Protozoologie*, 643 pp. Prague. The first modern Czechoslovakian text-book of protozoology, written by Czech experts on the major protozoan groups.

KUDO, R. R. (1954). *Protozoology*, 4th ed., 966 pp. Springfield, Ill.: Thomas. The standard American text-book. Careful attention is given to the taxonomy of all major groups and many species are characterized and figured.

MACKINNON, D. L. & HAWES, R. S. J. (1961). *An Introduction to the Study of Protozoa*, 506 pp. Oxford: Clarendon Press. A refreshingly modern, up-to-date consideration of the biology and systematics of all protozoan groups; intended particularly for the non-specialist.

MANWELL, R. D. (1961). *Introduction to Protozoology*, 642 pp. New York: St Martin's Press. An introductory text-book with comprehensive treatment of taxonomic problems encountered in all major protozoan groups.

RAABE, Z. (1948). An attempt of a revision of the system of Protozoa. *Ann. Univ. M. Curie-Skłodowska*, Sect. C, **3**, 259–76. (Polish with English summary.) A paper of considerable value as it represents one of the first recent efforts to improve the long-perpetuated conventional schemes of protozoan classification.

WENYON, C. M. (1926). *Protozoology. A Manual for Medical Men, Veterinarians and Zoologists*, 2 vols., 1563 pp. London: Baillière, Tindall and Cox. A useful introductory work, particularly for the less well studied groups of parasitic protozoa.

Reference works

BÜTSCHLI, O. (1880–89). Protozoa. Abt. I, Sarkodina und Sporozoa; Abt. II, Mastigophora; Abt. III, Infusoria und System der Radiolaria. In Bronn, H. G., *Klassen und Ordnung des Thier-Reichs*, **1**, 1–2035. Leipzig: C. F. Winter. An indispensable historic document; it lays the foundation for modern schemes of protozoan classification and contains a most helpful bibliography of the still older literature.

EDMONDSON, W. T. (editor) (1959). *Ward and Whipple's Fresh-Water Biology*, 2nd ed., 1248 pp. New York: Wiley and Sons. Chapters on the protozoa are contributed by G. Deflandre, J. B. Lackey and L. E. Noland; taxonomic keys are offered for forms belonging to the major free-living groups.

POCHE, F. (1913). Das System der Protozoa. *Arch. Protistenk.* **30**, 125–321. Old, but still valuable because it represents one of the few publications in which *nomenclatural* aspects of protozoan taxonomy—so very often neglected or ignored—are treated extensively and with care.

SMART, J. & TAYLOR, G. (editors) (1953). *Bibliography of Key Works for the Identification of the British Fauna and Flora*, 2nd ed., 126 pp. London: Systematics Association. Contains lists especially useful for identification and often covering exotic forms.

Some useful monographs and works on special groups

CORLISS, J. O. (1961). *The Ciliated Protozoa: Characterization, Classification, and Guide to the Literature*, 310 pp. London and New York: Pergamon Press. Offers a well-documented presentation of a modern scheme of classification of the protozoan subphylum Ciliophora; includes direct citation of some 1700 works, with emphasis on those of the past 25 years.

CUSHMAN, J. A. (1948). *Foraminifera. Their Classification and Economic Use*, 4th ed., 605 pp. Cambridge, Mass.: Harvard Press. The standard treatment of the taxonomy of the major protozoan group which is found abundantly as fossils.

GRASSÉ, P. P. (editor) (1952). *Traité de zoologie. Anatomie, systématique, biologie,* Vol. 1, fasc. 1. *Phylogénie. Protozoaires: généralités, Flagellés*, 1071 pp. Paris: Masson et Cie. Chapters on the taxonomy of the various groups of flagellated protozoa are contributed by a number of French authorities.

GRASSÉ, P. P. (editor) (1953). *Traité de zoologie. Anatomie, systématique, biologie,* vol. 1, fasc. 2. *Protozoaires: Rhizopodes, Actinopodes, Sporozoaires, Cnidosporidies*, 1160 pp. Paris: Masson et Cie. Includes contributions by a number of French authorities.

JEPPS, M. W. (1956). *The Protozoa, Sarcodina*, 183 pp. Edinburgh and London: Oliver and Boyd. A comprehensive treatment of the biology and taxonomy of an important major group.

KAHL, A. (1930–35). Urtiere oder Protozoa. I: Wimpertiere oder Ciliata (Infusoria). In Dahl, F., *Die Tierwelt Deutschlands*, Parts 18, 21, 25, 30, pp. 1–886. Jena: G. Fischer. An indispensable although ageing treatment of the biology and taxonomy of the free-living ciliated protozoa of the world, including keys to groups at all levels; profusely illustrated with drawings of many of the hundreds of species described.

LOEBLICH, A. R., Jr. & TAPPAN, H. (1961). Suprageneric classification of the Rhizopodea. *J. Paleont.* **35**, 245–330. A modern treatment of a difficult taxonomic group with particular attention to long-neglected nomenclatural matters.

ALGAE

General and introductory works

FOTT, B. (1959). *Algenkunde*. Jena: G. Fischer. The best general introduction to almost all aspects of phycology. Many good illustrations.

FRITSCH, F. E. (1935, 1945). *The Structure and Reproduction of the Algae*, 2 vols. Cambridge University Press. Still a basic text. Has been reprinted but the quality of the reproduction of some of the figures has deteriorated.

CHADEFAUD, M. (1960). *Les Végétaux non vasculaires (Cryptogamie)*. Vol. **1** of Chadefaud, M. & Emberger, L., *Traité de Botanique*. Masson: Paris. Covers many of the advances since Fritsch (1935, 1945), but is not so comprehensive.

SMITH, G. M. (editor) (1951). *Manual of Phycology*, 375 pp. Waltham, Mass.: Chronica Botanica. Contains chapters by specialists which range from good to poor.

SCHUSSNIG, B. (1953, 1960). *Handbuch der Protophytenkunde*, 2 vols. Jena: G. Fischer. A massive treatise on the morphology, anatomy, cytology, and life-histories of algae and protozoa.

WEST, G. S. & FRITSCH, F. E. (1927). *A Treatise on the British Freshwater Algae*, 534 pp. Cambridge University Press. [Out of print.] Generic keys; useful for preliminary sorting.

SMITH, G. M. (1950). *The Freshwater Algae of the United States*, 2nd ed. New York: McGraw-Hill. On similar lines to West & Fritsch (1927) and in print.

PRESCOTT, G. W. (1951). Algae of the Western Great Lakes area. *Bull. Cranbrook Inst. Sci. Mich.*, no. 31.

FOGG, G. E. (1953). *The Metabolism of Algae*. London: Methuen. A valuable little book.

PRINGSHEIM, E. G. (1946). *Pure Cultures of Algae, their Preparation and Maintenance*. Cambridge University Press.

THE FRITSCH COLLECTION OF ILLUSTRATIONS OF FRESHWATER ALGAE. This collection, kept at the Windermere Laboratory of the Freshwater Biological Association where it is freely available for the use of anyone who wishes to consult it, at present contains more than 170,000 figures (from nearly 3000 original works) covering 15,000 species (see *Ann. Rep. Freshwater biol. Ass.* **29**, 21–3, 1961).

Standard General Floristic Works

PASCHER, A. (editor). *Die Süsswasser-Flora Deutschlands, Österreichs und der Schweiz.* Jena: G. Fischer. Some parts out of date, others superseded by vols. in Rabenhorst's Kryptogamenflora. Vol. 10 entitled Mitteleuropas instead of Deutschlands, etc.

1. PASCHER, A. & LEMMERMANN, E. (1914). *Flagellatae,* I.
2. PASCHER, A. & LEMMERMANN, E. (1913). *Flagellatae,* II. *Chrysomonadineae, Cryptomonadineae, Euglenineae, Chloromonadineae und gëfarbte Flagellaten unsicherer Stellung.*
3. SCHILLING, A. J. (1913). *Dinoflagellatae (Peridineae).*
4. PASCHER, A. (1927). *Volvocales. Phytomonadineae Flagellatae,* IV. *Chlorophyceae* I.
5. LEMMERMANN, E., BRUNNTHALER, J. & PASCHER, A. (1915). *Chlorophyceae,* II. *Tetrasporales, Protococcales, einzellige Gattungen unsicherer Stellung.*
6. HEERING, W. (1914). *Chlorophyceae,* III. *Ulotrichales, Microsporales, Oedogoniales.*
7. HEERING, W. (1921). *Chlorophyceae,* IV. *Siphonocladiales, Siphonales.*
9. CZURDA, V. (1932). 2nd edition: *Zygnemales.*
10. HUSTEDT, F. (1930). *Bacillariophyta (Diatomeae). Süsswasser-Flora.*
11. PASCHER, A. (1925). *Heterokontae; Phaeophyceae;* SCHILLER (1925), *Rhodophyceae,* and MIGULA (1925), *Charales.*
12. GEITLER, L. (1925). *Cyanophyceae;* GEITLER & PASCHER (1925), *Cyanochloridinae, Chlorobacteriaceae.*

Rabenhorst's Kryptogamen-Flora von Deutschland, Oesterreich und der Schweiz. Jena. A most valuable series.

7. HUSTEDT, F. (1930–61). *Die Kieselalgen.* (Not yet complete.)
10 (2). SCHILLER, J. (1925). *Coccolithineae,* pp. 89–273.
10 (3). SCHILLER, J. (1933, 1937). *Dinoflagellatae (Peridineae).*
11. PASCHER, A. (1937–39). *Heterokonten.*
12 (4). GEMEINHARDT, K. (1939). *Oedogoniales.*
13. KREIGER, W. (1937–9). *Die Desmidiaceen.* (Incomplete.) To be completed, for *Cosmarium* at least, in KRIEGER, W. & GERLOFF, J., *Die Gattung Cosmarium. Nova Hedwigia,* Beihefte 1.
13 (2). KOLKWITZ, R. & KRIEGER, H. (1941). *Zygnemales.*
14. GEITLER, L. (1932). *Cyanophyceae.*

GOLLERBAKH, M. M., POLYANSKIĬ, V. I. & SAVICH, V. P. (editors). *Opredelitel' presnovodnȳkh Vodorosleĭ SSSR.* Moscow. A recent Russian parallel to *Die Süsswasser-Flora Deutschlands.*

1. GOLLERBAKH, M. M. & POLYANSKIĬ, V. I. (1951). *Obshchaya chast'.*
2. GOLLERBAKH, M. M., KOSINSKAYA, E. K. & POLYANSKIĬ, V. I. (1953). *Sinezelënȳe vodorosli.*
3. MATVIENKI, A. M. (1954). *Zolotistȳe vodorosli.*
4. ZABELINA, M. M., KISELËV, I. A., PROSHKINA-LAVRENKO, A. I. & SHESHUKOVA, V. S. (1954). *Diatomovȳe vodorosli.*
6. KISELEV, I. A. (1954). *Perofitovȳe vodorosli.*
8. DEDUSENKO-SHCHEGOLEVA, N. T., MATVIENKO, A. M. & SHKORBATOV, L. A. (1959). *Zelënȳe vodorosli. Klass: Vol'voksovȳe.*

DE TONI, G. B. (1889–1907). *Sylloge Algarum omnium hucusque cognitorum.* 5 vols. Pavia. [Available on microcards from Microcard Foundation, Washington, D.C.] Latin descriptions, no illustrations.

Special works and monographs

Euglenoids

PRINGSHEIM, E. G. (1956). Contributions towards a monograph of the genus *Euglena*. *Nov. Act. Leopoldina*, N.F. no. 125, 168 pp. Leipzig. Though not all the species are considered in detail this is the best monograph of the genus and also includes a valuable section on *Astasia*.

GOJDICS, M. (1953). *The Genus* Euglena. Madison. Concerning this monograph see Pringsheim (1956), p. 9.

POCHMANN, A. (1942). Synopsis der Gattung *Phacus*. *Arch. Protistenk.* 95, 81–252.

CONRAD, W. (1935). Étude systématique du genre *Lepocinclis* Perty. *Mém. Mus. Hist. nat. Belg.*, Ser. 2, 1.

DEFLANDRE, G. (1926–7). Monographie du genre *Trachelomonas*. *Rev. gén. Bot.* 38, 358–86, 449–69, 515–28, 580–92, 640–58, 687; 39, 26–51, 73–98. Also printed separately at Nemours, 1926.

Chlorophyceae (green algae)

PRINTZ, H. (1927). Chlorophyceae. In Engler, A., *Die natürlichen Pflanzenfamilien*, 2. Aufl., 3. Leipzig. Still a useful account of the majority of the genera.

GERLOFF, J. (1940). Beiträge zur Kenntnis der Variabilität und Systematik der Gattung *Chlamydomonas*. *Arch. Protistenk.* 94, 311–502. A review of the genus together with critical investigations of several species. Some 300 species are considered but since then over 200 more have been described.

KORSHIKOV, O. A. (1938). *Volvocineae. Viznachnik prisnovodnikh vodorostei Ukr. RSR. IV.* Kiev: Akad. Nauk Ukr. RSR. Contains observations and descriptions not in *Die Süsswasserflora* and should be looked at even if the Ukrainian text is not understood.

KORSHIKOV, O. A. (1953). *Viznachnik prisnovodnisk vodorostei Ukrains' koi RSR. Pidklas Protokokovi (Protococcineae).* Kiev: Ukr. Akad. Nauk. Though in Ukrainian, this outstanding flora cannot be overlooked by those studying coccoid green algae.

TRANSEAU, E. N. (1952). *The Zygnemataceae*. Ohio State University Press.

RANDHAWA, M. S. (1959). *Zygnemaceae*. I.C.A.R. monographs on algae. New Delhi.

WEST, W. & WEST, G. S. (1904–11). *The British Desmidiaceae*, 1–4. London: Ray Soc.

WEST, G. S. & CARTER, N. (1922). *The British Desmidiaceae*, 5. London: Ray Soc. Still very useful starting-points.

Planktonic algae and diatoms

SKUJA, H. (1948). Taxonomie des Phytoplanktons einiger Seen in Uppland, Schweden. *Symb. bot. Upsaliens.* 9 (3), 399 pp. Uppsala.

SKUJA, H. (1956). Taxonomische und biologische Studien über das Phytoplankton Schwedischer Binnengewässer. *Nov. Act. Soc. Sci. Upsaliens.*, Ser. IV, 16 (3), 404 pp. Uppsala. These are two of the most important works on plankton algae, protozoa and some large bacteria. Richly and beautifully illustrated.

HUBER-PESTALOZZI, G. (1938–61). *Das Phytoplankton des Süsswassers. Die Binnengewässer*, 16, 1, Teil; 2. Teil, 1–5. Five volumes covering generalities, Cyanophyta, bacteria and fungi; Chrysophyceae, colourless flagellates and Xanthophyceae; diatoms; Cryptophyceae, Chloromonadophyceae and Peridineae; Euglenophyceae; Chlorophyceae: Volvocales.

KOMÁREK, J. & ETTL, H. (1958). *Algologische Studien*. Československa Akad. Ved. Praha. Contains valuable sections on planktonic Cyanophyta, Chlorangiales and Volvocales.

SCHMIDT, A. (1874–). *Atlas der Diatomaceenkunde.* Over 400 large plates of drawings.
CLEVE-EULER, A. (1951–55). *Die Diatomeen von Schweden und Finnland.* Ser. 4, **2** (1), **3** (3), **4** (1), **4** (5), **5** (4).
HELMCKE, J. G. & KRIEGER, W. (1953–54). *Diatomeenschalen im elektronenmikroskopischen Bild,* **1** (1953), **2** (1954). Berlin: Wilmersdorf. This and the coming new edition give a good idea of the variety of fine structure in diatoms.
SKABICHEVSKIĬ, A. P. (1960). *Planktonȳe diatomovȳe Vodorosli presnȳkh vod SSSR.* Moscow.

Chrysophyceae

BOURRELLY, P. (1957). Recherches sur les Chrysophycées: Morphologie, phylogénie, systématique. *Rev. algol. Mem. Hors Ser.* **1**, 412 pp. A valuable account.

Cyanophyceae (blue-green algae)

DROUET, F. & DAILY, W. A. (1956). Revision of the coccoid Myxophyceae. *Butler Univ. bot. Stud.* **12**, 218 pp. A thorough revision based on the examination of herbarium material, not at present generally supported.
ELENKIN, A. A., GOLLERBACH, M. M., POLYANSKIĬ, V. I. & KOSINSKAYA, E. K. (1936–49). *Monographia algarum cyanophycearum aquidulcium et terrestrium in finibus URSS inventarum.* Inst. Bot. Acad. Sci. U.R.S.S.
DESIKACHARY, T. V. (1959). *Cyanophyta.* I.C.A.R. monographs on algae. New Delhi.
GEITLER, L. (1960). *Schizophyzeen.* Berlin: Nikolassee. A general account.

Rhodophyceae (red algae)

KYLIN, H. (1956). *Die Gattungen der Rhodophyceen.* Lund: CWK Gleerups Förlag. The standard work.

FUNGI

General works

BESSEY, E. A. (1950). *Morphology and Taxonomy of Fungi,* 791 pp. Philadelphia: Blakiston Co. [Reprinted, 1961.] A comprehensive general introduction with particularly good references to the taxonomic literature.
SMITH, G. (1960). *An Introduction to Industrial Mycology,* ed. 5, 399 pp. London: Arnold. A useful introduction to methods for culturing and examining fungi with special reference to a range of common and ubiquitous moulds.
AINSWORTH, G. C. (1961). *Ainsworth and Bisby's Dictionary of the Fungi,* ed. 5, 547 pp. Kew: Commonwealth Mycological Institute. Summarizes the characteristics of the major groups of fungi, lists generic names, gives explanations of mycological terms and many references to taxonomic literature. Includes G. W. Martin's useful key to the families of fungi.
CLEMENTS, F. E. & SHEAR, C. L. (1931). *The Genera of Fungi,* 496 pp., 58 plates. New York: H. W. Wilson Co. [Reprinted, 1957.] Though now rather dated still a very useful source book with extensive keys.
Index of Fungi. Kew: Commonwealth Mycological Institute. This half-yearly publication lists the names of new species and varieties of fungi, new combinations and new names proposed since 1940 with the citations for the places of publication. Ten-yearly cumulative indexes. The years 1920–39 are covered by Petrak's Lists issued or re-issued in the same series. [See SACCARDO, *Sylloge* below.]

Bibliography of Systematic Mycology. Kew: Commonwealth Mycological Institute. A half-yearly publication listing publications on all aspects of the taxonomy of fungi and actinomycetes.

BARNETT, H. L. (1960). *Illustrated Genera of Imperfect Fungi*, ed. 2, 225 pp. Minneapolis: Burgess Publishing Co. 462 genera are briefly characterized and there is a generic key.

Standard reference works

SACCARDO, *Sylloge fungorum*, 1882–1931 (25 vols.) has short Latin descriptions of most species proposed up to 1920 but no illustrations. [See *Index of Fungi* above.]

Rabenhorst's Kryptogamenflora von Deutschland, Oesterreich, und der Schweiz, **1, 8**, 1881–1938 (10 vols.). [Available on microcards or fiche from Micro Methods Ltd., East Ardsley, Wakefield, Yorks.] Covers all groups.

Special monographs of particular interest to microbiologists

THOM, C. & RAPER, K. B. (1945). *A Manual of the Aspergilli*, 373 pp. Baltimore: Williams and Wilkins Co.; London: Baillière, Tindall and Cox.

RAPER, K. B. & THOM, C. (1949). *Manual of the Penicillia*, 875 pp. Baltimore: Williams and Wilkins Co.; London: Baillière, Tindall and Cox.

LODDER, J. & KREGER-VAN RIJ, N. W. J. (1952). *The Yeasts*, 713 pp. Amsterdam: Netherland Publishing Co. [VERONA, O. & MONTEMARTINI, A., *Atti Ist. bot. Univ. Pavia*, Ser. 5, **17**, 1–123, 1959, have compiled the descriptions of new yeasts proposed during 1952–58.]

SPARROW, F. K. (1960). *Aquatic phycomycetes*, ed. 2, 1187 pp. Ann Arbor, Michigan: University of Michigan Press.

BONNER, J. T. (1959). *The Cellular Slime Moulds*, 150 pp. Princeton, New Jersey: Princeton University Press.

LISTER, A. & GULIELMA (1925). *A Monograph of the Mycetozoa*, ed. 3, 296 pp. London: Brit. Mus. (Nat. Hist.).

HAGELSTEIN, R. (1944). *The Mycetozoa of North America*, 306 pp. Mineola, N.Y.: Author.

BACTERIA

General works

Bergey's Manual of Determinative Bacteriology, 1957. BREED, R. S., MURRAY, E. G. D. & SMITH, N. R. (editors). 7th ed., 1094 pp. London: Baillière, Tindall and Cox. The current standard treatment of bacterial systematics. (The 6th edition, 1948, includes full references to the more obscure bacteria. The 1st edition, 1923, gives a full review of the older systems of bacterial classification and lists most of the important early work.)

SKERMAN, V. B. D. (1959). *A Guide to the Identification of the Genera of Bacteria*, 217 pp. Baltimore: Williams and Wilkins. The most comprehensive and useful set of diagnostic generic keys available, intended as a companion to *Bergey's Manual*, 7th ed., together with many technical details on a very wide range of tests.

KRASSILNIKOV, N. A. (1949). *Guide to the Bacteria and Actinomycetes*. (In Russian), 430 pp. Moscow and Leningrad: U.S.S.R. Acad. Sci. This comprehensive manual includes much little-known work from Russia.

ENLOWS, E. M. (1920). The generic names of bacteria. *Bull. U.S. hyg. Lab.*, no. 121, 115 pp. An annotated check-list.

BUCHANAN, R. E. (1925). *General Systematic Bacteriology. History, Nomenclature, Groups of Bacteria*, 597 pp. Baltimore: Williams and Wilkins. A valuable review on nomenclature with a large bibliography.

MIGULA, W. (1897, 1900). *System der Bakterien, Handbuch der Morphologie, Entwickelungsgeschichte und Systematik der Bakterien*, 2 vols. 368 and 1068 pp. Jena: Fischer. The 2nd volume (1900), the fullest of the early works on bacterial systematics, has extensive and accurate references.

GRAINGER, T. H., Jr. (1958). *A Guide to the History of Bacteriology*, 210 pp. New York: Ronald Press Co. An extensive annotated bibliography to a wide range of subjects, including systematics.

Pathogenic bacteria

WILSON, G. S. & MILES, A. A. (1955). *Topley and Wilson's Principles of Bacteriology and Immunity*, 4th ed., 2 vols. London: Arnold. Primarily bacteria of medical and veterinary interest. The earlier editions are still useful.

HAUDUROY, P., GUILLOT, G., MAGROU [J.], PRÉVOT, A.-R., ROSSET & URBAIN, [A.] (1953). *Dictionnaire des bactéries pathogènes pour l'homme, les animaux et les plantes suivi de la liste des êtres microscopiques conservés dans les collections des cultures types*, 2nd ed., 692 + 64 pp. Paris: Masson. A useful work but not very critical.

COWAN, S. T. & STEEL, K. J. (1961). Diagnostic Tables for the Common Medical Bacteria. *J. Hyg. Camb.* **59**, 357. [Available as a reprint, Cambridge University Press.]

ELLIOTT, C. (1951). *Bacterial Plant Pathogens*, 2nd ed., 186 pp. Waltham, Mass.: Chronica Botanica Co. Descriptions and detailed bibliographies.

DOWSON, W. J. (1957). *Plant Diseases Due to Bacteria*, 232 pp. London: Cambridge University Press.

STAPP, C. (1958). *Pflanzenpathogene Bakterien*, 259 pp. Berlin: Paul Parey. [English translation, 1961. Oxford: Oxford University Press.] General accounts.

Some useful monographs

CIOGLIA, L. (1957). *Filogenesi e tassonomia delle enterobacteriaceae*, 319 pp. Cagliari: Istituto di Igieni della Universita di Cagliari.

ELEK, S. D. (1959). Staphylococcus pyogenes *and its Relation to Disease*, 767 pp. London: Livingstone.

FRATEUR, J. (1950). Essai sur la systématique des acetobacters. *Cellule*, **53**, 287–392.

ITERSON, W. VAN (1958). Gallionella ferruginea Ehrenberg *in a different light*, 185 pp. Amsterdam: N. V. Noord-Hollandsche Uitgevers Maatschappij.

JAHN, E. (1927). *Beiträge zur botanischen Protistologie; I. Die Polyangiden*, 107 pp. Leipzig: Bornträger.

JENSEN, H. L. (1934). Studies on saprophytic mycobacteria and corynebacteria. *Proc. Linn. Soc. N.S.W.* **59**, 19–61.

KAUFFMANN, F. (1954). *Enterobacteriaceae*, 2nd ed., 382 pp. Copenhagen: Munksgaard.

KRZEMIENIEWSCY, H. I. S. (1926, 1927). Miksobakterje Polski (Die Myxobakterien von Polen). *Acta Soc. Bot. Polon.* **4**, 1–54; **5**, 1–20.

NIEL, C. B. VAN (1928). *The Propionic Acid Bacteria*, 187 pp. Haarlem: Boissevain.

NIEL, C. B. VAN (1944). The culture, general physiology, morphology and classification of the non-sulfur purple and brown bacteria. *Bact. Rev.* **8**, 1–118.

ORLA-JENSEN, S. (1919). *The Lactic Acid Bacteria*, 2nd ed., 196 pp. Copenhagen: Munksgaarde. Still valuable: largely a reprint from *K. dansk. vidensk. Selske* (Sec. Sci., ser. 8), **5**, no. 2.

PRINGSHEIM, E. G. (1949). Iron bacteria. *Biol. Rev.* **24**, 200–45.

SHERMAN, J. M. (1937). The streptococci. *Bact. Rev.* **1**, 3–97.

SMITH, N. R., GORDON, R. E. & CLARK, F. E. (1952). Aerobic sporeforming bacteria. *Agric. Monogr. U.S. Dep. Agric.*, no. 16, 148 pp.

SNEATH, P. H. A. (1960). A study of the bacterial genus *Chromobacterium*. *Iowa St. Coll. J. Sci.* **34**, 243–500.

WINOGRADSKY, S. N. (1888). *Beiträge zur Morphologie und Physiologie der Bakterien.* Heft I. *Zur Morphologie und Physiologie der Schwefelbakterien*, 120 pp. Leipzig: Felix. Historically valuable.

WINSLOW, C.-E. A. & WINSLOW, A. R. (1908). *The Systematic Relationships of the Coccaceae*, 300 pp. New York: Wiley. Historically valuable.

ACTINOMYCETES

WAKSMAN, S. A. (1959, 1961). *The Actinomycetes*, Vol. I, *Nature, Occurrence and Activities*, 327 pp.; Vol. II, *Classification, Identification and Descriptions of Genera and Species*, 372 pp. Baltimore: Williams & Wilkins.

Bergey's Manual of Determinative Bacteriology, 7th edition, pp. 694–829, 1957. Descriptions and keys. (The 6th edition, pp. 892–977, 1948, gives references to many obscure and poorly described actinomycetes.)

KRASSILNIKOV, N. A. (1941). *Actinomycetales*, 148 pp. (In Russian.) Moscow: Acad. Sci. U.S.S.R. A taxonomic account.

LESSEL, E. F. (1960). The nomenclatural status of the generic names of the Actinomycetales. *Int. Bull. Bact. Nomen. Tax.* **10** (Suppl.), 87–192. A useful annotated list of almost all the generic names applied to actinomycetes.

VIRUSES

General

BURNET, F. M. & STANLEY, W. M. (editors) (1959–60). *The Viruses, Biochemical, Biological and Biophysical Properties*, 3 vols. New York and London: Academic Press. A general treatment; of particular interest to systematists are the articles by F. M. Burnet on animal virus classification and K. M. Smith on insect viruses in vol. **3**.

Bergey's Manual of Determinative Bacteriology, 6th ed., pp. 1127–96, 1948. Gives short general descriptions. The viruses are designated by Latin binomials and arranged in families.

Animal viruses

RIVERS, T. M. & HORSFALL, F. L. (editors) (1959). *Viral and Rickettsial Infections of Man*, 3rd ed., 967 pp. Philadelphia: Lippincott.

MINER, R. W. (editor) (1953). Virus and rickettsial classification and nomenclature. *Ann. N.Y. Acad. Sci.* **56**, 381–622. General treatments.

Insect viruses

STEINHAUS, E. A. (1949). *Principles of Insect Pathology*, chapter 11 (pp. 417–545). New York (Toronto and London): McGraw-Hill.

Plant viruses

SMITH, K. M. (1957). *A Textbook of Plant Virus Diseases*, 2nd ed., 652 pp. London: J. and A. Churchill Ltd. This standard text gives short illustrated accounts of most plant viruses.

Common names of virus diseases used in the *Review of Applied Mycology* (*Rev. appl. Mycol.* **35**, Suppl., 78 pp., 1957). As there is no internationally agreed method for virus nomenclature this list of plant virus names and synonyms, prepared by the Commonwealth Mycological Institute in co-operation with the American Phytopathological Society, is frequently followed.

For a list of Latin binomial names for plant viruses as suggested by the Commission on Virus Nomenclature of the International Botanical Congress, see ROLAND, G., *Taxon*, **8**, 126–30, 1959.

INDEX

DATE DUE